THE PEOPLE'S EMERGENCY GUIDE

THE PEOPLE'S EMERGENCY GUIDE

Edited by Jeffrey Weiss

A DELL TRADE PAPERBACK

A DELL TRADE PAPERBACK BOOK
Published by
Dell Publishing Co., Inc.
1 Dag Hammarskjold Plaza
New York, New York 10017

Dell ® TM 681510, Dell Publishing Co., Inc.

ISBN: 0-440-56911-7

Reprinted by arrangement with St. Martin's Press, Inc.

Printed in the United States of America

First Dell Trade Paperback printing—January 1982

INTRODUCTION

No matter how careful you are, the chances are that you will have to face a variety of emergencies during your lifetime. Some are life-threatening, while others may destroy property and deplete savings. Here are some sobering government figures: 16,000 children die each year from accidents, and 20 million are injured severely enough to require professional medical care. Over 6,000 people die annually from house fires, countless others are injured, and millions of dollars' worth of property is lost.

These statistics are indeed alarming, but they should not make you a fatalist. By facing an emergency in a calm and knowledgeable way, you can reduce the potential for disaster. You owe it to yourself and your family to be able to act competently.

For example, a person is choking. In four minutes he may be dead. He can save himself, or someone else can save him—provided either person knows the Heimlich Maneuver, a technique that can be learned in a matter of minutes.

The last decade has seen the publication of numerous guides dealing with health, house, car, boat, or pet emergencies. But until now there has been no comprehensive book that covered *all* of these topics. *The People's Emergency Guide* fills this gap, providing up-to-date information on what to do in all of the most common and potentially dangerous emergencies.

The size of this book makes it important that you know how to use it *before* an emergency occurs. Familiarize yourself with the format now; then when an emergency occurs, you can turn quickly to the information you need.

There are six illustrated sections: YOURSELF, YOUR HOUSE, ON THE ROAD, AT SEA, YOUR PET, and NATURAL DISASTERS. The first section, YOURSELF, is subdivided into 38 chapters covering common medical emergencies. The first chapter, "Principles of First Aid," explains the basics of recognizing an emergency and giving first aid for the life-threatening conditions of impaired breathing, circulatory failure, severe bleeding, and shock. It also provides important information on transporting a victim safely, applying dressings and bandages, stocking a medicine chest, and keeping lists of emergency telephone numbers and family members' blood types. The next 36 chapters deal with specific emergencies, such as burns, fractures and dislocations, and stroke, in alphabetical order for quick reference. Remember in using these chapters that the first aid given does not eliminate the need for a physician, but it can keep a victim alive until medical personnel arrive. The last chapter in this section, "Health Insurance," gives important information on how to obtain the kind of medical coverage you and your family need at a cost you can afford.

The other five sections are also subdivided into chapters: YOUR HOUSE covers such common household-related emergencies as electrical and plumbing breakdowns, and household pests. ON THE ROAD deals with emergencies involving automobiles, bicycles, motorcycles, travel and camper trailers, motorhome and pickup campers, and camping outdoors. AT SEA covers boat-related emergencies, including rescuing a person who has fallen overboard. YOUR PET tells how to provide first aid for the family dog or cat. And finally, NATURAL DISASTERS covers thunderstorms, winter storms, strong winds, flash floods, tornadoes, hurricanes, earthquakes, and radiation, and also tells how to stockpile food for surviving any of these disasters.

This book represents thorough research with the help of many experts who provided important information and checked the chapters for accuracy (a list of sources follows). In addition, several individuals deserve mention for their part in producing this book: Barbara B. Buchholz for assembling the text; Albert T. Hamowy for designing the imaginative and easy-to-follow layouts; Natalie Siegel for drawing all the precise diagrams; Kim Dalton for editing and proofing the entire manuscript at all stages; Barbara Taylor Hackney for doing the mechanicals; Paul H. Bonner and Elaine Greene Weisburg for reading the manuscript and offering countless suggestions; and Louis O. Gropp for seeing that this project got off the ground, and for his invaluable support throughout.   J.W.

SOURCES

The following list provides the sources for important information in the book. Individuals and organizations that reviewed chapters are indicated by an asterisk (*).

YOURSELF

Principles of First Aid: Joseph Ballinger, M.D.,* Clinical Associate Professor of Medicine at Albert Einstein College of Medicine and Attending Physician at Montefiore Hospital, Bronx, N.Y.; Medic Alert Foundation International; U.S. Department of Health, Education, and Welfare; U.S. Department of the Interior, Safety Manual No. 3, "First Aid."

Abdominal Pain: Joseph Ballinger, M.D.*

Alcohol Abuse: Joseph Ballinger, M.D.*; National Council on Alcoholism, Inc., questionnaire, "What Are the Signs of Alcoholism?"; U.S. Department of Health, Education, and Welfare; U.S. Department of Transportation.

Allergic Reactions: Joseph Ballinger, M.D.*; U.S. Department of Agriculture; U.S. Department of Health, Education, and Welfare.

Amputation: Joseph Ballinger, M.D.*

Burns: Joseph Ballinger, M.D.*; U.S. Department of the Interior, Bureau of Mines Instruction Manual and Safety Manual No. 3, "First Aid"; Milton Zaret, M.D.,* Clinical Associate Professor of Ophthalmology at New York University Medical Center.

Cancers: Joseph Ballinger, M.D.*; U.S. Department of Health, Education, and Welfare.

Chest Injuries: Joseph Ballinger, M.D., U.S. Department of the Interior, Safety Manual No. 3, "First Aid."

Emergency Childbirth: The American College of Obstetricians and Gynecologists and *Redbook* Magazine for "How to Deliver a Baby in an Emergency"; Jon R. Snyder, M.D.,* Attending Physician at Booth Memorial Medical Center in Queens, N.Y., and Assistant Clinical Professor at New York University Medical Center.

Choking: Henry J. Heimlich, M.D.,* Professor of Advanced Clinical Sciences at Xavier University in Cincinnati, Ohio, and inventor of the Heimlich Maneuver.

Convulsions: Joseph Ballinger, M.D.*

Diabetes: Joseph Ballinger, M.D.*; Estelle Ballinger, M.A., R.D.,* former Adjunct Professor of Foods and Nutrition at Westchester Community College in

Purchase, N.Y.; U.S. Department of the Interior, Safety Manual No. 3, "First Aid"; U.S. Department of Health, Education, and Welfare.

Drowning and Water Safety: Joseph Ballinger, M.D.*; U.S. Department of Commerce.

Drug Abuse: Joseph Ballinger, M.D.*; U.S. Department of Health, Education, and Welfare; U.S. Department of Justice.

Ear Injuries: Joseph Ballinger, M.D.*

Electric Shock: Joseph Ballinger, M.D.*; U.S. Consumer Product Safety Commission.

Epilepsy: Joseph Ballinger, M.D.*; Epilepsy Foundation of America; U.S. Department of Health, Education, and Welfare.

Eye Injuries and Diseases: U.S. Department of Health, Education, and Welfare; Milton Zaret, M.D.*

Fainting: Joseph Ballinger, M.D.*

Fever: Joseph Ballinger, M.D.*

Food Illnesses: Joseph Ballinger, M.D.*; Estelle Ballinger*; Center for Science in the Public Interest; U.S. Department of Agriculture; U.S. Department of Health, Education, and Welfare.

Fractures and Dislocations: Joseph Ballinger, M.D.*; U.S. Department of the Interior, Safety Manual No. 3, "First Aid"; George Uris, M.D.,* orthopedist.

Frostbite: U.S. Air Force manual; U.S. Department of the Interior, Bureau of Mines Instruction Manual and Safety Manual No. 3, "First Aid"; Joseph Ballinger, M.D.*

Head Injuries: Joseph Ballinger, M.D.*; Richard Freedman, D.D.S.*; U.S. Department of the Interior, Safety Manual No. 3, "First Aid."

Headache: Joseph Ballinger, M.D.*; U.S. Department of Health, Education, and Welfare.

Heart Disease (and **Stroke**): Joseph Ballinger, M.D.*; U.S. Department of the Interior, Safety Manual No. 3, "First Aid"; U.S. Department of Health, Education, and Welfare.

Heat Exposure: Joseph Ballinger, M.D.*; U.S. Department of the Interior, Safety Manual No. 3, "First Aid"; U.S. Department of Commerce; U.S. Department of Health, Education, and Welfare.

Hypothermia (Exposure to Cold): U.S. Department of the Interior, Bureau of Mines Instruction Manual and Safety Manual No. 3, "First Aid"; Joseph Ballinger, M.D.*

Immunization: Joseph Ballinger, M.D.*; U.S. Department of Health, Education, and Welfare.

Lung Diseases: Joseph Ballinger, M.D.*; U.S. Department of Health, Education, and Welfare.

Meningococcal Meningitis: Joseph Ballinger, M.D.*; U.S. Department of Health, Education, and Welfare.

Poisoning: Joseph Ballinger, M.D.*; Estelle Ballinger*; U.S. Department of the Interior, Safety Manual No. 3, "First Aid"; U.S. Consumer Product Safety Commission; U.S. Department of the Army; U.S. Department of Health, Education, and Welfare.

Stroke: (see *Heart Disease*)

Suicide Prevention: Joseph Ballinger, M.D.*; Calvin J. Frederick, M.D., Ph.D.,* Professor in the Department of Psychiatry, George Washington University Medical School, Washington, D.C.; U.S. Department of Health, Education, and Welfare.

Tooth Problems: Richard Freedman, D.D.S.*; U.S. Department of Health, Education, and Welfare.

Unconsciousness: Joseph Ballinger, M.D.*

Wounds: Joseph Ballinger, M.D.*; U.S. Department of the Interior, Safety Manual No. 3, "First Aid."

Health Insurance: Paul Gross,* writer and expert on financial matters.

YOUR HOUSE

Getting Started: Department of the Navy Training Manual; U.S. Consumer Product Safety Commission; U.S. Department of Agriculture.

Electrical Emergencies: Association of Home Appliance Manufacturers, "Consumer Recommendations on the Safe Use of Appliances"; General Services Administration; Deanne Raffel,* home repair consultant; Underwriters Laboratories Inc. (Charles Salit,* Public Information and Educational Services); U.S. Consumer Product Safety Commission; U.S. Department of Agriculture; U.S. Department of the Army; U.S. Department of Housing and Urban Development.

Plumbing, Heating, and Cooling Emergencies: Deanne Raffel*; U.S. Department of Agriculture.

Fire Safety: Engine Co. No. 40, Ladder Co. No. 35, New York City Fire Department (Capt. Ken McGowan*); U.S. General Services Administration; U.S. Consumer Product Safety Commission; U.S. Department of Agriculture; U.S. Department of Commerce; U.S. Department of Housing and Urban Development.

Household Security: New York City Police Department ("Protective Measures to Prevent Rape"); U.S. Department of Commerce; U.S. Department of Housing and Urban Development.

Childproofing Your House: U.S. Consumer Product Safety Commission; U.S. Department of Health, Education, and Welfare.

Controlling Household Pests: U.S. Department of Agriculture; U.S. Department of Health, Education, and Welfare; F. E. Wood, Ph.D., entomologist at the University of Maryland, who provided original material on head lice and reviewed the entire chapter.

Removing Stains and Mildew; Cleaning Household Surfaces: U.S. Department of Agriculture; The Soap and Detergent Association.

In the Garden: U.S. Consumer Product Safety Commission; U.S. Department of Agriculture.

Exterior Repairs: Olin, "Easy Spin Guide to Pool Water Care"; U.S. Consumer Product Safety Commission; U.S. Department of Agriculture.

ON THE ROAD

Automobiles; Bicycles; Motorcycles; Travel and Camper Trailers; Motor-home and Pickup Campers; Camping Outdoors: U.S. General Services Administration; Shell Answer Books (information on changing a flat tire on a car and diagram of the parts of a car); U.S. Consumer Product Safety Commission; U.S. Department of Agriculture; U.S. Department of Health, Education, and Welfare; U.S. Department of Transportation.

AT SEA

Boats: National Safety Council, Man Overboard section from "Suddenly in Command"; U.S. Department of Transportation, U.S. Coast Guard (Lt. Cmdr. W. R. Ladd*).

YOUR PET

First Aid: The American Society for the Prevention of Cruelty to Animals*; U.S. Department of Agriculture; U.S. Department of Health, Education, and Welfare.

NATURAL DISASTERS

Weather Emergencies; Earthquakes; Radiation; Family Food Stockpile for Survival: U.S. Department of Agriculture; U.S. Department of Commerce, National Oceanic and Atmospheric Administration, National Weather Service (Charles G. Thomas and Charna Lester*); U.S. Department of Defense; U.S. Department of Energy; U.S. Department of Housing and Urban Development; U.S. Dept. of the Interior.

CONTENTS

9

RECORDS OF YOUR FAMILY'S HEALTH

NAME _____

DATE OF BIRTH _____

SOCIAL SECURITY NUMBER _____

BLOOD TYPE _____

ALLERGIES _____

_____

_____

DESCRIPTION OF PREVIOUS HEALTH PROBLEMS
AND HOSPITALIZATIONS_____

_____

_____

_____

IMMUNIZATION RECORD

DPT   First _____

Second _____

Third _____

Fourth _____

Boosters _____

POLIO   First _____

Second _____

Third _____

Booster _____

Booster _____

MEASLES _____

RUBELLA _____

MUMPS _____

RECORDS OF YOUR FAMILY'S HEALTH

NAME _____

DATE OF BIRTH _____

SOCIAL SECURITY NUMBER _____

BLOOD TYPE _____

ALLERGIES _____

_____

_____

DESCRIPTION OF PREVIOUS HEALTH PROBLEMS
AND HOSPITALIZATIONS_____

_____

_____

_____

IMMUNIZATION RECORD

DPT   First _____

          Second _____

          Third _____

          Fourth _____

          Boosters _____

POLIO First _____

          Second _____

          Third _____

          Booster _____

          Booster _____

MEASLES _____

RUBELLA _____

MUMPS _____

RECORDS OF YOUR FAMILY'S HEALTH

NAME _____

DATE OF BIRTH _____

SOCIAL SECURITY NUMBER _____

BLOOD TYPE _____

ALLERGIES _____

_____

_____

DESCRIPTION OF PREVIOUS HEALTH PROBLEMS
AND HOSPITALIZATIONS_____

_____

_____

_____

IMMUNIZATION RECORD

DPT   First _____

        Second _____

        Third _____

        Fourth _____

        Boosters _____

POLIO   First _____

        Second _____

        Third _____

        Booster _____

        Booster _____

MEASLES _____

RUBELLA _____

MUMPS _____

RECORDS OF YOUR FAMILY'S HEALTH

NAME _____

DATE OF BIRTH _____

SOCIAL SECURITY NUMBER _____

BLOOD TYPE _____

ALLERGIES _____

_____

_____

DESCRIPTION OF PREVIOUS HEALTH PROBLEMS
AND HOSPITALIZATIONS_____

_____

_____

_____

IMMUNIZATION RECORD

DPT　　First _____

Second _____

Third _____

Fourth _____

Boosters _____

POLIO　　First _____

Second _____

Third _____

Booster _____

Booster _____

MEASLES _____

RUBELLA _____

MUMPS _____

13

YOURSELF

1

PRINCIPLES OF FIRST AID

What should you do if a family member or co-worker is injured or suddenly becomes ill? Right after an accident or illness occurs and before medical help arrives may be the critical period when a person skilled in first aid may make the difference between life and death for the victim.

First aid does not replace the physician, but it can help keep the victim alive and in the best possible condition until medical assistance arrives. All people called upon to give first aid should know how to send for medical help in cases of serious injury and know to instruct the victim to visit a physician as soon as possible in the case of a minor injury.

The following sections include instructions on recognizing an emergency, and giving first aid for the life-threatening conditions of impaired breathing, circulatory failure, severe bleeding, and shock. There is also important information on transporting a victim safely, applying dressings and bandages, stocking your medicine chest, and keeping lists of emergency telephone numbers and family members' blood types.

RECOGNIZING AN EMERGENCY

When a person is injured or ill, someone must take charge, send for a doctor or ambulance, and apply first aid. If you are the person taking charge, you must make a rapid but effective examination to determine the nature and extent of the injuries.

Do not move the injured person any more than necessary until you have a clear idea of the injury and have applied first aid—unless the victim is exposed to further danger at the accident site (see pages 21–23 for transporting a victim safely). If the injury is serious but the victim can remain safely where he is and medical aid will be readily obtainable, it is generally best not to move the person. Unnecessary movement may aggravate certain conditions such as fractures.

When making an initial survey, a first aider should consider reports of any witnesses to the accident, his own observations of the victim, and anything the victim tells him. The first aider must not assume that the obvious injuries are the only injuries. He should look for the causes of the injury; these may provide clues to the extent of physical damage.

While there are several conditions that can be considered life-threatening, impaired breathing and circulatory failure require the most immediate attention. Next, a rescuer should administer aid for severe bleeding and for shock.

Once life-threatening conditions have been alleviated, the first aider should attend to other obvious needs, such as sealing open chest or abdominal wounds, immobilizing open fractures, covering burns and dressing less serious bleeding wounds.

The first aider should then make a secondary survey to detect less easily noticed injuries that may be aggravated by mishandling. For example, a victim with a spinal injury who is mishandled can suffer further spinal damage leading to paralysis, or a victim with a closed fracture may develop an open fracture if his wound is not immobilized. The secondary survey is a head-to-toe examination. Start with the victim's head and go on to the neck, trunk and extremities, looking for abnormalities such as swelling, discoloration, lumps or tenderness that might indicate an unseen injury.

Medical identification

Check for medical identification on the victim indicating a need for treatment for a hidden and life-threatening medical condition. One out of every five Americans—over 40 million persons—has such a problem (severe allergy, diabetes, epilepsy, etc.).

There are several organizations that provide persons who have hidden medical problems with wallet cards and signal devices. This vital information will allow a rescuer to aid a victim properly and help prevent tragic or even fatal mistakes when a victim cannot communicate. For example, an epileptic having a seizure may be confused with an alcoholic.

Medic Alert: Medic Alert Foundation International, a nonprofit, charitable and tax-exempt organization, provides an excellent three-part system of emergency medical protection:

1. *Emblem.* Each member wears a metal emblem or alerting device in either bracelet or necklace form (see Fig. 1-1). The emblem bears the insignia of the medical profession and the words "Medic Alert" in red so as to attract attention. On the reverse side are engraved the hidden medical problem or problems of the wearer, the wearer's membership number and the telephone number of the Medic Alert emergency answering service.

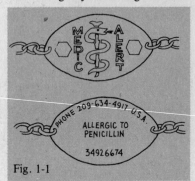

Fig. 1-1

2. *Wallet card.* The members annually receive a wallet card that contains personal and medical information in addition to that on the emblem. Along with the card, the member receives a computer printout of his or her entire emergency record so that it can be verified. It can be changed or updated at any time and as often as needed.

3. *Emergency answering service.* When a medical emergency involves a Medic Alert member, emergency personnel can place a collect call to the telephone number engraved on the emblem and printed on the card from any world location, around the clock, and receive in seconds emergency information in addition to that on the emblem and wallet card. Each member can update his record at any time for a $3 charge.

Individuals interested in obtaining the Medic Alert protection should write to the Medic Alert Foundation International, P.O. Box 1009, Department ZE, Turlock, California 95380, for an application. The basic lifetime membership is acquired for a one-time fee of $10.

Other organizations: Through the American Medical Association, you can obtain an emergency medical identification card and signal device. Write to the AMA, attention Order

Department OP-2, 535 North Dearborn Street, Chicago, Illinois 60610. The Metropolitan Life Insurance Company also offers an emergency medical identification wallet card. Write to Box T, Health and Safety Education Division, Metropolitan Life, 1 Madison Avenue, New York, N.Y. 10010.

FIRST-AID PROCEDURES FOR LIFE-THREATENING CONDITIONS

This section outlines the first-aid measures that should be used whenever life-threatening conditions exist. These conditions include impaired breathing, circulatory failure, severe bleeding and shock. The first and paramount concern is to recognize and correct these conditions immediately. Emergency treatment should be given in this order: (1) Clear the air passage; (2) restore breathing and heartbeat; (3) stop bleeding; and (4) administer treatment for shock.

Impaired breathing

When breathing stops, it becomes necessary to force air in and out of a victim's lungs until he can resume breathing on his own. If his pulse (see page 18 for feeling for a pulse) and circulation also fail, it will be necessary for a rescuer to perform cardiopulmonary resuscitation (see pages 18–19).

Causes: The causes can be quite varied; they include suffocation, gas poisoning, electrical shock, drowning and heart failure.

Signs/symptoms: The chest or abdomen does not rise and fall. Air cannot be felt exiting from the nose or mouth.

First-aid treatment

There are several methods of artificial respiration to open the airway and restore breathing. Mouth-to-mouth is the most effective. Use the mouth-to-nose method if the victim has a severe jaw fracture, neck injury, or mouth wound, or has his jaw tightly closed. Simply breathe into his nose instead of his mouth. Use back-pressure method only when mouth-to-mouth and mouth-to-nose cannot be used, for example, if the victim has severe facial injuries, is trapped or pinned face down, or

when you are in a toxic environment and both you and the victim are wearing masks which do not contain a resuscitation device.

Seconds count when a person is not breathing. Start artificial respiration at once. Do not take time to move the victim unless the accident site is unsafe.

Mouth-to-mouth and mouth-to-nose techniques. Position victim on his back on a flat, hard surface. If it is necessary to roll the victim over, try to roll him over as a single unit, keeping the back and neck straight and not twisting the body. This is to prevent further aggravation of any possible spinal injury.

Kneeling at victim's side, tilt victim's head back so chin is pointing up, by placing one hand under the neck and the other hand on the forehead.

Quickly glance in victim's mouth for any obstruction. If an obvious obstruction is present, carefully turn the victim on his side, tilt his head down, and sweep his mouth out with your fingers. When the mouth is clear, move the victim onto his back again and tilt his head back.

Check for breathing by bending over the victim, and placing your ear close to victim's mouth and nose. For at least five seconds, listen and feel for air exchange and look for chest movements.

If an adult victim is not breathing, pinch the nose closed with the hand that is resting on the forehead, form an airtight seal by placing your mouth over the victim's mouth, and breathe into the victim's mouth until his chest rises. If using the mouth-to-nose method, seal the victim's mouth with your hand and breathe into his nose. If it is necessary to open the airway when using mouth-to-nose method, use a modification of the jaw thrust maneuver. Rescuer places his hands on either side of victim's head, holding it stationary. He then uses his index fingers to displace the jaw forward without tilting head backward or turning to either side. If necessary, artificial respiration usually can be given in this position. If unsuccessful, rescuer should tilt head back slightly and make another attempt to ventilate victim using the modified jaw thrust maneuver.

For a child or infant, cover both his mouth and nose with your mouth when giving artificial respiration.

Give a victim a total of four quick breaths (see Fig. 1-2). Keep victim's head tilted back. Continue breathing into mouth or nose, removing your mouth each time to allow air to escape. Do this at the rate of 12 times per minute for an adult, or every five seconds; and 20 times per minute for a small child or infant, or once every three seconds. Use deep breaths for an adult, less for a child, and gentle puffs of the cheeks for infants. As the victim begins to breathe, maintain head tilt. If it is impossible to do mouth-to-mouth or mouth-to-nose methods, use back-pressure, arm-lift method.

Fig. 1-2

Back-pressure, arm-lift method. Clean mouth. Place victim face down. Bend his elbows and place his hands one upon the other at eye level under victim's head. Turn his head to one side, making sure the chin juts out. This method will be done on a five-beat count.

• Kneel at victim's head, placing your hands on victim's back so palms lie just below an imaginary line between armpits (count 1).
• Rock forward until arms are vertical and the weight of your body exerts steady pressure on your hands (count 2).
• Rock back, grasping victim's elbows (count 3).
• Draw victim's arms up toward you until you feel resistance at his shoulders (count 4).
• Lower victim's arms to the ground (count 5).

Repeat about 12 times per minute, or every five seconds, for an adult; 20 times per minute for a child or infant, or once every three seconds. Keep checking to see if victim's mouth is clear, airway is open and heart is beating. If heart is not beating, begin external cardiac compressions (see pages 18–19).

Mouth-to-stoma method. This method is for individuals who have had their larynx removed and their trachea connected to the skin of the lower neck, known as laryngectomees. It is through an opening in the neck called a stoma that these persons breathe. When such an individual needs artificial respiration, direct mouth-to-stoma resuscitation should be performed. The rescuer should keep victim's head straight with the neck level (see Fig. 1-3).

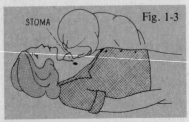
STOMA   Fig. 1-3

Rescuer seals his mouth around victim's stoma and blows air in until chest rises. He then removes his mouth to allow victim to exhale passively. It is not necessary for rescuer to seal off victim's mouth or nose.

Whatever method you employ, do not stop. Continue until victim breathes normally, until a more qualified person takes charge, or until you are physically unable to continue. If victim must be moved, continue artificial respiration while transporting the victim.

Circulatory failure

When the heart stops abruptly (cardiac arrest), irreversible brain damage begins after four to six minutes, and death will certainly occur if cardiopulmonary resuscitation is not given. Cardiopulmonary resuscitation (CPR) is an emergency procedure designed to keep a victim alive by keeping the airway open, by restoring breathing, and by maintaining circulation when the heart stops beating. With CPR a rescuer is providing both mouth-to-mouth (nose) respiration and chest compressions.

To perform CPR effectively, it is essential to take a certified course of at least four hours' duration sponsored by the American Heart Association or the Red Cross. The course will include practice on a mannikin. CPR is dangerous if done improperly or when it is not required. CPR may not be helpful with victims of severe emphysema, crushing chest injuries, or perforated hearts. Every CPR victim must be brought to a hospital quickly for follow-up treatment by a physician.

Remember, if it is necessary to transport a victim away from an accident scene when you are giving CPR, do not stop. Place victim on a flat board and continue CPR during transportation.

Causes: The causes of circulatory failure are commonly heart attack, impaired breathing, shock and electrical shock.

Signs/symptoms: No breathing and no pulse.

First-aid treatment

The following steps should be performed in the order given.
1. *Check for a response.* Gently shake the victim and shout "Are you okay?" If no response, shout for help. If victim is not lying flat on his back on a flat, hard surface, roll him over, moving entire body at one time as a unit.
2. *Check and open airway.* Remove any foreign matter from mouth. Open victim's airway by lifting up the neck or chin gently with one hand while pushing down on forehead with other to tilt head back.
3. *Check and restore breathing.* For at least five seconds, listen and feel for air exchange and look for chest movements. If victim is not breathing, give four quick, full breaths, using the mouth-to-mouth or mouth-to-nose technique (see page 17).

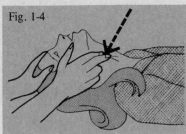
Fig. 1-4

4. *Check pulse.* After giving four quick breaths, check the pulse, using the carotid artery in the neck (see Fig. 1-4). To find the carotid artery, locate the voice box and slide index and middle fingers into the groove between the voice box and the large neck muscle. Press firmly but gently to feel for the pulse and hold for at least five seconds. You can also feel for a pulse over the artery of the wrist, on the thumb side below the base of wrist. Feel for a pulse on both wrists. Count the number of beats per minute. The average adult has a pulse of 72. For a child or infant, place tips of fingers over precordium, which is below the left nipple line, to feel the aortic heart beat. An infant has a much higher pulse, usually about 120.

If a pulse is present, continue rescue breathing at 12 times per minute for an adult and at 20 times per minute for a child. If pulse is not present, begin cardiac compressions immediately (see below).
5. *Cardiac compressions.* Kneel at the victim's side near his chest. (Victim should be lying on a hard, flat surface.) To determine the pressure point for adult cardiac compressions, locate the bony tip of the breastbone (sternum) with your ring finger and place two fingers just above that point—about $1\frac{1}{2}$ inches

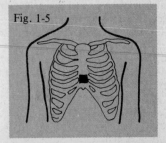
Fig. 1-5

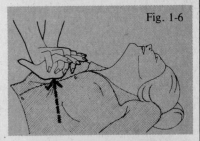
Fig. 1-6

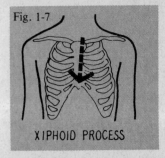
Fig. 1-7

XIPHOID PROCESS

above (see Fig. 1-5). Place the heel of one hand adjacent to your fingers and the second hand on top of the first (see Fig. 1-6). Be sure not to compress over the lower part of the sternum known as the xiphoid process (see Fig. 1-7).

Position your shoulders directly over victim's breastbone and press downward, keeping arms straight. Depress the sternum $1^{1}/_{2}$ to 2 inches for an adult. The time spent depressing and releasing the sternum should be equal. Do not remove hands from victim's sternum. Continue CPR once started until victim begins to breathe spontaneously and heartbeat begins or until physician arrives.

It is best to perform CPR with two rescuers. If two rescuers are present, they should be on opposite sides of the victim. One rescuer should perform compressions at a rate of 60 per minute, while the second rescuer is interposing a breath (artificial respiration) after every fifth compression. Compressions should not be interrupted by the breathing maneuver.

If there is only one rescuer, compressions should be at a rate of 80 per minute with two breaths (artificial respiration) after each 15 compressions. You must perform both rescue breathing and cardiac compressions. Remember, after the two breaths, check your hand position on the sternum before resuming compressions.

Note. To perform CPR on infants and children, first check pulse. For an infant, feel below his left nipple. Be careful not to overextend the infant's head when tilting it back; it is so pliable that you may block the breathing passage instead of opening it. Do not blow too hard into infant's lungs. You can cover both infant's nose and mouth with your mouth and use less air volume; give a breath every three seconds.

In both infants and small children, only one hand is used for compressions. For infants, use only the tips of the index and middle fingers to depress the mid-sternum $1/_{2}$ to $3/_{4}$ of an inch at a rate of 80 to 100 compressions per minute. For small children, use only the heel of one hand to depress the chest at mid-sternum and

depress the mid-sternum $3/_{4}$ to $1^{1}/_{2}$ inches, depending on the size of the child. The rate should be 80 to 100 compressions per minute. In both infants and small children, breaths should be interposed after every fifth chest compression.

Check pupils. Check pupils to see if CPR is effective, but while doing so do not stop procedure. If pupils are widely dilated and do not react to light, victim may have suffered brain damage or may soon do so (see Fig. 1-8). Dilated but reactive pupils are less threatening. Check victim's pupils every few minutes. Also check pulse.

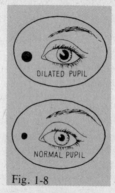
Fig. 1-8

Precordial chest thump. In certain cases, a single blow or thump over the precordium can restart a heart by giving it an electrical impulse. The precordium is the area of the chest directly in front of the heart, slightly to the left of the area occupied by the lower two-thirds of the breastbone. To be effective, rescuer must give victim a thump at the exact moment he is stricken or within the first minute of cardiac arrest. Precordial chest thump is not a substitute for cardiac compression, but can be a preliminary step to reviving a victim.

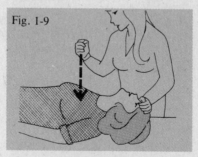
Fig. 1-9

Tilt victim's head to open the airway, and simultaneously palpate the carotid pulse. If pulse is absent, give a precordial thump: Place a clenched

fist eight to twelve inches above the chest and give a blow over the mid-sternum with the fleshy portion of the fist (see Fig. 1-9). If victim is not breathing, give four quick breaths. If still no response, begin cardiopulmonary resuscitation (CPR) at once.

Severe bleeding

Severe bleeding quickly weakens the victim and can lead to shock and death. Loss of more than one quart of blood requires immediate attention. Bleeding can come from an open wound, from the mouth, from internal sources such as the stomach, bowel, uterus and vagina.

Bleeding from open wounds: Blood from an open wound can come from an artery, a vein or a capillary. From an artery, the blood will spurt and be bright red in color. From a vein, there will be a continuous flow of blood, dark red in color. From a capillary, blood will ooze from a wound and be medium in color. The amount of blood that can be lost from a capillary is small, however.

First-aid treatment

There are four methods to stop bleeding. They are listed in the order in which you should use them.
1. *Direct-pressure method.* Cover wound with the cleanest cloth that is immediately available or cover with your bare hand and apply direct pressure on the wound. You can stop most bleeding this way. Secure the cloth in place with a bandage (see pages 23–25) when flow ebbs.
2. *Elevation method.* If an arm or leg is involved and no bone is broken, elevate limb higher than the heart and continue to apply direct pressure. Bleeding should stop.
3. *Pressure-point method.* Use finger pressure at a pressure point if it is necessary to control bleeding from an arterial wound (spurting bright red blood) that does not stop with the first two methods. Apply your fingers, keeping them flat, to the appropriate pressure point—a point where the main artery supplying blood to the wound is located (see Fig. 1-10). Hold the pressure point tightly for about five minutes; bleeding should stop. Do not hold pressure point much longer since you do not want to stop the circula-

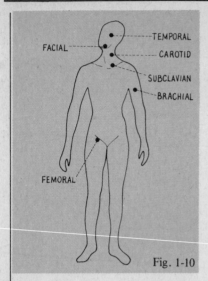

FACIAL
TEMPORAL
CAROTID
SUBCLAVIAN
BRACHIAL
FEMORAL

Fig. 1-10

tion in the arm, leg or other part of the body. The three pressure points in the head and neck should be used only as a last resort—when there is a suspected skull fracture and direct pressure cannot be used. If direct pressure can be used, it will stop the bleeding on the head in about 95 percent of the injuries. When using the pressure-point method, keep applying direct pressure to the wound with your other hand, and have the victim continue to elevate the injured part if it is a limb.

4. *Tourniquet method.* A tourniquet, a device for compressing a blood vessel to stop bleeding, should be applied to an arm or leg *only as a last resort* after all other methods have failed. When an artery is bleeding, apply a tourniquet above the wound as close to the wound as possible but never on a wound or fracture. When a vein is bleeding, apply the tourniquet just below the wound. If both an artery and a vein are bleeding, apply tourniquets above and below the wound. If you have trouble determining whether an artery or a vein is involved, it is best to follow procedure for a bleeding artery.

For an improvised tourniquet, the material should be preferably flat and about two inches wide. You can use a strap, a belt, handkerchiefs, necktie, cravat bandage. Never use a wire, cord or anything that will cut into the flesh. Wrap the tourniquet twice around the limb and half-knot it loosely. Place a stick or similar ob-ject on the half knot and tie a full knot. Twist the stick to tighten the tourniquet only until the bleeding stops—not more. Secure the stick firmly in place with the loose ends of the tourniquet, another strip of cloth or other improvised material.

Once the tourniquet is put in place, do not loosen it. Note the time the tourniquet was applied and attach a note to the victim to let people know he has a tourniquet in place. Get the victim to a doctor or hospital as soon as possible. If a tourniquet is left on too long, it can result in gangrene from cut-off circulation. But only a doctor should loosen or remove a tourniquet because doing so can increase the risk of shock and cause bleeding to resume.

Bleeding from the mouth: Blood in the mouth may originate from the mouth, from the lungs or from the stomach.

Coming from the mouth. Bleeding from the mouth is mostly due to gum disease. Rinse the mouth with a solution of table salt in cool or luke-warm water. Use approximately one teaspoon salt to one pint water. Consult a dentist.

Coming from the lungs. Blood from the lungs or any other part of the respiratory tract may be coughed up in the form of clots, bright red or dark brown in color. Have the victim lie down flat. Turn victim's head to allow the blood and any vomit to drain out of his mouth easily. Do not move the victim unless it is essential, and then move him only on a stretcher in a lying-down position. Consult a doctor immediately.

Coming from the stomach. Blood from the stomach or digestive tract may be vomited up. It is usually dark brown in color. Have the victim lie down flat. Turn victim's head to allow him to vomit the blood. Place an ice bag over his stomach. Give him nothing orally. Keep victim warm. Move him only if necessary, and then move only on a stretcher in a lying-down position. Consult a doctor quickly.

Internal bleeding: Internal bleeding poses a serious threat. The signs/symptoms of internal bleeding, which are similar to those of shock, can be due to an ulcer, cancer, or a ruptured aorta. They include cold and clammy skin, weak and rapid pulse, dull eyes and enlarged pupils, thirst, nausea and vomiting, pain in the suspected affected area, sudden collapse and shock.

Treat the victim for shock (see page 21). Anticipate that the victim may vomit, and give nothing by mouth. Get victim to a doctor or hospital as quickly and safely as possible.

Bleeding from the rectum: Bleeding from the rectum can appear as bright red lines in bowel movements or as blood passed in sizable amounts. It may be due to hemorrhoids or to more serious conditions such as tumors, polyps, or ulcerative colitis. Consult a doctor, especially if bleeding is in the form of black, tarry stool.

Bleeding from the vagina: Bleeding from the vagina, when not part of the menstrual cycle, demands medical help. Bleeding that takes place during pregnancy may be due to a ruptured tubal pregnancy or to a miscarriage. Bleeding after menopause can be a sign of cancer. Have the victim rest in bed until a doctor arrives, or quickly get victim to a doctor or hospital emergency room.

Nosebleed: Although a nosebleed is normally not an emergency, it can be a cause for concern. Sit the person down. Blow out from the nose all blood and clot. Apply pressure on the outside of the nostril which is bleeding for at least five minutes with a cold compress. If bleeding continues, put a wedge of cotton, moistened with cold water, into the bleeding nostril. Apply pressure again, for another five to ten minutes. If the bleeding stops, leave the cotton in place for a few more minutes; if the bleeding continues, get medical help promptly.

Diagram of main pressure points

Apply pressure to the pressure point closest to the wound:

1. *Carotid*—one of two large arteries on each side of the head, it controls bleeding from wounds in the neck, mouth or throat. Apply pressure on side of neck.

2. *Temporal*—pertains to point situated near the temporal bone in the skull and controls bleeding from wounds in the upper part of the head. Apply pressure in front of the ear.

3. *Facial*—controls bleeding from wounds of face below the eye and

above the jawbone. Apply pressure at jawbone.

4. *Subclavian*—artery beneath the clavicle, a part of the shoulder, it controls bleeding from wounds in the extreme upper part of the arm, the armpit, and the shoulder. Apply pressure at collarbone.

5. *Brachial*—pertains to the arm and controls bleeding from the hand and forearm. Apply pressure midway between shoulder and elbow.

6. *Femoral*—one of two main arteries of the thigh supplying blood to the leg, it controls bleeding from the foot, leg or thigh. Apply pressure at middle of groin.

Shock

Shock is a disorder of the circulatory system, caused by a serious illness, injury or a sudden psychic disturbance. It is characterized most prominently by a decrease in blood pressure and a weak, rapid pulse. Shock often accompanies extreme loss of blood, an impairment of breathing, heart failure, severe burns, poisoning, or an overdose of drugs.

The degree of shock varies from faintness and shallow breathing to unconsciousness and death. You must treat a person in shock immediately.

Signs/symptoms: Shallow breathing; rapid (usually over 100), weak pulse; nausea and vomiting; shivering; pale, moist skin; confusion; drooping eyelids; dilated pupils; and collapse.

First-aid treatment

Establish and maintain an open airway. Control bleeding, if present. Keep victim lying down. Exceptions are if victim has suffered head and chest injuries, a heart attack, a stroke, sunstroke. Then, if the person has no spinal injury, he may be more comfortable and breathe more easily in a semireclining position with his head raised a few inches. If in doubt, keep the victim lying flat. Elevate the feet about 12 inches unless injury would be aggravated by this position and cause pain. Maintain normal body temperature. Place blankets under and over the victim. Be sure victim is not too warm or he will begin to sweat. Give nothing by mouth, especially stimulants or alcoholic beverages. The only exception is if the injured person is conscious, is not vomiting and does not have an abdominal injury, and if medical help will not arrive for an hour or more. Then give victim a solution of one teaspoon salt and $\frac{1}{2}$ teaspoon baking soda in one quart of water. Give an adult four ounces of this solution—approximately $\frac{1}{2}$ glass—every 15 minutes for one hour. Give a child two ounces, and an infant one ounce. Always treat for shock in lesser injuries.

TRANSPORTING THE VICTIM

A seriously injured person often requires transportation to a hospital, to a physician's office or to his own home. It is always best to transport the victim by ambulance with trained personnel, but sometimes proper transportation is not immediately available. It is the responsibility of the first aider then to insure that the victim is transported in a manner which prevents further injury and avoids subjecting the victim to any unnecessary pain or discomfort. No matter how expert the first-aid emergency care has been, improper handling and careless transportation often add to the severity of the original injuries, increase the possibility of shock, and frequently endanger life.

Do not move a victim until you have made a thorough examination and treated any life-threatening conditions, including severe bleeding, impaired breathing and shock. The only exception is if you and the victim are in immediate danger at the accident scene, such as in the case of a fire or an explosion.

Seriously injured persons should be moved only in a lying-down position. If proper transportation is not immediately available, continue care of the victim to conserve his strength until adequate means of transportation can be found.

Pulling the victim

If a person is in a life-threatening situation and must be pulled or dragged to safety, pull him in the direction of the long axis of his body, preferably from the shoulders—not sideways (see Fig. 1-11). Avoid bending or twisting the neck or the trunk. If a blanket, board or cardboard is available, move the victim on that (see Fig. 1-12).

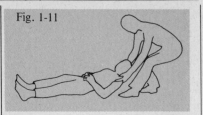
Fig. 1-11

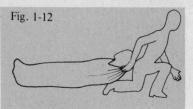
Fig. 1-12

Various carries

The stretcher is the preferred method of transportation, but various carries can be used in emergencies when a stretcher is not available. The following methods should be used only when it is certain that transporting will not aggravate an injury, such as a neck or spinal injury.

If the victim is conscious and has no neck or spinal injury, you may assist him to walk from the accident. Place one of his arms around your neck, hold his hand at your chest and place your other arm around his waist.

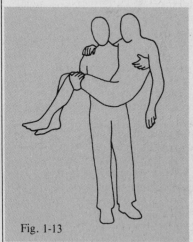
Fig. 1-13

One adult can usually support and carry a lightweight adult or child if the victim does not have a spinal or neck injury or any other serious wounds. The best method is to support the victim under his knees and under his upper back and armpit (see Fig. 1-13). Sometimes the victim can be carried on the rescuer's back (see Fig. 1-14).

PRINCIPLES OF FIRST AID

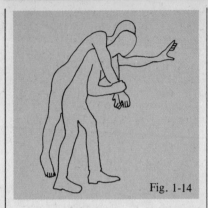

Fig. 1-14

Two adults can take the victim from the accident scene in a chair-lift carry (see Fig. 1-15). If an actual chair is available, two rescuers can support the victim in it (see Fig. 1-16). Both of these methods are useful if the victim must be carried up or down stairs.

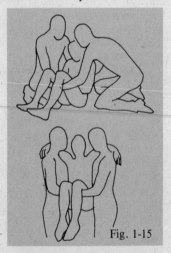

Fig. 1-15

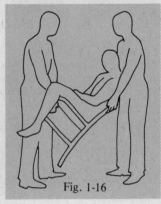

Fig. 1-16

Three- or four-man lift and carry

Three or four people using the lift-and-carry method can move an injured person with a minimum of further injury or discomfort to the victim. Use this method when moving an injured person a short distance or through a narrow passageway, or when a stretcher is not available and the victim must be kept in a lying-down position. You can also use this lift when an injured person is being placed on or taken off a stretcher.

Three persons are required for this lift and a fourth is desirable. A fourth person is necessary if the victim has suffered a spinal injury, because his head must be held securely. Proper lifting must be done by commands of a leader or by one of the bearers, usually the one at the victim's head.

Each of the three persons kneels (on his knee nearest the victim's feet). One person should be opposite the victim's shoulders, one opposite his hips, and the third opposite the victim's knees. Unless the nature of the victim's injuries makes it undesirable, the bearers kneel by the victim's uninjured or less injured side.

The first person should place his hands under the victim's shoulders and neck; the second person should place his hands under the victim's thighs and small of the back; the third person should place his hands under the victim's ankles and knees (see Fig. 1-17); and the fourth person, if available, should help support the trunk from the opposite side, to prevent the victim from rolling.

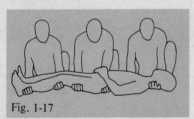

Fig. 1-17

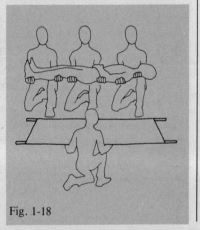

Fig. 1-18

Step 1: The leader will tell the bearers "Prepare to lift victim."
Step 2: The leader will then say "Lift victim." The bearers slowly lift the victim and support him on their knees. If a stretcher is available, stop in this position and slide stretcher under the victim (see Fig. 1-18). Then lower the victim on command of the leader. If stretcher is not available and cannot be brought to the victim, proceed to Step 3.
Step 3: The leader will tell the bearers "Prepare to rise with victim." Bearers turn victim slowly to his side until he rests against their chests.
Step 4: When the leader says "Rise with victim," the bearers rise slowly with the victim and carry him away from the scene of the accident (see Fig. 1-19). To place victim down, the rescuers reverse the procedure.

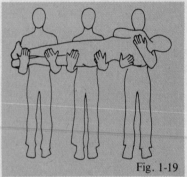

Fig. 1-19

Stretchers

Test a stretcher before you place a victim on it. Use a person about the same weight as the victim. The person should be face down so that if the stretcher should break or tear when it is picked up, he will be able to catch himself.

Stretcher boards:

Long boards. Stretcher boards can be made from a wide board, approximately 1½ inches thick, or from laminated plywood, about ¾ of an inch thick. They are usually about 78 inches in length and about 18 inches in width. They have slots about one inch wide placed along the edges through which cravat bandages are passed to secure the victim to the board (see Fig. 1-20). The slots may also serve as hand holds. Some variations have additional slots in the center of the boards so that each leg may be secured separately to the board (see Fig. 1-21). Some also have foot rests (see Fig. 1-22).

22

YOURSELF

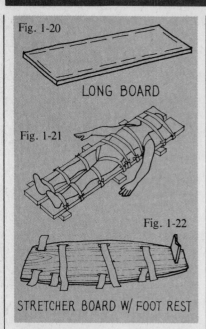

Fig. 1-20
LONG BOARD

Fig. 1-21

Fig. 1-22

STRETCHER BOARD W/ FOOT REST

To place a victim on the board, roll him on his side, then roll him onto the board. Always turn the victim's body as a unit so as not to twist it and cause further injury. It is essential to use several rescuers: one at the victim's head, one at his feet, and one on each side. Again, pick a leader and follow his commands of "Lift" and "March."

Fig. 1-23
SHORT BOARD

Short boards. Use a short board (see Fig. 1-23) if the victim is in a sitting position such as in a car or if a long board is not available. Position the board to the victim before any attempt is made to move him. Placing a cloth or some padding between the board and the back of the victim's neck provides additional comfort. Use a bandage to secure the victim's head and arms to the board.

Improvised stretchers: You can improvise a stretcher with a blanket, brattice cloth of similar size, a rope, or a strong sheet and two poles or pieces of pipe each seven to eight feet long (see Fig. 1-24). Place one pole or pipe about one foot from the center of the unfolded blanket. Fold the short side of the blanket over the pole to-

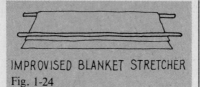

IMPROVISED BLANKET STRETCHER
Fig. 1-24

ward the other side. Place the second pole or pipe on the two thicknesses of blanket about two feet from the first and parallel to it. Fold the remaining side of the blanket over the second pole toward the first pole. When the injured person is placed on the blanket, the weight of the body secures the folds. Be sure that the victim will not roll during transportation. It is helpful to have four rescuers present when you use this method.

Transporting victim in a vehicle

If an ambulance is not available and you must transport the victim to a hospital or doctor, do so in a flat-bottomed vehicle such as a station wagon or van. (Two-door passenger cars are unsatisfactory.) In transporting the victim, be sure to support his vital functions and keep his airway open.

APPLYING DRESSINGS AND BANDAGES

Dressings and bandages protect wounds and burns from further injury and from the threat of infection. The dressing is applied to the site of the injury, and the bandage is put on top to hold the dressing in place. The size of both dressing and bandage depends on the size and type of injury and the materials you have at hand.

In applying a dressing and bandage, remember not to touch the wound or burned area with your hand, your clothing or anything that is not sterile.

Dressings

A dressing, also known as a compress, must be clean and sterile. Most dressings, available in a variety of shapes and sizes, come in sterilized individual packages. Always leave a dressing in its package until you need to use it. Then when applying it, try not to touch the part of the dressing which will come in contact with the wound or burned area so that you keep the dressing sterile.

Cotton gauze is the best material for a dressing, but when that is not available, you can substitute a handkerchief, towel, napkin or sheet. Wash

and iron the improvised fabric to sterilize it. If that is impossible, take the cleanest cloth available, such as a strip torn from a sheet, and sterilize it by holding it close to an open flame until you have evenly scorched the fabric. Do not, however, burn the cloth. When the cloth has cooled, apply it to the site of injury. If you cannot do that or don't have time, use the cleanest cloth at hand.

Note. Never use absorbent cotton as a dressing because it will stick to the wound, and never place adhesive directly on a wound or burn. If blood saturates the dressing, put another on top of the original dressing.

Selecting dressings: There are many dressings to choose from at your local drugstore. Be sure any dressing you use is wide enough to completely cover the wound and the surrounding areas. Following are the more common dressings that you should have in your home first-aid kit. An adhesive compress, or bandage (also known as a plastic strip adhesive or bandaid), consists of a small area of gauze fixed to a plastic or fabric adhesive. Available in a variety of sizes, the adhesive compress (see Fig. 1-25)

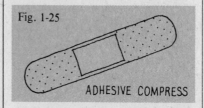

Fig. 1-25
ADHESIVE COMPRESS

is sold under many trade names. Be sure you buy ones that are individually packaged.

Nonadherent gauze compress. A nonadherent gauze compress is a pad of several thicknesses of folded gauze available in many sizes, usually individually packaged (see Fig. 1-26).

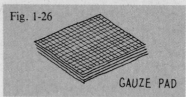

Fig. 1-26
GAUZE PAD

Bandage compress. A bandage compress is a pad of several thicknesses of sterile gauze sewn to the middle of a strip of muslin (see Fig. 1-27). Available in different widths, the

23

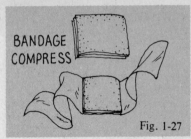

BANDAGE COMPRESS

Fig. 1-27

bandage compress is folded so that its sterile gauze pad can be applied directly to the open wound with no exposure to the air or the fingers. Place a sterile bandage compress over a wound and tie it in place with a bandage.

Bandages

Bandages hold dressings or splints in place, control bleeding through pressure, and provide support for muscles and injuries by immobilizing a part of the body through a sling or other device. Cotton gauze and muslin are the preferred materials for a bandage, but when these are not available, you can improvise a bandage from a handkerchief, scarf, pillowcase, or sheet. Use the cleanest fabric available, but do not worry if it is not sterile since you will not place the bandage directly against a wound.

Bandage wounds firmly—but never tightly—placing the part to be bandaged in the position in which it is to be left. Because swelling frequently follows an injury, a tight bandage may interfere with the supply of blood and damage surrounding tissue. In bandaging arms or legs, leave the tips of the fingers or toes uncovered where possible so that you can watch for swelling and changes of color and feel for coldness—all of which signal interference with circulation. If these signals do appear or if a victim complains of numbness or a tingling sensation, loosen the bandage at once. On the other hand, never apply a bandage too loosely because it may slip off and expose the wound. Do not apply a wet bandage except in treating burns and abdominal wounds.

Always tie bandages with a square, or reef, knot unless instructed otherwise. To tie a square knot, take an end of the bandage in each hand, pass the end in the right hand over the end in the left hand and tie a single knot. Then pass the end now in the left hand over the end in the right hand

and complete the knot. The free ends after the second knot are in the same place as they were after the first knot. The rule to remember in tying a square knot is: right over left, then left over right.

Selecting bandages: Following are the most common bandages you will need to use in covering wounds and burns. Keep an ample supply in your home first-aid kit.

Triangular bandage. The standard triangular bandage is made from a piece of cloth 40 inches square by folding the square diagonally and cutting along the fold. It is usually made from unbleached cotton cloth, although any kind of cloth will do. In emergencies, a triangular bandage can be improvised from a clean handkerchief, clean piece of shirt, or clean sheet. Use the triangular bandage to improvise a tourniquet, to support a fracture or dislocation, to apply a splint or form a sling (see Fig. 1-28), to cover an injury of the chest, back or shoulder.

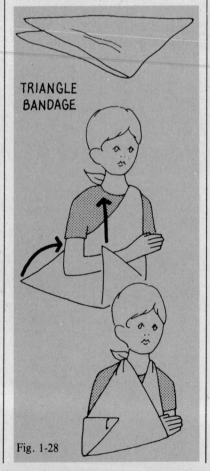

TRIANGLE BANDAGE

Fig. 1-28

Cravat bandage. A triangular bandage can be used open or folded. When folded, it is known as a cravat bandage and gives additional support, as for a sprained ankle or elbow. It is especially helpful when used for smaller areas such as a wound of the cheek. To prepare a cravat bandage, make a $1^1/_2$-inch fold along the base of the triangular bandage (see Fig. 1-29). Then bring the point to the center of the folded base, placing the point underneath the fold. This makes a wide cravat bandage (see Fig. 1-29). The bandage may be divided again by folding lengthwise along a line midway between the base and the new top of the bandage. This makes a medium cravat bandage (see Fig. 1-29). If folding is repeated, a narrow cravat bandage is made (see Fig. 1-29).

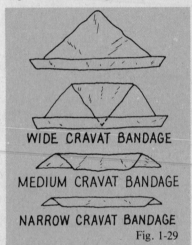

WIDE CRAVAT BANDAGE

MEDIUM CRAVAT BANDAGE

NARROW CRAVAT BANDAGE

Fig. 1-29

This method of making different-size cravat bandages offers the advantage of having different widths to suit different-size wounds. To complete the bandage, tie the ends together. Place knots where they do not cause discomfort and may be easily reached.

Gauze roller bandage. The gauze roller bandage, available in different widths for different parts of the body, can fit snugly around irregular parts of the body such as the fingers and toes. When using, unwind the roll only as you apply it in order to keep it clean. Apply the bandage according to how you use it. For example, around fingers and toes, use a spiral turn (see Fig. 1-30); for arms and legs, use a spiral reverse turn (see Fig. 1-31); and for an injury on the palm or ankle, use a figure 8 (see Fig. 1-32). Whatever technique you use, be care-

24

SPIRAL TURN

Fig. 1-30

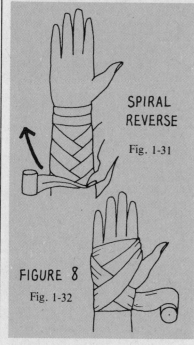

SPIRAL REVERSE

Fig. 1-31

FIGURE 8

Fig. 1-32

ful not to make turns of the bandage successively tighter.

Muslin binder bandage. The muslin binder bandage holds in place bulky dressings for wounds or burns of the chest, abdomen and back. If no muslin is available, you can use a sheet or towel. Be sure the material is wide enough to completely cover the dressing and long enough to go

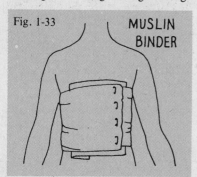

Fig. 1-33

MUSLIN BINDER

around the part of the body it must cover. Fasten binder together with safety pins (see Fig. 1-33).

Elastic bandage. An elastic bandage is made of a woven material in varying lengths and widths. Never apply an elastic bandage too tightly. In securing, begin at the lower part of the wound. After two circular turns, proceed upward, overlapping as you go (see Fig. 1-34). Use metal clips or safety pins to secure the bandage.

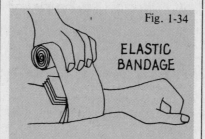

Fig. 1-34

ELASTIC BANDAGE

FIRST-AID SUPPLIES

Every home should have a medical supply chest with a lock to keep out children, and smaller versions for the car, camper, and boat. You can put together your own kit, including enough supplies for the number of members in your family and any prescription drugs for specific medical problems, or you can buy some already stocked first-aid kits from such companies as White Cross and Johnson & Johnson. These kits usually allow you to add refills. No matter what kind of kit you buy or put together, sterility of the supplies is of prime importance.

Make it a habit to routinely check your medical supply chest to be sure you have all necessary items, and dispose of any items that may have become dated.

Medical supply chest for the home

Absorbent cotton (4 oz.)
Oval eye pads ($2\frac{1}{2}$" $\times$ $2\frac{5}{8}$")
Plastic strip bandages (a variety of sizes: $\frac{3}{4}$" $\times$ 3", $\frac{3}{8}$" $\times$ $1\frac{1}{2}$", 1" $\times$ 3", 2" wide)
Lomotil
Sheer strip bandages (1" wide)
Splint
Adhesive tape ($1\frac{1}{2}$" $\times$ $2\frac{1}{2}$ yards, $\frac{1}{2}$" $\times$ 5 yards)
Nonadherent gauze pads (2" $\times$ 3", 2" $\times$ 2", 4" $\times$ 4")
Aromatic spirits of ammonia

Anti-motion-sickness tablets
Oil of cloves
Antiseptic wipes
Measuring cup
Activated charcoal
Syrup of ipecac
Tweezers
Scissors
Aspirin, for children and adults (or Tylenol)
Calamine lotion
Petroleum jelly
Triangular bandage
Rubbing alcohol
Tongue depressors
Thermometers, oral and rectal
Tourniquet
Elastic bandage (3" wide)
Cotton-tipped swabs
Gauze roller bandage (2" $\times$ 10 yards, 1" $\times$ 5 yards)
First-aid cream such as Neosporin ointment
Sunburn lotion
Cotton balls
Adhesive pads ($2\frac{7}{8}$" $\times$ $4\frac{1}{2}$")
Bandage compress (2", 3" or 4" widths)
Short board for splint
Safety pins

Camping first-aid kit

Plastic strip bandages ($\frac{3}{4}$" $\times$ 3")
Adhesive tape ($\frac{1}{2}$" $\times$ $2\frac{1}{2}$ yards)
Absorbent cotton ($2\frac{1}{2}$ oz.)
Gauze roller bandage (2" wide $\times$ 5 yards)
Nonadherent gauze pads (2" $\times$ 3")
Aromatic spirits of ammonia
Anti-motion-sickness tablets
Aspirin, for children and adults (or Tylenol)
Antiseptic wipes
Scissors
Tweezers
Thermometers, oral and rectal
Lomotil
Elastic bandage (3" wide)

Boating first-aid kit

Plastic strip bandages ($\frac{3}{4}$" $\times$ 3")
Sunburn lotion
Adhesive tape ($\frac{1}{2}$" $\times$ $2\frac{1}{2}$ yards)
Absorbent cotton ($\frac{1}{2}$ oz.)
Gauze roller bandage (2" wide $\times$ 5 yards)
Nonadherent gauze pads (2" $\times$ 3")
Aromatic spirits of ammonia
Anti-motion-sickness tablets
Antiseptic wipes
Scissors
Tweezers

Elastic bandage (3" wide)
Thermometers, oral and rectal
Lomotil
Aspirin, for children and adults (or Tylenol)
Salt tablets
Hot-water bottle
Oval eye pads

Travel first-aid kit

Plastic strip bandages ($^3/_4$" $\times$ 3")
Adhesive tape ($^1/_2$" $\times$ 2$^1/_2$ yards)
Absorbent cotton ($^1/_2$ oz.)
Gauze roller bandage (2" wide $\times$ 5 yards)
Nonadherent gauze pads (2" $\times$ 3")
Scissors

FAMILY MEMBERS' BLOOD TYPES

Name	Type
_____	_____
_____	_____
_____	_____
_____	_____
_____	_____

FAMILY MEMBERS' KNOWN ALLERGIES

Name	Allergy
_____	_____
_____	_____
_____	_____
_____	_____

EMERGENCY TELEPHONE NUMBERS

(Keep these numbers handy in several places in your home.)

Physician _____
Alternate Physician _____
Pediatrician _____
Dentist _____
Hospital Emergency Room _____
Fire Department _____
Police Department _____
Ambulance _____

Life-support Service _____
Poison-control Center _____
All-night Pharmacy _____
Father at Work _____
Mother at Work _____
Neighbor _____
Alternate Neighbor _____

IMMUNIZATION RECORD

Names				
Birth Dates				
DPT	First			
	Second			
	Third			
	Fourth			
	Boosters			
Polio	First			
	Second			
	Third			
	Booster			
	Booster			
Measles Rubella Mumps				

The following chapters, arranged in alphabetical order, are designed both for quick reference during an emergency and for periodic review.

2
ABDOMINAL PAIN

Abdominal pain can be caused by anything from an upset stomach to an acute appendicitis that requires surgery. Pain may vary from dull to stabbing, and from occasional to constant. Nausea and vomiting may also accompany the abdominal pain. Pain that persists, especially when accompanied by a fever, requires the immediate attention of a physician. While victim awaits medical help, have him rest. Do not give him any food, or laxative, purgative or cathartic.

The five most common causes of abdominal pain, besides food allergies (see pages 37–38) and food illnesses (see pages 57–69), are appendicitis, hernia, gallstones, kidney stones and swallowing of a foreign object.

APPENDICITIS

The appendix is a tube which extends from the large intestine in the lower right part of the abdomen. It has no digestive function and is probably vestigial. An infected appendix will develop into a condition known as appendicitis, which if neglected may result in the rupturing of the appendix. If the appendix does rupture, the infection will spread throughout the abdomen and cause a serious illness known as peritonitis (an infection of the tissues lining the abdominal cavity and enclosing many of the organs).

Appendicitis can occur at any age, but is most frequent in adults between the ages of 20 and 30.

Signs/symptoms: The pain of appendicitis begins high in the center of the abdomen and is followed by nausea and sometimes vomiting. Pain then shifts to the area over the appendix in the lower right portion of the abdomen, and usually becomes more severe.

Symptoms may vary, however. The pain may occur in the back or pelvis, or the person may experience no pain. Fever often accompanies an appendicitis attack.

Diarrhea, often associated with other abdominal illnesses, is usually not present in appendicitis.

First-aid treatment

Get victim to a physician, even if pain subsides. Do not apply heat to the site of pain while awaiting help. Give nothing to eat or drink. Physician will perform a rectal examination to locate the points of tenderness and take a white-blood-cell count. If the cause of the pain is appendicitis, then the appendix will be removed by a surgeon.

HERNIA

A hernia is a rupture of tissue or an organ through a weak wall that normally holds it in place. The most common type of hernia is the protrusion of the loop of the intestine through a weak part of the abdominal wall. Although both men and women may develop hernias, they are most common in men—especially overweight men.

Causes: A hernia usually develops following a strenuous activity that produces a marked increase in pressure within the abdomen.

Signs/symptoms: The main sign of a hernia is a globular swelling that is tender to touch. At the exact moment of protrusion, a victim may feel a sharp pain, although a hernia can occur with little or no pain. Nausea and vomiting may accompany a hernia.

First-aid treatment

Do not push a bulging hernia back inside. Instead have the victim lie down on his back and draw up his knees to his chest. If the bulging does not disappear, have the victim turn over on his stomach and bring his knees up under his chest so that he raises his buttocks. If this method also doesn't work, have the victim lie on his back. Apply cold compresses to hernia area. If hernia still does not disappear, call a physician. Surgery may be necessary, especially for a strangulated hernia that may shut off the essential blood supply of the loop of the bowel. If the patient is in great pain and must be transported, do so with him lying down on a stretcher (see pages 22–23).

GALLSTONES

In the gallbladder, a pear-shaped sac under the liver, bile manufactured by the liver is chemically changed and temporarily stored to help digest fat. The gallbladder can become inflamed, stop working and become filled with stones—gallstones—that can obstruct the flow of bile to the small intestine.

Causes: Some of the frequent causes of gallstones are a diet high in fats, oral contraceptives, menopausal estrogens, diabetes, pregnancy. (A typical candidate is "fat, fair, forty and female.")

Signs/symptoms: Pain in the upper mid-abdomen that is severe and colicky and radiates to the right side along the rib cage and then around the side to the back is a strong indication of gallstones. Pain may be followed by protracted nausea and vomiting, and sometimes by jaundice. If the gallbladder becomes inflamed, a victim may also develop a fever.

First-aid treatment

Seek prompt medical attention. If the patient is in severe pain, do not let him walk; transport him lying down on a stretcher (see pages 22–23). A physician will do an X ray and sometimes an ultrasound examination. Many people who have frequent attacks of gallstones or who develop complications may have to have their gallbladder removed. In the future, drugs may dissolve the most common types of gallstones, formed primarily of cholesterol.

KIDNEY STONES

The kidneys, two reddish, bean-shaped organs lying below the ribs near the spine, separate water and waste products from the blood and excrete them as urine through the bladder and ureter. Kidney stones, formed from phosphates, urates, and other chemicals, block the ureter and if not removed obstruct the flow of urine. The kidneys then become swollen, and severe pain and infection develop.

Causes: The most frequent known causes of kidney stones are gout, which produces uric acid stones, and diseases of the parathyroid gland. Moreover, some people have a tendency to form crystals of calcium in the kidney for no known reason.

Signs/symptoms: An excruciating pain that may begin in the back or anywhere along the course of the ureter toward the groin characterizes the development of kidney stones. The pain may become severe enough to produce shock. Microscopic, or blood, urine may also develop.

First-aid treatment

Take the victim to a physician. If victim is in severe pain, do not let him walk, but transport him lying down on a stretcher (see pages 22–23). A physician will examine victim's urine, X-ray the kidneys and relieve pain with an injection. Surgery may be necessary.

SWALLOWED OBJECT

Objects that are swallowed and will not dissolve in the stomach can perforate or block the intestine. Have the person check his bowel movements to see if the object has passed. If object does not pass and victim has severe pain, vomits or has difficulty in breathing or coughing, take him to a physician. The physician can locate and follow the foreign object by X rays. Surgery may be necessary.

3

ALCOHOL ABUSE

The drinking of alcohol is widely accepted socially in the United States. Two thirds of the adult population drink at least occasionally. A recent survey found that most American adolescents have had at least some experience with alcoholic beverages, and over one half of them drink at least once a month. Among this large percentage of drinkers, there are some who abuse alcohol, consuming large amounts over a long period. This can cause social and economic detriment as well as physical damage that may lead to death.

Alcohol, the major active ingredient in wine, beer and distilled liquor, is a natural substance formed by the reaction of fermenting sugar with yeast spores. There are many alcohols, but the kind in alcoholic beverages is ethyl alcohol, a colorless, flammable liquid with an intoxicating effect. Alcohol is a drug which can produce feelings of well-being, sedation, intoxication or unconsciousness, depending on the amount or manner in which it is drunk. It can also be classified as a food since it contains calories, although it has no nutritional value.

Unlike other foods, alcohol does not have to be digested. When a person drinks, 20 percent of the alcohol is absorbed immediately into the bloodstream through the walls of the stomach. The other 80 percent enters the bloodstream after being quickly processed through the gastrointestinal tract. The alcohol is carried to the liver, then to the heart and other body tissues, and to the secretions of the body. Intoxication results when the liver receives more alcohol than it can metabolize. The alcohol eventually acts on the brain's central control areas, slowing down or depressing brain activity.

A low level of alcohol in the blood, such as would result from consumption of a 12-ounce can of beer, has a mild tranquilizing effect on most people. A sedative, alcohol seems to act temporarily as a stimulant for many people when they first start to drink. This is because alcohol's initial effects are on those parts of the brain affecting learned behavior patterns such as self-control. After a drink or two, this learned behavior may temporarily disappear, making a person lose inhibitions, talk more freely, or feel like the "life of the party." On the other hand, a person could feel aggressive or depressed after a little drinking.

Higher blood alcohol levels depress brain activity to the point that memory as well as muscle coordination and balance may be temporarily impaired. Still larger alcohol intake within a relatively short period of time depresses deeper parts of the brain, severely affecting judgment and dulling the senses.

If steady, heavy drinking continues, the alcohol anesthetizes the deepest levels of the brain and can cause coma or death by depressing the heart functions and breathing. It can also cause inflammation of the stomach lining, leading to alcoholic gastritis and internal bleeding. Cirrhosis of the liver and destruction of brain cells may also follow.

How fast does alcohol take effect?

The rapidity with which alcohol enters the bloodstream and exerts its effects on the brain and body depends on a number of factors.

How fast you drink: If you sip your drink slowly and do not have more than one drink every 2 hours, the alcohol will not have a chance to jolt your brain or build up significantly in your blood, and you will feel few unpleasant effects. Gulping drinks, however, produces immediate intoxicating effects and depression of deeper brain centers.

Whether your stomach is empty or full: Eating, especially before you drink but also while you drink, will slow down alcohol's rate of absorption into your bloodstream and produce a more even response to the alcohol.

What you drink: Most beer contains about 4 percent pure alcohol. Ordinary table wines contain up to 14 percent pure alcohol. Liquors are distilled beverages containing about 40 to 50 percent pure alcohol. Diluting the alcohol with water slows the absorption but mixing it with carbonated beverages such as club soda and ginger ale increases the rate of absorption. Whether the alcohol is cold or hot also makes a difference. Cold drinks take longer to be absorbed than warm drinks do.

How much you weigh: The effect of alcohol on the body varies according to a person's weight. Alcohol is quickly distributed uniformly within the circulatory system. Therefore, if the same amount is drunk by two people with different weights, the alcohol becomes more concentrated in the bloodstream of the lighter individual and is more intoxicating to that person.

Whether or not you drink regularly: Heavy drinkers develop a tolerance to alcohol and may not be as affected as people who do not drink as often.

The setting, mood or expectations: If you are sitting down relaxed while having a drink with a friend, alcohol will not affect you as much as when you are standing and drinking at a cocktail party. If you are emotionally upset, under stress or tired, alcohol may have a stronger impact on you than normally. Your expectations will also have an influence. If you think you are going to become drunk, you are likely to get drunk more quickly.

DRUNKENNESS

Drunkenness is characterized by temporary loss of control over physical and mental powers caused by excessive alcohol intake. The symptoms vary, but they can include impaired vision, distorted depth perception, thick speech, bad coordination, reduced ability to solve problems, unpredictability of mood, impairment of memory and bad judgment. In most states, a person is considered legally drunk when he or she has a 0.10 percent blood alcohol level.

It is illegal to drive a car after the specified blood alcohol concentration is reached. It is also extremely dangerous. There is strong evidence that alcohol plays a role in roughly half of all fatal automobile crashes, and a role in a fourth to a third of all serious accidents (see chart, below). One cannot

solid food and take an aspirin.

Heavy drinking can cause severe physiological damage, especially cirrhosis of the liver, and is associated with ulcers, heart disease and diabetes. Heavy drinking can also lead to mental or nervous disorders or cause permanent brain damage. It can be physiologically addictive, producing withdrawal symptoms when the alcohol intake ceases abruptly.

First-aid treatment

Alcohol intoxication, whether due to an acute overdose or prolonged abuse, requires treatment.

If the person is resting or sleeping and is breathing normally, there is no need to take any action. If the person, however, is in shock (see page 21) or if he does not respond, get medical help immediately. Maintain an open airway, give artificial respiration if necessary (see pages 17–18), and cover the person with a blanket or apply a hot-water bottle to keep him warm. If the person is

serious psychological, physical or social problems, alcoholism is developing or is already present. It is a disease that affects one of every 15 drinkers.

Alcoholism cannot be cured, but it can be arrested. If it is not, it will shorten a person's life by 10 to 12 years. At present, alcohol represents the third greatest killer in the United States, and the reason behind one-third of all suicides.

Warning signs of alcoholism

The following questions will help a person learn if he has some of the symptoms of alcoholism, or if a member of his family does.

Yes No

□ □ 1. Do you occasionally drink heavily after a disappointment, a quarrel, or a conflict with the boss?

□ □ 2. When you have trouble or feel under pressure, do you always drink more heavily than usual?

□ □ 3. Have you noticed that you are able to handle more liquor than you could when you were first drinking?

□ □ 4. Did you ever wake up on the "morning after" and discover that you could not remember part of the evening before, even though your friends tell you that you did not pass out?

□ □ 5. When drinking with other people, do you try to have a few extra drinks when others will not know it?

□ □ 6. Are there certain occasions when you feel uncomfortable if alcohol is not available?

□ □ 7. Have you recently noticed that when you begin drinking you are in more of a hurry to get the first drink than you used to be?

□ □ 8. Do you sometimes feel a little guilty about your drinking?

□ □ 9. Are you secretly irritated when your family or friends discuss your drinking?

DRINK CHART											
Number of Drinks (over two-hour period) 1½ ozs. 86-proof liquor or 12-oz. can of beer											
Your Weight											
100	1	2	3	4	5	6	7	8	9	10	11	12
120	1	2	3	4	5	6	7	8	9	10	11	12
140	1	2	3	4	5	6	7	8	9	10	11	12
160	1	2	3	4	5	6	7	8	9	10	11	12
180	1	2	3	4	5	6	7	8	9	10	11	12
200	1	2	3	4	5	6	7	8	9	10	11	12
220	1	2	3	4	5	6	7	8	9	10	11	12
240	1	2	3	4	5	6	7	8	9	10	11	12

Social	Warning	Intoxicated
Drive with caution BAC to .05%	Driving impaired .05% – .09%	Do not drive 10% & up

Note: This table is only a guide. Information presented is based on averages and may vary according to circumstances, or from individual to individual. Courtesy of the U.S. Department of Transportation, National Highway Traffic Safety Administration.

sober up by drinking black coffee, taking a cold shower or breathing pure oxygen. It takes a specific amount of time for the body to burn up a quantity of alcohol, generally at the rate of 7 grams of pure alcohol per hour. Once alcohol is in the bloodstream, nothing can be done about its effects except to wait until it is metabolized by the body.

A hangover is the body's reaction to excessive drinking. The miseries of hangover may include nausea, gastritis, anxiety and headache. Fatigue almost always accompanies a hangover. The best first aid is to rest, eat some

unconscious, place him on his side with his head facing downward. His saliva may then drool from his mouth. Sometimes an intoxicated person may be hallucinating or may be violent. If so, you will have to handle him carefully to prevent him from harming himself or another person.

ALCOHOLISM

Alcoholism is a serious progressive illness, marked by dependence on alcohol—a loss of control over one's drinking. When a person continues to drink despite the fact that it is causing

Yes No

☐ ☐ 10. Have you recently noticed an increase in the frequency of your memory blackouts?

☐ ☐ 11. Do you often find that you wish to continue drinking after your friends say they have had enough?

☐ ☐ 12. Do you usually have a reason for the occasions when you drink heavily?

☐ ☐ 13. When you are sober, do you often regret things you have done or said while drinking?

☐ ☐ 14. Have you tried switching brands or following different plans for controlling your drinking?

☐ ☐ 15. Have you often failed to keep the promises you have made to yourself about cutting down on your drinking?

☐ ☐ 16. Have you ever tried to control your drinking by making a change in jobs or moving to a new location?

☐ ☐ 17. Do you try to avoid family or close friends while you are drinking?

☐ ☐ 18. Are you having an increasing number of financial and work problems?

☐ ☐ 19. Do more people seem to be treating you unfairly?

☐ ☐ 20. Do you eat very little or irregularly when you are drinking?

☐ ☐ 21. Do you sometimes have the "shakes" in the morning and find that it helps to have a little drink?

☐ ☐ 22. Have you recently noticed that you cannot drink as much as you once did?

☐ ☐ 23. Do you sometimes stay drunk for several days at a time?

☐ ☐ 24. Do you sometimes feel very depressed and wonder whether life is worth living?

☐ ☐ 25. Sometimes after periods of drinking, do you see or hear things that are not there?

☐ ☐ 26. Do you get terribly frightened after you have been drinking heavily?

If you answered "yes" to any of the questions, you have some of the symptoms that may indicate alcoholism.

"Yes" answers to several of the questions indicate the following stages of alcoholism:

Questions 1-8:   Early Stage
Questions 9-21:   Middle Stage
Questions 22-26:   Beginning of Final Stage

(Reprinted from the pamphlet "What Are the Signs of Alcoholism?" by the National Council on Alcoholism, 733 Third Avenue, New York, N.Y. 10017.)

Help for alcoholism

Help can be provided by a doctor, clergyman, local welfare agency, clinic, social worker, psychiatrist or psychologist, or a group such as Alcoholics Anonymous. This organization, whose local chapters are listed in telephone books, is a self-help group in which members participate in a type of group therapy that utilizes members' experiences for mutual support. Recovery requires total abstention, and anonymity is protected for all. There are also Alanon family groups to help relatives of alcoholics, and Alateens to help teenagers understand and cope with their parent's excessive drinking. The National Council on Alcoholism is a national voluntary health organization which also has local chapters in many communities for alcoholics seeking help. Whatever treatment an alcoholic pursues, the primary goal is to help him overcome his dependence on alcohol and develop a way of life that does not revolve around its use. The chances of improvement seem greatest if total abstinence is the goal.

As an individual, you can try to prevent alcoholism in yourself by following certain rules: drink slowly; drink while also eating; never have more to drink than you intended; never drink alone; try not to have a drink until evening. Be especially careful if alcoholism runs in your family.

You can also assume responsibilities as host or hostess to your friends. At dinner parties and other social gatherings, food should be served both before and with drinks. Food slows the rate at which the body absorbs alcohol. Soft drinks should be made available as an alternative to alcoholic beverages. These can be supplemented by nonalcoholic punches, fruit juices, tea and coffee. The guest who does not choose to drink alcoholic beverages should never be cajoled or shamed into doing so, whether the person is an abstainer, recovered alcoholic or social drinker who recognizes he has had enough. One effective method of giving your guests some extra time for alcohol effects to wear off is to close the bar at least one or two hours before you plan to break up the party. If someone is really drunk, insist on his not driving. If another guest cannot take him, call a taxi for him.

Note. Delirium tremens (DTs) is a major symptom complex of sudden alcohol withdrawal, requiring a doctor's supervision and hospitalization.

Mixing alcohol and other drugs

Alcohol does not mix well with any drug. The best advice is to avoid drinking when taking any kind of medication. For example, taking alcohol and aspirin together can produce bleeding of the stomach and intestine.

Alcohol and pregnancy

Alcoholism can have serious consequences for an unborn child. A child born with serious defects, physical or mental, is said to suffer from "fetal alcohol syndrome." Some children are even born experiencing withdrawal symptoms. A pregnant woman should abstain from drinking during the first six to eight weeks of pregnancy.

4

ALLERGIC REACTIONS

An allergy is a sensitivity or overreaction of the body to a substance which for most people causes no problems. The substance, known as an allergen, may be poison ivy, the chemical from an insect sting, a drug, a food, house dust, animal hair, cosmetics, or pollens from trees, grasses or weeds. The reaction may take many forms—for example, the sneezing and runny nose of hay fever, the wheezing and difficulty in breathing of asthma, or the itching of hives. The reactions to some substances can be serious and lead to life-threatening conditions. Some allergic reactions develop within minutes of exposure to the allergen (and are therefore called immediate hypersensitivity reactions), while others are delayed (and are thus known as delayed hypersensitivity reactions). This chapter will focus on allergies that cause reactions resulting in emergency situations.

Scientists have not yet been able to prove what causes allergies. Some people become allergic after exposure to a potential allergen, while others remain symptom free. In allergic individuals, cells in organs and tissues become sensitive to an allergen after one or more exposures. These cells become coated with a special antibody, immunoglobulin E (IgE). Normally, antibodies protect the body. However, when antibody IgE reacts with an allergen on the cell's surface, certain chemicals are released which, in turn, produce symptoms of allergy.

With proper care and treatment, allergies can be controlled. There are many kinds of medicine that can help, but true control is dependent on finding the cause. It is important to consult a doctor if you are troubled by allergies so that the doctor can find the cause of the allergy by questioning you and by performing laboratory and skin tests. In some cases, allergy shots may be a means to minimize or prevent allergic reactions.

POISON IVY ALLERGY

Allergic reactions to three native plants—poison ivy, poison oak and poison sumac, all members of the same plant genus—have long been a source of misery to residents of the United States and Canada.

The allergic response to poison ivy, oak and sumac occurs many hours or days after exposure. An estimated seven out of every ten Americans might be allergic if exposed to these plants, and possibly five out of every ten have had such a reaction.

An allergy to poison ivy, oak or sumac is most common in adults, but rare in very young children, probably because they are less exposed. Research has not been able to demonstrate family tendency toward an allergy to poison ivy, oak or sumac. A sensitivity to them usually lasts many years.

How does exposure occur?

The sticky sap of all three plants contains an active ingredient known as urushiol. The urushiols of these three plants are not identical, but are similar enough so that a person allergic to one will often react to the other two as well.

Cases of poison ivy allergy occur most frequently in the spring and summer when people spend a lot of time outdoors. The reaction can still develop in the winter, however, because the urushiol is present in dead or decaying plants. Since the urushiol is in the sap of the plant, rubbing or crushing the plant or a leaf provides sufficient contact for an allergic reaction. Exposure may occur in other ways, too. Smoke from burning plants may contain the urushiol on particles borne in the air and thus expose susceptible persons on their skin or in their nose, throat and lungs. Clothing or tools that touch the plants, or pets that rub against them, can pick up the sap and pass it to a person indirectly. Neglecting to clean these items after contact with poison ivy will reexpose the sufferer whenever he touches them.

What are the symptoms?

Symptoms of an allergy to poison ivy, oak or sumac usually develop within 12 to 48 hours after contact with the urushiol. The time may be as short as four hours or as long as 72, depending on one's sensitivity. The lesions are at their worst after about five days. They improve in a week or two even without therapy. However, extremely sensitive persons exposed to urushiol over large areas of the body may become quite ill.

At first the area which touched the plant becomes red, and then bumps and blisters appear. This is usually accompanied by itching and sometimes by swelling. After reaching their peak in several days, the oozing lesions begin to crust over and disappear. These lesions remain localized and appear only wherever the sap has touched the body. They rarely occur on the palms of the hands because the outer skin there is very thick and hard to penetrate. Contrary to common belief, scratching the lesions will not cause them to spread. The urushiol is not present in the blister fluids, but if it has not been completely washed off the skin, touching the lesion and then touching another area of the body can transfer the urushiol.

How is the allergy treated?

Most people are afraid of developing scars and of spreading the rash, so they tend to overtreat the condition, but these allergies leave no scars unless there is a secondary infection. The first and most important part of treatment is to make sure the skin and clothes are free of all sap. Adequate sudsing of the skin with an alkali soap (such as yellow laundry soap) or the use of 70 percent alcohol and rewashing of any clothing suspected of harboring urushiol should prevent spread of the lesions. With the source of urushiol eliminated, very mild cases of rash then require little or no further care; they will usually clear quickly by themselves. Wet, cold compresses of water, boric acid or liquid aluminum acetate may relieve any inflammation during the oozing period. Calamine lotion is a good drying agent and helps relieve itching. In more severe cases in extremely sensitive persons, a severe rash and swelling may develop, and the person may become quite ill. Those persons require immediate medical help.

In general, complications from poison ivy, oak or sumac allergy are rare, but a secondary infection can develop as a result of scratching which has introduced bacteria into the open sores. A doctor should always be consulted if this happens so that he can prescribe drugs to fight the infection. Infrequently, kidney problems can develop in a highly sensitive person with a severe, widespread case.

Treatment itself can lead to complications if the poison ivy sufferer overuses nonprescription lotions. These contain antihistamines, which may sensitize a patient to such an extent that he is unable to use the medications when needed in the future.

Prevention of the allergy

The surest way to prevent poison ivy allergy is to avoid contact with the

31

three plants. Learn to identify them.

Poison ivy: Poison ivy has slightly glossy green leaves which grow in groups of three, and its flowers and berries, when present, are greenish-white. It is usually a vine, but sometimes a trailing or erect shrub. Poison ivy is most common in the eastern and central portions of the United States (see Fig. 4-1).

Fig. 4-1

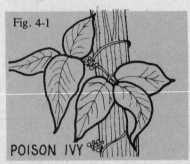

POISON IVY

Poison oak: Western poison oak closely resembles poison ivy, although it is usually more shrublike, and its leaves are shaped somewhat like oak leaves. This plant is found on the west coast of this continent (see Fig. 4-2). Another variety grows in such states as New Jersey, Tennessee, Kansas and Texas, also as a shrub.

Fig. 4-2

POISON OAK

Poison sumac: Poison sumac is found chiefly in uninhabited areas, especially in swampy locations. Thus, hikers, hunters, and other outdoors people should become familiar with it. A small tree about five or six feet high, poison sumac is distinguished from other sumacs by its drooping green berries (see Fig. 4-3); harmless sumacs have red, erect berry clusters. Poison sumac is most common east of the Mississippi River in swampy areas.

Avoiding these plants is difficult. Poison ivy and poison oak grow almost everywhere, in backyards as well as in woods and in pastures. Long

Fig. 4-3

POISON SUMAC

sleeves, long trouser legs and gloves will help you guard against exposure in heavily weeded areas. Animals do not usually react to urushiol, but since the resin may be on their fur, care should be taken in handling them. The family pet should be given a thorough bath if there is a chance it has contacted the plants.

To destroy poison ivy and oak around the home, the United States Department of Agriculture recommends the use of chemical weed killers. Check with the department to find out what is permissible to use. Since these chemicals can damage valuable vegetation, they should be carefully sprayed or even painted on the plant's leaves. The directions for using herbicides should be followed carefully because these chemicals can also be harmful to humans.

Grubbing out poison ivy and oak is a good method of eradication, but care must be taken not to touch the plants with bare hands. Grubbed-out plants should be buried, not burned or left for the unsuspecting trash collector. Urushiol can be carried in smoke.

Allergy shots

Avoidance is the best method of prevention for most people allergic to poison ivy, oak or sumac. For individuals like foresters or gardeners who would have to change occupations in order to avoid the plants, immunotherapy (more commonly called allergy shots) may be helpful. The shots may also be helpful for extremely sensitive people for whom careful avoidance is insufficient. As with other allergies, allergy shots for poison ivy, oak and sumac consist of frequent administration of a small amount of diluted poison ivy, oak or sumac extract. These shots are given before the season begins and never during an active attack of the allergy. The extract for the poison ivy, oak or sumac has

been given by mouth, rather than by injection, with varying degrees of temporary suppression. One of the disadvantages of this method can be gastrointestinal side effects. This therapy must be continued for some time, possibly six months or longer, and should be repeated every year, as the protection it provides is temporary.

INSECT ALLERGY

Scientists have long known that some bugs carry disease-causing microorganisms. Only in this century has it been recognized that insect bites or stings may also trigger allergic reactions. No one knows for sure how many people have insect allergy, although it may be as many as 4 per 1,000. Every year approximately 50 to 100 people in this country die from reactions to insect stings. More people are killed in this country each year by hymenoptera—bees, wasps, hornets, yellow jackets and fire ants—than by any other venomous creature, including rattlesnakes. Anyone—allergic or not—will react to some degree to an insect sting because the venom contains materials which are irritating to the body cells.

In insect allergy, allergens may be inhaled, injected, or taken by mouth, although the usual exposure is by a sting or a bite, which involves injection of the allergen by the offending insect. It is usually not the whole insect, but the venom or salivary secretions that cause the allergy.

People who are allergic to insects usually have other allergies and are most prone to severe reactions after age 30. A person's previous reaction to an insect sting is no clue to the severity of future reactions. The response could be entirely normal on one occasion, and the next sting might spark a serious allergic reaction. Insect sting reactions are most common during the summer months when insects are abundant and most active. During those months, people are outdoors and will therefore encounter insects more frequently.

Which insects cause allergy?

The stinging insects are the most dangerous, although the salivary secretions of biting insects (such as mosquitoes, flies, lice, fleas and kissing bugs) or the irritating substances left on the skin by crawling insects also may lead to a reaction, but a far less serious one.

Hymenoptera: There are many types of membrane-winged insects, or hymenoptera (see Fig. 4-4), but only a few of the stinging hymenoptera—bees, wasps, hornets, yellow jackets, and fire and harvester ants—cause serious allergic reactions in man. The yellow jacket and bee cause the most serious reactions.

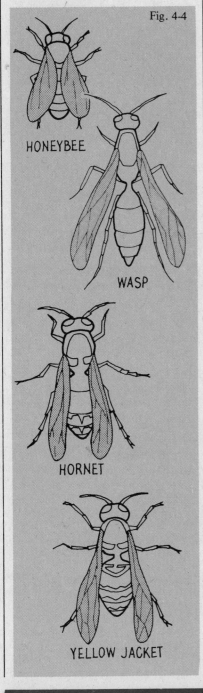

Fig. 4-4

HONEYBEE

WASP

HORNET

YELLOW JACKET

In the hymenoptera, the stinger works like a hypodermic syringe. Found only in the female, the stinger has small, venom-filled sacs located at its base. The venom is injected through a hollow tube in the center of the stinger. Most stinging hymenoptera can remove their stinger and use it again and again, but the stinger of the honey bee is barbed. Thus, when the honey bee tries to remove its stinger from human skin, both stinger and venom sacs are torn off and left in the victim as the injured bee flies away and dies.

Bees sting only to protect themselves or their hive, but yellow jackets, wasps and hornets sting in order to kill smaller insects, which are used as food. All hymenoptera stingers may be contaminated with bacteria and occasionally cause infections in man, although this seems to occur less commonly with honey bees.

The most common wasp, or vespid, threats to man are the hornets, yellow jackets and the polistes wasps, which are very protective of their nests. Usually dark blue, yellow or reddish brown, wasps can be identified by their narrow waists. Wasps are most interested in other insects for food, but are also attracted to nectars and overripe fruit.

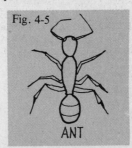

Fig. 4-5

ANT

Ants: Ants (see Fig. 4-5) are found almost everywhere, but only two kinds are believed to cause allergic reactions in man. These are harvester, or agricultural, ants and fire ants. The aggressive harvester ant lives in warm, dry, sandy areas and builds mounds that are easily recognized and avoided. The fire ant, especially the imported fire ant, is common in the southeastern United States. It constructs large mounds, but these are harder to avoid because they are low and sometimes naturally camouflaged. The ant's stinger is much like that of the bee, but it does not have barbs. Ants seem to sting because of

what they see or hear and sometimes what they smell. They bite for stability before stinging, but probably only the sting—when venom is released—is significant for allergy sufferers.

Other insects that cause allergy

Some biting insects cause allergic reactions, but fewer people seem to be bothered by them, and reactions are less severe. Mosquitoes (see Fig. 4-6),

Fig. 4-6

MOSQUITO

for example, bite humans to obtain blood for food. Usually the allergic reaction to their bites consists of hives or an eczemalike rash with red, itchy lesions which become moist and then crusted when scratched. This allergy is diagnosed by the location of the reaction, medical history and the circumstances surrounding the bites. Measures to prevent exposure to mosquitoes are generally sufficient treatment.

Some flies—but *not* the house fly—bite and may cause allergic reactions. These include black flies (see Fig. 4-7), biting midges, deer flies and the

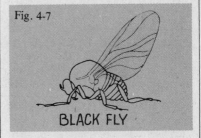

Fig. 4-7

BLACK FLY

stable fly. Bites from these cause pain, swelling, severe itching and, in unusual situations, anaphylactic shock. Local reactions can be treated by oral antihistamines or by steroid creams applied to the affected area. Systemic (throughout the body) reactions should be treated just like those resulting from hymenoptera stings.

33

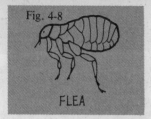

Fig. 4-8

FLEA

Fleas (see Fig. 4-8) usually cause only a local rash consisting of grouped, itchy, raised lesions. Antihistamines and applied medications will relieve itching due to flea bites. The best prevention is to treat the environment and pets.

Kissing bugs bite at night and cause a full range of reactions from local itching to extensive swelling and shock. Antihistamines or injections of epinephrine or corticosteroids are the proper treatment, depending on the type and severity of the symptoms.

Fig. 4-9 CATERPILLAR

Some caterpillars (see Fig. 4-9) are covered for their protection by tiny hairs which seem to contain an irritating substance. If these larvae crawl on the skin of a sensitive person, or if the hairs are swallowed or inhaled, the resulting symptoms may range from a local rash to a severe systemic reaction. The puss caterpillar is the worst offender. A rash will follow the grid-like track of the insect on the skin. If a sticky tape is applied to the skin as soon as possible, some of the hairs can be removed for examination. Ice packs and antihistamine tablets, as prescribed by a doctor, are used to treat local reactions.

Some insects cause allergic reactions when accidentally inhaled or swallowed. For example, extremely small insects like the mayfly and caddisfly (see Fig. 4-10) are abundant near bodies of water in late summer. They can usually be breathed in. Also, insect parts, such as scales, wings, bits of the hard outer body covering, and

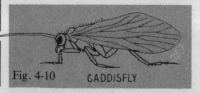

Fig. 4-10 CADDISFLY

dried secretions, may be blown around by the wind. Such materials, along with the minute house dust mite dermatophagoides and the cockroach, can be components of house dust allergy. These insects cause respiratory allergies with symptoms resembling those of hay fever or asthma and can result in positive skin-test reactions.

Insects are found wherever there is food, especially grains or cereals. Most common are the cockroach, weevil, moth, beetle, mite and silverfish. Insects contaminating food may actually cause some cases of food allergy.

What are the symptoms?

Insect stings or bites can cause a variety of reactions, depending on the type of insect, the amount of venom injected, the presence or absence of specific type of allergy in the person attacked, and the site of the sting or bite. Reactions usually fall into three groups.

Normal reactions involve pain, redness, swelling, itching, and warmth at the site of the sting. These symptoms last for a few hours and may be quite severe, but as long as they are confined to the area of the sting, they are considered normal inflammatory responses.

Toxic reactions are the result of multiple stings. Five hundred stings injected in one individual within a short time produce enough venom to kill. Fewer stings, but usually at least ten, closely spaced over time can cause serious illness and discomfort. Muscle cramps, headache, fever and drowsiness are the most common symptoms of a toxic reaction.

Allergic reactions produce some of these same symptoms but differ in that they can be triggered by only one sting or a minute amount of venom. If there is confusion as to whether a specific reaction is toxic or allergic in nature, it should be treated as though it is the more serious allergic type. Any reaction to a single sting involving extensive swelling in a limb beyond the site of the sting should probably be considered allergic until proven otherwise.

Allergic reactions can be immediate or delayed. In most causes, the shorter the time between the sting and the start of symptoms, the more se-

vere the reaction will be. Slight allergic reactions may result in widespread hives, itching, fatigue, and a feeling of anxiety. Moderate reactions may also include swelling, chest tightness, dizziness, stomach cramps, nausea and/or vomiting. Severe allergic reactions produce some of those symptoms but also result in more serious difficulty in swallowing or breathing, weakness and disorientation.

The most serious form of allergic reaction to insect stings is shock, or anaphylaxis. The patient may develop a sudden lowering of blood pressure, collapse, and have problems resulting from impairment of respiration, heart action, and circulation. Anaphylaxis may lead to death if not promptly treated. This condition usually develops within minutes or hours after a sting. (See shock treatment, page 21.)

A delayed reaction, occurring several hours to two weeks after a sting, is similar to a drug reaction known as serum sickness. In this situation, painful joints, fever, hives or other skin rashes, and swollen lymph glands may develop. Both immediate and delayed reactions can develop in the same person following a sting, although immediate reactions are more common in the allergic individual. Treatment is symptomatic, as prescribed by a doctor.

Most ant stings cause very little pain or itching. Those of the imported fire ant, however, can produce severe local or generalized reactions. In the normal local reaction, pain and a small raised area at the site of the sting are followed in a few hours by several fluid-filled blisters, which eventually break or dry up. After the first day, the sting site itself becomes red and filled with pus. Days later, this spot crusts over and scar tissue forms. A generalized allergic reaction involves progressively larger local reactions and, in time, may even develop into symptoms of anaphylactic shock.

Treatment of stings

In the event of any insect sting, the stinger and attached venom sac, if left behind, should be removed immediately by gently scraping them out with a fingernail or knife and not by squeezing or pressing them. The honey bee's venom sac continues to push venom through the stinger for some time after being torn from the insect, so the sooner it is removed, the less venom is injected. The affected area should then be washed thoroughly.

In a normal reaction, ice—not heat—applied to the spot may help lessen the pain and swelling. To relieve the itching and discomfort, apply calamine lotion or a paste made of baking soda and a small amount of water. Aspirin or codeine, as recommended by your doctor, may relieve pain. Some physicians suggest $1/4$ teaspoon of meat tenderizer be dissolved in one or two teaspoons of water and rubbed on the skin to lessen the pain and swelling. To diminish the stinging sensation of ant bites, try household ammonia diluted to half strength with water. Avoid the eyes when applying this treatment.

A toxic reaction to an insect sting is treated in the same manner as described in the above section, but other medication may be needed. Antibiotics to control secondary infections may also be necessary. Your doctor will prescribe necessary drugs.

Treatment of insect sting allergy

When a reaction to an insect sting is presumed to be allergic, three general approaches used in handling all allergies may be considered: (1) medication to lessen the symptoms of the allergic reaction; (2) measures to reduce the sensitivity to the allergenic substance; and (3) avoidance of the causative substances.

An allergic person should try to keep the amount of venom in the blood low by removing any stinger as soon as possible. In addition, he should place a tourniquet above the sting site if it is on an arm or leg and loosen the tourniquet every ten minutes so that circulation is not impaired. A physician should be consulted immediately and an ambulance called.

Every allergic reaction to a sting is an emergency because there is no way to predict when a slight or moderate allergic reaction will progress to anaphylactic shock. Epinephrine (adrenalin) will be given by a doctor by injection as soon as possible and may have to be repeated if symptoms do not improve. It does not always relieve shock, however; it may be necessary for some patients to be treated in

a hospital with intravenous fluids and electrolytes, pressor agents or other measures. Antihistamines given by injection or by mouth reduce later-appearing symptoms but do not constitute effective emergency treatment. Adrenal corticosteroids may be given for persistent symptoms such as severe itching, swelling and hives. Intravenous fluids, oxygen and a tracheotomy may also be necessary in acute shock. Antihistamines and epinephrine given by mouth and sometimes steroids are given for several days for a delayed allergic reaction to a sting. Promptness in treating any person with a history of allergic reactions to insect stings is vital. Because most stings occur at some distance from a doctor's office or hospital, anyone who has had any form of an allergic reaction to a sting should take two precautionary steps:

First, he should wear a bracelet or necklace and/or carry an identification card which states that he is allergic to specific insects and needs special treatment. A Medic Alert tag is vital if the wearer should faint or become unconscious. Tags can be ordered from the Medic Alert Foundation International, Department ZE, Box 1009, Turlock, California 95380 (see page 16 for more on Medic Alert). Identification tags may also be obtained by writing EMI, c/o The American Medical Association, Attention Order Department OP-2, 535 North Dearborn Street, Chicago, Illinois 60610.

Second, he should always have an emergency insect sting treatment kit available, one for the home and one for the car. This kit should contain epinephrine in a syringe, ready for injection, antihistamine tablets, a tourniquet, and alcohol swabs for cleansing the injection site. The syringe should be checked periodically. If the fluid has turned brown, the syringe should be replaced. Such kits are only available with a doctor's prescription. When a doctor prescribes one, he will also instruct the allergic person how to use it. The emergency treatment will provide the precious time needed to get the allergic person to a physician or a hospital. Some doctors also recommend that a pocket-sized inhaler containing epinephrine be carried. This can be useful for children or others unable to give themselves injec-

tions, especially because swelling of the throat may sometimes accompany an allergic reaction to a sting. An inhaler can be helpful in preventing or reducing such swelling because it causes the blood vessels to constrict.

Are tests available?

For many years skin tests have been used to determine whether individuals are allergic to insect stings. The tests consist of injections or skin scratches using a small amount of venom. There is also a new test in which a blood sample from the person is exposed to specially prepared venom from the suspected insect.

Allergy shots

This form of immunotherapy is believed to build up the body's supply of protective or blocking antibody. immunoglobulin G (IgG). This is thought to combine with the allergen before it can attach to IgE on the cell surface. In insect allergy the doctor employs filtered, sterilized extracts of the body of the insect or insects involved in the reaction. These shots have been used to reduce or prevent future symptoms of allergy.

Protection against insects

There are ways to make yourself less appealing and vulnerable to insects. Close-fitting clothes will prevent the insect from getting between the material and the skin. Subdued solid colors, like gray or white, rather than bright colors, or a print, will make the wearer appear less like a flower. Scented soaps, perfumes and cosmetics should be avoided, as should shiny buckles or jewelry. Shoes, not sandals, should be worn out of doors because some hymenoptera nest in the ground and others, attracted to low-growing plants, can attack unprotected feet.

Feeding areas of the hymenoptera—flower beds, clover fields, garbage cans and ripe fruit—must be avoided. Car windows should be kept closed, if possible. While repellants are generally not effective, an insecticide spray carried in the glove compartment may be helpful if an insect does get in the car.

In and around the house, screens on windows and doors should be checked for holes, and garbage cans should be kept clean, sprayed with an insecticide if necessary and closed tight. Nests should be removed from under eaves, in trees, or in the ground. A professional exterminator should be called.

Weather can affect the activity of hymenoptera. For example, rain may wash pollen from the flowers and anger bees. At such times an allergic person must take special care to avoid attack. If hymenoptera are nearby, an allergic person should move away slowly and calmly. In the event of an attack, he should lie on the ground and protect his face with his arms. Wild motion of the arms or frantic running will only anger and further provoke an insect.

Preventing attack by ants involves taking special care with food, covering arms and legs, and locating and eliminating any nests indoors (between the floor and subfloor, under cracked basement floors, or in decaying wood). Entrances to the home, as well as suspicious areas in the yard, can be treated with appropriate chemicals that are safe to use.

DRUG ALLERGY

An adverse drug reaction is any effect of drug therapy that is undesirable and not of benefit to the patient. Whatever the reasons for an allergic drug reaction, there are three steps in its development. First, there is an initial exposure to the drug. Second comes a latent period during which the antibodies, or cells sensitized to the drug, are formed. Usually this takes about one or two weeks. Third, the drug is administered again, and this time the sensitized cells lead to the symptoms of allergy.

Many factors seem to be involved in allergies to drugs, including the manner of administration and dosage. Application to the skin carries the greatest risk of a reaction to certain drugs and injection comes next. Thus, giving a drug orally is preferable. Intermittent administration of a drug rather than prolonged, continuous use appears to be more likely to lead to an allergic reaction. The age and general health of a patient are also factors in drug allergy. Children are less likely to have a serious reaction than adults, possibly because they are given fewer medications. An individual who has a history of drug reactions may be more inclined to have an allergic reaction to a new drug.

What are the symptoms?

Immediate reactions occur within minutes or a few hours after contact with the specific allergen, while a delayed response may develop many hours or even days after exposure. Since drugs may affect the whole body, it is often difficult to separate the allergic reaction from the symptoms of the illness being treated.

Contact dermatitis is a delayed reaction to a drug and often occurs where the medication was applied to the skin or mucous membranes. Dermatitis medicamentosa includes generalized itching, hives, angioedema (giant swelling of body tissue), fixed drug eruptions, allergic photosensitivity reactions and various widespread eruptions accompanied by redness and scaling of the skin, particularly on the trunk. A fixed drug eruption is one of the few reactions that is virtually always associated with drug allergy. It is found at the same body site each time the drug is administered and is a well-outlined welt (round or oval), swollen and red. There are usually only one or two such lesions. Similar reactions may develop in the sensitized person if he receives the drug by mouth or injection.

Allergic photosensitivity reactions may follow any form of drug administration and are characterized by redness, skin lesions, scaling and swelling, often resembling contact dermatitis. The symptoms are found only on those areas of the skin exposed to sunlight.

Drugs are the most common cause of hives. Characterized by swollen, itching, reddened areas on the skin, this illness may occur in acute or chronic form, and may be either widespread or localized. The chronic cases are usually those in which the hives continue for three or more weeks. In its severest form, it affects deeper body tissues, especially around the eyelids, lips, hands, feet, tongue, larynx, central nervous system, and gastrointestinal tract.

What are the systemic effects?

Systemic symptoms of drug allergy may appear in almost every organ in the body. Anaphylaxis, probably the most serious form of drug allergy, occurs within minutes after taking the allergenic drug. It may involve four major organ systems in the body—the skin, the respiratory system, the gastrointestinal tract and the circulatory system. A significant drop in blood pressure, weakness and loss of consciousness are the most serious aspects of anaphylaxis and can even lead to shock and death. (For treatment, see page 21.) More common and less life-threatening manifestations include hives and generalized itching, tightness in the chest and wheezing.

Serum sickness, another generalized allergic drug reaction, can develop following use of certain medications. The first dose both sensitizes and brings on the symptoms of allergy—fever, rash, joint pain, itching and inflammation of certain glands in the body. This reaction usually lasts about a week. In accelerated serum sickness, the patient is already sensitive to the therapy due to a previous exposure, so the reaction develops in about two days. The symptoms are similar to those of primary serum sickness, but may be more severe. Treatment is symptomatic, as prescribed by a doctor.

Lung problems may also result from drug allergy. Most common are asthma, and an illness known as hypersensitivity lung disease, which results from inhaling a drug. It causes an inflammation of lung tissue and can result in shortness of breath, coughing and weight loss.

Fever may be the only symptom of a drug reaction, especially if the medication is given for a relatively long period of time at high doses. Drug fever develops within seven to ten days after therapy begins and may be difficult to diagnose if the person might be expected to run a fever as a result of his underlying illness.

A drug allergy may also destroy various blood cells. Such a reaction develops quite quickly, but recovery is also generally rapid once the drug is withdrawn.

A doctor should be consulted for treating systemic drug-allergy effects.

Which drugs are the culprits?

Three common drugs are the most frequent causes of drug allergy—penicillin, aspirin and sulfonamides.

Penicillin is the most common cause of drug allergy and should not be used unless clearly indicated. Hives and other rashes are the most common allergic reactions to penicillin. Anaphylaxis and serum sicknesslike illnesses are more serious reactions.

Aspirin is an important cause of hives, swelling of body tissues, asthma attacks and anaphylaxis. In some asthmatics in whom no allergic cause can be found for their asthma, taking aspirin will lead to a severe asthma attack within 20 minutes to two hours.

There are now fewer allergic reactions with the newer sulfonamides, but the longer-acting sulfa drugs are still potentially troublesome. Sulfa drugs may cause many of the symptoms described above. Included in this category of medications are sulfa antibiotics, diuretics, and oral hypoglycemics.

Other drugs that may cause allergic reactions include antituberculosis medications and antibiotics other than penicillin, anticonvulsants, barbiturates, local anesthetics, vaccines, tranquilizers and antithyroid drugs. The contrast media containing iodides, used for some X rays, may also cause severe reactions.

First-aid treatment

For a bad reaction to penicillin, get medical help quickly. Have the victim stop taking the drug immediately. Treat for shock if necessary (see page 21).

One possible allergic reaction to aspirin is asthma. If the reaction is mild, give an antihistamine tablet according to a doctor's directions. If the reaction is severe, give epinephrine and get victim to a doctor or hospital immediately.

Hives may result from some reactions to drugs. They will appear as pinkish or reddish patches (wheals) which suddenly develop on the skin. They can vary in size from a dot to a dime, often with a white center and an irregular shape. Bathe the wheals with a soda solution consisting of three teaspoons baking soda to one glass cold water. Apply with gauze or a clean cloth. Calamine lotion can relieve any itching and burning. If hives are not relieved, consult a doctor.

Is there a cure?

As is true of all allergies, there is no actual cure for drug allergy. A doctor must be consulted. The first step in treating drug allergy is for a doctor to identify and remove the drug allergen. After that, therapy depends on the symptoms. If these are mild, they will disappear on their own. If more severe, either local or systemic therapy will help to alleviate them. Local treatments include soothing baths and lotions, steroid creams and possibly antibiotics if secondary infections develop. More general therapy involves medications such as antihistamines and corticosteroids. On occasion enzymes have been used to speed the breakdown of the drug in the body.

Prevention of drug allergy

Several kinds of skin tests are available to diagnose allergies before drugs are administered. In one test, allergens are applied to a scratch on the skin, or a needle containing the allergen is used to prick the skin, or the allergen is injected under the skin. A raised red welt should appear within 15 minutes if the person is allergic to a test substance that induces the formation of skin-sensitizing antibodies. The other test is a patch test for contact dermatitis in which the suspected allergen is applied to the skin, covered for 48 hours, and then observed for the appearance of delayed redness or scaling.

In the case of drug allergy, skin tests, except for the patch test for contact dermatitis, are relatively unreliable and possibly dangerous because of the explosive nature of some allergic drug reactions.

Once an allergy to a drug has developed, several steps can be taken to prevent a reoccurrence. A physician should warn the patient and his family about the allergy, and the patient might consider carrying a special identification card or wearing a Medic Alert tag. He should be aware of hidden sources of the drug also; for example, aspirin is included in many over-the-counter drugs.

For those with a drug allergy, substitute medications are generally available. For example, there are acceptable replacements for aspirin. And if a patient knows his allergies, he should always report them to a hospital or doctor treating him without having to be asked.

There are ways to prevent or forestall the initial development of drug allergy. Any drug with a reputation for producing allergic reactions should be used selectively, especially for people with a history of eczema, hay fever or asthma. Patients with asthma and nasal polyps should be very careful in their use of aspirin. The use of several drugs in combination as well as drugs and alcohol should also be avoided unless approved by your physician.

When drugs are given, the oral route is preferable, and the patient and his family should be warned about possible reactions.

FOOD ALLERGY

Eating is something most people do almost without thinking. To some, however, a single bite of the wrong food can bring on unpleasant and sometimes frightening food allergies. Allergic food reactions can resemble symptoms of food poisoning, but with food allergy there is often a history of previous attacks. Symptoms involve the skin, the respiratory or the gastrointestinal tract, or, rarely, the body's vital organs, resulting in a serious state of shock.

This allergic response appears in two forms—immediate, within minutes after eating the culprit food, and delayed, up to several hours later.

Besides an individual's allergic tendency, the time, severity and duration of symptoms are affected by many factors such as the quantity of the food, the effect of cooking, and the number of allergenic foods eaten in combination. The problem of food allergy is further complicated by the fact that food does not have to be eaten to cause symptoms. If the aroma of the culprit food is inhaled or a related product is injected, it can produce the same effect in an allergic person.

What are the symptoms?

The symptoms of food allergy are varied and complex. Most commonly associated with sensitivity to food are hives, eczema, vomiting and diarrhea. Asthma, rhinitis, migraine headache, sweating of body tissues, and serious shock also may occur. Although digestion breaks down food into particles that tend to become less allergenic, even this process cannot completely suppress symptoms in those who are highly sensitive. Other allergic reactions that occur solely in the digestive tract are called gastrointestinal allergies and may mimic other gastro-intestinal problems.

What causes food reactions?

The number of foods and food additives that can cause allergic reactions is even greater than the number of symptoms they cause. Usually an allergy develops after a number of exposures to the food.

If you have a tendency toward allergy, you may develop a sensitivity to food at any age. Young children, however, are especially prone. Because changes can occur in environmental factors, diet, and body chemistry, food sensitivities sometimes disappear, although the allergic state or tendency remains.

Treatment of food allergy

In most cases, a food allergy will not produce an emergency. The first procedure in treatment is to identify the food allergen and to stop eating it if it repeatedly causes problems. (Unfortunately, the ingredients of many packaged foods are not listed on labels. The Food and Drug Administration is now seeking to modernize the 1938 provisions that permitted standardized foods such as catsup not to include their ingredients on the label.)

Symptoms of food allergy should be treated on an individual basis. For example, for hives, bathe the wheals with a soda solution consisting of 3 teaspoons baking soda to 1 glass cold water and then apply gauze. Use calamine lotion to relieve any itching and burning.

If a food allergy happens regularly, a doctor should be consulted. He will collect a careful medical history and ask the patient to keep a diary of what he eats to reveal likely causes. Extracts of the suspected foods might then be used for skin testing. Once the allergist or doctor has a list of suspicious foods, he can recommend carefully controlled and supervised elimination diets. Suspect foods are slowly reintroduced individually to pinpoint those that cause the allergic symptoms.

Once the offending foods are identified, avoidance—either partial or complete—is the most effective method of treatment. Sometimes temporary avoidance causes the allergy to disappear, although it may be triggered again at a later time.

Thorough cooking and boiling may enable the allergic individual to tolerate the food. If symptoms return, however, the food must be eliminated from the diet. Food substitutes, such as soybean formulas for cow's milk and artificial flavors for fresh fruits, may be used in place of some troublesome foods. Vitamin and mineral supplements, as prescribed by a physician, may help by compensating for those lost through the elimination of essential, but allergenic, foods.

For people who must eliminate wheat, eggs or milk from their diets because of allergy, the U.S. government has a pamphlet, "Baking for People with Food Allergies," Home and Garden Bulletin No. 147. Write to the Superintendent of Documents, U.S. Government Printing Office, Washington, D.C. 20402.

5
AMPUTATIONS

When all or part of a limb or digit of the body is cut off in an accident, medical help must be sought quickly.

First-aid treatment

While waiting for help, control the bleeding with direct pressure (see page 19). If not successful, try pressure-point method (see pages 19–20). If these two methods fail, apply a tourniquet as a last resort (see page 20). Treat for shock if necessary (see page 21).

Collect dismembered part, since surgeon may be able to restore it to the body. Wrap dismembered part in a cold, clean cloth and place in a bag packed with ice (not dry ice) in order to preserve it. Take the package to the doctor or medical facility when you transport the victim.

6
BURNS

Burns are caused by heat, chemicals, electricity or radiation. They vary in severity from slightly reddened skin to destroyed tissue and damaged red-blood cells. In its most serious state, a burn may become infected, lead to shock and even result in death.

Burns are classified by the depth or degree of the injury to body tissues. A 1st-degree burn is the mildest reaction, a 2nd-degree burn is potentially serious, and a 3rd-degree burn is the most severe. Often a person suffers a combination of burns of different degrees with 3rd-degree burns surrounded by less severely burned areas.

DEGREE OF BURN

1st-degree burns

Common causes: Over-exposure to the sun, contact with hot-water bottle and other hot objects, contact with electrical wires.

Signs/symptoms: Reddened skin, mild pain, sometimes mild swelling.

First-aid treatment

Immerse burned area in cold but not ice water until pain subsides. Blot dry with a clean cloth. You can apply a dry, sterile dressing if necessary. Aspirin may ease any pain. Seek medical help if burns involve face or hands.

Healing: Takes place rapidly because only the outermost layer of the skin is involved.

2nd-degree burns

Common causes: Deep sunburn, contact with very hot liquids such as grease, burns from gasoline.

Signs/symptoms: Reddened skin, blister formation, swelling, more pain than with 1st-degree burn.

First-aid treatment

Cut away loose clothing. Cover burned area with several layers of cold, moist dressings. If a limb is involved, immerse in cold water for relief of pain and to prevent infection. Then cover with a cold, moist dressing and loose bandage. Elevate limb. Do not break any blisters that develop.

For severe 2nd-degree burns, especially to the face or hands, go quickly to a hospital emergency room or to a doctor. If the burns are extensive, it may be necessary to treat for shock (see page 21).

Healing: Because only an outer layer of the skin is involved, new skin will grow as long as an infection does not develop. Healing takes longer than with a 1st-degree burn.

3rd-degree burns

3rd-degree burns are always serious because they can be complicated by infection and/or shock.

Common causes: Scalding water, flames, electrical contact.

Signs/symptoms: Skin underneath surface layers destroyed and tissues charred, red blood cells and blood vessels damaged, severe pain unless nerve endings in area also destroyed.

First-aid treatment

Get medical help as quickly as possible. Until help arrives, treat in the following manner: Cut away loose clothing, but do not try to remove any clothing that adheres to the skin. Cover with several layers of sterile, moist dressings for relief of pain and to stop the burning action. Do not use ice water or ice because the intense cold may lead to shock. Blot area dry with a clean cloth, and apply dry cloth as a protective dressing. Separate any burned areas such as the fingers that may come in contact with each other when bandaging. Bandages should be loose enough to prevent pressure on burned surfaces. Apply new dressings as necessary; remove old dressings by wetting well to free the dressings from the skin. Elevate any injured limb. Make victim lie down unless he has severe face burns. Then he should sit or be propped up. Be sure to keep airway open. Do not induce vomiting. Treat for shock if necessary (see page 21).

If victim is conscious and not vomiting and you cannot get him to a hospital for an hour or more, give a weak solution of one teaspoon salt and ½ teaspoon baking soda in one quart of water. Give an adult four ounces, or ½ glass, over 15 minutes. Give a child two ounces and an infant one ounce. If victim begins to vomit, give no more fluid.

Healing: Healing is prolonged in all cases of 3rd-degree burns, and skin will often require grafting.

Note. Never use ointments or butter on any type of burn. Never break blisters. Never give victim any alcohol.

PERCENTAGE OF BODY AFFECTED

Burns can also be described according to the percentage of the body affected. For example, if an adult suffers burns over 15 percent or more of his body, he will require hospitalization because shock may result. If 50 percent or more of the body is burned, he may well die.

TREATMENT FOR SPECIAL TYPES OF BURNS

Chemical burns

Chemicals on the skin pose an immediate burn problem. The chemicals that cause burns include acids, alkalis and corrosive chemicals.

First, wash the chemical away as quickly as possible with water from a shower, hose or faucet. If clothing has been contaminated, cut it away quickly. Then follow first-aid instructions, according to the degree of the burn.

Eyes: Special attention must be given to chemical burns of the eyes since vision may be impaired or lost. If victim wears contact lenses, have him remove them first. Flush away the chemicals immediately with plenty of water. Turn head so the injured side is down. Flood the inner corner of the eye with cool water for at least five minutes, or hold the eye under a stream of water from a water faucet. Hold eyelids open. Be sure the chemical does not wash into the other eye if only one eye is burned. Cover eyes with clean compresses, but not with absorbent cotton, whose fibers can become lodged in the eye. Remove clothing because the chemical may be retained on the clothing. Give first aid as for burns, according to the severity of the burn. Go immediately to a doctor, preferably an eye specialist, or a hospital emergency room.

For an acid burn, you can also clean the eye with a solution of one teaspoonful of baking soda mixed in one quart of water. Pour solution over burned eye area. (Never use this solution for an alkali burn.) Then cover

eye with dry protective dressing, not absorbent cotton.

If the chemical was an alkali such as a strong laundry or dishwasher detergent, lift off any particles of dry chemicals that may be on the eye.

If you cannot get medical help for victim within an hour and he requests fluid and is not vomiting, you can give him a weak solution of one teaspoon salt and ½ teaspoon baking soda in one quart of water. Give an adult four ounces, or ½ glass, over 15 minutes. Give a child two ounces and an infant one ounce. If the victim begins to vomit, give no more fluid.

Sunburn

Too much sunlight will cause any type of complexion to burn. When the skin is burned, tiny blood vessels at the surface dilate to produce a scorched look. A mild sunburn will result in some of the skin reddening, possibly followed by peeling of the skin, and dryness. If the skin turns red, dust the area with talcum powder. Moderately bad burns will make the skin turn even redder, and will also make it slightly swollen, tender and possibly itchy. Blisters and peeling may also result. Apply wet dressings of gauze dipped in a solution of baking soda and cornstarch, using one tablespoon of each to 2 quarts of cool water. In an emergency, use cool milk or water. A severe burn may be accompanied by chills, fever and large blisters, which may become infected. For a severe burn, it is wise to consult a physician immediately. For whatever type of sunburn you suffer, drink plenty of fluids and eat salty food to replace the salt you have lost from perspiration. Rest indoors in a cool room.

To avoid sunburn, don't stay too long in the direct rays of the sun in hot weather. Always use a good sun-screening lotion containing either the chemical PABA or benzophenone, even on smoggy, hazy or cloudy days. Apply it to all exposed parts of your body before you go out in the sun, and reapply it after going into the water, after exercising and after sweating profusely. Be careful of the sun's rays when you are resting on the beach and when you are in or near the water. Sand and water and also snow all absorb the ultraviolet rays of the sun, making you tan and burn faster.

Light, tightly woven clothing helps protect your skin. Hats also help.

Always let your skin become accustomed to the sun gradually. Begin your first day of sunbathing by spending only about 40 minutes in the sun, 45 minutes your second day, and 50 minutes on your third and fourth days. Avoid sunbathing at midday when the sun is strongest.

Electric burns

Follow first-aid instructions according to the degree of the burn. Be sure to keep an open airway. If breathing becomes impaired, give artificial respiration (see pages 17–18). Administer treatment for shock, if it develops (see page 21).

Many young children experience disfiguring burns when they put electrical cord plugs into their mouths. To avoid this injury, cover unused extension cord receptacles with electric tape or plastic safety caps. Be sure that no plug prongs are exposed when the extension cord receptacle is being used. Return a defective cord or throw it away. Instruct children not to go near plugs and outlets, and not to attempt to unplug cords.

Electric wall outlets also pose a hazard to infants and toddlers. Most outlets are placed at their level; if children insert metal objects into empty outlets, they can receive serious burns and severe, possibly fatal shocks. If an outlet is not in use, do not leave it exposed. Insert a plastic safety cap, which can be purchased at a drug or hardware store.

7

CANCERS

You can protect yourself and your family by being alert to the seven danger signs of cancer. The presence of one of the signs does not necessarily mean that you have cancer, but it does mean that you should make an immediate appointment with your doctor. The best weapon against cancer is still early diagnosis followed by prompt medical treatment. Every person should, in addition, have a complete physical examination once a year.

Possible signs of cancer

- Unusual bleeding or discharge
- A lump or thickening in the breast or elsewhere
- A sore that does not heal
- A change in normal bowel or bladder habits
- Repeated hoarseness or coughing
- Repeated indigestion or difficulty in swallowing
- Change in a wart or mole

If your symptom lasts longer than two weeks, go to your doctor to find out if it signifies cancer. Do not wait for symptoms to become painful because frequently pain does not occur until cancer has become more advanced.

Treatment

There are three ways to arrest and in some instances cure cancer. (1) *Surgery* removes cancerous growths and nearby tissue that may contain cancer cells. (2) *Radiation* from X rays and radioactive elements destroys cancer cells. (3) *Chemotherapy*, or treatment with drugs, sometimes relieves symptoms and shrinks tumors when other types of treatment are of no benefit.

Prevention

Medical science still does not know how the change from a normal to an abnormal cell takes place, but research has produced important information about the causes of some forms of cancer. For instance, cigarette smoking has been identified as the major cause of lung cancer. Other cancer hazards include repeated or prolonged exposure to sunlight and to X rays; to the fumes of certain industrial chemicals, household solvent cleaners, garden and lawn chemicals; and to car fumes and polluted air. You should also decrease the quantity of smoked and fatty foods in your diet and avoid excess caloric intake.

You cannot "catch" cancer from another person. It is generally believed that parents do not pass cancer on to their children, but physicians occasionally find that two or more members of a family develop the same type of cancer.

BREAST EXAMINATION

Women should examine their breasts once a month. This is best done after the menstrual period.

Stand in front of a mirror and look

Stand in front of a mirror with the upper body unclothed. Look for changes in the shape and size of the breast and for dimpling of the skin or pulling in of the nipples. Be aware of any discharge from the nipples or scaling of the skin of the nipples. Abnormality in the breast may be accentuated by a change in position of the body and arms. Follow these steps:
1. Stand with arms down.
2. Lean forward.
3. Raise arms overhead and press hands behind your head (see Fig. 7-1).

Fig. 7-1

4. Place hands on hips and tighten chest and arm muscles by pressing firmly inward (see Fig. 7-2).

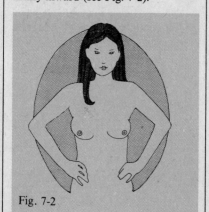

Fig. 7-2

Lie flat on your back and feel

Lie flat on your back with a pillow or folded towel under your shoulders and feel each breast with the opposite hand. With the hand slightly cupped, feel for lumps or any change in the texture of the breast or skin; also, note any discharge from nipples. Avoid compressing the breast between the thumb and fingers as this may give the impression of a lump when there is none. Follow these steps:

1. Place the left arm overhead. With the right hand, feel the inner half of the left breast from top to bottom and from nipple to breastbone.

2. Feel the outer half from bottom to top and from the nipple to the side of the chest (see Fig. 7-3).

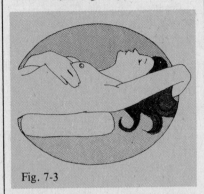

Fig. 7-3

3. Pay special attention to the area between the breast and armpit, including the armpit itself (see Fig. 7-4).

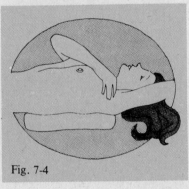

Fig. 7-4

4. Repeat the above procedure for the right breast, using your left hand to feel.

Feel gently, carefully and thoroughly. If you find something that you consider abnormal, contact your doctor for an examination. Most breast lumps are not serious, but all should be brought to the doctor's attention for an expert opinion. You may have a condition that will require treatment or further study. If necessary, your doctor may recommend laboratory tests or X rays as part of a more detailed examination. Follow your doctor's advice, as your early recognition of a change in your breast and his thorough investigation will determine the safest course. Keep up this important health habit even during pregnancy and after menopause.

8
CHEST INJURIES

The chest contains the heart and the lungs, and therefore any chest injury should be considered an emergency for which medical aid should be sought promptly. Following are four of the most common chest emergencies and treatment for them.

OPEN CHEST WOUND

Cover wound with an airtight material such as aluminum foil or plastic wrap after the victim has exhaled. Secure in place. If no airtight material is available, use your hand. Place victim on injured side to give the uninjured lung room to expand. If the victim's condition worsens, air may be trapped inside the lung or the lung may have collapsed. Remove airtight material, quickly listen for escape of air, then promptly replace material.

If breathing stops, give artificial respiration (see pages 17–18). Treat for shock if necessary (see page 21).

Get victim immediately to a hospital emergency room or physician, preferably by ambulance. If you must transport victim yourself, do so with victim lying down on a stretcher (see pages 22–23).

EMBEDDED OBJECT

Do not move the victim. Do not remove embedded object, but cut off a long object a few inches from the wound if possible. Cut clothing away from the site of injury. Stabilize the object with bulky dressing. Apply bandage to prevent movement (see pages 23–25). Give artificial respiration if breathing ceases (see pages 17–18). Treat for shock if necessary (see page 21).

Get victim immediately to a hospital emergency room or physician, preferably by ambulance. If you must transport victim yourself, do so with the victim lying down on a stretcher (see pages 22–23).

RIB FRACTURES

When ribs are fractured, pain is usually localized at the site of the fracture. If the victim is conscious, ask him to place his hand on the exact area of the pain. Common signs/symptoms include: rib may be deformed or lacerated; deep breathing, coughing or movement becomes painful; victim often leans toward injured side with his hand held over the injury site in an attempt to ease the pain and immobilize chest.

For simple rib fractures, current medical therapy is not to bind the chest because the bandaging may interfere with respiration and produce complications in the lungs. Instead, get the patient to a doctor or hospital immediately. Give aspirin for relief of any pain.

If the patient's lung is punctured (he will have extreme difficulty breathing), rush patient to a doctor or hospital for immediate treatment.

CRUSHED CHEST

Signs of a crushed chest include broken ribs, and a chest collapsing rather than expanding upon inhalation.

Open victim's airway by tilting back head. If injury is limited to one side, turn victim onto injured side. If the injury occurs in the center of chest or on both sides, prop victim up with pillows or bulky materials. If breathing stops, begin artificial respiration (see pages 17–18). If circulation fails, begin cardiopulmonary resuscitation (see pages 18–19).

Get victim immediately to a hospital emergency room or physician, preferably by ambulance. If you must transport victim yourself, do so with victim lying down on a stretcher (see pages 22–23).

9
EMERGENCY CHILDBIRTH

The emergency birth of a baby can be safe as well as a rewarding experience for mother and first-aid assistant if the delivery process is thoroughly understood. Normally the mother will deliver the baby by herself with the assistant helping and providing encouragement. This chapter explains the signs of the approach of labor and the delivery process. It also covers special problems such as bleeding dur-

41

ing pregnancy, breech delivery, tubal pregnancy, eclampsia, and prolapse of the umbilical cord.

Note. A physician should always be called once labor has begun.

BLEEDING DURING PREGNANCY

During the first three months of a pregnancy, a woman may notice some bleeding. There may be no cause for alarm, but sometimes bleeding indicates the beginning of a miscarriage, also known as a spontaneous abortion. In a miscarriage, which occurs in 10 to 20 percent of all pregnancies, the fetus detaches itself from the uterus and is expelled, causing bleeding and cramps in the lower abdomen. In the event of any bleeding, a pregnant woman should contact her gynecologist immediately.

Bleeding can also occur toward the end of a pregnancy, sometimes due to the detachment or faulty position of the afterbirth, or placenta. This, too, calls for a doctor's immediate attention. The doctor will probably admit the woman to a hospital for evaluation, even though the bleeding may ultimately be found to be due to a minor problem.

APPROACH OF LABOR

The typical indications that the baby is about to make its descent are blood mucus, known as "bloody show"; an uncontrollable flow of water from the vagina, caused by breakage of the sac of water enclosing the baby; or, the most reliable indicator, regular contractions of the uterus. If for an hour the contractions are about 30 seconds long and occur about 10 to 15 minutes apart, it is time for the pregnant woman to call her doctor. The doctor will decide when she should go to the hospital. With the birth of a first child there is usually more time to reach the hospital because the interval between contractions is greater and the labor longer. If she cannot reach her doctor, she should proceed to the hospital anyway as a safety precaution.

EMERGENCY DELIVERY

Sometimes even with nature's warning signs that birth is imminent, a woman may hesitate and not allow sufficient time for her to get to a hospital or a doctor to get to her. This is

more likely to happen with the birth of a second child, when the interval between contractions and the entire labor may be shorter. If bad weather or lack of transportation threatens to delay an expectant mother from reaching a hospital in time, she should call an ambulance, the police or fire department. Still, emergency birth may be necessary. A woman should always try to call her physician once labor has begun so that he can give step-by-step instructions to her, her husband or a friend over the telephone.

If the baby's head can be seen in the birth canal without separating the lips of the vagina, she should be prepared for an emergency delivery.

Choose a delivery area and make it as sterile as possible. Get together clean sheets, towels and cloth or string (for tying the umbilical cord). You should also have on hand a pair of scissors or a fresh razor blade, alcohol, sanitary napkins or clean cloths, and a blanket for wrapping the newborn baby.

Wash your hands thoroughly with hot water and soap to prepare for delivering the baby. Have the expectant mother lie down on her back with her knees bent and her thighs spread apart. Spread a clean towel under her buttocks and a sterile sheet just below that for the baby to arrive on.

Let the mother deliver the baby by herself. Encourage her to push down and to breathe in and out using short breaths. As the baby's head appears, move to the side of the mother. Get ready to cradle the baby's head as it appears. Try to avoid allowing the head to deliver rapidly. If the umbilical cord is wrapped around the baby's neck, loosen it or tie and cut it to prevent it from strangling the baby. As soon as the baby's shoulders appear, lift the baby upward—without pulling it—to support its head and neck as it emerges. Many babies arrive with their mouth and nose full of blood and mucus. Wipe out both with a clean cloth. The baby should begin to cry. Wrap a towel around the baby's legs and, holding its ankles, lift the baby into the air upside down, tipping its forehead back gently to let any additional mucus run out. If the baby still has not begun to breathe, give mouth-to-mouth resuscitation by placing your mouth over the baby's

nose and mouth and gently blowing short puffs of air into the infant's lungs every five seconds.

When the umbilical cord has changed from full, blue and pulsating to limp, pale and pulseless, tie a strip of clean, sterile cloth or string around it about four to six inches from the baby. Tie a second knot about three inches from the first. Then cut the cord between the ties with a clean razor blade or a pair of scissors boiled in water or wiped well with alcohol. Make the cut not closer than four inches from the infant's navel. If you have no instrument with which to cut the cord, you can keep mother and baby attached until you get them to a hospital. An exception, however, is if the cord is tightly bound around the baby's neck. Then you must find some way of separating mother and baby. Shoelaces to tie and a knife to cut the cord will work. Next place the baby on the mother's breast with its face to the nipple.

The mother will expel the placenta approximately 15 minutes after you have cut the cord. There will probably be some vaginal bleeding. Place your hand on the mother's abdomen and massage her uterus for a few minutes to help the uterus contract. Tell the mother to lower her legs and place them together. Clean the vaginal area with a clean cloth wet with water and cover with a sanitary napkin or clean cloth. If severe bleeding occurs, this is usually due to poor uterine tone or a vaginal tear. Vigorous massage and rapid transport to a hospital are essential. Apply ice packs en route to a hospital.

Wrap baby in a clean blanket. Do not wash baby's ears, eyes or nose. Take mother and baby to the nearest hospital. Also take the placenta wrapped in a clean towel to the hospital for examination for completeness.

SPECIAL PROBLEMS

Certain conditions require immediate care by a physician.

Breech delivery

If the baby's buttocks emerge first instead of the head, the woman is about to have a breech delivery. Take her to the nearest hospital as quickly as possible. Have her lie down during transport and do not attempt to pull the baby out by the feet.

42

Tubal pregnancy

A ruptured tubal pregnancy will cause internal bleeding. Signs include shock (light-headedness, fainting, cold extremities) due to the bleeding and pain in the lower abdomen. Take her to the nearest hospital as quickly as possible.

Eclampsia

Convulsions in the last trimester of a pregnancy, known as eclampsia, are a life-threatening condition caused by high blood pressure. Take the pregnant woman to the nearest hospital as quickly as possible. Protect her from injuring herself en route.

Prolapse of the umbilical cord

Rarely, with breakage of the bag of water, the umbilical cord may slide, or prolapse, through the vagina and appear. This is life-threatening for the baby. Bring the woman immediately to the hospital. Elevate her feet and lower her head during transport.

Note. Taking a class in childbirth, in a hospital or with a qualified private instructor, and reading some of the many books on the subject can help prepare a woman for childbirth, whether it is an emergency or not. You can obtain two excellent pamphlets put out by The American College of Obstetricians and Gynecologists—"Bleeding in Pregnancy" and "How to Deliver a Baby in an Emergency"—by sending a stamped, self-addressed envelope to that organization, 1 East Wacker Drive, Suite 2700, Chicago, Illinois 60601.

10
CHOKING

Choking on food lodged in the air passage is a common cause of accidental death. It often results from poor chewing of large pieces of food. Coughing will sometimes dislodge the mass, and a victim should always be encouraged to try this if his breathing is only partially obstructed and he is not getting worse. For the victim unable to breathe, death occurs in about four minutes.

Signs/symptoms

The most common signs of choking are gasping for breath, then inability to talk or breathe, and complexion turning from pale to blue as oxygen supply diminishes. The choking victim is often mistaken for a heart attack victim, but there is no reason to confuse the two conditions. The significant difference between these two emergencies is that the heart attack victim can talk and breathe initially, while the choking victim cannot. Everyone should learn the universal Heimlich sign for choking (see Fig. 10-1).

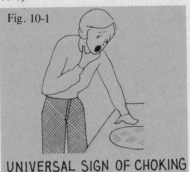

Fig. 10-1

UNIVERSAL SIGN OF CHOKING

First-aid treatment

If a choking victim cannot breathe, perform the Heimlich Maneuver described below. After the object is expelled from the throat, should the victim still not be breathing and if his pulse stops, perform mouth-to-mouth resuscitation and cardiopulmonary resuscitation (see pages 17–19). *Note:* Mouth-to-mouth resuscitation is useless until the object is removed.

Heimlich Maneuver

The Heimlich Maneuver is a life-saving rescue technique endorsed by the American Medical Association and named for its inventor, Dr. Henry J. Heimlich, Professor of Advanced Clinical Sciences at Xavier University in Cincinnati, Ohio. The Heimlich Maneuver is based upon the theory that by applying sudden pressure below the rib cage with a clenched fist you can push up the diaphragm, compress the lungs and force enough air up from the lungs to push out the object. The victim should see a physician immediately after the rescue. Performing the maneuver could result in injury to the victim. However, this

risk is justified because the victim will survive only if his airway is quickly cleared.

Victim standing or sitting: Stand behind the victim and wrap your arms around his waist. If he is sitting down, get behind his chair to do this. Place your fist with the thumb side against the victim's abdomen slightly above the navel and below the rib cage. Grasp your fist with your other hand and pull your fist into the victim's abdomen with a quick upward thrust. Repeat this movement several times if necessary (see Fig. 10-2).

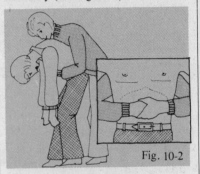

Fig. 10-2

Victim lying down: With the victim lying on his back, face him and kneel astride his hips. With one of your hands on top of the other, place the heel of your bottom hand on the abdomen slightly above the navel and below the rib cage. Press into the victim's abdomen with a quick upward thrust. Repeat several times if necessary (see Fig. 10-3).

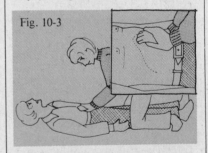

Fig. 10-3

This position is often better if the rescuer is a smaller, weaker or lighter person than the victim and must therefore use his weight rather than strength. This position is also useful if the victim has collapsed onto the floor, for he is then seconds from death.

For the infant victim: There are two methods you can use for an infant. Hold him in your lap and place the index and middle fingers of both

43

hands against his abdomen above the navel and below the rib cage. Press into abdomen with a quick upward thrust (see Fig. 10-4). Or, place infant face upward on a firm surface and perform the maneuver while you face him (see Fig. 10-5).

Fig. 10-4

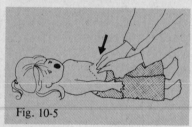

Fig. 10-5

Note. The American Red Cross recommends four sharp slaps between the shoulder blades before applying the abdominal thrusts. The American Heart Association also has adopted the Red Cross's method.

Heimlich Maneuver using chest compression

If a victim is fat or markedly pregnant and you cannot get your fist under the rib cage, you may want to use chest compression. Stand behind a standing or sitting victim and place your arms under his arms through the armpits.

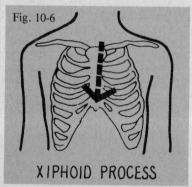

Fig. 10-6

XIPHOID PROCESS

Clench your fist and grasp it with your other hand. Place the thumb side of your fist on the breastbone, but *not* on the lower tip of the breastbone, also known as the xiphoid process (see Fig. 10-6). Press sharply inward so you compress the chest. This forces air out of the lungs (see Fig. 10-7).

If victim is lying on his back, kneel astride his hips facing him and place one of your hands on top of the other. Put the heel of the bottom hand on the breastbone, as above, and then press quickly inward.

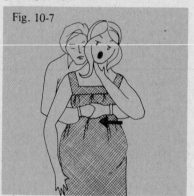

Fig. 10-7

If victim is an infant, use two fingers and a gentler thrust.

Note. According to Dr. Heimlich, you must be very careful when using this method not to crush the chest. Compressing the chest should be used only if pressure under the diaphragm is not possible.

If you are choking

If you begin to choke and no one is present to aid you, you can save your own life. Press your fist into your abdomen with your other hand, or lean forward to press your abdomen over a solid object such as a piece of furniture.

Prevention of choking

Following the suggestions below will make you less vulnerable to choking:
- Do not eat while running.
- Do not eat while laughing or talking, and be particularly cautious when eating after drinking alcohol.
- If you feel you are about to sneeze, get rid of any food in your mouth.
- Always cut food into small pieces. Eat slowly.
- Chew carefully, particularly if you wear dentures.
- Infants and small children are par-

ticularly susceptible to choking. Keep hard candies and small objects away from children so that they do not put such things into their mouth and try to swallow them.

You can obtain a wallet-size card explaining the Heimlich Maneuver by sending $1 and a self-addressed, stamped envelope to Edumed, P.O. Box 52, Cincinnati, Ohio 45201.

11

CONVULSIONS

Most convulsions—violent, involuntary contractions or spasms of the muscles—stop within a few minutes. Common causes are epileptic seizures (see pages 53–54), high fever, overdoses of narcotics. Your main goal in aiding someone experiencing a convulsion is to prevent the victim from injuring himself.

Signs/symptoms

A convulsion is often characterized by falling down, frothing at the mouth, stiffening of muscles, loss of consciousness, jerking movements, muscle spasms, loss of bladder and bowel functions, vomiting.

Some convulsions, such as those due to grand mal epilepsy, begin with a warning known as an aura, in which the victim experiences unusual colors, smells, sounds or a numbness or tingling sensation. Some victims will also utter a sharp cry prior to an attack.

First-aid treatment

Keep calm. Do not restrain victim or interfere with his movements in any way. Prevent him from hurting himself, however, by clearing the area of any objects that may be hazardous, such as furniture.

If victim's mouth is open and you can do so without using force, place a padded object, such as a folded handkerchief, between his teeth. This will prevent victim from biting his tongue or cheek. Do not force victim's jaws open if he has already clamped them shut.

Loosen tight clothing around the neck.

If breathing stops, institute arti-

44

ficial respiration (see pages 17–18). Mouth-to-nose resuscitation may be the only effective way to ventilate a victim if his mouth is tightly closed.

Once convulsive movements stop, get victim to lie down. Turn him on his side to allow his tongue to fall forward and excess saliva to drain out of his mouth. This will also prevent him from breathing any vomit into his lungs. Allow victim to rest or sleep.

Always report any convulsions to a doctor; they may indicate a serious underlying illness.

If victim experiences repeated convulsions, get him immediately to a hospital emergency room.

Convulsions due to high fever

Note. For convulsions due to high fever, sponge victim's body with cool water. Apply cool compresses to his head.

12
DIABETES

Diabetes, also known as diabetes mellitus or sugar diabetes, is a disease in which the body is unable to convert sugar and starch (carbohydrates) into the heat and energy necessary for normal activity. Ordinarily, the sugars and starches in the food we eat are processed by our digestive juices into a form of sugar called glucose, which circulates in our blood. This glucose, or blood sugar, is the fuel for our body's functioning. It is burned as needed for energy or stored for later use. Insulin, a hormone produced by the pancreas, is one of the major regulators of the use of our fuel supply. When the right amount of insulin is present at the right time, the right amount of glucose is burned or released for use by the body. In the diabetic individual, insulin activity is impaired. Either the body does not produce enough insulin or the available insulin is somehow blocked or inactivated by other substances within the body, preventing the insulin from performing its primary function. Because of this impairment, glucose is not properly utilized by the body, accumulating in the blood and tissues

and overflowing into the urine. Too much glucose in the blood and glucose in the urine are signs of diabetes.

The basic cause of the loss of insulin production or activity in diabetes is not known. While there appears to be a tendency to develop diabetes because of a hereditary factor, there are cases that do not fall into this category. Other factors are obesity and middle age; together these factors are especially predisposing to diabetes.

Signs/symptoms

The early symptoms stem from the increased amount of sugar in the blood and sugar in the urine. With the kidneys excreting extra water along with excess sugar, the uncontrolled diabetic is likely to urinate frequently and to be constantly thirsty. Because the sugar in the blood is not being converted to energy, the diabetic will be weak and tired; and because calories are lost in the urine, he will lose weight no matter how much he eats. This also accounts for the frequent, intense hunger felt by many uncontrolled diabetics.

In addition to excessive urination, increased thirst, rapid weight loss with increased appetite and general weakness, common symptoms that should be brought promptly to the attention of a physician include: visual disturbances such as blurred vision; slow healing of cuts and bruises; and skin disorders such as boils, infections and intense itching, especially in the genital areas. Some diabetics may, however, experience none of these symptoms. The only way to detect this so-called hidden form of diabetes is in a regular checkup by a doctor.

Detection

A doctor can detect the possibility of diabetes by performing a chemical test of the urine and blood. This test is not, however, foolproof. Another, more complicated but more dependable test is called the glucose tolerance test (GTT). It measures the amount of glucose in the blood before and after a sweet sugar syrup is swallowed. An unusually large amount of sugar remaining in the blood after a specified length of time establishes the diagnosis of diabetes.

Treatment

There is no known cure for diabetes,

but many thousands of people who have diabetes live full and productive lives with only minor restrictions. Treatment must be prescribed by a physician on an individual basis to alleviate the symptoms, or if there are no symptoms to prevent them from occurring and to forestall certain complications associated with inadequate diabetic control. The three main concerns are diet, exercise and insulin intake.

Years ago, the diet of the diabetic was rigid and unappealing. Today, it may be varied. For the most part, the patient can eat and drink the same foods and liquids as other people but must cut down on sugars and sugar-rich foods such as pastries, sweets and soft drinks. The diabetic cannot increase his output of insulin promptly and adequately when he eats a large carbohydrate meal. Therefore, the more carbohydrates he eats, the larger his dose of insulin or oral drugs must be. The amount of food eaten must also be regulated. With the help of exchange lists, menus can be varied. For the overweight patient, some form of weight-reducing diet is essential to accommodate the abnormality of sugar metabolism.

Exercise in the form of work and play is also important to the diabetic. A normal amount of regular exercise increases the body's ability to use food. On the other hand, a lack of activity causes sugar to build up in the blood, which can bring on symptoms. If a diabetic is inactive all week and then engages in strenuous activity on the weekend, the unaccustomed activity uses up more than the usual amount of sugar in his diet. With the insulin having no sugar left to work upon, the result may be a hypoglycemic reaction (see page 46).

Insulin, a hormone prepared from an extract of pancreas of cattle and hogs, must be taken by injection, as the digestive juices in the stomach would destroy it if taken by mouth. All juvenile and some adult diabetics must take insulin in order to use carbohydrates in a comparatively normal manner. For the rest of his life, the juvenile diabetic must give himself insulin injections daily, and balance the dosage with his food intake and physical activity. Several times a day, as an indirect check on his blood-sugar level, the diabetic must perform urine tests. Infants, the very young and the disabled need the assistance of an individual who is trained in the procedure. People who develop diabetes after the age of 40 have a type of diabetes called adult-onset diabetes. Most patients with this type can control it by diet alone, although some may also require daily insulin injections. Insulin in the adult-onset type is usually present in the system, often in excessive amounts, but it is hindered in some way from performing its normal functions in body metabolism.

The role of the oral antidiabetic drugs in the management of diabetes is in a state of professional dispute at present. Many physicians believe that strict dietary measures are preferable to the use of the antidiabetic drugs.

As diabetics are more susceptible to infections than other individuals, they must take special care of cuts and bruises and avoid foot infections.

INSULIN SHOCK

Insulin shock, or insulin reaction due to hypoglycemia (too little sugar in the blood), may result when the diet-exercise-insulin balance is disrupted. The person may not be eating enough, may be engaging in too-strenuous exercise, or may be taking too much insulin. It can also be brought on by emotional factors. The onset can be sudden and include tremor, hunger, sweating, headache, nausea, blurred vision, excitability, moist skin and, if not promptly treated, loss of consciousness.

First-aid treatment

For prompt relief, give the conscious diabetic candy, orange juice or some other sugary food or beverage in order to raise the blood-sugar level. Give the semiconscious diabetic orange juice in teaspoonfuls or place small sugar cubes under the tongue. In all cases, get the victim to a doctor or to the emergency room of a hospital.

Note. Insulin-treated patients should always carry wrapped lumps of sugar or hard candy.

DIABETIC COMA

Diabetic coma accompanied by hypoglycemia (too much sugar in the blood) can occur when a patient fails to take sufficient insulin or oral antidiabetic drug, does not follow his meal plan, or gets an infection. Other illnesses can also contribute to coma. The onset is usually gradual. In this condition—which is the opposite of insulin shock—fat is burned to supply energy, which produces an increasingly acid condition of the blood and other body fluids (acidosis) due to the accumulation of ketone substances, including acetone. The usual symptoms are nausea, drowsiness, extreme thirst, lack of hunger, dry skin, headache, blurred vision, abdominal pain, deep and rapid breathing, fruity breath odor. Acetone can be detected by the patient in the routine urine tests and should be immediately reported to a physician. If this condition progresses, it can lead to a loss of consciousness and coma.

First-aid treatment

There is no adequate treatment. Treat as you would for shock (see page 21). If the victim is conscious and not vomiting, give him fluids, such as broth or tea. Rush victim to a medical facility or doctor.

Note. Every diabetic should carry an identification card with his prescribed insulin dosage marked on it in case of emergency.

13

DROWNING AND WATER SAFETY

Water sports can provide countless hours of happy recreation, but swimming, boating, ice skating, fishing and diving can also result in drowning if proper safety measures are not observed. Drowning can also occur in a bathtub. This chapter is intended to help you cope with a drowning emergency; it may help you save a life.

Signs/symptoms

Drowning victims look dead. Their skin is blue and cold to the touch; they have no detectable heartbeat or breathing; and their eyes are fixed and pupils dilated. In short, there are no external signs of life.

First-aid treatment

Water rescue: Try to reach a person who is drowning from land first with your hand outstretched. Hold on to something with your other hand so the victim cannot pull you into the water. If the victim is too far from you, try extending a long pole or throwing a ring buoy. Again, hold on to something else so the victim cannot pull you into the water. If the victim is close enough to the shallow water for you to wade in and hand or throw him the assist, do so.

If a boat is available, row to the victim. If not and you would have to swim to victim, do so only if you are an experienced and strong swimmer; otherwise you may also require help. Bring along a floating assist when you swim to the victim, throw it to him and then pull the victim to shore.

Begin artificial respiration at once if necessary to restore respiratory function (see pages 17–18). If victim's heart stops, give cardiopulmonary resuscitation (see pages 18–19). Do not worry about getting water out of victim's lungs; the body will absorb it quickly. Keep the victim warm by covering him with a blanket, but do not overheat him. Improper rewarming may harm the victim. Get victim to nearest medical facility quickly.

Ice rescue: Never walk close to open ice. Tell a person who has fallen through ice not to try to climb out. Instead he should slide his arms onto frozen ice and hold on until a rescuer can reach him. Try to reach the victim from land by extending your hand. If victim is too far away, try using a pole. If you still cannot reach the victim, form a human chain with each person lying on the ice and holding the ankles of the person in front of him. The farthest person can then pull the victim out.

Give artificial respiration if the victim's breathing has stopped (see pages 17–18). Give cardiopulmonary resuscitation if heartbeat ceases (see pages 18–19). Observe for shock and treat accordingly (see page 21). Also watch for signs of frostbite (see page 72) and hypothermia (see pages 81–82). Warm the victim with blankets.

46

Preventing drowning

If you work or play near water, you should learn how to swim. The American Red Cross offers courses in swimming, water safety and lifesaving across the country, as do many community groups. If you cannot swim, assuming the fetal or heat-escape-lessening posture (HELP) will give you a better chance of survival.

Swim safely: Swim at a pool or beach where a lifeguard is on duty or where another adult is present. Always check the depth of the water before you venture into it. Wait at least an hour before swimming after having eaten. Do not swim when you are cold, overheated or tired. Do not swim after dark unless there is good illumination. Do not swim if there are strong currents or undertows, and do not swim during an electric storm or in cold weather. Young children require adult supervision even if a lifeguard is present.

If you find yourself in a difficult current, swim diagonally across the current. If you find yourself in an undertow, do not fight it. Swim parallel to the shore across the current and then, when free, swim to shore.

Dive safely: Before diving, be sure you are thoroughly trained and familiar with all equipment. Dive only if you are in good health, with no head or chest colds. It is safest to get a physical examination and have your doctor approve your diving. Be familiar with the area where you plan to dive. Know where the closest medical facility is and where there is a decompression chamber.

When you dive, display a diving flag at least three feet above the surface of the water. Be alert to currents, tides, and water temperature. Be aware of environmental dangers such as polluted water, hazardous marine animals, bottom conditions.

After diving, be sure you are free of symptoms indicating any diving illness. Allow time for bodily adjustments if you plan to fly.

Ice-skate safely: Stick to shallow ponds and be sure the ice is frozen and hard everywhere. Skate in groups.

Boat safely: Be sure your boat is in good working order and properly equipped with medical supplies, personal flotation devices (PFDs), fire extinguishers, basic tools and parts.

Watch the weather before you go out boating and while boating; don't get caught in a storm. Let someone know where you are going. Read "Boating Emergencies" to know how to handle possible problems while at sea.

If you are in a boat that capsizes, stay near the boat and cling to the bottom of the overturned boat. Or sit in a flooded boat and paddle back to shore.

Fish safely: It is best to fish in pairs. Wear a life jacket when venturing into deep water or when wading in swift currents.

Use bathtubs safely: Never leave a baby, small child or invalid unattended in a bathtub; the person may drown.

Tubs and the areas around them can be slippery. Use caution to avoid a fall that may knock you unconscious. You may want to attach nonslip padding to the bottom of your tub or shower stall and to the area just beyond it.

14

DRUG ABUSE

Consumers spend billions of dollars each year on medicine. There are two basic types of medicine available: over-the-counter (OTC) drugs and prescription (Rx) drugs. All drugs have a potential for harm as well as good. It is important, therefore, not to use medicines more than necessary, and to follow the directions for use, whether they come from the label on an OTC medicine you buy in a drugstore or supermarket, or from a pharmacy as prescribed and directed by your physician.

This chapter explains what you need to know about buying and using medicine and how to prevent adverse reactions. It also details the main drugs of abuse: narcotics, depressants, stimulants, hallucinogens, cannabis.

OVER-THE-COUNTER DRUGS

Over-the-counter drugs include the vast assortment of medicines you can buy in drugstores and in many supermarkets without a doctor's prescription. OTC drugs do not—and are not meant to—cure disease. They should be used for temporary relief of minor symptoms such as a headache, indigestion or constipation.

Improper use of OTC drugs may aggravate your symptoms, hide a condition that needs a doctor's attention, or lead to undesirable results. Symptoms that persist require the attention of a doctor for proper diagnosis and treatment.

Federal law requires that OTC drugs be properly labeled. The label must give a name or statement of identity of the product, the symptoms which the product will relieve, the net quantity of the contents, the active ingredients, and the name and place of business of the manufacturer, distributor or packer. It must also give directions: the amount of each dose, how frequently it can be taken, and in what manner (for example, by mouth with water). It must give warnings: total dose that may be taken in a day, limit on the length of treatment or number of days it can be taken, statement of possible side effects such as drowsiness or constipation, circumstances which require a doctor's supervision for taking the medicine. Many OTC medicines should not be used by people when they are taking certain other drugs. Soon all labels will be required to have a warning against use of the medicine when it could cause a hazardous interaction. An example of such warning is: "Do not take this product if you are presently taking a prescription antibiotic drug containing any form of tetracycline." Some information now on labels is particularly helpful to people with special health problems. For example, some labels now contain the sodium content per dose, if it is 5 mg or higher, to alert people who must limit their intake of salt.

Large doses of OTC drugs can cause serious reactions. There have been numerous reports of accidental poisoning of young children who swallow too many aspirin. So although a medicine may be ordinary enough not to require a doctor's prescription, it can cause harm and sometimes death.

PRESCRIPTION DRUGS

For more serious problems, doctors prescribe more powerful medicines.

47

Prescription, or Rx, drugs can be sold only by licensed pharmacists. These drugs can be extremely dangerous if not used properly.

Prescription drugs also have a label, written especially for you by your pharmacist as directed by your doctor. Instructions on the label tell you how much to take and how often. If you feel you need to take more—or less—ask your physician. Unlike the labels on OTC drugs, the label on a prescription medicine does not usually tell you what it will do for you, any side effects that may occur, or special precautions you should take, and perhaps it will not even give the name of the medicine. This information must come from your physician. Always ask the doctor what the drug is supposed to do for you, possible undesirable effects you might watch for, and how to handle them if they arise. You should ask him the name of the drug he is prescribing and write it down so you can keep it for ready reference. You should get his specific instructions for taking the drug too. Brief instructions will be on the label, but it is a good idea to be sure you understand his directions completely. Besides asking questions, you should tell your doctor about any special drug problem you have (such as allergies or side effects from drugs you have taken in the past) and also what medicines you may now be using, to help him determine the best medication for your needs. If you find a drug is not doing for you what the doctor expected it to do, check with him. He may wish to change the dosage or prescribe a different drug. If after you start to take the drug you have a new and unexpected symptom such as nausea, a rash or headache, report the problem to your doctor immediately.

Do not stop taking a prescription drug just because you are feeling better and think you no longer need it. You may prevent the drug from doing its work completely, and you may have a relapse. Follow your doctor's instructions.

Some prescriptions cannot be refilled without permission from your doctor. He knows that some drugs should not be taken continually, or he may want to see you again to determine what effects the drug is having before continuing its use. When the medicine is one that he considers necessary and safe for continued use, the label will state that it can be refilled.

Do not keep prescription drugs that are no longer needed. If your doctor takes you off a medicine before it is used up, destroy what is left. Clear out your medicine cabinet regularly, getting rid of old drugs. An exception is if you suffer from a chronic illness and need the medication over a long period of time. An example would be medicine to lower high blood pressure.

Always store drugs correctly. Some drugs must be kept cool and dry; others should be refrigerated.

Choose a pharmacy that will keep a record of all the prescriptions filled for you and other family members.

When traveling, be sure to take along any prescription medicines that you might need. Carry them in the original labeled containers. Pharmacists often do not fill prescriptions written by out-of-state doctors. In an emergency, contact a nearby hospital.

PREVENTING ADVERSE REACTIONS

All medicines are double-edged swords. They can alleviate symptoms and in some cases cure disease. When you take a drug, you hope it will fulfill the primary function for which it was intended. But medicines may also cause undesirable or unexpected side effects. They can be caused by medicines bought with a doctor's prescription as well as medicines purchased over the counter. The more powerful the drug, the greater the potential for an adverse reaction. Unexpected effects can be mild, such as a slight rash, a headache, nausea or drowsiness. They can also be severe, such as prolonged vomiting, bleeding, marked weakness or impaired vision or hearing. These symptoms are nature's way of telling you that the medicine is acting adversely, and that you should do something about it.

If a prescription drug you are taking causes an unexpected or undesirable effect, call your physician right away. He will know whether you should continue taking the medicine.

If an unusual or undesirable reaction occurs from taking a medicine you bought over the counter, you should stop taking it immediately. With side effects, use common sense. If, for example, you become drowsy, do not drive a car until the effect of the medicine wears off.

Remember that mixing two types of medicine can cause an unexpected and sometimes very severe reaction. You should never mix two medicines unless your doctor tells you it is proper. If your physician prescribes a drug for you, make sure he knows what other drugs you are taking. No drug is too unimportant to mention. Knowledge about drug interaction is by no means complete. Even if your doctor recommends a second drug, you could become ill. Report any side effects to your physician. Numerous OTC drugs contain more than one ingredient. For example, Bufferin, a headache remedy, contains aspirin as well as an antacid. This other active ingredient could cause a side effect. Be sure always to read the label carefully. Again, report any side effects to your physician.

Remember that alcohol is a drug. Do not drink alcohol when taking medicine without first consulting your physician; the combination can be dangerous. For example, a person taking nitroglycerin for angina pectoris, a heart ailment, who also drinks alcohol may suffer hypotension, or low blood pressure, and then failure of the circulatory system.

Individuals react differently to medicines. Just because someone you know had no side effects from a drug, it does not mean you will not. For this reason, never take medicine prescribed for someone else, even if you feel your symptoms are the same and the medicine is similar in color and size to medicine you take. Likewise, never give anyone a medicine that has been prescribed for you.

If after buying medicine you notice it seems off-color or stale, do not use it. Return it to the pharmacy where you purchased it. At regular intervals, clean out your medicine cabinet and dispose of prescription and OTC drugs.

When buying medicine, look for safety packaging closures which are difficult for children to open. Then store these medicines out of children's reach on a high shelf. Never refer to medicine for children as candy. Children may then try to get more of it.

More than twenty states have laws to help you save money on prescriptions by allowing you to substitute generic equivalent drugs for the higher-priced brand-name drugs. Generic drugs are usually not inferior to brand-name drugs, although some pharmaceutical companies claim that their quality-control procedures insure a better product.

Watch out for aspirin

When some of us feel the slightest ache or pain, we reach for an aspirin. Aspirin is also found in many headache and pain remedies. Taking too much aspirin can produce an adverse reaction, however, just as with more powerful drugs. An overdose can cause ringing in the ears, loss of hearing, rapid breathing, blueness of the fingernails and lips, nausea and vomiting, hemorrhages, convulsions, delirium, and even coma.

First-aid treatment

In case of an overdose, call your local poison-control center or physician. If you cannot reach either, proceed with the following steps:

If victim is conscious and not convulsing, give water—three or four glasses for an adult and one or two glasses for a child. The poison-control center, hospital emergency room or doctor may tell you to induce vomiting. If so, give victim syrup of ipecac. For a child under a year give two teaspoonfuls; for a child a year or older one tablespoonful (1/2 ounce), and for an adult two tablespoonfuls followed by one cup of water. If victim does not vomit in 20 minutes, repeat the dose. If vomiting still does not occur, or if you do not have syrup of ipecac on hand, give water and then try to make person vomit by tickling back of throat with spoon or blunt object or by placing finger down the throat. When victim begins to vomit, keep his head down and turned sideways to prevent him from choking on the vomit. Save a sample for examination by a doctor.

The poison-control center or doctor may tell you to give activated charcoal after vomiting occurs. Ask how much to give. Do not give charcoal unless a doctor recommends it.

Treat for shock if necessary (see page 21).

Notes on using aspirin: Many OTC products contain aspirin, so read all labels. Always take aspirin with food to avoid stomach irritation. Do not mix alcohol and aspirin. Pregnant women should avoid taking aspirin. Doctors often recommend acetaminophen for aspirin-sensitive people.

PSYCHOACTIVE DRUG ABUSE

Drugs that are safe in a dose recommended by a doctor or by the label on an over-the-counter drug may be dangerous in large doses. People of all ages, from all walks of life and in all economic and social circumstances, however, abuse drugs—sometimes out of ignorance.

The drugs which can cause the most serious problems are psychoactive drugs because they can influence behavior. Some psychoactive drugs are available legally; others are not. The five main categories of psychoactive drugs are narcotics, depressants, stimulants, hallucinogens, cannabis.

With each type of drug, there is a potential for producing psychological and/or physical dependence. Drug abuse refers to the use of a psychoactive substance so that the person taking it hurts himself and/or threatens society's well-being. The section on treatments (pages 51–52) shows the uses and effects of the five main types of psychoactive drugs. Following is a brief description of each type.

Narcotics

The term *narcotic*, which originally referred to a variety of substances inducing an altered state of consciousness, in current usage means opium, its derivatives, or synthetic substitutes that produce tolerance and dependence, both psychological and physical. (Tolerance means that a progressive increase in dose is required to produce the same degree of pharmacologic activity or the same pleasurable experience.)

Narcotics are especially useful in the practice of medicine for the relief of intense pain; they are the most effective analgesics known. They are also used as cough suppressants and as a centuries-old remedy for diarrhea.

Relief of physical or psychic suffering through the use of narcotics may result in a short-lived state of euphoria. They also tend to induce drowsiness, apathy, lethargy, decreased physical activity, constipation, pinpoint pupils, and reduced vision. Except in cases of acute toxication, there is no loss of motor coordination or slurred speech. A larger dose may induce sleep, but there is an increased possibility of nausea, vomiting, and respiratory depression.

Methods of administration include oral ingestion, sniffing or smoking, and the more direct—and correspondingly more rewarding—routes of subcutaneous (skin popping), intramuscular, and intravenous (mainlining) injections. Because addicts tend to become preoccupied with the procuring and taking of drugs, they often neglect themselves and may suffer from malnutrition, infections, and unattended diseases or injuries. Among the hazards of addiction are contaminated drugs and needles as well as unsterile injection techniques, resulting commonly in abscesses, blood poisoning, hepatitis, and endocarditis.

Opium: There were no restrictions on the importation or use of opium in the United States until the early 1900s. Patent medicines in those days often contained opium without any warning label, and many persons became physically dependent on medicines that were bought and sold without restriction. Today there are state, federal, and international laws governing the production and distribution of narcotic substances, and there is little abuse of opium in this country. At least 25 organic substances can be extracted from opium. These are alkaloids of two general categories, each producing markedly different effects. In the first, morphine and codeine are used as analgesics and cough suppressants. In the second, papaverine (an intestinal relaxant) and noscapine (a cough suppressant) have no significant influence on the central nervous system.

Heroin: First synthesized from morphine in 1874, heroin was not extensively used in medicine until the beginning of this century. Pure heroin is a white powder with a bitter taste. Illicit heroin may vary in color from white to dark brown because of impurities left from the manufacturing process or the presence of diluents such as food coloring, cocoa, or brown sugar. Pure heroin is rarely sold on the street. The first comprehensive control of heroin in the United States was established with the Harrison Narcotic Act of 1914. Today it is the most widely abused opiate, acting on the central nervous system to produce euphoria, drowsiness, respiratory depression, constricted pupils, and mental confusion. The effects of an overdose are slow and shallow breathing, clammy skin, convulsions, coma and possibly death. Heroin is one narcotic that has no medical use at present in the United States.

Depressants

Taken in amounts prescribed by a physician, depressants can be beneficial in the symptomatic treatment of insomnia, anxiety, irritability, and tension. In excessive amounts, however, depressants produce a state of intoxication that is remarkably similar to that of alcohol. As in the case of alcohol, these effects may be expected to vary not only from person to person but from time to time in the same individual. Low doses produce mild sedation; higher doses, insofar as they relieve anxiety or stress, may produce a temporary state of euphoria, but they may also produce depression and apathy. Intoxicating doses invariably result in impaired judgment, slurred speech, and an often unrealized loss of motor coordination. They may also induce drowsiness, sleep, stupor, coma and even death. The dangers of depressants multiply when used in combination with other drugs or alcohol. Depressants also serve as a means of suicide, a pattern especially common among women, who take an overdose of barbiturates

Barbiturates: Among the drugs most frequently prescribed by physicians to induce sedation and sleep are the barbiturates, the largest group of depressants. Small therapeutic doses tend to calm nervous conditions, and larger amounts cause sleep from 20 to 60 minutes after taken orally. If a user increases the dosage, the effects of the barbiturates may progress through successive stages of sedation, sleep, and coma to death from respiratory arrest and cardiovascular complications. Barbiturates are legally available only with a prescription.

Stimulants

The consumption of chemical agents that stimulate the central nervous sys-

tem is an accepted part of modern life. The two most prevalent stimulants are nicotine, contained in tobacco products, and caffeine, the active ingredient in coffee, tea and some bottled beverages sold in every supermarket. When used in moderation, they tend to have the effects of relief from fatigue, and increased alertness.

There is also a broad range of stronger stimulants that may produce mood elevation and a heightened sense of well-being, but because of their dependence-producing potential are under regulatory control. The controlled stimulants are available on prescription, and they are also clandestinely manufactured in vast quantities for the illicit market. Chronic users tend to rely on stimulants to feel stronger, more confident, decisive and self-possessed. They often follow a pattern of taking "uppers" in the morning and "downers" such as alcohol or sleeping pills at night. Such chemical manipulation, however, interferes with normal body processes and can lead to mental and physical illness.

The oral consumption of stimulants may result in a temporary sense of exhilaration, superabundant energy, hyperactivity, and extended wakefulness; it may also induce irritability, anxiety, and apprehension. These effects are greatly intensified with administration by intravenous injection, which may produce a sudden sensation known as a "flash." The continued use of stimulants is followed, however, by a period of depression known as "crashing" that is invariably described as unpleasant. Because the depression can be counteracted by a further injection of stimulant, this abuse pattern becomes increasingly difficult to break. Heavy users may inject themselves every few hours, a process sometimes continued to the point of delirium, psychosis or physical exhaustion.

Dizziness, tremor, agitation, hostility, panic, headache, flushed skin, chest pain with palpitations, excessive sweating, vomiting, and abdominal cramps are among the symptoms of a sublethal overdose. In the absence of medical intervention, high fever, convulsions, and cardiovascular collapse may signal the onset of death.

The most widely used stimulants are amphetamines (found in many

diet pills). Other stimulants include cocaine, methylphenidate and phenmetrazine.

Cocaine: Cocaine is the principal active ingredient of the South American coca plant and the strongest stimulant of natural origin. Some cocaine is legally exported to the United States where the leaves—decocainized—yield flavoring extracts for cola beverages, and the pure cocaine extract supplies a dwindling world market for medical purposes. Its medical application is now mainly restricted to ear, nose and throat surgery. While the demand for licit cocaine has been going down, the supply of illicit cocaine in recent years has been rapidly rising. It is sold on the street in the form of a white crystalline powder containing usually from 5 to 10 percent pure cocaine "cut" with other white powders such as lactose. It is administered by sniffing or snorting and for heightened effect by intravenous injection, producing intense euphoria with increased heartbeat, blood pressure, and body temperature. Due to the intensity of its pleasurable effects, a strong psychic dependency can develop. Effects of overdose include agitation, increase in body temperature, hallucinations, convulsions, and possibly death.

Hallucinogens

The hallucinogenic drugs are substances, both natural and synthetic, that distort perception. If taken in large doses, they cause hallucinations—the apparent perception of unreal sights and sounds. Under the influence of hallucinogens, a user may speak of "seeing" sounds and "hearing" colors. His senses of direction, distance, and time become disoriented. Restlessness and sleeplessness are common until the drug wears off. Recurrent use produces tolerance of the drug, inviting the use of greater amounts. The greatest hazard of the hallucinogens is that their effects are unpredictable each time they are taken. Toxic reactions that precipitate psychotic behavior and even death can occur. Persons in hallucinogenic states should be closely supervised to keep them from harming themselves and others. At present, hallucinogens have no accepted use in medicine.

LSD: The most powerful hallucinogen is LSD. It is an abbreviation of

50

the German expression for lysergic acid diethylamide. It was first synthesized in 1938, and its effects were discovered in 1943 when a chemist accidentally took some. As he began to experience the effects now known as a "trip," he noticed a sense of vertigo and restlessness; objects and other workers in the laboratory appeared to undergo optical changes; light was intensified and bizarre visions with bright colors appeared. This condition lasted for about two hours.

Along with the mental changes described above, physical reactions may include dilated pupils, lowered temperature, nausea, goose bumps, profuse perspiration, increased blood sugar, and rapid heartbeat. "Flashbacks" days or months after pharmacological effects have worn off have also been reported. One of the dangers of the use of LSD is the unpredictability of its effects. While some users have a "good trip," others may experience a "bad trip." Many LSD users often believe they can do anything they attempt, and many have as a result walked out of windows to try to fly and died.

Cannabis

Cannabis sativa L. grows throughout the temperate and tropical regions of the world. As a psychoactive drug, cannabis is usually smoked in the form of loosely rolled cigarettes ("joints"), although it may also be taken orally. Low doses tend to produce initial restlessness and an increased sense of well-being, followed by a dreamy, carefree state of relaxation; alteration of sensory perceptions, including an illusory expansion of time and space; a more vivid sense of touch, sight, smell, taste, and sound; hunger, especially a craving for sweets; and subtle changes in thought formation and expression. Moderate doses may result in a state of intoxication that intensifies these reactions. The individual may experience rapidly changing emotions, shifting sensory imagery, a flight of fragmentary thoughts with disturbed associations, a dulling of attention, and impaired memory, accompanied by an altered sense of self-identity and commonly a sense of enhanced insight. High doses can result in distortions of body image, loss of personal identity, fantasies, and hallucinations.

Very high doses may precipitate a toxic psychosis. This state will clear as the drug is eliminated from the body. Heavy users may experience withdrawal syndrome, including sleep loss, irritability, restlessness, hyperactivity, decreased appetite, sweating, sudden weight loss, increased salivation, and increased pressure within the eyes.

Hashish: A drug-rich resinous secretion from the flowers of the cannabis plant, hashish is processed by drying to produce a drug several times as potent as marijuana. The resin from the flowers is richer in cannabinols than the leaves and tops.

Marijuana: The popular name of the cannabis plant, marijuana also denotes the drug that is prepared by drying the leaves and flowering tops of the plant to make a tobaccolike material. Marijuana at present has no therapeutic uses in the practice of medicine in this country, although there are several experiments for its use as a painkiller. Small doses of marijuana may affect a person's driving ability enough to lead to accidents.

First-aid treatment for overdose and adverse reaction

For any overdose or severe adverse reaction, call your local poison-control center or physician immediately for help. For ingested overdoses, give victim water if conscious and not convulsing. Give an adult three or four glasses and a child one or two glasses. The poison-control center, hospital emergency room or physician may tell you to induce vomiting. If so advised, give victim syrup of ipecac. Give a child under a year two teaspoonfuls, give a child a year or older one tablespoonful (1/2 ounce), and give an adult two tablespoonfuls. Afterward give one cup of water. If victim does not vomit in 20 minutes, give another dose. If vomiting still does not occur, or if you do not have syrup of ipecac on hand, give water and then try to induce vomiting by tickling the back of throat with spoon or blunt object or by placing finger down the throat. When victim begins to vomit, keep his head down and turned sideways

to prevent him from choking on the vomitus. Save a sample for examination by a doctor.

A poison-control center or doctor may tell you to give activated charcoal after vomiting occurs. He will tell you how much to give. Do not give unless doctor recommends it, however.

Follow the first-aid measures below for specific psychoactive drug overdoses.

Narcotics: Try to arouse victim by splashing with cold water or having him walk around. Keep victim awake until you get medical help. Reassure victim that everything will be all right. Observe breathing. If it stops, begin artificial respiration at once (see pages 17–18). Sustain cardiac function, including blood pressure, by cardiopulmonary resuscitation (see pages 18–19). Treat for shock if necessary (see page 21), and stay with victim if convulsions begin (see pages 44–45). Maintain body temperature. Seek medical help promptly.

Depressants: Observe breathing. If it stops, begin artificial respiration at once (see pages 17–18). Sustain cardiac function, including blood pressure, by cardiopulmonary resuscitation (see pages 18–19). Treat for shock if necessary (see page 21), and stay with the victim if convulsions begin (see pages 44–45). Maintain normal body temperature, and seek medical help promptly.

Stimulants: Prevent self-inflicted damage. If breathing stops, begin artificial respiration (see pages 17–18). Maintain normal body temperature, and seek medical help promptly, especially for a victim who is hallucinating.

Hallucinogens: Protect a person from inflicting damage on himself. Restrain a person who is experiencing a bad trip. Reassure the person. Seek medical help promptly.

Cannabis: You will not have to give any special first-aid treatment unless the person is having a very bad reaction. Then you should help the person as you would for a bad LSD trip (see directly above). Protect the person from inflicting damage on himself. You may have to restrain the person. Reassure him that everything will be fine. Seek medical help promptly.

15

EAR INJURIES

The following are the most common ear emergencies.

Perforated eardrum

An eardrum that is perforated by an explosion, injury to the side of the head, or a dive can be painful. It will have to be diagnosed by a doctor. If you have severe pain in the ear, do the following until you can secure medical help: Place a cotton ball or small pad of gauze loosely into the outer ear canal. Get immediate help.

Bleeding cuts

For cuts on the ear that bleed, cover with the cleanest cloth available or with your hand and apply direct pressure on the wound. Elevate victim's head. Apply a bandage to secure the cloth in place, and continue pressure to stop the bleeding.

Foreign object

If a foreign object becomes lodged in the ear, do not try to remove the object yourself or have victim dislodge it. Instead, turn victim's head on injured side so any fluid can drain out of the ear. Get medical help quickly.

Earache

Blowing the nose too hard during a cold can lead to an earache. Symptoms include a fever and ear pain. Treat with aspirin to ease the pain and also apply heat through a heating pad or hot-water bottle for temporary relief. Call a physician if pain does not subside.

An earache can also develop during air travel because air pressure changes in taking off and landing. Pain in the ear will often be sharp and stabbing. Try swallowing, yawning or chewing gum or taking nose drops right before takeoff and landing. If pain continues after the flight, consult a physician.

Severed ear

If an ear is severed, pack it in a cold, clean cloth and place in a bag with ice (not dry ice). Take the package to a doctor or hospital emergency room when you transport the victim.

In the meantime, control bleeding with direct pressure (see page 19). If not successful, try pressure-point method to control bleeding (see pages 19–20).

16

ELECTRIC SHOCK

An electric shock is caused by a current flowing through the body, most often from a wire downed by a storm, a short circuit in a home appliance, or a bolt of lightning. A fraction of one ampere can kill you. If you are not kicked free by the initial shock, your muscles may contract and cause your hand to freeze around the appliance or the conductor which you are touching. Someone else will have to free you by using an insulated object to push you away, or by turning off the current.

Signs/symptoms

Symptoms vary, depending upon the strength and duration of the current passing through the body. Typical symptoms include shallow breathing; rapid, weak pulse; pale, moist skin; confusion; muscle contractions; burns ranging from mild to severe; unconsciousness.

First-aid treatment

Do not touch the victim until he is free of the electricity because you can also receive a shock. Try to cut off the current by removing the fuse or unplugging the electrical cord from the outlet. If you cannot cut off the circuit, use a nonconductive material such as a dry board, loop of cloth or wood pole to push the victim away from the source of current. Always stand on something dry such as a rubber mat.

If breathing stops, begin artificial respiration (see pages 17–18). If circulation stops, give victim cardiopulmonary resuscitation (see pages 18–19). Treat burns (see pages 38–39). Call a doctor immediately or get victim to a hospital.

Safety precautions

Rather than use two-prong adapters, it is safer to have wall outlets rewired by qualified electricians so that the outlets can accept three-prong plugs. If you must use an adapter, be sure to attach the pigtail third wire to the screw holding the faceplate to the wall receptacle. If the screw itself is properly grounded (which an electrician can determine), this should provide a line to carry any leaking current directly to the ground. If it is not grounded, a wire from the ground to the outlet box must be installed.

Keep your body from becoming part of a circuit or conducting current to the ground. Don't touch any appliance if you are wet, standing on a wet surface or in water, or if the appliance cord has broken insulation or a damaged plug.

Don't use ordinary electrical appliances where they can get wet or where it is raining because the water can cause a short circuit, which may result in fatal electric shock. Special outdoor electrical appliances are available which prevent short circuiting in wet weather.

If you are not experienced with electrical work, don't attempt to make repairs yourself. Hire a qualified electrician. If you do make the electrical repairs, insulate yourself from becoming part of the electric circuit. Wearing dry rubber gloves or standing on a rubber mat can prevent current from running through your body. Don't use metal ladders when making repairs.

If you feel even a slight shock when you touch an appliance, cease using it. Unplug it and have it repaired.

Disconnect tools by pulling the plug, not the cord.

When changing light bulbs, disconnect the lamp plug first to avoid potential electrical shock.

If an overhead wire falls on an automobile you are in, it is best to remain inside until rescuers arrive unless fire is an immediate threat.

Never touch downed power lines.

17

EPILEPSY

Epilepsy is a disorder of the nervous system centered in the brain in which there is an abnormal release of energy. The symptoms, called seizures, are characterized by muscle spasms, partial or total loss of consciousness for periods ranging from a few seconds to several minutes, and, possibly, abnormal social behavior.

CAUSES OF EPILEPSY

Epilepsy can result from a congenital malformation of the brain, from a scar that formed within the brain after an injury, or from damage to brain tissue following a childhood infection such as meningitis or encephalitis. Neurosurgeons occasionally find tumors and abscesses in the brain that may irritate nearby nerve cells and cause seizures. Chemical imbalance, poor nutrition, and some poisonous substances are additional causes of the disease. In most cases, no cause can be found.

REASONS FOR A SEIZURE

In some epileptics who are not well controlled by medication, a seizure can apparently be traced to a time of great nervous tension, a sudden noise, or a bright flickering light. Generally, no clear precipitating cause can be found.

KINDS OF SEIZURES

There are many types of epileptic seizures, and a person can suffer from more than one at the same time. The three main types are grand mal, petit mal, and psychomotor seizures.

Grand mal

Grand mal means "great sickness" or "major attack" in French. Despite its fearsome name, grand mal epilepsy is generally the easiest type to bring under control and is also the most common form of the disease. During a seizure, which usually lasts less than five minutes but sometimes as long as 20 minutes, the patient may turn blue and appear to be suffering from a lack of oxygen in the blood. He may fall to the ground with convulsive move-

ments, vomit, and froth at the mouth because of heavy breathing and an uncontrolled flow of saliva. There may be an involuntary movement of the bowels and bladder. At the end of the seizure, the condition will disappear. The person's muscles will relax, and he will become conscious again. The seizure may be followed by another seizure. When the seizure or seizures are finally over, the person may feel confused or drowsy for a while and prefer to recover by sleeping.

Many people with grand mal epilepsy experience a warning before the seizure, called an aura. They sense unusual colors, smells or sounds, and experience a numbness or tingling sensation. Some persons will also utter a sharp cry prior to the onset of an attack.

First-aid treatment

A person experiencing a grand mal seizure does not require special medical aid. Your main goal should be to keep the person from hurting himself. Use the following suggestions as a guide:
1. Keep calm. Nothing can be done to stop the attack once it starts. The person is not going to die; he does not need a doctor unless—and this does not happen usually—he seems to pass from one seizure to another without regaining consciousness. Then the victim is experiencing a status epilepticus and should be placed in a hospital or under the care of a physician.
2. The condition is not contagious. Ordinarily the grand mal attack will be over in a few minutes.
3. Try to get the victim in a position where he will not hurt himself by knocking against a sharp object or piece of furniture. Clear the area of harmful objects. Do not interfere with his movements.
4. If you can do it without using force, slip something like a folded handkerchief or a piece of rubber between the teeth to keep the victim from biting his tongue or cheek. Do not try to force the jaws open if the victim has already clamped them shut.
5. Loosen tight clothing, particularly around the neck area.
6. Give artificial respiration if breathing stops. Mouth-to-nose re-

suscitation may be the only effective way to ventilate a victim if the mouth is closed tightly (see page 17).
7. Once convulsive movements stop, you may turn the person on his side to assist his tongue to fall forward and excess saliva to drain out of the mouth. As the victim recovers, let him rest if he wants to. Treat him matter-of-factly. If possible, observe details for a full medical report to his doctor.
8. After the seizure is over, encourage the epileptic to rest.

Petit mal

Petit mal is French for "little sickness" or "minor attack." It is a form of epilepsy prevalent in children ages four to ten. The seizures occur without convulsions and without the epileptic's knowledge. They also occur without any forewarning. The petit mal seizure lasts from 5 to 20 seconds and can occur a few times a day or as many as 50 times a day. During the seizure, the victim may blink his eyes, nod his head or jerk his arms for a few seconds. This type of seizure may disappear at puberty.

Some neurologists consider two other types of seizures to be variations of the petit mal seizure. In one case, all the muscles go limp at one time and the person falls to the ground. After the attack, he usually picks himself up and goes about whatever he had been doing. In the other type of seizure, the muscles of the arms or trunk suddenly begin to move jerkily, and then in a little while that movement stops. Some authorities classify these types of petit mal seizures as minor motor seizures.

First-aid treatment

A petit mal seizure does not require emergency treatment. Keep the victim from hurting himself. It is sometimes hard to recognize this form of epilepsy because there are no convulsions. The person, in fact, may appear drunk or addicted to drugs. Do not restrict him in any way unless it is essential for his personal safety. The seizure will end quickly.

Psychomotor epilepsy

Another type of seizure is known as

53

psychomotor epilepsy because the abnormally discharging brain cells act on the mental process as well as on the muscles. It is characterized by irrational—or at least odd—behavior that generally lasts only a few minutes, but may continue for several hours. The patient does not remember the seizure afterward.

A psychomotor epilepsy seizure can occur at any age, but is more common in adolescence and adulthood. It involves such complex activities as lip-smacking, as well as staring and confusion, abdominal pains, headaches, spots before the eyes, changes in color perception, dizziness, fear, anger, buzzing and ringing in the ears. When the seizure ends, the patient may prefer to sleep.

First-aid treatment

It is difficult to recognize psychomotor epileptic seizures. Sometimes the person's unusual behavior is mistaken for that of a drunk or drug addict. It is best not to restrain him during a seizure unless it is essential for his safety. The person may react violently to restraint.

CONTROL OF EPILEPSY

Epilepsy is not curable, but seizures can be controlled in approximately 80 percent of all cases by use of anticonvulsant medication. The drugs sometimes lead to side effects such as dizziness, drowsiness, unstable gait. These symptoms may be eliminated by reduced dosage. Most epilepsy medicines are not habit-forming and none leads to addiction. In a few cases, brain surgery may provide relief. Sometimes epilepsy that begins in childhood disappears in adult years. Epileptic patients should drink as little alcohol as possible.

Identification during a seizure

A free Emergency Medical Identification card for the wallet may be obtained from the American Medical Association (AMA), 535 North Dearborn Street, Chicago, Illinois 60610. This helps protect the person in a seizure from being mistaken for a person in a coma. The AMA also encourages persons experiencing seizures or other health problems to wear an emergency signal device around the neck or wrist at all times. A source for signal

devices is the Medic-Alert Foundation International, P.O. Box 1009, Turlock, California 95390 (see page 16).

If you have further questions, contact your local chapter of the Epilepsy Foundation of America, or EFA at 1828 L Street, N.W., Washington, D.C. 20036.

Note. Not all seizures are epilepsy. Other conditions can cause convulsions. These include chemical poisoning, high fever in young children, meningitis and encephalitis.

18

EYE INJURIES AND DISEASES

The human eye (see Fig.18-1) is a remarkable organ, which, in addition to giving us our vision, also displays early warning signs of many illnesses, including high blood pressure, diabetes, multiple sclerosis and kidney diseases. To do their work effectively, the eyes must be taken care of, guarded from infections, injuries and serious illnesses. The following descriptions tell how to protect the eyes.

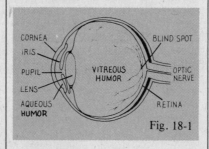

Fig. 18-1

INFECTIONS

Eye products

Pseudomonas is a type of bacteria found in contaminated eye products that can cause eye infections. Fortunately, most infections do not lead to blindness. But even if the infection results only in a swollen eyelid or inflamed mucosa, the potential for serious harm must be recognized and held in check. The Food and Drug Administration has encouraged the manufacturers of eye cosmetics to include in their products preservatives that will retard the growth of micro-

organisms. But no matter how good the preservative in an eye cosmetic, if the product is misused by the consumer, infections can still develop. The FDA advises women to heed the following precautions in the use of eye cosmetics:

1. Discontinue immediately the use of any eye product that causes irritation. If irritation persists, see a doctor.
2. Your hands contain microorganisms that, if they get into the eye, could cause infections. Wash your hands before applying cosmetics to your eyes.
3. Make sure that any instrument you place in the eye area is clean.
4. Do not allow eye cosmetics to become covered with dust or contaminated with dirt or soil. Wipe off the container with a damp cloth if visible dust or dirt is present.
5. Do not use old eye cosmetics. If you have not used the product for several months, it is better to discard it and purchase a new one.
6. Do not spit into eye cosmetics. The microorganisms in your mouth may grow in the cosmetic and subsequent application to the eye may cause infection. Boiled water can be added to products which have thickened.
7. Do not share your cosmetics. Another person's microflora in your cosmetic can be hazardous.
8. Do not store cosmetics at temperatures above 85° F. Cosmetics held for a long period of time in hot cars, for example, are more susceptible to deterioration of the preservative.
9. Avoid using eye cosmetics if you have an eye infection or the skin around the eye is inflamed. Wait until the area is healed.
10. Take particular care in using eye cosmetics if you have any allergies.
11. When removing eye cosmetics, be careful not to scratch the eyeball or the other sensitive areas of the eye.

Note. The instructions given for use of eye cosmetics also apply to sterile eye drugs.

Hard and soft lenses

Many persons become so adept at using hard lenses that they forget to exercise reasonable precautions to limit lens contamination. Retrieving a lost lens from a dirty floor, using saliva in-

54

stead of wetting solution, and inserting a lens into the eye with unwashed hands are fraught with danger. Such careless handling only invites infections to develop.

Wearing soft contact lenses also requires certain precautions. Because they absorb fluid, soft lenses have the potential for harboring microorganisms that can lead to infections. Soft lenses are accompanied by sanitizing kits. It is up to the individual who wears the lenses to follow carefully the instructions in the use of the lenses.

Note. Every person who wears contact lenses should carry identification stating this fact. In case of an accident, the lenses can be removed to prevent corneal damage.

INJURIES

The following are only a few of the precautions that should be observed to prevent eye injuries. In industries where there is a potential hazard of eye injury, employees should be required to use safety eyewear. Students working in laboratories and workshops where eye damage can occur should be required to wear safety goggles. Only eyeglasses and sunglasses that have impact-resistant lenses should be worn; sunglasses should be worn to protect eyes from both bright sun and airborne particles such as sand in a desert area. Household chemicals and hazardous objects should be kept out of reach of young children. Driving in fog, a heavy snow-storm, a cloudburst—any time when visibility is poor—should be avoided.

Note. Television watching is not harmful to the eyes. Excessive viewing over a long period, however, can result in eye fatigue. The screen should be viewed from about six feet, or five times the width of the picture, and there should be some light in the room. The set should always be in perfect focus.

Injury to the eyeball by an object embedded in the eye

Injuries to the eyeball can occur from a piece of wood accidentally stuck in the eye, a BB shot, a flying piece of glass. In case of eyeball injury, do not rub the eye and do not try to remove the object. Cover the injured eye with a paper cup or cardboard cone to protect it, and to prevent the object from being driven further into the eye. Cover the other eye, even if it is not injured, with a sterile dressing. Both eyes should be covered because one eye cannot move without the other eye moving. Calm and reassure the victim. He may panic with both eyes covered. Go immediately to your physician or to the emergency room of a hospital.

Injury to the eyelid

Stop any bleeding by applying direct pressure. Cleanse the wound and apply a clean dressing. Tape dressing securely to the injured area.

Foreign bodies in the eye

Foreign bodies can become lodged on the inner surface of the upper or lower eyelid, on the eyeball, or between the eyeball and eyelid. Never rub the eye; this may force the foreign body in deeper and scratch the eyelid or eyeball. Wash your hands well before touching any part of the eye.

Bring upper eyelid down over the lower lid and hold it there for a moment while the person looks up. Tears should flow, helping to wash away the foreign body. If the object remains, place fingers below the lower eyelid and pull down on the lower lid. Look for the foreign body on the inside of lower lid. If the object is there, lift it out carefully with the corner of a moistened clean cloth. If the object still remains, try flushing the eye with water, using either an eye dropper or a small cup of water. If the object still does not become dislodged or if it cannot be seen, cover both eyes with clean, dry compresses and go to a physician or hospital emergency room.

Chemical burns of the eye

Special attention must be given to chemical burns of the eyes since vision may be impaired or lost. If victim wears contact lenses, have him remove them first. Flush away the chemicals immediately with plenty of water. Turn head so the injured side is down. Flood the inner corner of the eye with cool water for at least five minutes, or hold the eye under a stream of water from a water faucet. Hold eyelids open. Be sure the chemical does not wash into the other eye if only one eye is burned. Cover eyes with clean compresses, but not with absorbent cotton, whose fibers can become lodged in the eye. Remove clothing because the chemical may be retained on the clothing. Give first aid as for burns, according to the severity of the burn. Go immediately to a doctor, preferably an eye specialist, or a hospital emergency room.

For an acid burn, you can also clean the eye with a solution of one teaspoonful of baking soda mixed in one quart of water. Pour solution over burned eye area. (Never use this solution for an alkali burn.) Then cover eye with dry protective dressing, not absorbent cotton.

If the chemical was an alkali such as a strong laundry or dishwasher detergent, lift off any particles of dry chemicals that may be on the eye. Do *not* use baking soda solution given above.

If you cannot get medical help for victim within an hour and he requests fluid and is not vomiting, you can give him a weak solution of 1 teaspoon salt and ½ teaspoon baking soda in 1 quart of water. Give an adult 4 ounces, or ½ glass, over 15 minutes. Give a child 2 ounces and an infant 1 ounce. If the victim begins to vomit, give no more fluid.

GLAUCOMA

Glaucoma is an eye disease which produces an increased fluid pressure within the globe of the eye and a loss of vision. When the aqueous humor, which bathes the lens and cornea, fails to flow out in its normal path, it puts an increased pressure on the rear of the eye. Usually the disease progresses slowly and painlessly, unnoticed by its victim until vision is severely impaired. This form of the disease is called chronic glaucoma. Sometimes, however, the disease strikes suddenly, in as little as a few hours, clouding vision and causing pain in and around the eyes. This sudden form is known as acute glaucoma. Sight already destroyed by glaucoma cannot be restored, but early detection and treatment can stop its progression.

The drugs used to control glaucoma, however, sometimes cause side effects. When drugs fail, surgery can

55

create a tiny opening through the white of the eye to filter fluid out. This procedure lowers eye pressure in many cases.

If a person suffers from any of the following symptoms, he should immediately seek help from a physician: loss of side vision, blurred or foggy vision, colored rings around lights, trouble focusing on close work, inability to adjust his sight in a dark room, the need to change eyeglasses frequently in order to maintain proper vision.

Glaucoma can usually be prevented with a regular eye examination, preferably once a year between ages 6 and 20, every two years between ages 20 and 45, and every year over the age of 45. Glaucoma runs in families. If a relative has had glaucoma, you should be especially suspicious if you suffer from any of the above symptoms.

CATARACTS

Cataracts, the leading cause of blindness in the United States today, are a clouding of the eye's lens. They can be congenital or can result from eye injuries, diabetes or other medical problems.

At first spots form in the lens and there is some blurring of vision. Gradually the lens becomes more clouded until the victim cannot see objects distinctly. Occasionally cataracts occur in both eyes.

Surgery is the only known cure for a cataract. It is successful in more than 95 out of 100 cases.

RETINAL DETACHMENT

Retinal detachment is a separation of the inner layer of the retina from its outer layer. This detachment can cause permanent vision impairment. It occurs most frequently when the retina develops a tear. Then fluid from the vitreous humor can flow through this tear, seep between the retinal layers and cause the detachment.

Symptoms which require prompt medical attention include seeing light flashes, sootlike spots or a feeling of having a curtain drawn across the eyes. Prompt care can lead to reattachment of the retina through surgery. Without it the detachment may become complete and permanent blindness may result.

19
FAINTING

Fainting, a temporary or partial loss of consciousness caused by an inadequate supply of blood to the brain, can be due to physical or emotional factors. It is important to report all instances of fainting to a physician because it may be an indication of a serious underlying illness.

If a person feels faint, have him sit down with his head between his knees or have him lie down.

Signs/symptoms

Weakness; dizziness, spots before the eyes; pallor and/or sweaty appearance; nausea. Fainting may occur without warning.

First-aid treatment

After a person faints, place him on his back with his head lower than his feet. Loosen clothing, especially around the neck. Keep victim warm. If victim vomits, turn him on his side to allow the vomit to drain out of mouth. Do not give any food or liquid and do not splash water on his face. After victim regains consciousness, have him rest for at least 10 minutes.

If victim does not regain consciousness after several minutes, send for an ambulance or transport victim by stretcher to a hospital emergency room (see pages 22–23).

If breathing stops, immediately give artificial respiration (see pages 17–18).

20
FEVER

The average body temperature when taken orally is 98.6° F and when taken rectally about 99.6° F. When a person's temperature exceeds 102° F or when any above-normal temperature persists for more than 24 hours, it may constitute an emergency situation. If a person has a temperature of 104° F for just a few hours, however, it is an emergency. A person with an abnormal temperature—called fever—may experience hot, dry skin, dehydration and chills. Fever is a symptom that can have a number of causes.

First-aid treatment

Call a doctor immediately. Do not give victim any medication, alcohol or ice rubs unless the doctor prescribes them.

If you cannot reach a doctor, proceed with the following method as an interim treatment for a victim with a temperature exceeding 102° F.

Undress the victim. Place in a tub of lukewarm water that is not completely filled and sponge body for at least 15 minutes. If no tub is available, give victim a sponge bath, also using lukewarm water. Dry victim well. Repeat cooling process if temperature does not go down or recurs. Give victim fluids to replace those lost.

Taking a person's temperature

To take a person's temperature, you can use an oral or a rectal thermometer. Rectal thermometers are usually more accurate and are best for babies, small children and unconscious adults. Whichever thermometer you use, be sure the column of mercury is below 95° F before you use it. Give the thermometer several vigorous shakes by snapping your wrist. Always clean a thermometer before and after you use it by washing it in cool water and gently drying it. Do not take a person's temperature for at least an hour after he has had a warm or cold drink or a warm or cold shower or bath. Temperature fluctuates during the day, being lowest in the morning. Always, therefore, make note of the time you took temperature.

Orally: Place thermometer under person's tongue and have person close his lips tightly. Leave thermometer in place for about four minutes.

Rectally: Have person lie on his stomach. Lubricate thermometer with petroleum jelly. Insert about one inch into rectum and leave in place for approximately four minutes.

The mercury rises from the bulb end of the thermometer. To determine temperature, twist the thermometer until you can see where the mercury line ends, and then read the temperature.

21
FOOD ILLNESSES

Poor food-handling practices in and out of the home often cause illness, even though the foods were safe to eat when purchased and first prepared. Lack of sanitation, insufficient cooking, and improper storage can allow bacteria in food to increase to dangerous levels. Bacteria account for 95 percent of all cases of food poisoning, causing illness in two ways. Disease-producing bacteria may enter the body in contaminated food, multiply and set up infections in the digestive tract, and, in some cases, in the bloodstream. Other bacteria produce poisonous substances called toxins in food. Eating this contaminated food causes illness, outbreaks of which are especially common during hot summer months when perishable foods are carried on picnics and cookouts without proper refrigeration. Food poisoning is rarely fatal, but many people, especially infants and elder

---

BACTERIA THAT CAUSE FOOD-BORNE ILLNESS

Name of illness: *Salmonellosis*
Examples of foods involved: poultry, red meats, eggs, dried foods, dairy products.

What causes it: Salmonellae. Bacteria widespread in nature; live and grow in intestinal tracts of human beings and animals; cause infection.

Symptoms: Severe headache, followed by vomiting, diarrhea, abdominal cramps and fever. Infants, elderly, and persons with low resistance are most susceptible. Severe infections cause high fever and may even cause death.

Characteristics: Transmitted by eating contaminated food, or by contact with infected persons or carriers of the infection. Also transmitted by insects, rodents and pets.
Onset: Usually within 12 to 36 hours after consumption.
Duration: 2 to 7 days.

Preventive measures: Salmonellae in food are destroyed by heating the food to 140° F and holding for 10 minutes, or to higher temperatures for less time; for instance, 155° F for a few seconds. Refrigeration at 40° F inhibits the increase of salmonellae, but they remain alive in dried foods. Stored foods should be fully reheated before use. Personal cleanliness is essential.

First-aid treatment: Put the victim to bed. Give nothing by mouth until nausea and vomiting subside. Then give fluids by mouth such as hot tea and broth. Do not give purgatives, cathartics or laxatives in case another substance is the cause of the poisoning. Consult a physician immediately; diagnosis will be made by physician taking a culture of victim's vomitus and any residual food.

Name of illness: *Staphylococcal poisoning, or staph*
Examples of foods involved: custards, egg salad, potato salad, chicken salad, macaroni salad, ham, salami, cheese.

What causes it: Staphylococcus aureus. Bacteria fairly resistant to heat. Bacteria growing in food produce a toxin that is extremely resistant to heat.

Symptoms: Salivation, vomiting, diarrhea, prostration, abdominal cramps. Generally mild and often attributed to other causes.

Characteristics: Transmitted by food handlers who carry the bacteria and by eating food containing the toxin.
Onset: Usually within 3 to 8 hours after consumption of food.
Duration: 1 to 2 days, depending on degree of illness.

Preventive measures: Growth of bacteria that produce toxin is inhibited by keeping hot foods above 140° F and cold foods at or below 40° F. Toxin is destroyed by boiling for several hours or heating the food in a pressure cooker at 240° F for 30 minutes. Personal cleanliness by food handlers is essential.

First-aid treatment: Put victim to bed. Give nothing by mouth until vomiting subsides. Then give fluids by mouth such as hot tea and broth. Do not give cathartics, purgatives or laxatives to anyone with these symptoms in case the actual cause is another form of food poisoning or appendicitis. Consult a physician immediately; he will make the diagnosis after taking a culture of victim's vomitus and any residual foods.

Name of illness: *Perfringens poisoning*
Examples of foods involved: stews, soups, or gravies made from poultry or red meat.

What causes it: Clostridium perfringens. Spore-forming bacteria that grow in the absence of oxygen. Temperatures reached in thorough cooking of most foods are sufficient to destroy vegetative cells, but heat-resistant spores can survive and produce toxins.

Symptoms: Nausea without vomiting, diarrhea, acute inflammation of stomach and intestines.

Characteristics: Transmitted by eating food contaminated by abnormally large numbers of the bacteria.
Onset: Usually within 8 to 20 hours.
Duration: May persist for 24 hours.

Preventive measures: To prevent growth of surviving bacteria in cooked meats, gravies and meat casseroles that are to be eaten later, cool rapidly and refrigerate promptly at 40°F or below, or hold them above 140°F.

First-aid treatment:	Put victim to bed. For diarrhea, give a drug such as Lomotil. When nausea subsides, give fluids by mouth such as hot tea and broth with a little sugar or salt. Avoid food for at least 24 hours. Consult a physician immediately; he will make the diagnosis after taking a culture of victim's stool and any residual food.
Name of illness:	*Botulism* Examples of foods involved: canned low-acid foods, smoked fish, improperly cooked meats.
What causes it:	Clostridium botulinum. Spore-forming organisms that grow and produce toxin in the absence of oxygen, such as in a sealed can.
Symptoms:	Double vision, nausea, vomiting, inability to swallow, speech difficulty, progressive respiratory paralysis. Fatality rate, once high in the United States, is now down to approximately 12 percent of victims.
Characteristics:	Transmitted by eating food containing the toxin. Onset: Usually within 12 to 36 hours after consuming food. Duration: 3 to 6 days.
Preventive measures:	Boiling at 212° F for 10 to 20 minutes will destroy the vegetative form of the bacteria in high-acid foods. Spores may survive, but they are unable to germinate and grow in high-acid canned foods. Higher temperatures, attained only by pressure-cooking at 240° F, are required to kill the spores in low-acid foods. Low-acid foods include meat and poultry, fish, string beans, beets, corn, some fruits. Prevention is based on five principles: (1) In canning foods of low acidity, use pressure cookers and cook long enough with high enough temperature and pressure to destroy the spores; (2) in canning of foods of high acidity, cook at boiling temperatures in accordance with canning instructions in order to kill the vegetative form and yeasts and molds (spores cannot grow in high-acid foods); (3) avoid tasting or eating canned foods in containers showing defects; (4) avoid tasting any canned foods that spurt liquid when opened or any canned food that has abnormal odor; and (5) boil low-acid canned foods for 10 minutes prior to serving.
First-aid treatment:	Put victim to bed at once. Call a physician immediately, or get victim to hospital. Persons who are contaminated but have not yet developed serious symptoms can usually be saved if given an antitoxin in time. As the victim seems to feel better, give liquids such as hot tea and broth to prevent dehydration. Withhold food, however, for at least 24 hours.

persons, can be severely affected, experiencing nausea, vomiting, diarrhea and stomach cramps.

Food can also be contaminated by parasitic animals such as the roundworm, which primarily infests swine, and can cause the disease known as trichinosis. Eating raw or undercooked pork containing parasitic animals is a primary cause.

Without added preservatives, many foods would quickly spoil. The chart on pages 66–69 will help guide you in choosing foods with safe additives.

BACTERIA THAT AFFECT FOOD

There are four main types of bacteria which can cause food-borne illness: salmonellae, *Staphylococcus aureus*, *Clostridium botulinum*, and *Clostridium perfringens* (see charts, pages 57–58).

Salmonellae

Foods containing salmonellae can cause an infection called salmonellosis. The disease is difficult to control because it spreads easily. Salmonella infections result from eating food in which large numbers of salmonellae are growing or from personal contact with an infected person or carrier of the infection such as a rodent. There are approximately 1,300 different types of salmonellae.

Salmonella bacteria do not change the taste, odor, or flavor of contaminated food, so they are difficult to detect.

Staphylococcus aureus

Staphylococcus aureus, also known as staph, is probably the most common food-borne disease in the United States. It is caused by bacteria producing toxins in food. Bacteria responsible for staph food poisoning seem to prefer ready-to-serve foods such as custards, potato salads, ham. The bacteria are introduced into the food during preparation, particularly by food handlers who may have an infected skin wound such as boils, pimples or acne. If the food is allowed to stand at temperatures above 44° F for 2 hours or more, the bacteria begin to multiply rapidly. As the food temperature rises, growth of the staphylococci increases. As the bacteria grow, they produce the toxins. These bacteria also do not change the taste, odor or flavor of food, making it difficult to detect them. The toxin is not destroyed by ordinary cooking methods.

Clostridium botulinum

Clostridium botulinum can cause botulism, the rarest and deadliest form of food poisoning. When these bacteria are in a low-acid food, they multi-

ply and produce a toxin that is the agent responsible for the disease. These bacteria, called anaerobes, grow in the absence of oxygen, which accounts for their presence in canned and preserved foods. Most cases result from improperly home-canned foods which are then eaten without adequate cooking.

Clostridium perfringens

Another class of bacteria is *Clostridium perfringens*. These bacteria often cause diarrheal upsets which are rarely fatal. The spores of the bacteria require warmth and certain anaerobic conditions to survive.

TRICHINOSIS

Trichinosis is a parasitic disease which can affect humans and is transmitted by animals. It is caused by a parasitic worm which primarily infests swine.

Early signs include cramps and diarrhea. Later the legs and areas around the eyes begin to swell, muscles become sore and painful, and sweating, chills and fever develop. The disease can prove fatal. Anyone experiencing those symptoms should immediately consult a physician.

The cause of trichinosis is eating raw or undercooked pork containing the parasitic animals. To prevent

58

trichinosis, you should thoroughly cook all pork and pork products before you eat them. Use a meat thermometer to be safe and wait for the temperature of fresh pork to reach 170° F, and for the meat to be without traces of pink coloring. For cured pork, cook according to directions on page 64. Never taste raw pork. You can also freeze the pork at temperatures sufficiently low to kill the parasites.

HOW TO PREVENT FOOD ILLNESS

The most important thing to remember is that you can prevent food poisoning in most cases.

1. Stress personal hygiene for all members of your household. Strict cleanliness of person and surroundings is the best way to prevent contamination of foods and spread of illness at home. Any member of the household who has an infectious disease should be discouraged from handling, preparing or serving food. Do not permit anyone with an infected cut or other skin infection to work with food because the bacteria causing the infection may also be the source of the food illness. Anyone handling food should observe the following rules:

● Always work with clean hands, clean hair, clean fingernails and clean clothing.

● Wash hands thoroughly with soap and water and then rinse after using the toilet or assisting anyone using the toilet.

● Wash hands thoroughly with soap and water after smoking or blowing your nose.

● Keep hands away from your mouth, nose and hair when handling food.

● Cover your mouth with disposable tissues when coughing or sneezing.

● Wash hands thoroughly with soap and water after touching raw meat, poultry or eggs, and before working with other foods. Be sure to get under the fingernails where bacteria hide along with dirt. Rinse with plenty of water afterward.

● Avoid using hands to mix foods; use clean utensils instead.

● Avoid using the same spoon more than once for tasting food while preparing, cooking or serving it.

● Never eat any food directly from a

STORING FOODS PROPERLY

Breads and cereals

Breads: Store in original wrapper in breadbox or refrigerator. Use within 5 to 7 days. Breads will retain their good quality for 2 to 3 months if frozen in original wrappers.
Cereals, flours, spices, sugar: Store at room temperature, away from the heat of a range or a refrigerator. Store in tightly closed containers to keep out dust, moisture and insects. In summer, inspect for weevils.
Dry mixes: Cake, pancake, cookie and roll mixes may be held at room temperatures indefinitely, away from the heat of a range or a refrigerator.

Eggs and egg-rich foods

Keep eggs clean and cold. Put eggs in the refrigerator promptly after purchasing. Use eggs within one to two weeks. Refrigerate leftover egg yolks or whites in a covered container; use within 2 to 4 days. Always hold uncooked and cooked foods containing eggs in refrigerator.
 Refrigerate cream, custard or meringue pies and foods with custard fillings, including cakes, cream puffs or eclairs. Do not allow them to stand at room temperatures after they cool slightly. If you carry foods of this type on summer outings, keep them in a cooler with ice or reusable cold packs until you are ready to serve. Follow the same precaution for salads and sandwiches made with salad dressings containing eggs or milk products and foods with little vinegar or other acids.

Fats and oils

Most fats and oils need protection from air, heat and light. Fats and oils in partially filled containers keep longer if they are transferred to smaller containers in which there is little or no air space.
Butter, margarine, fat drippings: Store tightly wrapped or covered in the refrigerator. These products are best used within 2 weeks.
Cooking and salad oils: Keep small quantities at room temperature and use before flavor changes. For long storage, keep oils in the refrigerator. Some may cloud and solidify in the refrigerator. This is not harmful. If warmed to room temperature, they will become clear and liquid.
Hydrogenated shortening and lard: Most of the firm vegetable shortenings and lard have been stabilized by hydrogenation or anti-oxidants. These can be held at room temperature without damage to flavor. Lard that is not stabilized should be refrigerated. Keep these products covered.
Mayonnaise and other salad dressings: Keep all homemade salad dressings in the refrigerator. Purchased mayonnaise and other ready-made salad dressings should be refrigerated after jars have been opened.

Fruits

Plan to use fresh fruits promptly while they are sound and flavorful. Because fruits are fragile, they need special handling to keep them from being crushed or bruised. Sort fruits before storing. Bruised or decayed fruit will contaminate sound, firm fruit. Some fruits can be stored for longer periods in cellars at cool temperatures.
Apples: For immediate use, store uncovered in the refrigerator and use within a month.
Apricots, nectarines and peaches: These fruits may be ripe when purchased. If not, store at room temperature until flesh begins to soften. Then refrigerate uncovered and use within 3 to 5 days.
Avocados, bananas and pears: Allow these fruits to ripen at room temperature. Refrigerate avocados and pears. Use within 3 to 5 days.
Berries and cherries: Store covered in refrigerator to prevent moisture loss. Do not wash before storing. Use within 2 to 3 days.
Cranberries: Store covered in refrigerator. Use within 1 week.
Grapes: Grapes are ready to use when purchased. Store covered in refrigerator and use within 3 to 5 days. Grapes can also be stored in a fruit storage cellar near 32° F for 1 to 2 months.
Citrus fruits: These are best stored at a cool room temperature or refrigerated uncovered. Use within 2 weeks. Citrus fruits can be stored in a fruit storage cellar near 32° F and used within 4 to 6 weeks.
Melons: Keep at room temperature until ripe, then refrigerate uncovered. Use when ripe.
Pineapples: Use as soon as possible. Once cut, a pineapple may be stored in a tightly covered container for 2 to 3 days.
Canned fruits, canned fruit juices: Store them in the refrigerator after opening.
Plums: Hold at room temperature until ripe. Then refrigerate uncovered and use within 3 to 5 days.
Dried fruits: Keep in tightly closed containers. The fruits may be stored in a cool place about 6 months. In warm, humid weather, store in refrigerator.
Jellies, jams, preserves: After these have been opened, store them covered in the refrigerator.

Meat, poultry, fish

Store unfrozen raw meat, poultry and fish in the refrigerator as purchased in plastic wrap for a day or two. For longer periods, remove food from store wraping and wrap loosely in wax paper or plastic film. If you are not planning to use the food for at least 3 days, place in freezer, wrapping tightly in freezer paper, plastic film or foil. Freeze.

jar or can; you may spread any illness to the utensil and then contaminate the remaining food.

● Scrub raw food products such as potatoes before using.

2. Make sure all dishes, utensils, kitchen equipment and work surfaces are clean.

3. Safely store, prepare, cook and preserve all foods.

4. When eating out, choose clean restaurants. Order foods that do not spoil easily, especially in summer.

5. Drink only pasteurized milk.

6. Do not eat wild foods such as mushrooms and berries, which if poisonous can cause convulsions and death.

7. After a flood, drink bottled water.

8. In certain foreign countries, drink only bottled water. Check with your doctor before you go on vacation.

PURCHASING FOODS

Examine each item you buy at the food store to detect possible spoilage. Never buy food in a torn package, in an imperfectly sealed package or in a bulging can.

Check display cases to determine if frozen foods are stored above the frostline or load lines. Never buy frozen food that has softened; it may be spoiled.

Always pick up meat, poultry and dairy products last when shopping.

Never leave a sackful of groceries in the car on a hot day; it hastens spoilage. Make the grocery store the last stop before returning home. Have perishable groceries packed in an insulated bag for a long trip home.

Once home, put groceries in the refrigerator, freezer or storage cupboards quickly.

STORING FOODS

See pages 59–62 for a complete listing of how to store different foods, including meats, fish and poultry.

Storing canned goods

Never store food in a cabinet with a drainpipe running through it, such as under the kitchen sink. This is an unsafe practice because of possible leakage, and because it is difficult to seal off the opening through which the pipes pass. Also, do not store canned goods in a cabinet above the range or near any heat source such as steam pipes, radiators, furnaces. Instead,

Milk, cream, cheese

Fresh milk and cream: Store in original container in the refrigerator after purchase. For best quality, use within 1 week. Some creams may be stored longer if they have been ultra-pasteurized.

Nonfat dry milk: It will keep in good condition for several months on the cupboard shelf. Refrigerate reconstituted dry milk like fresh fluid milk.

Evaporated milk and condensed milk: Store at room temperature until opened, then cover tightly and refrigerate like fresh fluid milk.

Hard cheeses: Keep in the refrigerator. Wrap tightly to keep out air. They can be kept for several months. Cut off mold if it develops on the surface of the cheese.

Soft cheeses: Store tightly covered. Use cottage cheese within 5 to 7 days, other soft cheeses within 2 weeks.

Vegetables

With only a few exceptions, vegetables keep best in the refrigerator, stored in plastic bags or plastic containers. The exceptions—potatoes, sweet potatoes, mature onions, hard-rind squashes, eggplant, rutabagas—keep well in a cool place, away from bright light.

Asparagus: Use within 2 or 3 days after being stored.

Broccoli and brussels sprouts: Store and use within 3 to 5 days.

Cabbage, cauliflower, celery, snap beans: For immediate use, place in refrigerator and use cabbage within 1 or 2 weeks; use cauliflower, celery and snap beans within 1 week. These vegetables can also be stored for longer periods outside the refrigerator. Store cabbage in a pit, trench or outdoor cellar near 32° F through fall and winter. Store cauliflower in a storage cellar near 32° F for 6 to 8 weeks. Store celery in a pit or trench; roots in soil in storage cellar, near 32° F through late fall and winter. Store snap beans in any cool, dry place between 32° F and 40° F as long as desired. Be sure humidity is low.

Carrots, beets, parsnips, radishes, turnips: Remove tops, and place in refrigerator. Use within 2 weeks. Parsnips can be stored in a storage cellar near 32° F through fall and winter. Root crops can be stored in a pit or storage cellar near 32° F also through fall and winter.

Green peas and lima beans: Store in refrigerator and use within 3 to 5 days. You can also store them in any cool, dry place about 35° F for as long as desired.

Lettuce: Use within 1 week. Wash and dry before using.

Onions: Store at room temperature in a cool, dry place near 32° F through fall and winter. Keep green onions, however, cold and moist. If you place regular onions in the refrigerator, use within 1 week.

Peppers and cucumbers: Wash and dry. Store in refrigerator for up to 1 week. Or store in an unheated basement near 45° F for 2 to 3 weeks.

Potatoes: Store in a dark, dry place with good ventilation away from any source of heat, with a temperature of about 35° to 40° F for the fall and winter. Be careful that there is no light; it causes greening. High temperatures hasten sprouting and shriveling. If stored at room temperature, use within 1 week.

Rhubarb: Store in refrigerator and use within 3 to 5 days.

Spinach, kale, collards, chard, beet, turnip, mustard greens: Store in refrigerator and use within 3 to 5 days.

Squash and pumpkins: Store in refrigerator and use within 3 to 5 days. Or store in a cellar or basement at a moderately dry temperature of 55° F through fall and winter.

Sweet corn: Store, unhusked and uncovered. Use as soon as possible.

Sweet potatoes, hard-rind squashes, eggplant, rutabagas: Store at cool room temperature, around 60° F. These will then keep several months. They will only keep about 1 week at room temperature.

Tomatoes: Store ripe tomatoes uncovered in the refrigerator, for up to 1 week, depending on the ripeness when stored. Keep unripe tomatoes at room temperature away from direct sunlight until they ripen. Mature green tomatoes can be stored in a home cellar or basement at 55° to 70° F for 4 to 6 weeks.

Nuts

Store in airtight containers in the refrigerator or freezer. Unshelled nuts may be stored at room temperature about 6 months. Shelled nuts, in moisture-vapor-proof wrapping, can be refrigerated for up to 6 months.

Peanut butter: After a jar has been opened, it should be kept in the refrigerator.

Storage cellars

You can store some vegetables and fruits without refrigeration in basements, cellars, outbuildings and pits, but you need cool outdoor air to cool the stored products. The kind of storage facility that you need depends largely on the climate of your area. For most areas, you need an outdoor temperature during winter averaging 30° F or lower.

Basement: In a house with a basement that has a furnace, you need to partition off a room and insulate it to store the food products over winter. Store them in wood crates or boxes rather than in bins.

Cellar without central heat: These cellars usually have an outside entrance and a dirt floor. The door is a means of ventilating the cellar and regulating the temperature. If the room has a window, shade it to stop potatoes from turning green.

Outdoor storage cellar: Cellars constructed below ground maintain a desirable temperature longer and more uniformly than above-ground cellars.

Outbuilding: Storing vegetables and fruits in above-ground storage buildings is practical only where the climate is consistently cold, but not below freezing.

Pit: Cone-shaped outdoor pits can be used, built on the ground or in a hole 6 to 8 inches deep in a well-drained location. Pits should have a bedding material such as straw or leaves on the ground. Do not store vegetables and fruits in the same pit. Cover them with more bedding, and cover the entire pile with 3 or 4 inches of soil. Make sure pit is waterproof. Dig a drainage ditch around the pit. Pits should be made in a different place every year. Leftovers usually are contaminated.

Keep your storage area clean. Get rid of vegetables and fruits that show signs of decay. At least once a year, remove all containers from your storeroom. Clean and air them in the sun. Wash and whitewash the walls and ceiling before putting containers back. Maintain proper humidity.

STORAGE FOR MEATS, FISH AND POULTRY

	Days (in refrigerator at 35° to 40° F)
Fresh meats	
Roasts (beef and lamb)	3 to 5
Roasts (pork and veal)	3 to 5
Steaks (beef)	3 to 5
Chops (lamb)	3 to 5
Chops (pork)	3 to 5
Ground and Stew Meats	1 to 2
Variety Meats	1 to 2
Sausage (pork)	1 to 2
Processed meats	
Bacon	7
Frankfurters	7
Ham (whole)	7
Ham (half)	5
Ham (slices)	3
Luncheon Meats	3 to 5
Sausage (smoked)	7
Sausage (dry and semidry)	14 to 21
Cooked meats	
Cooked Meats and Meat Dishes	3 to 4
Gravy and Meat Broth	1 to 2
Fresh poultry	
Chicken and Turkey (whole)	1 to 2
Chicken (pieces)	1 to 2
Turkey (pieces)	1 to 2
Duck and Goose (whole)	1 to 2
Giblets	1 to 2
Cooked Poultry	
Pieces (covered with broth)	1 to 2
Pieces (not covered)	1 to 2
Cooked Poultry Dishes	1 to 2
Fried Chicken	1 to 2
Fresh fish	1 to 2

store canned or dried foods in a cool, dry cabinet.

Food cabinets should be clean. Frequently remove dust, which could contaminate opened cans or packages of food with microorganisms. Food storage areas should not be used for other purposes. Household chemicals should be stored in a separate cabinet.

The length of time canned foods keep depends on the type of food, the processing it received, how long it was handled, and the conditions under which it was stored. A regular turnover, about once a year, is a good rule to follow. Date each canned good you place in your food cabinets so that you use the oldest items first.

Storing food in the refrigerator

Proper refrigeration of foods can hold the number of bacteria to a safe level. Perishables should be refrigerated at 40° F or lower. Refrigerator shelves should never be covered with foil or any material that keeps down the air circulation. Be sure your refrigerator is clean and that you have an accurate thermometer.

Produce should be held in the lower compartments of the refrigerator to prevent crystallization.

Opened canned food should be refrigerated as you would any other

cooked food. If the opened food is to be kept for a substantial period of time, it should be tightly covered and frozen. If you have not refrigerated an item, throw it out.

Frequent opening and closing of the refrigerator door on warm, humid days, or an accumulation of thick frost on the freezing unit raises the refrigerator's temperature and hastens spoilage.

Among the signals that can indicate dangerous bacterial spoilage are an off odor, and a sour taste in bland foods. Some kinds of spoilage are harmful to health; others are not and just make the food distasteful to eat. Sometimes, however, the bacteria do not change the taste, odor or flavor of the food, making it difficult to detect their presence.

Never leave leftovers on the table after a meal. Store them immediately in the refrigerator.

PREPARING AND COOKING FOODS

Serve food soon after cooking, or refrigerate it promptly. Hot foods may be refrigerated if they do not raise the temperature of the refrigerator above 45° F. Keep these foods in the refrigerator until it is time to serve or reheat them. Speed the cooling of large quantities of food by refrigerating the food in shallow containers. Keep hot foods hot, above 140° F, and cold foods cold, below 40°F (see chart, page 63). Food may not be safe to eat if held for more than two or three hours at temperatures between 60° F and 125° F, the zone where bacteria grow rapidly. Remember to count all time during preparation, storage and serving.

Holding of food for several hours in an automatic oven prior to cooking is not safe if the food is in the temperature zone of 60° F to 125° F.

Thoroughly clean all dishes, utensils and work surfaces with soap and water after each use. It is especially important to clean equipment and work surfaces that have been used for raw food before you use the area for cooked food. This prevents the cooked food from becoming contaminated with bacteria that may have been present in the raw food. Bacteria can be destroyed by rinsing utensils and work surfaces with chlorine laundry bleach in the proportion recom-

61

SUGGESTED MAXIMUM STORAGE FOR FROZEN FOODS

Food	Approximate holding period at 0° F (in months)	Food	Approximate holding period at 0° F (in months)
Fruits and vegetables		Frankfurters	½
Fruits:		Ham (whole)	1–2
Cherries	12	Ham (half)	1–2
Peaches	12	Ham (slices)	1–2
Raspberries	12	Luncheon meats:	*Do*
Strawberries	12	Sausage (smoked)	*not*
Fruit juice concentrates:		Sausage (dry & semidry)	*freeze*
Apple	12	Cooked meat:	
Grape	12	Meat dinners	2–3
Orange	12	Meat pie	2–3
Vegetables:		Swiss steak	2–3
Asparagus	8	Gravy & broth	2–3
Beans	8	**Poultry**	
Cauliflower	8	Chicken:	
Corn	8	Cut-up	9
Peas	8	Livers	3
Spinach	8	Whole	12
Baked goods		Duck, whole	6
Bread and yeast rolls:		Goose, whole	6
White bread	3	Turkey:	
Cinnamon rolls	2	Cut-up	6
Plain rolls	3	Whole	12
Cakes:		Cooked chicken and turkey:	
Angel	2	Chicken or turkey dinners	
Chiffon	2	(sliced meat and gravy)	6
Chocolate layer	4	Chicken or turkey pies	6
Fruit	12	Fried chicken	4
Pound	6	Fried chicken dinners	4
Yellow	6	Giblets	3
Danish pastry	3	**Fish and shellfish**	
Doughnuts:		Fish:	
Cake type	3	Fillets:	
Yeast raised	3	Cod, flounder, haddock, halibut, pollack	6
Pies (unbaked):		Mullet, ocean perch, sea trout, striped bass	3
Apple	8	Pacific Ocean perch	2
Boysenberry	8	Salmon steaks	2
Cherry	8	Sea trout, dressed	3
Peach	8	Striped bass, dressed	3
Meat		Whiting, drawn	4
Beef:		Shellfish:	
Stew meats	2–3	Clams, shucked	3
Hamburger or chipped (thin) steaks	2–4	Crabmeat:	
Roasts	6–12	Dungeness	3
Steaks	6–12	King	10
Lamb:		Oysters, shucked	4
Chops	6–9	Shrimp	12
Patties (ground meat)	4	Cooked fish and shellfish:	
Roasts	6–9	Fish with cheese sauce	3
Pork, cured	2	Fish with lemon butter sauce	3
Pork, fresh:		Fried fish dinner	3
Chops	3–4	Fried fish sticks, scallops, or shrimp	3
Roasts	4–8	Shrimp creole	3
Sausage	2	Tuna pie	3
Veal:		**Frozen desserts**	
Cutlets, chops	9	Ice cream	1
Roasts	4–9	Sherbet	1
Processed meat:			
Bacon	1		

CRITICAL TEMPERATURES FOR SAFE FOOD HANDLING

Operation	Internal Temperature in Degrees Fahrenheit
Home canning	240–260
Cooking	165 or more
Warm holding	140 or more
DANGER ZONE	45–115
Refrigeration	35–45
Frozen storage	0 or less

mended on the package. Cutting boards, meat grinders, blenders, food processors, and can openers particularly need this protection. Always wipe up spills with paper towels or other disposable material.

Certain foods, discussed below, require special attention.

Eggs and egg-rich foods

Use only fresh, clean, unbroken and odor-free eggs in any recipe in which eggs are not thoroughly cooked, such as egg-milk drinks, uncooked salad dressings, ice cream. Cracked or soiled eggs may contain harmful bacteria. They should be used only in foods that are to be cooked thoroughly, such as baked goods or casseroles. Cool hot foods containing a high proportion of eggs if they are not to be served hot. Set custards and puddings, for example, in ice water and stir large batches of pudding to speed cooling. Then refrigerate promptly until serving time.

Meat, poultry and fish

Thaw frozen raw meat or unstuffed raw poultry or fish in the refrigerator. For a quicker method, immerse the package in its watertight wrapper in cold water. Thaw until meat is pliable. Cook soon after thawing.

You can cook frozen meat, poultry or fish without thawing first, but you must allow more cooking time to be sure that the center of the meat is properly cooked. Allow at least one-and-a-half times as long to cook as required for unfrozen or thawed products of the same weight and shape. Undercooked foods may not be safe to eat.

Stuff fresh or thawed meat, poultry or fish just before roasting, not a day or two ahead of time. Put the stuffing in lightly, without packing, to allow heat to penetrate more quickly throughout the stuffing. Be sure that the stuffing reaches a temperature of at least 165° F during cooking. To check the temperature of the stuffing afterward, insert a meat thermometer into the stuffing for about five minutes. Cook longer if necessary. Any stuffing cooked separately in the oven should also reach 165° F.

Cook meat and poultry according to a reliable timetable (see page 64). *Ground meat* should be thoroughly cooked because it is handled often in

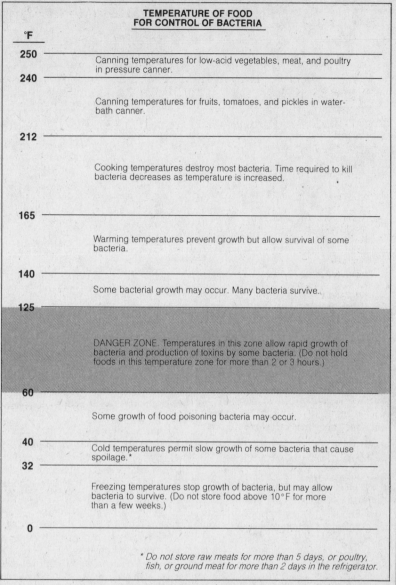

preparation, allowing germs to get mixed into it. Do not eat raw ground meat. Some *hams* need to be cooked; others are fully cooked and can be eaten as they come from the package. Check the label, and if you have doubts, cook the ham. Cook *poultry* products fully. If you prepare the poultry ahead of the day you plan to cook it, store the giblets and the rest of the bird separately in the refrigerator. Use *hot dogs* and *lunch meat* within a week after purchasing. Open and close packages as few times as possible. Handle cold meats with a fork, not with your fingers. Fingers spread germs.

Do not partially cook meat, poultry

or fish one day and complete the cooking the next day. Keep cooked meat, poultry and fish hot, above 140° F, until serving.

Refrigerate leftover meat and stuffing in separate containers. Heat leftovers thoroughly. Boil broth and gravies several minutes when reheating them.

Safe brown-bag lunches

To keep food cold, put lunch in the refrigerator. If no refrigerator is available, try freezing these types of sandwiches; they will thaw in time for lunch. Letting your lunch sit in a warm locker or room will encourage bacteria to grow. No lunch should be

FOOD ILLNESSES

COOK MEAT TO TEMPERATURES SHOWN	
(thermometer inserted into meat)	
Fresh beef	
Rare	140° F
Medium	160° F
Well done	170° F
Fresh veal	170° F
Fresh lamb	
Medium	170° F
Well done	180° F
Fresh pork or Cured pork	170° F
Ham, raw (cook before eating)	160° F
Ham, fully cooked (to warm)	140° F
Shoulder (cook before eating)	170° F
Canadian bacon (cook before eating)	160° F
Poultry	
Turkey	180°–185° F
Boneless turkey roasts	170°–175° F
Stuffing (inside or outside bird)	165° F

Press fingers on flesh of thigh or breast; if meat is soft, it is done.

left at room temperature for more than three hours. The familiar vacuum bottle is a good way to keep certain kinds of food, especially liquids, hot or cold. Be sure fruits and vegetables are clean and well scrubbed before eating them. Lunch boxes, especially insulated ones, hold in the cold much better than brown bags do. If you must use brown bags, use them only once and then throw them away.

FREEZING FOODS

Keep all food to be frozen and everything that touches it clean. Freezing does not kill the bacteria in food; it simply stops the multiplication. The bacteria begin to multiply as the food thaws.

Protect all foods to be frozen by wrapping or packing them carefully in moisture-vapor-resistant coverings. These coverings will keep the food from drying out during freezing and will prevent air from entering the closed package and causing oxidation. Label each package with the date and type of food. Dating the food will help you to know when it is time to remove the food from the freezer (see chart on page 62). Limit the amount of food frozen at one time in a home freezer to 2–3 pounds per cubic foot of total storage space. Overloading slows down the freezing process and foods may spoil. After freezing, packages may be stored closer together.

Frozen foods should be kept in a freezer at 0° F or below.

When a freezer fails

A fully loaded freezer usually will stay cold enough to keep foods frozen for two days if the door is kept closed. In a cabinet with less than half a load, food may not stay frozen more than one day. The colder the food, the longer it will stay frozen. Also, the larger the freezer, the longer the food will stay frozen.

If normal operation cannot be resumed before the food starts to thaw, add dry ice to the freezer. Twenty-five pounds of dry ice placed in a 10-cubic-foot freezer with half a load soon after the power goes off should keep the temperature of the freezer below freezing for two to three days. If the freezer is fully loaded, the food should keep for three to four days. Handle the dry ice with care. Wear gloves and be sure the room is well ventilated when you are working with it. Never touch dry ice with bare hands. Place the dry ice on cardboard or on small boards on top of packages and do not open the freezer again except to put in more dry ice or to remove it when normal operation of the freezer resumes.

You can also move your frozen food to a locker plant if one exists in your community. Use insulated boxes or thick layers of paper to prevent the food from thawing during transportation.

Refreezing food

Whether or not partially or completely thawed food can be safely refrozen depends on the temperature at which the food was held and the length of time it was held after thawing. You may safely refreeze frozen foods that have thawed if they still contain ice crystals, or if they are still cold—about 40° F—and have been held no longer than one or two days at refrigerator temperature after thawing.

Thawed ground meats, poultry or fish that have a peculiar odor or color should not be refrozen and should not be eaten. Thawed ice cream should not be refrozen. If the odor or color of any food is poor or questionable, do not taste it. Throw it out. The food may be dangerous. Even partial thawing and refreezing affect the eating quality—the taste and nutritional value—of the food, particularly of fruits, vegetables and prepared dishes. The eating quality of red meat is reduced less than that of other foods. Foods that have been frozen and thawed require the same care as foods that have not been frozen. Use refrozen foods as soon as possible to save as much of their eating quality as you can.

Defrosting the freezer

Frost on freezer shelves reduces storage space and makes the freezer inconvenient to use. Defrost refrigerator completely before frost reaches a depth of one-half inch over a large area of the refrigerated surfaces. Defrost completely when the amount of food in the freezer is very low because all food will have to be removed from the freezer during defrosting. Work quickly. Placing pans of hot water in the freezer speeds defrosting.

CANNING FOODS

Commerically canned foods are considered safe because they are processed under carefully controlled conditions. But, if a canned food shows any sign of spoilage—bulging ends of can, leakage, spurting liquid, off-odor or mold—do not use it. Do not even taste food from the can.

Home-canned vegetables (except for pickled ones), meat and poultry may contain the toxin that causes botulism if they are not properly processed. It is not safe to can vegetables, meat or poultry in a boiling-water bath, an oven, a steamer without pressure or an open kettle. None of these methods will heat the products sufficiently to kill the dangerous bacterial spores of clostridium botulinum.

64

Tomatoes, pickled vegetables and fruits can be processed safely in a boiling-water bath because they are more acid than other vegetables, meat and poultry. Allow 2 to 4 inches above jar tops for a brisk boiling. The can must have a tight-fitting cover. Do not use overripe tomatoes for canning. Tomatoes lose acidity as they mature.

There is no danger of botulism, however, if foods are canned properly in a pressure canner. Be sure that the pressure canner is in perfect order and that each step of the canning process, including the time and temperature specified, is followed exactly. The internal temperature of every can must reach 240°–260° F for the specified time.

Boil all home-canned vegetables and meats as described below. Heating usually makes any odor of spoilage more noticeable. Bring home-canned vegetables to a rolling boil. Then cover and boil for at least 10 minutes. Boil spinach and corn 20 minutes. Boil home-canned meat and poultry 20 minutes in a covered container. If food looks spoiled, foams or has an off-odor, do not taste; destroy it instead.

Use containers in perfect condition. Glass jars may be widemouthed or regular. There are two types of jar closure: flat metal lid with sealing compound and a metal screw band; and porcelain-lined zinc cap with a shoulder rubber ring which must be tightened to complete the seal immediately after food is canned. Discard jars that have cracks or chips, or lids and bands with dents or rust. Jars must be clean before they are used. Tin cans are also acceptable if in good condition. Make sure that cans, lids and gaskets are perfect. Discard ones that are badly bent, dented or rusty; discard lids with damaged gaskets.

Use a thermometer so that you can be sure the proper heat is attained during canning.

Check for leaks when jars or cans are cool. On the day after canning, examine each jar for good sealage. Label each jar and can to show the contents, and date each one. Select a cool, dry place for storing them. Be alert to signs of spoilage when you take canned foods from storage. Bulging jar lids or rings, gas bubbles, leaks, bulging can ends—all of these may indicate that a seal has broken and that

the food has spoiled. Test each container by pressing the end; ends should not bulge or snap back. Check the contents as you open the container. Spurting liquid, off-odor and color changes in food are danger signals.

Caution. Never use preservatives in home canning. They may be harmful.

KEEPING HOUSEHOLD INSECTS UNDER CONTROL

Certain household insects, particularly houseflies and cockroaches, can carry some of the bacteria discussed in this chapter. It is easier to prevent these pests from infesting your home than it is to get rid of them after they get indoors. Keep all windows and doors tightly screened. Make sure screen doors swing outward. These steps will keep out most flies.

Sanitation measures, including prompt disposal of garbage, will help control cockroaches. Caulk openings and cracks around washbasins, drainpipes, water pipes and radiator pipes. Make sure that cockroaches are not entering your home in containers and cardboard cartons brought in from the outside. Get rid of any infested containers at once.

If you need an insecticide to supplement these sanitation measures, buy a product specifically labeled for control of the kind of insect you want to kill. Read the label before you buy it. Read the label again before each use, and follow all directions. Used improperly, many household insecticides can be injurious to humans and to household pets. Be careful not to get insecticide on food, dishes, or cooking utensils.

If you cure meat at home, be sure to sweep out your storeroom and scrub it with hot, soapy water before you store meat in it. Seal any cracks with putty or plastic wood after you clean them. To keep pests out, see that doors and windows fit tightly. Install screens on windows and doors. Keep the temperature of the storeroom between 55° F and 60° F. If meat becomes infested in spite of these preventive measures, remove it from the storeroom and trim out infested parts.

FOOD ADDITIVES

Without added preservatives, many foods would quickly spoil. A common concern today is whether these food

additives are safe. The following chart from the Center for Science in the Public Interest will help guide you regarding food additives selection.

A simple rule about additives is to avoid sodium nitrite and artificial coloring. Not only are these the most questionable additives, but they are used primarily in foods of low nutritional value.

Good nutrition

Knowing about additives is important, but so is knowing about the foods themselves. Eat whole grains, vegetables, fruit, lean meat, low-fat dairy foods, and dried beans. This nutritious diet is low in fat, cholesterol, and sugar, and high in fiber. Eating such a diet will help prevent tooth decay, obesity, heart disease, certain cancers, and high blood pressure. Nutritious, natural foods also contain few additives.

Glossary

Antioxidants retard the oxidation of unsaturated fats and oils, colorings, and flavorings. Oxidation leads to rancidity, flavor changes, and loss of color. Most of these effects are caused by the reaction of oxygen in the air with fats.

Chelating agents trap trace amounts of metal atoms that would otherwise cause food to discolor or go rancid.

Emulsifiers keep oil and water mixed together.

Flavor enhancers have little or no flavor of their own, but accentuate the natural flavor of foods. They are usually used when very little of a natural ingredient is present.

Thickening agents are natural or chemically modified carbohydrates that absorb some of the water that is present in food, thereby making the food thicker. Thickening agents "stabilize" factory-made foods by keeping complex mixtures of oils, water, acids, and solids well mixed.

The *Delaney Clause* is part of the Food, Drug, and Cosmetic Act. This important consumer protection clause specifically bans any additive that "is found to induce cancer when ingested by man or animal."

CHEMICAL ADDITIVES

Caution: The additive may be unsafe, is poorly tested, or is used in foods we eat too much of.

Avoid: The additive is unsafe in the amounts consumed or is very poorly tested.

Alginate, Propylene glycol alginate Thickening agents; foam stabilizer *Ice cream, cheese, candy, yogurt*	Alginate, an apparently safe derivative of seaweed (kelp) maintains the desired texture in dairy products, canned frosting, and other factory-made foods. Propylene glycol alginate, a chemically-modified algin, thickens acidic foods (soda pop, salad dressing) and stabilizes the foam in beer.
Alpha Tocopherol (Vitamin E) Antioxidant, nutrient *Vegetable oil*	Vitamin E is abundant in whole wheat, rice germ, and vegetable oils. It is destroyed by the refining and bleaching of flour. Vitamin E prevents oils from going rancid.
Artificial Colorings Most artificial colorings are synthetic chemicals that do not occur in nature. Though some are safer than others, colorings are not listed by name on labels. Because colorings are used almost solely in foods of low nutritional value (candy, soda pop, gelatin desserts, etc.), you should simply avoid all artificially colored foods. In addition to problems mentioned below, there is evidence that colorings may cause hyperactivity in sensitive children. The use of coloring usually indicates that fruit or other natural ingredient has not been used.	
Blue No. 1 Artificial coloring *Beverages, candy, baked goods*	Very poorly tested; possible risk. Avoid.
Blue No. 2 Artificial coloring *Pet food, beverages, candy*	Very poorly tested; should be avoided.
Citrus Red No. 2 Artificial coloring *Skin of some Florida oranges only*	Studies indicate that this additive causes cancer. The dye does not seep through the orange skin into the pulp.
Green No. 3 Artificial coloring *Candy, beverages*	Needs to be better tested; avoid.
Orange B Artificial coloring *Hot dogs*	Was used to color some hot dogs; the FDA had approved it in 1966, despite shamefully poor tests. In 1978 the producer stopped making it upon discovering that it contained a cancer causing impurity.
Red No. 3 Artificial coloring *Cherries in fruit cocktail, candy, baked goods*	This complex, synthetic dye may cause cancer.
Red No. 40 Artificial coloring *Soda pop, candy, gelatin desserts, pastry, pet food, sausage*	The most widely used coloring promotes cancer in mice; should be outlawed.
Yellow No. 5 Artificial coloring *Gelatin dessert, candy, pet food, baked goods*	The second most widely used coloring is poorly tested, with one test suggesting it might cause cancer. Some people are allergic to it.
Yellow No. 6 Artificial coloring *Beverages, sausage, baked goods, candy, gelatin*	Appears safe, but can cause occasional allergic reactions; used almost exclusively in junk foods.
Artificial Flavoring Flavoring *Soda pop, candy, breakfast cereals, gelatin desserts; many others*	Hundreds of chemicals are used to mimic natural flavors; many may be used in a single flavoring, such as for cherry soda pop. Most flavoring chemicals also occur in nature and are probably safe, but they may cause hyperactivity in some sensitive children. Artificial flavorings are used almost exclusively in junk foods; their use indicates that the real thing (usually fruit) has been left out.
Ascorbic Acid (Vitamin C), Erythorbic Acid Antioxidant, nutrient, color stabilizer *Oily foods, cereals, soft drinks, cured meats*	Ascorbic acid helps maintain the red color of cured meat and prevents the formation of nitrosamines (see *sodium nitrite*). It helps prevent loss of color and flavor by reacting with unwanted oxygen. It is used as a nutrient additive in drinks and breakfast cereals. Sodium ascorbate is a more soluble form of ascorbic acid. Erythorbic acid (sodium erythorbate) serves the same functions as ascorbic acid, but has no value as a vitamin.

Beta Carotene
Coloring; nutrient
Margarine, shortening, non-dairy whiteners, butter

Used as an artificial coloring and a nutrient supplement. The body converts it to Vitamin A, which is part of the light-detection mechanism of the eye.

Brominated Vegetable Oil (BVO)
Emulsifier, clouding agent
Soft drinks

BVO keeps flavor oils in suspension and gives a cloudy appearance to citrus-flavored soft drinks. The residues of BVO found in body fat are cause for concern. BVO should be banned; safer substitutes are available.

Butylated Hydroxyanisole (BHA)
Antioxidant
Cereals, chewing gum, potato chips, vegetable oil

BHA retards rancidity in fats, oils, and oil-containing foods. It appears to be safer than BHT *(below)*, but needs to be better tested. This synthetic chemical can often be replaced by safer chemicals.

Butylated Hydroxytoluene (BHT)
Antioxidant
Cereals, chewing gum, potato chips, oils, etc.

BHT is poorly tested, is found in body fat, and causes occasional allergic reactions. BHT is unnecessary in many of the foods in which it is used; safer alternatives are available.

Caffeine
Stimulant
Coffee, tea, cocoa (natural); soft drinks (additive)

Caffeine may cause miscarriages or birth defects and should be avoided by pregnant women. It also keeps many people from sleeping.

Calcium (or Sodium) Propionate
Preservative
Bread, rolls, pies, cakes

Calcium propionate prevents mold growth on bread and rolls. The calcium is a beneficial mineral; the propionate is safe. Sodium propionate is used in pies and cakes, because calcium alters the action of chemical leavening agents.

Calcium (or Sodium) Stearoyl Lactylate
Dough conditioner, whipping agent
Bread dough, cake fillings, artificial whipped cream, processed egg whites

These additives strengthen bread dough so it can be used in bread-making machinery and lead to more uniform grain and greater volume. They act as whipping agents in dried, liquid, or frozen egg whites and artificial whipped cream. Sodium stearoyl fumarate serves the same function.

Carrageenan
Thickening and stabilizing agent
Ice cream, jelly, chocolate milk, infant formula

Obtained from "Irish Moss" seaweed, it is used as a thickening agent and to stabilize oil-water mixtures.

Casein, Sodium Caseinate
Thickening and whitening agent
Ice cream, ice milk, sherbet, coffee creamers

Casein, the principal protein in milk, is a nutritious protein containing adequate amounts of all the essential amino acids.

Citric Acid, Sodium Citrate
Acid, flavoring, chelating agent
Ice cream, sherbet, fruit drink, candy, carbonated beverages, instant potatoes

Citric acid is versatile, widely used, cheap, and safe. It is an important metabolite in virtually all living organisms; especially abundant in citrus fruits and berries. It is used as a strong acid, a tart flavoring, and an antioxidant. Sodium citrate, also safe, is a buffer that controls the acidity of gelatin desserts, jam, ice cream, candy, and other foods.

Corn Syrup
Sweetener, thickener
Candy, toppings, syrups, snack foods, imitation dairy foods

Corn syrup is a sweet, thick liquid made by treating cornstarch with acids or enzymes. It may be dried and used as corn syrup solids in coffee whiteners, and other dry products. Corn syrup contains no nutritional value other than calories, promotes tooth decay, and is used mainly in low-nutrition foods.

Dextrose (Glucose, Corn Sugar)
Sweetener, coloring agent
Bread, caramel, soda pop, cookies, many other foods

Dextrose is an important chemical in every living organism. A sugar, it is a source of sweetness in fruits and honey. Added to foods as a sweetener, it represents empty calories, and contributes to tooth decay. Dextrose turns brown when heated and contributes to the color of bread crust and toast.

EDTA
Chelating agent
Salad dressing, margarine, sandwich spreads, mayonnaise, processed fruits and vegetables, canned shellfish, soft drinks

Modern food manufacturing technology, which involves metal rollers, blenders, and containers, results in trace amounts of metal contamination in food. EDTA (ethylenediamine tetraacetic acid) traps metal impurities, which would otherwise promote rancidity and the breakdown of artificial colors.

Fumaric Acid
Tartness agent
Powdered drinks, pudding, pie fillings, gelatin desserts

A solid at room temperature, inexpensive, highly acidic, it is the ideal source of tartness and acidity in dry food products. However, it dissolves slowly in cold water, a drawback cured by adding dioctyl sodium sulfosuccinate (DSS), a poorly tested, detergent-like additive.

Gelatin
Thickening and gelling agent
Powdered dessert mix, yogurt, ice cream, cheese spreads, beverages

Gelatin is a protein obtained from animal bones, hoofs, and other parts. It has little nutritional value, because it contains little or none of several essential amino acids.

Glycerin (Glycerol) Maintains water content *Marshmallow, candy, fudge, baked goods*	Glycerin forms the backbone of fat and oil molecules and is quite safe. The body uses it as a source of energy or as a starting material in making more complex molecules.
Gums Guar, Locust Bean, Arabic, Furcelleran, Ghatti, Karaya, Tragacanth Thickening agents, stabilizers *Beverages, ice cream, frozen pudding, salad dressing, dough, cottage cheese, candy, drink mixes*	Gums derive from natural sources (bushes, trees, or seaweed) and are poorly tested. They are used to thicken foods, prevent sugar crystals from forming in candy, stabilize beer foam (arabic), form a gel in pudding (furcelleran), encapsulate flavor oils in powdered drink mixes, or keep oil and water mixed together in salad dressings. Tragacanth, sometimes used in McDonald's ''Big Macs'' and many other foods, has caused occasional severe allergic reactions.
Heptyl Paraben Preservative *Beer*	Heptyl paraben—short for the heptyl ester of para-hydroxybenzoic acid—is used as a preservative in some beers. Studies suggest this chemical is safe, but it has not been tested in the presence of alcohol.
Hydrogenated Vegetable Oil Source of oil or fat *Margarine, many processed foods*	Vegetable oil, usually a liquid, can be made into a semi-solid by treating with hydrogen. Unfortunately, hydrogenation converts much of the polyunsaturated oil to saturated fat. We eat too much oil and fat of all kinds, whether natural or hydrogenated. Additive needs better testing.
Hydrolyzed Vegetable Protein (HVP) Flavor enhancer *Instant soups, frankfurters, sauce mixes, beef stew*	HVP consists of vegetable (usually soybean) protein that has been chemically broken down to the amino acids of which it is composed. HVP is used to bring out the natural flavor of food (and, perhaps, to use less real food).
Invert Sugar Sweetener *Candy, soft drinks, many other foods*	Invert sugar, a 50-50 mixture of two sugars, dextrose and fructose, is sweeter and more soluble than sucrose (table sugar). Invert sugar forms when sucrose is split in two by an enzyme or acid. It represents ''empty calories,'' contributes to tooth decay, and should be avoided.
Lactic Acid Acidity regulator *Spanish olives, cheese, frozen desserts, carbonated beverages*	This safe acid occurs in almost all living organisms. It inhibits spoilage in Spanish-type olives, balances the acidity in cheese-making, and adds tartness to frozen desserts, carbonated fruit-flavored drinks, and other foods.
Lactose Sweetener *Whipped topping mix, breakfast pastry*	Lactose, a carbohydrate found only in milk, is Nature's way of delivering calories to infant mammals. One-sixth as sweet as table sugar, it is added to food as a slightly sweet source of carbohydrate. Milk turns sour when bacteria convert lactose to lactic acid.
Lecithin Emulsifier, antioxidant *Baked goods, margarine, chocolate, ice cream*	A common constituent of animal and plant tissues, it is a source of the nutrient choline. It keeps oil and water from separating out, retards rancidity, reduces spattering in a frying pan, and leads to fluffier cakes. Major sources are egg yolk and soybeans.
Mannitol Sweetener, other uses *Chewing gum, low-calorie foods*	Not quite as sweet as sugar and poorly absorbed by the body, it contributes only half as many calories as sugar. Used as the ''dust'' on chewing gum, it prevents gum from absorbing moisture and becoming sticky. Safe.
Mono- and Diglycerides Emulsifier *Baked goods, margarine, candy, peanut butter*	Makes bread softer and prevents staling, improves the stability of margarine, makes caramels less sticky, and prevents the oil in peanut butter from separating out. Mono- and diglycerides are safe, though most foods they are used in are high in refined flour, sugar or fat.
Monosodium Glutamate (MSG) Flavor enhancer *Soup, seafood, poultry, cheese, sauces, stews; many others*	This amino acid brings out the flavor of protein-containing foods. Large amounts of MSG fed to infant mice destroyed nerve cells in the brain. Public pressure forced baby food companies to stop using MSG. MSG causes ''Chinese Restaurant Syndrome'' (burning sensation in the back of neck and forearms, tightness of the chest, headache) in some sensitive adults.
Phosphoric Acid; Phosphates Acidulant, chelating agent, buffer, emulsifier, nutrient, discoloration inhibitor *Baked goods, cheese, powdered foods, cured meat, soda pop, breakfast cereals, dehydrated potatoes*	Phosphoric acid acidifies and flavors cola beverages. Phosphate salts are used in hundreds of processed foods for many purposes. Calcium and iron phosphates act as mineral supplements. Sodium aluminum phosphate is a leavening agent. Calcium and ammonium phosphates serve as food for yeast in bread. Sodium acid pyrophosphate prevents discoloration in potatoes and sugar syrups. Phosphates are not toxic, but their widespread use has led to a dietary imbalance that may be causing osteoporosis.
Polysorbate 60 Emulsifier *Baked goods, frozen desserts, imitation dairy products*	Polysorbate 60 is short for polyoxyethylene-(20)-sorbitan monostearate. It and its close relatives, Polysorbate 65 and 80, are synthetic, but appear to be safe. These chemicals work the same way as mono- and diglycerides, but smaller amounts are needed. They keep baked goods from going stale, keep dill oil dissolved in bottled dill pickles, help coffee whiteners dissolve in coffee, and prevent oil from separating out of artificial whipped cream.

Propyl Gallate Antioxidant *Vegetable oil, meat products, potato sticks, chicken soup base, chewing gum*	Retards the spoilage of fats and oils. It is often used with BHA and BHT because of the synergistic effect these additives have in retarding rancidity. Propyl gallate has not been adequately tested, frequently is unnecessary, and should be avoided.
Quinine Flavoring *Tonic water, quinine water, bitter lemon*	This drug can cure malaria and is used as a bitter flavoring in a few soft drinks. There is a slight chance that quinine may cause birth defects, so pregnant women should avoid quinine-containing beverages and drugs. Very poorly tested.
Saccharin Synthetic sweetener *"Diet" products*	Saccharin is 350 times sweeter than sugar and 10 times sweeter than cyclamate. Studies have not shown that saccharin helps people lose weight. There is some evidence that saccharin causes cancer, although tests have proven inconclusive. It may nonetheless be wise to avoid it.
Salt (Sodium Chloride) Flavoring *Most processed foods: soup, potato chips, crackers*	Salt is used liberally in many processed foods. Other additives contribute additional sodium. A diet high in sodium may cause high blood pressure, which increases the risk of heart attack and stroke. Everyone should eat less salt: avoid salty processed foods, use salt sparingly, enjoy other seasonings.
Sodium Benzoate *Fruit juice, carbonated drinks, pickles, preserves*	Manufacturers have used sodium benzoate for over 70 years to prevent the growth of microorganisms in acidic foods.
Sodium Carboxymethylcellulose (CMC) Thickening and stabilizing agent; prevents sugar from crystallizing *Ice cream, beer, pie fillings, icings, diet foods, candy*	CMC is made by reacting cellulose with a derivative of acetic acid. Studies indicate it is safe.
Sodium Nitrite, Sodium Nitrate Preservative, coloring, flavoring *Bacon, ham, frankfurters, luncheon meats, smoked fish, corned beef*	Nitrite can lead to the formation of small amounts of potent cancer-causing chemicals (nitrosamines), particularly in fried bacon. Nitrite is tolerated in foods because it can prevent the growth of bacteria that cause botulism poisoning. Nitrite also stabilizes the red color in cured meat and gives a characteristic flavor. Companies should find safer methods of preventing botulism. Meanwhile, *don't bring home the bacon.* Sodium Nitrate is used in dry cured meat, because it slowly breaks down into nitrite.
Sorbic Acid, Potassium Sorbate Prevents growth of mold and bacteria *Cheese, syrup, jelly, cake, wine, dry fruits*	Sorbic acid occurs naturally in the berries of the mountain ash. Sorbate may be a safe replacement for sodium nitrite in bacon.
Sorbitan Monostearate Emulsifier *Cakes, candy, frozen pudding, icing*	Like mono- and diglycerides and polysorbates, this additive keeps oil and water mixed together. In chocolate candy, it prevents the discoloration that normally occurs when the candy is warmed up and then cooled down.
Sorbitol Sweetener, thickening agent, maintains moisture *Dietetic drinks and foods; candy, shredded coconut, chewing gum*	Sorbitol occurs naturally in fruits and berries and is a close relative of the sugars. It is half as sweet as sugar. It is used in non-cariogenic chewing gum because oral bacteria do not metabolize it well. Large amounts of sorbitol (2 oz. for adults) have a laxative effect, but otherwise it is safe. Diabetics use sorbitol, because it is absorbed slowly and does not cause blood sugar to increase rapidly.
Starch, Modified Starch Thickening agent *Soup, gravy, baby foods*	Starch, the major component of flour, potatoes, and corn, is used as a thickening agent. However, it does not dissolve in cold water. Chemists have solved this problem by reacting starch with various chemicals. These modified starches are added to some foods to improve their consistency and keep the solids suspended. Starch and modified starches make foods thicker and richer than they really are.
Sugar (Sucrose) Sweetener *Table sugar, sweetened foods*	Sucrose, ordinary table sugar, occurs naturally in fruit, sugar cane, and sugar beets. Americans consume about 100 pounds of refined sugar per year. Sugar makes up about one-sixth of the average diet, but contains no vitamins, minerals, or protein. Sugar and sweetened foods may taste good and supply energy, but most people eat too much of them. Unless you enjoy large dentist bills and a large waistline, you should eat much less sugar.
Sulfur Dioxide, Sodium Bisulfite Preservative, bleach *Sliced fruit, wine, grape juice, dehydrated potatoes*	Sulfur dioxide (a gas) and sodium bisulfite (a powder) prevent discoloration of dried apricots, apples, and similar foods. They prevent bacterial growth in wine and other foods. These additives destroy vitamin B-1, but otherwise are safe.
Vanillin, Ethyl Vanillin Substitute for vanilla *Ice cream, baked goods, beverages, chocolate, candy, gelatin desserts*	Vanilla flavoring is derived from a bean, but Vanillin, the major flavor component of vanilla, is cheaper to produce synthetically. A derivation, ethyl vanillin, comes closer to matching the taste of real vanilla. Vanillin is safe; ethyl vanillin needs to be better tested.

22

FRACTURES AND DISLOCATIONS

A fracture is a broken bone. It is a closed, or simple, fracture if there is no open wound; an open, or compound, fracture if there is an open wound. A dislocation is the separation of two bones that form a joint.

A doctor should set a broken bone and treat a dislocated one, but sometimes it is necessary to provide temporary aid with a splint. The general first-aid treatment for a fracture and a dislocation is the same, and is given below. Specific treatments follow.

Signs/symptoms

Fracture: Deformity, swelling, discoloration, grating sound, pain, exposed bone in an open fracture.

Dislocation: Deformity, swelling, pain, loss of function.

First-aid treatment

Treat for shock if it exists (see page 21). Control any bleeding and cover any wound with large, clean dressing. Do not wash wound.

If a fracture is suspected, immobilize the bone. Move the victim only if necessary to save life. Splint fracture where it lies. Handle as gently as possible. This work should be done by two persons if present, one person to immobilize the limb and one to apply the splint. Place a fracture in as nearly normal a position as possible by applying slight traction. Traction is applied by grasping the affected limb gently but firmly, with one hand above and one hand below the location of the fracture, and pulling the limb between your hands. This is maintained until the splint is secured in place. *Caution*: Never try to straighten if a joint or the spine is involved.

Immobilize dislocated joints in the position in which they are found; do not attempt to reduce or straighten any dislocation.

Splints should be applied to provide support for the injured part of the body. A splint should be long enough to support the joints above and below the fracture or dislocation, and rigid enough to support the fracture or dislocation. There are two main types of splints to choose from: an improvised splint such as a padded board, rolled blanket, newspaper, magazine or broomstick, and an inflatable splint.

Improvised splint

An improvised splint should be padded enough to insure even contact and pressure between the limb and the splint and to protect all bony prominences.

1. Apply slight traction to the affected limb.
2. A second person, if available, should place the padded splint under, above or alongside the limb.
3. Tie the limb and splint together with bandaging materials such as cotton or cloth so the two are held firmly together. Make sure the bandaging material is not so tight that it impairs circulation. Leave fingers and toes exposed, if they are not involved, so that the circulation can be checked constantly.

Inflatable splint

Inflatable splints can be used to immobilize a fracture of the lower leg or forearm.

1. To apply an air splint, gather splint on your own arm so that the bottom edge is above your waist.
2. Help support the victim's limb or have someone else hold it.
3. Inflate by mouth only until pressure with your thumb makes a slight indentation.
4. If it is a zipper-type air splint, lay the victim's limb in the unzipped air splint, zip it and inflate. Traction cannot be maintained when applying this type of splint.
5. A change in temperature can affect an inflatable splint. For example, going from a cold area to a warm area will cause the splint to expand. It may be necessary to deflate the splint until proper pressure is reached.

Rib fractures

Signs/symptoms: Pain is usually localized at the site of the fracture. Ask the victim to place his hand on the exact area of pain if he is conscious. Other signs or symptons may include possible rib deformity or lacerations, shallow breathing, pain aggravated by coughing or movement. The victim often leans toward the injured side with his hand held over the injury site in an attempt to ease the pain by immobilizing the chest.

First-aid treatment

For simple rib fractures, current medical therapy is not to bind the chest because the bandaging may interfere with respiration and produce complications in the lungs. Instead, get the victim to a doctor or hospital immediately. Give aspirin for relief of any pain.

If the victim's lung is punctured (he will have extreme difficulty breathing), rush him to a doctor or hospital for immediate treatment.

Skull fracture

Signs/symptoms: Unconsciousness, headache, deformity of the skull, open wound, blood or clear fluid coming from ears or nose, pupils unequal in size.

First-aid treatment

Maintain an open airway. Check for spinal injury. Keep victim quiet and lying flat. If there is no suspected neck injury, turn head so it does not rest on fracture. Raise head and shoulders or place in a three-quarter-prone position. Use light pressure or cold compresses to stop severe bleeding. Do not stop bleeding from ears or nose. If you must transport victim, do so with him lying down. Keep head immobilized with a head bandage.

Spine fracture or dislocation

Signs/symptoms: Pain or anesthesia in back or neck, paralysis, deformation, cuts and bruises, swelling.

Survey for a conscious victim. Ask if victim feels pain in the back. Look for cuts, bruises, and deformation. Feel along back for tenderness to your touch. Check for paralysis by having victim move fingers and toes. Check upper extremities for paralysis: Can victim feel your touch? Can victim grasp your hand? Can victim raise arms and wiggle fingers? Check lower extremities for paralysis: Can victim feel your touch? Can victim press against your hand? Can he wiggle his toes?

70

Survey for an unconscious victim. Look for cuts and bruises. Feel along back for deformation. Ask others what happened. Gently jab victim with something sharp on the soles of feet, ankles or on hands. If the spinal cord is intact, feet or hands may react. In an unconscious victim, it is difficult to determine a spine fracture or dislocation with any accuracy. If the accident looks as if it could have produced a spinal injury, treat for one even if you find no symptoms.

First-aid treatment

Do not try to make splinting easier by straightening any deformity. Straighten only to help open an airway. Apply traction to the head, supporting head in line with the body. The head should be held until the victim is secured to the splint.

Restore airway and make sure breathing is adequate.

If there is a suspected neck fracture and the victim is found on his face, apply traction to the head and roll the victim over. A minimum of three people is needed for this. Do not bend or twist the back or neck. Support the head in line with the body by using a cervical collar.

Control serious bleeding.

Immobilize before moving victim. Lift victim only high enough to slide stretcher under him. In a suspected neck fracture, the head should be kept from moving after the victim has been put on the stretcher by rolling a blanket around the head and securing it to the stretcher with two cravat bandages. Do not move the victim until there are enough rescuers and an adequate splint available.

The stretcher must be rigid; an ordinary canvas stretcher is not suitable. An improvised stretcher can be made from two long boards 84" by 6" by 1" each, and three short boards 22" by 4" by 1½" each. The three short boards will be crosspieces under the two long boards, nailed or tied at points corresponding to where the person's shoulders, hips and heels will be. Pad the long boards with blankets and secure in place. The victim is then placed on the stretcher with the body moved as a single unit and tied on with fifteen cravat bandages (see Fig. 22-1).

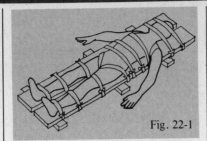

Fig. 22-1

For collarbone, shoulder, elbow and arm: Make a sling (see Fig. 22-2) to support the arm. Use cloth cut into the shape of a triangle or a triangular bandage. If no cloth or bandage is available, use a belt. Tie a band over the sling, and tie it to the chest so that you bind the arm to the chest. For collarbone fracture, make a sling. Get medical help immediately.

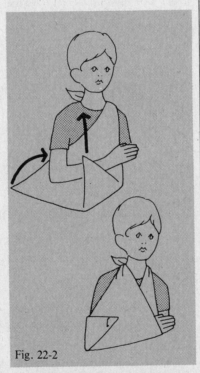

Fig. 22-2

For pelvis and hip: Immobilize the victim on a stretcher with bandages. Get medical help immediately.

For leg, ankle, foot and toe: For leg, immobilize with a padded splint. For ankle and toe, remove the shoe, cutting it off if necessary. Use a pillow for a splint. Get medical help.

For jaw: Put a bandage around chin and tie ends over head for support. Remove if the victim begins to vomit or bleed. Then put it back in place. Get medical help immediately.

For nose: Common signs of a broken nose include pain, swelling, discoloration and difficulty in breathing. Control bleeding as for a nosebleed. Tilt victim's head back and press cold compresses over nose. There is no need to apply a splint. Get medical help immediately.

SPRAINS

A sprain occurs when ligaments or other soft tissues around joints are torn or stretched.

Signs/symptoms: Pain on movement, swelling, discoloration.

First-aid treatment

Elevate injured part. Apply cold compresses to control bleeding. Treat as for a fracture (see page 70). Apply a bandage to keep joint from moving. Get medical help as soon as possible.

Have an X ray to be sure no bone is broken.

Sprains present basically the same symptoms as fractures. Because of this, treat all injuries to the bones and joints as fractures. Most sprains heal within a few weeks.

STRAINS

Strains are caused by overstretching of a muscle or tendon.

Signs/symptoms: Intense pain, moderate swelling, pain and difficulty in moving.

First-aid treatment

Rest injured muscle or tendon. Apply mild, dry heat to injured area, or apply ice.

SMASHED FINGERS OR TOES

Smashed fingers or toes are painful injuries.

Signs/symptoms: Swelling, pain, deformity, discoloration, lacerations of the skin, loss of function.

First-aid treatment

If the finger or toe is so injured as to be torn off or almost torn off, refer to the chapter "Amputations" (see page 38). If the finger or toe is intact, apply ice to injured area and get victim to a doctor or hospital immediately.

71

23

FROSTBITE

Frostbite is a result of exposure to extreme cold with inadequate protection. The parts of the body that are most frequently frostbitten are the extremities, including the toes, fingers, ears and nose. In severe cases of frostbite, damage can result in the death of tissue, a permanent sensitivity to the cold and the necessity to amputate a frozen part.

Poor circulation, in the case of diabetes or peripheral vascular disease, can increase one's chances of frostbite, as can the consumption of alcohol.

Signs/symptoms

In the mildest forms of frostbite, the frozen parts first feel cold, then painful and finally begin to feel numb. Sometimes, however, there is no pain. Damage is superficial and the underneath skin layers are not hurt if the victim is quickly brought inside and treated. In more severe cases, layers of the skin extending to the muscle tissue underneath are frostbitten, and the frozen parts begin to feel hard and doughy to the touch. In the most severe cases of frostbite, the bone underneath the muscles can become frostbitten, and the affected person may become incoherent, unconscious and even go into shock. The skin above the frozen parts will appear pale or grayish-yellow.

First-aid treatment

The first imperative is to get the victim inside, but until that can be done, he should be wrapped in woolen cloth and kept dry. Do not rub, chafe or manipulate frostbitten parts. Treat them gently. Warm affected parts with covers or place fingers or toes in a warm area of the body.

Once you bring victim inside, place him quickly in a tub of water at 102° F to 105° F, and make sure the water remains warm. Test water by pouring on the inner surface of your forearm. Do not use hot-water bottles or a heat lamp, and do not

place victim near a hot stove. With his lack of sensation in certain parts, he may easily burn himself. Have victim gently exercise frostbitten areas once they have thawed. Do not allow victim to walk if his feet were frostbitten. Try to keep toes and fingers separated with sterile gauze. Give victim a warm drink (but not alcohol) and an aspirin for pain. Do not break any blisters that later develop.

Always seek medical help, except for cases of superficial frostbite where color and sensation return quickly.

Note. Never thaw a victim if he has to go back out into the cold. That may cause the affected area to become refrozen and more difficult to rewarm later. It is better to leave part frozen and seek help quickly. Wrap frozen part while awaiting help.

Prevention

Dress warmly, using layers of clothing, if you anticipate going out in very cold weather. Especially cover your hands, ears and face, and feet. Cold winds increase the possibility of frostbite. If you feel chilled and tired, move indoors and warm up your body.

Never drink alcohol before going out in extremely cold weather.

Note. Mountain climbers, joggers and other outdoors people are particularly susceptible to frostbite.

SNOWBLINDNESS

Signs/symptoms

The signs of snowblindness are redness, burning, watering or sandy-feeling eyes, headaches, poor vision and disorientation. Snowblindness may not appear until four to six hours after exposure.

First-aid treatment

First-aid treatment includes protecting the eyes from light and relieving the pain by putting cold compresses on the eyes if there is no danger of freezing and by taking aspirin according to a doctor's instructions. Use no eye drops or ointment.

Most victims of snowblindness will recover within 18 hours without medical treatment, but it is important to contact a physician. The first attack of snowblindness makes a victim susceptible to future attacks.

24

HEAD INJURIES

Emergencies can involve any part of the head, including the skull, the face and jaw, the mouth, and the nose. (For injuries to eyes, teeth and ears, see separate sections under those headings.) A head injury can be more serious than you think because it may involve injury to the brain. Always watch victim's breathing and give artificial respiration if breathing stops (see pages 17–18). Also observe for symptoms of shock and treat if necessary (see page 21). Do not move a victim who has a serious head injury unless absolutely necessary, and then follow instructions on transporting the victim safely (see pages 21–23). Get prompt medical help from a doctor or at a hospital emergency room.

SERIOUS HEAD INJURIES

Signs/symptoms: Unconsciousness; impaired breathing; convulsions; vomiting; clear fluid or blood running from ears, nose or mouth; paralysis in some part of the body; loss of bowel or bladder control; pupils unequal in size; deformity of the skull; pale, moist skin.

First-aid treatment

Keep victim lying down. Do not give any fluids.

Open head injuries: Do not clean foreign matter from deep scalp wounds; it might cause bleeding. Control any bleeding by raising victim's head and shoulders without bending neck, and press with a clean cloth on the wound. Press lightly because a fracture may be involved. In serious open head injuries, always observe for symptoms of shock and treat accordingly (see page 21).

Clean minor wounds with soap and water, and when bleeding has

72

stopped, apply a dressing and bandage (see pages 23–25).

Closed head injuries: If there is no neck injury, place a pillow or cloth under victim's head and shoulders. Turn head to side so fluids and blood can drain from the mouth.

If there is a neck injury, immobilize victim's head in position found by placing clothing or towel around head and sides of neck and shoulders. If back is also injured, immobilize victim's body. If victim is found on back, slide a towel or other similar fabric under neck without moving his head. Do not use anything too bulky.

Suspected skull fracture: Maintain an open airway; check for spinal injury; keep victim quiet. If there is no suspected neck injury, turn victim's head so it does not rest on fracture. Raise head and shoulders or place in a three-quarter-prone position. Use ice pack to stop severe bleeding; do not stop bleeding from ears or nose. Get prompt medical help. Transport victim, if necessary, lying down on a stretcher (see pages 22–23).

Embedded objects: If an object is embedded in the cheek, it is safe to remove it if you can pull it out from the angle it entered without using force. Control bleeding by pressing inside of cheek with gauze.

Do not remove an object embedded in skull. Instead get medical help.

Face and jaw fractures: Remove broken teeth and any foreign matter from mouth. Save any teeth you can for replanting. The sooner the tooth is replanted into the jaw, the better the chances that it will take root. If possible, the tooth should be put back within 30 minutes. If the tooth is not too dirty, rinse it with cold water and wipe off remaining specks with clean, moist cloth. Preserve gum fibers still clinging to the tooth. Twist it back into place and go to the dentist. If the tooth is dirty or you are squeamish, put it in eight ounces of iced water with ½ teaspoon of salt and go straight to the dentist with it.

Observe victim for shock and treat accordingly (see page 21). Control bleeding using direct pressure with gauze or clean cloth. If

that does not work, use pressure-point method (see pages 19–20) until bleeding stops. Apply clean dressing or cloth and secure with a bandage (see pages 23–25).

For jaw injury, support lower jaw in position found with a cravat bandage. Tie ends of bandage over top of head. If victim vomits or continues to bleed, remove bandage, then replace when vomiting and bleeding stop. If victim is conscious and has suffered no neck injury, have him lean forward. If unconscious, turn his head to side so blood and saliva can drain from mouth. Follow additional instructions for treating closed head injuries (see page 73).

Mouth injuries: Remove broken teeth. Bring teeth to a dentist for replanting (see page 108).

Gums. With the direct-pressure method, control bleeding (see page 19). Use a clean cloth.

Teeth. Apply direct pressure on tooth socket to control bleeding (see page 19). Use a small packet of gauze or a clean cloth.

Lips. Press both sides of wound with a clean cloth to control bleeding.

Tongue. Press both sides of tongue to control bleeding.

Nose injuries:

Foreign object. Have victim keep both nostrils open and blow the object out. Do not try to remove object. If object does not appear, seek prompt medical help.

Nosebleed. Have person sit down and blow out any clotted blood. Pinch lower, soft part of nose and then apply cold compresses. If bleeding does not stop, pack nostril with cotton or gauze wet with cold water. Then pinch nose closed for approximately five minutes. If bleeding stops, leave packing in place for another five minutes. If bleeding does not stop, see a doctor immediately.

Broken nose. Common signs of a broken nose include pain, swelling, discoloration and difficulty in breathing. Control bleeding as for a nosebleed. Tilt victim's head back and press cold compresses over nose. There is no need to apply a splint. Get prompt medical help.

25

HEADACHE

What most people mean by a headache is a pain which lasts several minutes or hours, and covers the whole head, one side of it, or perhaps the front or the back of the head. The pain may be barely noticeable, steady and throbbing, or completely disabling.

HOW A HEADACHE OCCURS

Only in the 20th century have investigators studied the mechanism which causes headaches. The brain tissue does not feel pain on direct stimulation, nor does the bone of the skull. The scalp, blood vessels, and certain of the brain coverings, however, are extremely sensitive to pain.

A headache can occur because of a variety of factors:

1. *Swelling (dilation) of arteries of the head.* Fever, carbon monoxide poisoning and other toxic states, hangovers, and hunger are some of the headaches which relate to pain in the cranial arteries.

2. *Pulling (traction) on pain-sensitive structures within the head.* A brain tumor, abscess, or hemorrhage does not cause pain because of direct pressure on brain tissue but because it pulls on the arteries or other pain-sensitive structures.

3. *Prolonged tension in neck muscles.*

4. *Spreading pain.* Pain may spread into a general headache from local pain in the eye, ear, nose, sinuses or teeth.

5. *Psychogenesis.* An emotional conflict or anxiety is converted into a physical symptom: a headache.

THE DIFFERENT TYPES OF HEADACHE

Most doctors agree that a headache is not a disease but a symptom of an underlying problem. A headache can be classified as acute or chronic.

Acute headache

The acute headache occurs suddenly and occasionally, and can be the first warning of a serious condition that probably can be controlled if detected early. Therefore, if you remove the warning day after day with a painkiller, you are not dealing with the problem—you are merely masking the pain. Your family doctor will be alert to what your headache symptom points to and how it should be treated. For example, a headache accompanying infection may require antibiotics; the headache of high blood pressure is treated with medicines to reduce blood pressure. If necessary the doctor will refer you to an appropriate specialist such as a neurologist or to the special "headache clinics" that now exist at many hospitals. Some of the headaches that are alarm signals for a prompt and thorough medical checkup are:

1. A sudden, severe headache out of the blue
2. Daily or frequent headaches
3. A headache associated with fever
4. A headache associated with convulsions
5. A headache accompanied by confusion or lessening of consciousness
6. A headache following a blow on the head
7. A headache associated with local pain in the eye, ear or elsewhere
8. A headache beginning in an older person previously free of headaches
9. Recurring headaches in a child
10. A headache at any age which interferes with normal daily living.

Chronic headache

Chronic headaches are classified in several ways:

1. *Migraine and other headaches due to blood-vessel changes.* A temporary narrowing of the blood vessels in the head marks the early, painless stage of migraine. Some migraine patients experience a warning of the impending headache in the form of jagged streaks of light or other "fireworks" of vision, numbness, tingling and perhaps nausea. Some feel weak, tired or overexcited. This feeling or warning, called an aura, allows the individual to ward off head pain by lying down in a dark, quiet room or to take the medicine his doctor has prescribed.

The second and painful stage begins in minutes or hours with a severe, throbbing, one-sided or two-sided headache, and distended, throbbing arteries sensitized by certain chemical substances. Medicine to contract dilated arteries may end a migraine attack.

A third stage may follow—the steady headache—which is either part of the original migraine attack or a complicated muscle-contraction (tension) headache resulting from stiff muscles in the neck.

2. *Headaches caused by muscle contraction (tension).* The commonest of chronic headaches is the muscle-contraction headache, which comes from stiff muscles in the neck. The trigger which causes stiff muscles usually is some kind of conflict or stress. The trigger can also be physical, such as a cold draft from an air conditioner, eye-muscle fatigue, or pain elsewhere in the body.

The muscle-contraction headache comes without warning. It usually affects both sides of the head, or the back of the head and neck, or the forehead, face or jaw muscles, or a band around the head. The pain is steady, pressing or tight rather than throbbing. It may occur occasionally or frequently. At times such headaches disappear quickly, and at other times last for several days or weeks.

A massage of the neck muscles, heat from an electric pad, or a shower or warm tub bath will help relax the muscles. If pain continues, a doctor may prescribe muscle relaxants and/or tranquilizers.

3. *Headaches associated with various structural changes.* A small but important group of recurring headaches is associated with a variety of structural changes. These include headaches due to high blood pressure, virus infection, tumors, brain abscesses, defects and malformations of blood vessels, and certain diseases of the neck and spine, and headaches related to the menstrual cycle.

4. *Other headaches involving special causes:*

● Post-traumatic headaches following an injury, commonly a fall or an automobile accident. Every person who has been knocked unconscious should have a medical examination. Medical care should be continued as long as any headache continues. Headaches sometimes follow the neck strain called whiplash, or hyperextension. Bed rest helps relieve the neck from the stress of holding up the weight of the head. If necessary, pain relievers and muscle relaxants can help further. Next best to bed rest is the use of a cervical collar. After the initial phase

of recuperation, a doctor may prescribe wet hot packs and range-of-motion exercises and resistance exercises.

● Smoke, bad ventilation, and lack of sleep are invitations to headaches. A coffee-hunger headache afflicts heavy drinkers of coffee if they miss their usual cup. Fresh air and sleep should correct these problems.

● A headache from too much alcohol, known as a hangover headache, involves physical factors such as the swelling of blood vessels. The best treatment is to drink less or to stop drinking totally. Rest, an aspirin tablet or a combination pain reliever, and a stimulant such as coffee will relieve many sufferers.

● A headache from an allergy may be moderate and accompanied by swollen, runny nose and sneezing. Antihistamines and desensitization may help these sufferers. Although some kinds of antihistamines are sold over the counter, always consult your doctor before using them.

● Hunger is the source of many headaches. Make a habit of eating regular meals. If a meal must be postponed for more than an hour, a snack can help you avoid a hunger headache.

● A headache after prolonged use of the eyes. Rest your eyes occasionally to avoid eye strain and headache. If headache persists, it may be a signal for an eye examination.

● Excessive use of sedatives, even sedatives for treatment of a headache, can be dangerous and might even cause a headache. Do not take larger amounts of painkillers than your doctor prescribes. Do not take sedatives more often than he orders or over a longer period.

● Careless use of household and garden chemicals can cause a headache. Read directions on household and garden chemicals carefully and follow the warnings against skin contact and inhaling of these chemicals.

First-aid treatment

A doctor should be consulted regarding an acute headache, and as described above for some chronic headaches. While waiting for an appointment, you can try several emergency remedies, which also apply in the case of a chronic headache.

1. Try a prompt fresh-air break. This

74

will get you away from any noxious gases from a downdraft in heating equipment or leaky car exhaust, or out of a crowded, overexciting, tension-creating gathering.

2. Try lying down in a quiet room and falling asleep.

3. If pain continues, take an aspirin tablet. Unless a physician orders, never take more than two aspirin tablets at one time: More will have little or no effect on pain relief and may be harmful.

Note. Once your doctor has your headache under control, do not continue any medicine without supervision.

26

HEART DISEASE

Coronary heart disease is still the most common cause of death in the United States. Over half the heart emergencies are so sudden that the victim never makes it to the hospital alive. Our most important weapon against this epidemic is therefore prevention. Many of the deaths are due to arteriosclerosis, or hardening of the coronary arteries. The lessening of arteriosclerosis is a major focus of this chapter.

Arteriosclerosis may begin early in life. It is represented by tiny deposits of a fatty substance that thicken the innermost layer of the arterial walls. An important form of arteriosclerosis is atherosclerosis, a disease of the larger blood vessels characterized by the type of fatty deposits known as atheromata. The atheromata decrease the diameter of the inner channel of the vessel and thus reduce the blood supply to the heart. The deposits continue to thicken, often without producing any signs or symptoms, until they fully block the passageway, years or decades later. The arteriosclerosis then results in a variety of health problems for middle-aged and elderly persons, such as kidney failure and cerebrovascular disease including stroke, heart attacks, and loss of limbs. Often atherosclerosis is not discovered until an autopsy is performed.

MANIFESTATIONS OF ATHEROSCLEROSIS

Coronary atherosclerosis

Coronary atherosclerosis, also called coronary artery disease (because it affects the principal suppliers of blood to the heart muscle itself), often results in angina pectoris, acute myocardial infarction (heart attack), and sudden cardiac death.

When a heart emergency strikes, there is no time for delay. Many more victims could survive than do at present if they recognized the early warning signs and sought prompt medical attention, and if others knew how to give proper aid including cardiopulmonary resuscitation (see pages 18–19).

Angina pectoris: This disease literally means "chest pain." It is a condition in which the heart muscle receives an insufficient supply of oxygen and blood, causing pain or tightness in the chest and sometimes pain in the left arm and shoulder. The usual cause of angina pectoris is atherosclerosis of the coronary arteries. Angina usually occurs with physical exertion such as walking, emotional stress, or after a heavy meal. All of these instances temporarily increase the heart muscle's need for blood beyond the supply delivered by the affected coronary artery. The pain usually vanishes rapidly when the victim rests.

Angina pectoris most often persists in a stable form for many years with only brief, tolerable attacks. It is a serious disease, however, because the attacks can increase in frequency and intensity and will eventually respond less readily to rest and/or medication. Without warning, it can develop into a heart attack and cause death.

First-aid treatment

If the patient has suffered from angina before, he most likely will be carrying nitroglycerin tablets, which relax the muscles in the blood vessels of the heart. The victim should sit down, rest, and place the tablet under his tongue. If he is unable to take the tablet himself, place it under his tongue for him. Consult a physician immediately. He will prescribe drugs for angina pectoris to increase the coronary blood flow by dilating the coronary arteries and to decrease the heart's need for oxygen. Nitroglycerin tablets keep for months at room temperature, act within one to two minutes, and keep acting for 15 minutes to an hour.

Myocardial infarction: More commonly known as heart attack, myocardial infarction can strike anyone and claims some 670,000 American victims each year. It can strike a person who is resting, sleeping or exercising.

Unlike angina pectoris, a heart attack always involves some localized, fairly rapid heart-muscle death, or "myocardial infarction." This acute emergency happens when the closing-off process in one of the coronary arterial branches progresses so suddenly and completely that the local myocardium—the muscle area that was fed by the closed-off coronary branch—receives no blood or oxygen, stops contracting and dies over a period of hours. If the patient survives the attack, a scar tissue, or "healed infarct," will replace the muscle over a period of weeks.

Although some people have no symptoms prior to an attack and "have never been sick a day," most victims suffer pain or pressure in the chest within hours or days before the actual infarction. This chest pain may represent new symptoms or an increase in the severity and frequency of preexisting angina pectoris. The pain usually continues without interruption for as long as several hours if it is not relieved by rest or drugs such as nitroglycerin or morphine. Persons with symptoms of acute infarction (see below) must receive immediate medical help.

At least half of the deaths from acute coronary attacks occur before patients reach a health care facility. These early deaths result primarily because of two factors. First, serious abnormalities in heart rhythm, called arrhythmias, may lead to a stage of complete cardiac arrest. Early detection and treatment of these arrhythmias by drugs, cardiopulmonary resuscitation (CPR, see pages 18–19), or by electrical defibrillation equipment offer an important way to save lives. The second most common cause of death in the heart attack victim is extensive damage of the heart muscle

75

with loss of adequate pumping function resulting in congestive heart failure or cardiogenic shock.

Usual warning signs.

1. Pain may vary from mild uncomfortable pressure to severe aching or squeezing in the center of the chest under the sternum, or breastbone.
2. The pain may subside, or it may intensify, spreading to the entire chest and down the left arm.
3. The pain may continue to spread to both arms, to the shoulders, to the neck and even to the jaw.
4. Some people experience, in addition, a squeezing or fullness in the abdomen, which they mistakenly interpret as indigestion.
5. A victim may note other symptoms, including dizziness, faintness, profuse sweating, nausea and shortness of breath.
6. Color changes to ashen.
7. The victim may become unconscious. His heart may stop beating. He may stop breathing.

First-aid treatment

If someone you know has these symptoms, call for an ambulance with oxygen equipment immediately. If a hospital is not nearby (more than ten minutes away) and you can safely transport the victim quickly, do so. Some communities have mobile life-support units that carry vital equipment for sustaining a heart attack victim.

In the meantime, you can aid the victim:

1. If breathing stops, give artificial respiration; and if heart stops, give cardiopulmonary resuscitation (see pages 17–18 for former condition and pages 18–19 for latter condition).
2. If victim is breathing, place him in a semireclining or sitting position. Move victim without having him exert effort.
3. Loosen tight clothing at the neck and wrists.
4. Administer a nitroglycerin tablet under the tongue if victim is carrying one, and repeat in 15 minutes if necessary to relieve pain.
5. Keep onlookers away.
6. Keep victim warm.
7. Comfort and reassure victim; anxiety will only worsen his condition.

8. Do not allow victim to move around.
9. Give no stimulants or liquids, even if victim requests them.

Many complications are associated with myocardial infarction.

Cardiogenic shock is a dangerous complication of acute heart attacks. Over 85 percent of its victims die. In cardiogenic shock, extensive heart-muscle damage severely impairs the pumping effectiveness of the heart. In this case, the amount of blood pumped by the heart decreases dramatically, accompanied by a severe drop in blood pressure with inadequate flow to the body's vital organs.

Congestive heart failure develops most often as a consequence of a long-standing circulatory disorder, such as hypertension, that places a prolonged, heavy circulating burden on the heart; or it may stem from a loss of functioning heart-muscle tissue as a result of one or more heart attacks. Congestive heart failure can also be due to a variety of factors, such as alcoholism, bacterial and viral infections, and severe nutritional deficiencies. Whatever the cause, the failing heart is incapable of coping with the circulatory demands of the body. Infants and young children can also suffer from congestive heart failure caused by a congenital defect of the heart or vessel, or by rheumatic fever.

Heart failure, which may develop during or after a heart attack, is commonly accompanied by abnormal salt and fluid retention, and the accumulation of fluid in the lungs can be a serious complication. Treatment involves reducing the heart's workload, using medications such as digitalis to improve the heart's pumping efficiency, and relying on diuretics and a restricted salt intake to eliminate fluid from the body. Any person experiencing congestive heart failure should rest to reduce the heart's workload and should call a doctor immediately. If it is not treated promptly, shock may result.

Other symptoms—but not life-threatening—that can develop include swelling of the ankles and feet; lips, fingers and even earlobes turning blue; skin becoming cold and clammy; dizziness and faintness.

Heart arrhythmias may occur both during and after recovery from myo-

cardial infarction, occurring most often during the first few hours after onset of the episode. While some rhythm changes are relatively benign and require just rest, others are life-threatening and require emergency treatment such as electric shock to the heart through the chest wall, antiarrhythmic drugs, and perhaps the insertion of a cardiac pacemaker.

Atherosclerosis of the aorta

The aorta is the main trunk artery which receives blood from the lower left chamber of the heart. It originates from the base of the heart, arches up over the heart like a cane handle, and passes down through the chest and abdomen in front of the spine. It gives off many lesser arteries which conduct blood to all parts of the body except the lungs.

An aneurysm (a spindle-shaped bulge of a wall of an artery) of the thoracic aorta may result in pressure on adjacent structures, producing chest pain, breathlessness, hoarseness or signs of compression of the superior vena cava chamber of the heart. The aneurysm may rupture and cause death by bleeding.

Abdominal aortic aneurysms are usually located just below the origin of the renal arteries. Such an aneurysm can often be felt on abdominal examination by a doctor. Expansion of the aneurysm produces pain by pressing on nerve endings of abdominal organs and is a harbinger of impending rupture. The seriousness of the aneurysm is usually directly related to its size, though occasionally small aneurysms may also rupture.

If a person suffers severe and tearing pain, he should be rushed to the hospital because ruptured aneurysms may cause severe shock and death.

Peripheral vascular atherosclerosis

Atherosclerotic occlusion at or near the division of the abdominal aorta into the two large arteries to the legs causes severe cramps and pain in the buttocks and thighs upon walking. The victim should rest immediately, call a doctor or get to the emergency room of a hospital immediately.

PREVENTION OF ATHEROSCLEROSIS

Certain risk factors have been found

76

to increase an individual's chances of developing atherosclerosis of the major blood vessels of the body. A combination of two or more risks multiplies the potential danger. Many of the risk factors are easy to control. It is never too late to change habits that can be harmful to your heart, especially because the incidence of heart disease increases with age.

Established risk factors include high concentration of blood cholesterol, particularly low-density lipoproteins; high blood pressure; and cigarette smoking.

Probable risk factors include diabetes mellitus and impaired glucose tolerance; stress; post-menopausal state; genetic predisposition; and contraceptive pills.

Suspected risk factors include obesity and lack of physical exercise.

Large doses of alcohol are extremely harmful; moderate consumption may offer some protection against death from heart disease, according to recent medical reports.

Established risk factors

High concentration of blood cholesterol: High blood lipid or fat levels are very strongly associated with coronary heart disease. Excessive blood lipid levels may stem from certain metabolic disorders such as diabetes or hypothyroidism, but often blood lipid elevations can be traced to dietary habits.

The major blood lipids are cholesterol and triglycerides.

Cholesterol is a tasteless and odorless white fatty alcohol found in all animal tissues and is especially abundant in the fat and fatty products of milk, egg yolks and organ meats such as kidney and liver, and in seafood such as shrimp. Fruits, vegetables and vegetable oils have little or no cholesterol. The average American diet contains some 500–700 milligrams (mg) of cholesterol per day. The rest of the cholesterol in the blood is manufactured in the body—mostly by the liver. When we take in more cholesterol than our bodies need, the excess may be deposited in the arteries and can add to the buildup of atherosclerosis, and then lead to vascular disease. The "normal" range of blood cholesterol is still debated. For example, the average cholesterol level for American men—between 180 and 230 mg per ml—would be considered high for Japanese men.

Triglycerides are the predominant lipids of fat tissue. The elevation of triglycerides is often, but not always, associated with an elevation of cholesterol.

Cholesterol is the blood lipid most extensively studied because of its early identification as a risk factor. Studies show that up to age 55, the risk of developing coronary heart disease increases at the same rate as blood cholesterol levels increase. Blood triglycerides may also be an important determinant of risk. Thus, if an elevated blood level of cholesterol or triglycerides, or both, is found, even in an apparently otherwise normal adult or child, there is a cause for concern and for appropriate countermeasures.

However, such elevations can be a sign of a variety of disorders; not everyone with a high blood lipid level faces a high heart-attack risk. A high cholesterol level is diagnosed by a laboratory test. Once it is detected, there are several preventive countermeasures, and in most persons elevated blood lipids can be reduced—often to normal—by appropriate diet.

Lower intake of cholesterol. Carefully plan your diet to reduce your intake of cholesterol. Egg yolks, organ meats and shellfish contain lots of cholesterol; fruits, vegetables, and vegetable oils do not. Remember that no single food such as eggs has been implicated as a cause of atherosclerosis; rather it is a dietary pattern which results in elevated blood cholesterol levels.

Reduce total fat intake by counting calories. This may entail choosing leaner cuts of meat in all categories; substituting "low-fat" foods such as fish or poultry for pork or other meats high in fats; trimming meats closely to reduce visible fat, including skinning poultry before cooking; and cooking by methods that render out the fat of marbled meats. Avoid deep-fat frying. Instead bake, broil, roast, or stew meats. It may also entail other substitutions such as skim milk or nonfat dry milk for whole milk or cream.

By cutting calories and reducing fat intake, you can stay within your correct weight range. Maintaining a good weight will help preclude high blood pressure and diabetes. The heavier you are, the harder the heart has to work to pump blood. If you are overweight, ask your doctor for a sensible reducing plan.

Eliminate saturated fats. Saturated fats are solid animal fats which raise the level of cholesterol in the blood. The most common sources include animal products, butter, cheese, cream and whole milk. Chocolate and many solid cooking fats are also saturated. Saturated vegetable fats are found in many solid and hydrogenated shortenings and in coconut oil, cocoa butter and palm oil.

Saturated fats should be replaced with polyunsaturated fats such as those in liquid vegetable oils—corn, cottonseed, soybean and safflower oils; fish and poultry; skim milk and skim-milk cheeses; margarine. Polyunsaturated fats lower cholesterol in the blood by helping the body eliminate excess newly formed cholesterol, and thus lessen the hazard of fatty deposits developing in blood vessels.

High blood pressure: One in every seven adults has high blood pressure. Some do not even know they have it. Many who do know they have high blood pressure are not doing enough to control this disease, partly because they do not understand enough about it. Do you? Test your knowledge of high blood pressure by taking the quiz below. Answer true or false to the following. See page 78 for answers.

1. If I stay calm and relaxed, I will not have high blood pressure.
2. High blood pressure is the leading contributor to strokes, heart disease, and kidney disease.
3. I can tell when my blood pressure is high.
4. Once I have high blood pressure, it usually means I will have to take medicine to control it for the rest of my life.
5. Headaches and dizziness are symptoms of high blood pressure.
6. The only thing I can do about high blood pressure is watch my diet.

To deal with high blood pressure, we must understand what blood pressure is. Blood pressure is the force generated by the heart to propel blood through the vessels to all parts of the body. Your blood pressure can be determined by a doctor using a sphygmomanometer, and is generally expressed by two numbers. The first number represents the systolic pressure when the heart muscle is contracting; the second number represents the diastolic pressure when the heart muscle is relaxed between beats. A normal blood pressure for an adult is 120/80; fluctuations occur due to stress and other factors, however.

High blood pressure results from a breakdown in the system that maintains equilibrium between blood flow and constricting and dilating forces affecting arterial walls. In high blood pressure, known also as hypertension, the normal level or balance is shifted upward so that the blood circulated in the arteries is harder to pump, adding to the workload of the heart and arteries. If the high blood pressure continues, the heart and arteries will not function as well as they should, and the increased pressure can permanently damage the blood vessels and the heart and speed up the progression of atherosclerosis.

High blood pressure levels are directly related to an increased risk of developing coronary heart disease and stroke in the adult population. The risk of coronary disease and stroke increases as the level of blood pressure increases, especially when associated with other risk factors such as elevated cholesterol, diabetes, and cigarette smoking.

Although high blood pressure can be controlled, there is no cure. The condition will be with most victims for life. Most people with high blood pressure have no symptoms—which is why the disease is called a silent killer. There are usually no warning signs, especially in the early stages. Sometimes people suffer headaches, dizziness, fatigue, tension and shortness of breath for years without recognizing them as symptoms of high blood pressure. The only way to discover if you have high blood pressure is to have a checkup by your physician or at a health clinic.

If a person has high blood pressure, he should have his blood pressure checked periodically and should receive medical treatment. Medications, including antihypertensive drugs, can reduce and help control high blood pressure. A hypertensive person should also be kept on a low-fat and low-salt diet, lose weight if overweight and give up smoking if he has not already done so.

Many people confuse hypertension with tension caused by occasions of stress. Some people with high blood pressure take their pills only when they feel tense and dizzy or have a headache. Instead these pills should be taken as prescribed, which in most cases is daily. Those who should be especially careful about developing high blood pressure also include women on contraceptives, women who are pregnant, women who are menopausal and black men and women.

Answers to quiz: 1. False 2. True 3. False 4. True 5. False 6. False

Cigarette smoking: By an act of Congress, all cigarettes sold in the United States must bear the following legend: "Warning: The Surgeon General Has Determined That Cigarette Smoking Is Dangerous to Your Health." The latest report by the Surgeon General of the United States on cigarette smoking (January 1978) provides strong evidence that smoking is directly associated with an increased risk of coronary heart disease, including sudden death. The risk of death from coronary heart disease is directly related to the number of cigarettes smoked and applies equally to women and men. The risk is particularly high for people below age fifty-five.

The nicotine and carbon monoxide present in cigarette smoke appear to be important factors in the mechanism that produces coronary heart disease. Nicotine increases the demand of the heart for oxygen and other nutrients. Carbon monoxide decreases the ability of the blood to furnish the needed oxygen. Smoking makes the heart beat faster, raises the blood pressure, and narrows the blood vessels.

Cigarette smoking is closely associated with other respiratory and circulatory diseases, including lung cancer, emphysema, and chronic bronchitis. Smoking is especially dangerous for persons with blood vessel diseases in the legs, known as peripheral vascular diseases. Those who suffer from these diseases and continue to smoke increase the risk of gangrene, amputations and even death. Pregnant women who smoke may cause birth defects in their children.

Filters reduce only moderately the amount of harmful substances in cigarette smoking. As far as is known,

smoking a pipe or cigar involves no increased risk of heart attack, probably because the smoke is not inhaled. While 90 percent of the nicotine is absorbed into the body when smoke is inhaled, only 10 percent is absorbed when smoke is puffed without inhaling. Smoking a pipe or cigar, however, does increase the risk of mouth and throat cancer.

People who give up smoking have a lower death rate from heart attack than do those who continue to smoke. Some of the abnormal lung tissue of ex-heavy smokers can gradually revert to normal. The rate of decline appears to depend on the length of time the individual smoked and the number of cigarettes he smoked.

Probable risk factors

Diabetes mellitus and impaired glucose tolerance: Coronary heart disease, heart failure, stroke, sudden death and peripheral vascular disease are more common among diabetics, especially young ones, than among nondiabetics. Diabetes is often associated with hypertension and obesity.

Complications of diabetes that involve the cardiovascular system create trouble in the structure and function of the eyes, kidneys, heart, brain and peripheral blood vessels, especially in the legs. Diabetes is a systemic disorder that affects the whole body because blood sugar is needed to fuel all of the body tissues.

With regular medical checkups, diabetes can be detected early and brought under control. Treatment for diabetics includes a good diet and a weight-control plan limiting the intake of dietary cholesterol and saturated fats, avoidance of cigarette smoking, control of high blood pressure, regular exercise, and insulin injections or oral drugs prescribed by a physician.

Stress and coronary-prone behavior: The effect of stress on the development of atherosclerosis is currently being assessed by several investigations. Particular attention has been paid to the so-called Type A, or stress-ridden, behavior pattern. Everyone experiences pressures, but people who find coping with a stressful situation particularly difficult should seek professional help.

Post-menopausal state: Pre-menopausal women have significantly less chance of getting coronary heart disease than do women of the same age in whom artificial menopause has been induced.

Family history and genetic factors: There are some families in which premature and fatal heart attacks occur with frequency. It is uncertain to what extent this tendency may be due to genetic factors and to what extent it may be due to the fact that families share the same life-style, environment, and dietary habits. It seems that there is a genetic component to a number of risk factors, including some forms of high cholesterol, hypertension and diabetes mellitus.

If you have had a close relative who died between ages 40 and 50 from the complications of atherosclerosis, this could mean that a tendency toward the disease runs in your family. You may or may not inherit this tendency, but even if you do, it is not inevitable that you will have the disease. Your way of life will have a great influence.

If you have uncontrolled hypertension and if you add the risks of smoking, overeating, a diet rich in cholesterol and lipids, and a lack of exercise, you may set the disease process in motion. Heed the warning. Take steps to reduce the risks that are within your control.

Contraceptive pills: Studies have found that young women who take oral contraceptive pills are exposed to an increased risk of coronary heart disease. This risk is aggravated by cigarette smoking or other risk factors.

Suspected risk factors

Overweight: Obesity increases the risk of coronary disease and stroke. Much of its effect is related to certain other risk factors, such as high level of blood cholesterol and fats, hypertension, and diabetes.

Physical inactivity: Lack of exercise is generally regarded as a relatively minor reason for the development of atherosclerosis. But people who lead sedentary lives may run a higher risk of heart attack than those who get regular exercise. Exercise keeps the muscles in shape, improves circulation, keeps a person's weight down, and promotes a feeling of good health. There is some evidence that heart at-

tack victims who have exercised regularly survive longer than those who have not. But if you are not used to exercising, exercise does not mean shoveling snow in winter or playing several sets of tennis on a hot day. Strenuous and irregular exercise can bring on a heart attack in an apparently healthy person who has atherosclerosis of the coronary arteries. Begin an exercise program in consultation with your physician. Always increase your level of physical activity gradually. Discuss with your physician *any* health problems that develop during exercise. The benefits of exercise can be undermined, however, by bad habits of a high-fat diet and smoking.

Combination of risk factors

The incidence of acute heart attacks is far greater in persons with multiple risk factors than in those with no risk factor or only one risk factor. Persons with three, four or more definite risk factors form an especially high-risk group.

TREATMENT AND REHABILITATION OF HEART ATTACK VICTIMS

Most heart attack victims enter a hospital coronary care unit (CCU) for around-the-clock care, including access to emergency drugs and resuscitation equipment. In a hospital, the victim's heartbeat is monitored, and healing can begin. Blood vessels near the damaged area of the heart take over the work of the closed-off artery. As the heart heals, scar tissue forms at the damaged area. Recovery time for heart attack patients varies, depending upon the extent of heart muscle injury and on resulting complications. Sometimes surgery is required to bypass the blocked segments of the coronary arteries and remove destroyed heart tissue.

In an uncomplicated heart attack, the victim is usually hospitalized two to three weeks, followed by six to eight weeks of rest at home. The victim should cooperate with his physician and needs the cooperation of his family. He usually must take some medication and work on a program to control coronary risk factors. Gradually he will begin to increase his physical strength and activity to restore

himself to a productive, active and satisfying life. Three out of four survivors return to their old jobs after convalescence. The others must change their occupations or life-style to avoid another attack. A heart attack victim's doctor should draw up a long-term health plan to prevent a recurrence of the disease. Unfortunately, however, statistics show that a heart attack survivor's chances of having another attack are at least three or four times higher than those for the average person.

27

HEAT EXPOSURE

Hot weather can have an adverse effect on the body, causing it to lose large amounts of water or salt, or both, through profuse sweating and to become overheated and unable to eliminate excess heat. Each of the disorders caused by extremely hot weather—heat asthenia, heat cramps, heat exhaustion, and heatstroke—is most debilitating for older people and people with weak hearts. These individuals especially should avoid exertion and keep to a cool environment during very warm weather. Small children, chronic invalids, alcoholics and overweight individuals should also be more cautious during hot spells. Because heat-wave weather can kill, everyone should know the warning signs for the different types of heat illnesses, how to treat them, and how to prevent them (see the sections below). In addition, following the rules for beating a heat wave will make life during a hot spell much more bearable. And for those interested in getting a suntan, there are tips on how to avoid a sunburn.

HEAT SYNDROME: SYMPTOMS AND TREATMENTS

Sunburn

Signs/symptoms: Redness and pain caused by dilation of small blood vessels in skin. In more severe cases, tissue injury brings swelling of skin, blisters, and often fever and headache. Sunburn may be accompanied by other heat syndrome disorders.

First-aid treatment

Prevent severe sunburn by limiting the time of initial exposure, depending on comfort and conditions. Treat mild sunburn with cold cream or certain oils or greases (such as salad oil, shortening). Wash hands before applying. Do not apply butter or oleomargarine. Dressing should be used if blistering appears. Injured area should not be exposed to sunlight until healed. Medical care is needed for extensive or severe cases.

Heat asthenia

Signs/symptoms: Headache, profuse sweating, easy fatigue, high pulse rate, shallow breathing, poor appetite.

First-aid treatment

Move victim to a cooler, drier environment, give plenty of fluids, and unless diet prevents it, give a salt tablet. Encourage rest.

Heat cramps

Signs/symptoms: Painful spasms in voluntary muscles due to a loss of salt from sweating or from an inadequate salt intake. Pupils dilate with each spasm, possible heavy sweating, skin cold and clammy. Heat cramps can be an early sign of heat exhaustion.

First-aid treatment

Apply firm pressure and warm, wet towels on cramping muscles. Give three or four half-filled glasses of salty water at 15-minute intervals. Salty water means a teaspoonful of salt per glass. Make victim rest in a cool spot.

Heat exhaustion

Signs/symptoms: Fatigue, profuse sweating, vertigo, cold and pale skin that is clammy with sweat, thready pulse, low blood pressure, normal or subnormal temperature, possible nausea and vomiting.

First-aid treatment

Move victim to cooler environment immediately, but be careful not to chill. Loosen victim's clothing. Make victim rest in bed. Give three or four half-filled glasses of salty water at 15-minute intervals. Salty water means a teaspoonful of salt per glass. If victim vomits, do not give any more fluids. Have victim rest in a cool spot.

Heat stroke (sunstroke)

Signs/symptoms: Weakness; vertigo; nausea; heat cramps; mild heat exhaustion; excessive sweating (with sweating stopping just before heat stroke); sharp rise in temperature, possibly reaching 106° F; bounding and full pulse; elevated blood pressure; delirium or coma; skin flushed at first, later ashen or purplish. Victim's skin is usually hot, red and dry because the sweating mechanism is blocked. The mortality rate associated with heat stroke is high, and so it is essential to cool the victim's body quickly. Be careful, however, not to overchill the victim once his or her temperature goes below 102° F. Persons most likely to be victims are the aged, debilitated, malnourished, diabetic, and people with heart disease.

First-aid treatment

Heat stroke is a serious medical emergency. Summon a physician or get the victim to a hospital immediately. In the meantime, have the victim lie down in a cool room with head and shoulders raised. If the victim's temperature is *below* 106° F, reduce body temperature by sponging body with ice wrapped in a towel or with rubbing alcohol. If time does not permit removing victim's clothes, wet them with cold water. Use fans or air conditioner to promote cooling. Rub the victim's arms and legs toward heart to aid circulation. Check victim's temperature after 15 minutes. If temperature starts to escalate, begin the cooling process again. Do not give stimulants. If victim's temperature is *above* 106° F, give victim an iced-water tub bath. Watch for signs of shock and treat accordingly (see page 21).

PREVENTION

Avoid prolonged exposure to direct rays of the sun in hot weather or to high temperatures. Athletes in training and others who perform strenuous exercise or labor in hot, humid weather are especially susceptible to heat stroke. If you are going to exercise often in summer, let your body build up a tolerance to the heat over a period of several days. Drink enough water when exercising so your body can sweat properly. Take extra salt in the form of salty foods, salt tablets or salted drinking water to replace that lost in sweating. Never, however, take salt in any form unless you drink water.

Caution. People with heart or kidney trouble should check with a doctor before increasing their salt intake.

Rules for beating a heat wave

1. Slow down; your body cannot do its best in high temperatures.

2. Reduce your level of activity immediately when your body warns you that the heat is becoming too much for you. Warning signs include muscle cramps, dizziness, faintness. Move to a cooler environment.

3. Avoid thermal shock; treat yourself extra gently for those first two or three hot days while your body gets acclimated.

4. Vary your thermal environment. Try to get out of the heat for at least a few hours each day: Visit a cool store, restaurant, theater. If your apartment or house is not air conditioned, use a fan. Either method helps evaporate sweat and will keep your physiological cooling system working efficiently.

5. Take more baths in warm weather.

6. Do not get too much sun. Sunburn reduces the body's ability to cool itself.

7. Wear loose-fitting, loosely woven, absorbent, light-colored clothing. If you do not, you create a microclimate between the fabric and your skin which becomes humid, preventing the evaporation of sweat and inhibiting your cooling system. Your skin also becomes wet and uncomfortable.

8. Keep physically fit and exercise year round so that your sweat glands

80

are in training for a heat wave. Select the coolest and least humid time of day to be outdoors. Exercise for several days before attempting strenuous activity at midday. Increase your amount of activity slowly. If you feel faint, nauseated, dizzy or experience muscle cramps, stop and rest.

Getting a tan without sunburn

Different people can tolerate varying amounts of sun; too much can mean an aching sunburn rather than a healthy tan. The effect of the sun on a person depends on a variety of factors:

1. Your skin complexion (fair, medium, dark); the more pigment your skin has, the less chance you will burn.

2. Where in the world you are sunbathing, because the sun's rays are more direct at the equator than at more northerly latitudes.

3. What season it is, because seasonal changes affect the amount of ultraviolet light you receive.

4. What altitude it is, since high altitudes offer less atmosphere than low altitudes to filter ultraviolet rays.

5. What time of day you sunbathe, because the sun will cause more burns at noon when it is directly overhead than in the early morning or late afternoon hours.

6. Whether you are taking any medication which may make you more susceptible to sunburn.

7. Whether you are wearing any fragrances, including ones that contain the chemical bergapten, which is capable of reacting with sunlight to produce a phototoxic reaction in the skin.

No suntan lotion or cream will make you tan faster. The aim of such products is solely to help you stay outside in the sun a little longer without burning. It is best to buy a product that will screen out the harmful ultraviolet rays of the sun, and allow you to tan. The best sunscreens contain the chemical PABA or benzophenone. In August 1978, a Food and Drug Administration panel recommended that sun-protection factor (SPF) information be included on sunscreen products. The letters SPF plus a number give the amount of protection that a product offers from the sun's burning rays. The higher the SPF number, the greater the protection. For example, for moderate protection, you would choose a product with an SPF of four to six. By multiplying the SPF number by the amount of time you can stay in the sun before you begin to redden, you can figure out how long you can sunbathe without burning. Apply the sunscreen to all exposed parts of your body before you go out into the sun, and reapply it after going into the water, after exercising and after profusely sweating. Be especially careful of the sun's rays when you are resting on the beach and when you are in or near the water. Sand and water and also snow all absorb the ultraviolet rays of the sun, making you tan and burn faster. By wearing light protective clothing, you will also increase protection to your skin. You should also use a good sunscreening lotion on smoggy, hazy or cloudy days when you can still burn.

It is best to let your skin become accustomed to the sun gradually. If your skin is especially sensitive, begin your first day of sunbathing by spending only about 40 minutes in the sun. On your second day, you can spend 45 minutes, and on your third and fourth days about 50 minutes each. By your fifth day, you will be able to stay out for most of the day, your skin having built up a protective tan. It is always wise, however, to avoid sunbathing at midday when the sun is hottest.

Too much sunlight will cause any type of complexion to burn. When the skin is burned, tiny blood vessels at the surface dilate to produce a scorched look. There are three types of sunburn. Mild sunburn will result in some reddening of the skin, possibly followed by a slight scaling or peeling of the skin, and dryness. If the skin turns red, dust the area with talcum powder. Moderately bad burns will make the skin turn even redder, and will also make it slightly swollen, tender and possibly itchy. Blisters and peeling may also result. Apply wet dressings of gauze dipped in a solution of baking soda and cornstarch, using one tablespoon of each to two quarts of cool water. In an emergency, use cool milk or water. You can also try taking a lukewarm bath. A severe burn may be accompanied by chills, fever and bad blisters, which may become infected. For a severe burn, it is wise to consult a physician. For whatever type of burn you suffer, drink plenty of fluids and eat salty food to replace the salt you have lost from dehydration. Rest indoors in a cool room. Take aspirin to ease the pain.

Too much ultraviolet radiation from the sun is the leading cause of skin cancer. People with blue or green eyes, blond or red hair, fair skin with pronounced freckling, and people having a tendency to burn in the sun are especially vulnerable to skin cancer. Skin cancer usually shows up as waxlike, pearly nodules or red, scaly, sharply outlined patches. A rare type starts out as dark, molelike growths that increase in size. All three skin lesions are small—less than $\frac{1}{8}$ inch in diameter. If you are suspicious of a spot, see a dermatologist immediately. Skin cancer can be cured if it is detected early.

28

HYPOTHERMIA

Hypothermia chills the inner core of the body so the body cannot generate enough heat to stay warm. It happens in very cold weather, aggravated by wind and humidity, wet clothing, fatigue, and alcoholic intake. It is a medical emergency because the marked drop in body temperature can cause fatal heart attacks, severe changes in body chemistry, shock and infection. Older people are particularly susceptible, and although the energy shortage dictates lowered household temperatures, the elderly should not turn their thermostats below 65° F in cold weather.

Signs/symptoms

The entire body is affected by the lowering of the body's inner-core temperature. Shivering, except among some older persons, is usually the first sign. Then numbness and muscular weakness develop. The victim, especially an older person, will later become drowsy and begin to mumble. If the body temperature drops 10° to 20° and the condition is not corrected quickly, the victim may become unconscious, go into shock, and even die because of heart failure.

First-aid treatment

Bring victim into a warm room as quickly as possible. Remove any wet clothing. Wrap victim in pre-warmed blankets or place between two people for body warmth. In mild cases, put victim into a tub of warm water. Remove and dry victim.

If victim is conscious, give a warm drink such as tea or coffee, but not an alcoholic beverage. Give energy food such as a chocolate bar or raisins.

If victim is unconscious, give artificial respiration (see pages 17–18). Treat for shock if necessary (see page 21). Get medical help as soon as possible.

Prevention

Avoid consuming alcohol before going out in cold weather since it dilates peripheral blood vessels and promotes loss of body heat. Be sure the body has enough fuel by eating plenty of fats and carbohydrates. Wear warm clothing, preferably in layers. Especially cover ears, hands, feet in several layers, and wear waterproof garments. Do not smoke.

Do not overexercise in cold weather, particularly if past age 40. It produces a tremendous strain on the heart, and too much cold air taken into the lungs can prevent the body from warming itself. Whenever you begin to feel cold and shiver, immediately move indoors and warm yourself.

For how to prevent hypothermia in water accidents by assuming the fetal, or heat-lessening, position, see the chapter "Boating Emergencies."

29

IMMUNIZATION

Babies are immune to many diseases when they are born, but this immunity, which is received from their mothers, is only temporary and wears off during the first year of life. Young children need immunization programs to help them build their own permanent defenses against serious diseases such as measles, rubella (German measles), polio, mumps, diphtheria, pertussis (whooping cough) and tetanus.

With the exception of tetanus, these diseases are very contagious. They spread rapidly from child to child and from community to community. When children remain unprotected against them, serious outbreaks of disease—even epidemics—are possible.

It is important that parents understand what protection vaccines give and what risks, if any, vaccines present to their children. Vaccines are made of small quantities of live or dead organisms that cause a disease, or of materials produced from those organisms. These vaccines are injected into the body or are taken by mouth. The body reacts by producing disease-fighting substances—antibodies—that build up in the system and guard against infection for a long time, often for a lifetime. Immunization, therefore, stimulates the body to defend itself against a particular disease.

Generally, vaccines are among our safest and most effective medicines. Like most medicines, however, vaccines can cause side effects. These are usually mild—a slight fever, a sore arm, a mild rash—and do not last long. On rare occasions, however, they are serious, which is why vaccines should be given only by physicians or other qualified health professionals.

MEASLES

Measles is the most serious of the common childhood diseases. It can cause pneumonia, blindness and encephalitis, or inflammation of the brain, which often leads to permanent brain damage and deafness. Measles occurs most often in the late winter and spring, striking young children above the age of six months (although it has been occurring progressively later in life, with outbreaks in high schools and even in colleges).

The incubation period for measles is usually 9 to 12 days. When the disease strikes, it commonly lasts about two weeks. It begins with symptoms like those of a bad cold and a temperature that may rise as high as 104°. A few days after the beginning of the symptoms, a blotchy red rash appears on the face or eyes and body. This rash fades away gradually over a period of 7 to 10 days.

For uncomplicated measles, treatment should include aspirin to keep the fever down and a vaporizer for easing a bad cough. Your physician should monitor the course of the disease.

The complications of measles are another matter. As many as 3 out of every 10 cases of measles result in pneumonia. Encephalitis occurs once in every 1,000 reported cases. For serious forms of measles and resulting complications, a doctor should be consulted immediately.

Vaccination

All healthy babies who have never had measles should be vaccinated at the age of 15 months. The vaccine is effective, and one injection produces lasting—probably lifelong—protection. Measles vaccine can be given by itself or in a combination vaccine that also protects against rubella and mumps.

One out of every four children who receive measles vaccine will have a minor reaction—a slight fever or a mild rash. These reactions occur 7 to 18 days after vaccination, last only a day or two and usually do not harm the child in any way. About one out of every one million children who get the measles shot may have a more serious reaction, such as encephalitis. Medical authorities agree that the benefits of immunization against measles far outweigh any risks.

RUBELLA

Rubella, also called German measles, is a common, usually mild childhood disease (although it may also affect adults, and outbreaks are common among unvaccinated teenagers). Rubella occurs most often in the winter and spring and is highly contagious. It is caught by breathing in particles of rubella virus exhaled by sick people.

The incubation period is from 12 to 21 days. The usual symptoms are mild discomfort, a slight fever for perhaps 24 hours and most often a fleeting rash that appears on the face and neck and spreads to the trunk and extremities, lasting for a day or two. Young adults who get rubella may experience swollen glands in the back of the neck and some temporary pain and stiffness in the joints (arthritis).

Check with your doctor regarding treatment. Most suggest an aspirin to lower the fever and for any neck pain.

Recovery from rubella is almost always speedy and complete. A woman who gets rubella early in her pregnancy, however, stands a 20 to 25 percent chance of giving birth to a deformed baby. The possibility that she will have a miscarriage is even greater. The most common birth defects caused by the rubella virus are blindness, damage to the heart and major arteries, deafness, abnormally small brain and mental retardation. The best way to protect expectant mothers and their offspring from these tragic effects is to immunize children and thereby eliminate the source of infection. The child who cannot catch rubella cannot spread it to his or her mother or to other pregnant women. Blood tests are available to see if a pregnant woman is immune to the disease.

Vaccination

All healthy children who have never had rubella should be vaccinated after their first birthday. The vaccine is highly effective, and one injection produces lasting—probably lifelong—protection. Rubella vaccine is available by itself or in a combination vaccine that also protects against measles and mumps. A single shot of the combination vaccine, which is given at 15 months of age (because it includes measles vaccine), protects the child against all three diseases.

Rubella vaccine should be given to nearly everyone who is not already protected against the disease, but particularly to young girls. It should not, however, be given to pregnant women or to women who do not intend to take every precaution against becoming pregnant for three months after vaccination. It is possible that the rubella vaccine might cause the same kinds of problems for a pregnant woman as rubella disease itself.

Rubella vaccine can produce several side effects. About one out of every seven children will develop a rash or some swelling in the glands within a week or two following the shot. These effects usually last only a day or two. Some children and adults who receive the vaccine will have some pain and stiffness in the joints. This condition may appear anywhere from two to ten weeks after the shot. It is usually mild and lasts for only two or three days. About one out of every one million children who receive rubella vaccine may have a more serious reaction, such as encephalitis. The benefits of immunization against rubella far outweigh the risks.

POLIO

Poliomyelitis, or infantile paralysis, is a contagious viral disease that, in its severe form, can cause permanent paralysis and even death. Although it occurs only rarely today because of the widespread use of vaccines, polio is fatal in about one out of every ten cases.

Polio is caused by three types of virus that live in the noses, throats and the intestinal tracts of infected people. Polio occurs most often in children between the ages of one and sixteen. Many people who are infected by the polio virus have no symptoms but may still spread the disease to others.

The incubation period is from 8 to 10 days. The milder forms of polio usually begin abruptly and last, at most, a few days. When symptoms are present, they include fever, sore throat, nausea, headache and stomachache. Sometimes the patient will feel pain and stiffness in the neck, back and legs.

The disease will be treated symptomatically by your doctor. For example, for a headache he will suggest aspirin, for nausea he will tell you to avoid any food, for a stomachache he will suggest a hot-water bottle or prescribe an antispasmodic drug. Paralytic polio begins with these same symptoms, but severe muscle pain is usually present, and if paralysis occurs, it does so within the first week. There is no specific treatment for curing polio, and the degree of recovery varies from patient to patient. About half of all patients who recover have mild disabilities or none at all. The rest may suffer permanent paralysis.

While polio cases may be few today, the outlook for the future is ominous. Over the past several years, even as case rates have dropped, the number of children not protected by vaccination against polio has increased.

Vaccination

All healthy infants and young people between the ages of six weeks and 18 years who have never been immunized against polio should receive polio vaccine in a series of properly spaced doses.

Two kinds of vaccine are available. The preferred and most widely used vaccine is the trivalent oral polio vaccine, which is made from live but weakened polio virus. This vaccine is effective in preventing the spread of polio and gives protection for a long time, probably for life.

The second kind of polio vaccine is made from dead polio virus and is given in a series of injections. This vaccine is not widely used in the United States at this time, mainly because most polio experts do not feel that it is as effective in controlling polio in this country as the oral vaccine. However, injectable polio vaccine is most often recommended for persons who have low resistance to infections and for individuals who will be traveling to a destination where polio is common.

Young children should get two doses of oral vaccine in the first year of life, usually at two and four months of age, and a third dose at about 18 months of age. Some doctors, particularly in parts of the world where polio is still common, give three doses in the first year, at two, four and six months, and a dose at 18 months. To assure full and lasting protection, a booster dose should be given at four to six years of age, before the child enters school.

There is virtually no risk of side effects of any kind with injectable polio vaccine. Very rarely—only about once in every four million doses—a person who receives oral polio vaccine, or who comes into contact with someone who has received it recently, develops permanent paralysis and may die.

MUMPS

Mumps is a common disease of children that occurs most often in the first half of the year, from late winter to early summer. Mumps is highly contagious, spread by person-to-person contact. The favorite targets of this virus are children between the ages of five and ten, but it also strikes teenagers and adults, often with serious consequences. The incubation period is usually about 18 days.

The symptoms of mumps are painfully swollen glands in the face and neck, fever, headache, and earache.

83

The disease, which lasts about a week, should be treated symptomatically, including aspirin to reduce pain and fever according to a physician's directions. If solid food is hard to consume, the patient should take nutritious fluids. The patient should be kept away from other people and kept in bed.

There are usually no disabling complications and recovery is complete. Meningitis occurs occasionally. Early signs are fever, headache, pain in the back of the neck and spine. For this complication of the disease, a doctor should be consulted immediately. Most patients do recover fully from meningitis, and permanent damage, including deafness, occurs only rarely. In teenage and adult males, mumps may occasionally produce a painful inflammation of the testicles. This condition occurs in one out of every four patients and sometimes, but rarely, results in sterility. Some other complications of mumps are inflammation of the pancreas, thyroid and kidneys and, in female patients, inflammation of the ovaries and breasts.

Vaccination

All healthy children who have never had mumps should be vaccinated after their first birthdays. The vaccine can be given to older children and adults. It is highly effective, and one injection produces lasting—probably lifelong—protection.

Mumps vaccine is available by itself or in a combination vaccine that also protects against measles and rubella. One shot of the combination vaccine (which is given at 15 months of age because it includes measles vaccine) protects the child against all three diseases.

In rare instances, mumps vaccine produces a mild, brief fever which occurs one or two weeks after the shot. Occasionally, there is some swelling of the salivary glands. About one out of every one million children who get the mumps shot may have a more serious reaction, such as encephalitis. But since the disease itself can be painful and disabling, the benefits of immunization against mumps far outweigh the risks.

DIPHTHERIA, PERTUSSIS AND TETANUS

Diphtheria, pertussis (whooping cough) and tetanus (lockjaw) are serious diseases that usually occur in children, although each—especially tetanus—also strikes adults. Effective protection against these diseases, in the form of a combination vaccine called DPT, has been widely used since the early 1950s.

Diphtheria

Diphtheria is caused by a bacterium that is found in the mouth, throat and nose of an infected person. This germ is easily passed to others in the tiny droplets of moisture that are expelled by coughing and sneezing. Diphtheria also can be spread by carriers—people who harbor the bacteria but remain in apparent good health.

Diphtheria develops after an incubation period of from two to five days. It usually begins in the throat, where a patch or patches of grayish membrane may begin to form. Other early symptoms are sore throat, slight fever and chills. If the membrane continues to grow, it can interfere with swallowing. If it extends to the windpipe, it can block the passage of air and cause the patient to suffocate.

If diphtheria is suspected or if it develops, a doctor should be called immediately. If one is not available, the patient should be taken to the hospital. Emergency care is required in all cases of diphtheria.

Diphtheria is a treatable condition, but if treatment is inadequate, or if it is not begun in time, a powerful toxin, or poison, may be produced by the diphtheria bacteria and may spread throughout the body. The poison may cause serious complications such as paralysis that lasts for as long as three or four months, heart failure or bronchopneumonia. Five to ten percent of all diphtheria cases are fatal.

Pertussis

Pertussis, or whooping cough as it is more commonly known, is a highly contagious disease that occurs with greatest frequency in late winter and early spring and is most likely to strike children under the age of seven. It is caused by a bacterium that is found in the mouths, noses and throats of infected persons and is spread through the air to others. The incubation period is five to eight days.

When pertussis begins, it acts like a common cold, accompanied by an irritating cough. As the disease tightens its grip on the airways from the lungs, the cough increases in intensity and occurs in violent and prolonged spasms with high-pitched whooping sounds between each spasm as the patient fights to inhale air.

Steam and syrup of ipecac can relieve respiratory difficulty. The syrup can induce vomiting, which will rid the body of excess secretions. Medical help should always be sought.

A severe case of whooping cough prepares the way for a range of grave complications, among them convulsions, collapse of the lungs, pneumonia and brain damage. These effects are most likely to occur in the very young, and when they do, they can be fatal. Unless adequate treatment is given early in the course of the disease, one infant in four who get whooping cough before the age of six months will not survive.

Tetanus

Tetanus is caused by a bacterium that is present just about everywhere, but mostly in soil, dust, manure and in the digestive tracts of man and many animals. The germs of tetanus enter the body through a wound, sometimes one as small as a pinprick, but more often through deep, dirty puncture wounds and lacerations such as those made by nails and knives or by deep, crushing wounds. All such wounds are difficult to clean adequately. If the tetanus bacteria, which thrive on dying or dead tissue, were present on the nail or knife, they may remain deep in the wound where they produce poison that attacks the body's nervous system. The usual incubation period is from seven to twenty-one days.

First-aid treatment

Any wound that poses the risks of tetanus should be cleaned immediately with hydrogen peroxide, and if that is not available, soap and water. Be sure you remove foreign bodies from the wound. As an interim treatment until you can get medical help, elevate the affected area if it is the head, a hand, a leg or a foot. Apply heat to the area with warm towels over the wound. Continue applying warm packs for about 30 minutes; then cover the wound with a sterile dressing. Keep repeating this process until you get medical help.

A physician will decide upon immunization treatment, basing it on the history of previous tetanus vaccinations and the condition of the wound. A guide to wound management is given in the table below, provided by the U.S. Department of Health, Education, and Welfare's Center for Disease Control.

given, then a month later the second injection, and finally six months later the third injection is given.

DPT vaccination

The combination DPT vaccine provides a high degree of immunity for a number of years against diphtheria, pertussis and tetanus. This protection must be renewed throughout life, with booster doses for tetanus.

given every ten years to maintain a high level of protection.

Older children over six years of age and adults who have not been immunized should receive a series of shots for diphtheria and tetanus only and booster doses every ten years thereafter. Whooping cough vaccine is not included in the combination vaccine for older individuals or in the booster doses because this disease is not usually a threat beyond childhood.

Most children will have a slight fever and be cranky some time in the day or two after taking the DPT shot. Some children will develop soreness and swelling in the area where the shot was given. An aspirin can relieve discomfort; check with your doctor. A few children who get the shot will have a more serious side effect, such as a high fever or convulsions. A doctor should be consulted immediately. A child may also cry for several hours or go into shock and get pale. Still more rarely, encephalitis or brain damage may occur. Serious reactions are few and far between. Given the deadly seriousness of the diseases that the DPT vaccine prevents, parents have little choice but to make certain that their children are fully protected.

GUIDE TO TETANUS PROPHYLAXIS IN WOUND MANAGEMENT				
History of tetanus immunization (doses)	Clean, minor wounds		All other wounds	
	Td*	TIG†	Td*	TIG†
Uncertain	Yes	No	Yes	Yes
0-1	Yes	No	Yes	Yes
2	Yes	No	Yes	No[1]
3 or more	No[2]	No	No[3]	No

[1] Unless wound more than 24 hours old
[2] Unless more than 10 years since last dose
[3] Unless more than 5 years since last dose
* Td = Tetanus and Diphtheria Toxoids, Adult Type
† TIG = Tetanus Immune Globulin

If passive immunization is to be used, tetanus immune globulin is the product of choice. It causes no undesirable reactions, and provides longer protection than does antitoxin of animal origin.

The person who has not been immunized and develops tetanus has a 50-50 chance of surviving. The first symptoms are likely to be headache, irritability and muscular stiffness and pain in the neck and jaw, which accounts for its common name, lockjaw. As the poison steps up its attack, the jaw, neck and limbs become locked in spasm, the abdominal muscles grow rigid and the body may be wracked by waves of painful convulsions and coma.

Doctors treat the terrible symptoms of tetanus with powerful tranquilizers, antispasmodic drugs, antibiotics, antitoxins and special diets that are designed to preserve the patient's strength. Even with treatment, the convulsions may continue or increase in frequency until the patient dies of lack of oxygen, heart failure or simple exhaustion.

Note. If an adult was not immunized against tetanus as a child, he should receive a complete schedule of tetanus toxoid injections. First one injection is

All healthy infants should receive the DPT vaccine, beginning with a series of three shots, at two, four and six months of age. Early immunization is important. These diseases are deadly, and infants have no natural immunity to two of them, pertussis and tetanus. A fourth dose of vaccine should be given 12 months after the third, at about the age of 18 months; a fifth dose is needed when the child is four to six years old, before entering school. From then on, booster doses for diphtheria and tetanus should be

SCHEDULES FOR IMMUNIZATION

Vaccines work best when they are given at the recommended time and on a regular schedule. Your doctor may recommend schedules that differ somewhat from those given here (see schedules, page 86).

IMMUNIZATION RECORD				
Names				
Birth Dates				
DPT	First			
	Second			
	Third			
	Fourth			
	Boosters			
Polio	First			
	Second			
	Third			
	Booster			
	Booster			
Measles Rubella Mumps				

IMMUNIZATION SCHEDULE

If your child is six years of age or older...

First visit	Tetanus-Diphtheria (Td); Polio
1 mo. after first visit	Measles, Rubella, Mumps
2 mos. after first visit	Tetanus-Diphtheria (Td); Polio
8–14 mos. after first visit	Tetanus-Diphtheria (Td); Polio
Age 14–16 years	Tetanus-Diphtheria (Td)—repeat every 10 years

If your child is one through five years of age...

First visit	Diphtheria, Pertussis, Tetanus (DPT); Polio
1 mo. after first visit	Measles, Rubella, Mumps*
2 mos. after first visit	Diphtheria, Pertussis, Tetanus (DPT); Polio
4 mos. after first visit	Diphtheria, Petussis, Tetanus (DPT); Polio (optional)
10–16 mos. after first visit	Diphtheria, Pertussis, Tetanus (DPT); Polio
Age 14–16 years	Tetanus-Diphtheria (Td)—repeat every 10 years

*Not routinely given before 15 months of age.

If your child is two months old...

Age	Diphtheria Pertussis Tetanus	Polio	Measles	Rubella	Mumps
2 mos.	*	*			
4 mos.	*	*			
6 mos.	*	(optional)			
15 mos.			*	*	*
18 mos.	*	*			
4–yrs.	*	*			

Notes: Measles, rubella and mumps vaccines can be given in a combined form, at about 15 months of age, with a single injection.

Children should receive a sixth tetanus-diphtheria injection (booster) at age 14–16 years.

Note: The above schedule is based on information available as of May 1978. As new knowledge becomes available, recommendations for immunization schedules may change.

Your doctor or the staff at the clinic you visit will keep a record of your children's immunizations, but you should have one too. An up-to-date record, showing kinds of immunizations and dates received, helps you to cooperate with the doctor. It also serves as a reminder of visits coming up. On page 85, you will find an immunization record to use for your children.

ADULT IMMUNIZATION AND SAFE TRAVEL

Adults are not always immune to the communicable diseases of childhood, and most immunizations do not last for life. Consult your physician about renewing immunizations.

If you are going to travel abroad where diseases such as smallpox, typhoid fever, and cholera are prevalent, you should consult your family doctor; he will know the current requirements for vaccinations against communicable diseases in other countries. Pregnant women should consult their doctor on whether the vaccine(s) are safe to take.

Summary of requirements for United States travelers to countries most frequently visited

Europe: There are no vaccination requirements for travel directly between the United States and countries in Europe. The areas that are considered to comprise Europe are:

Albania
Austria
Azores
Belgium
Bulgaria
Czechoslovakia
Denmark
Faroe Islands
Finland
France
Germany (East)
Germany (West)
Gibraltar
Greece
Guernsey, Alderney, and Sark
Hungary
Iceland
Ireland
Isle of Man
Italy
Jersey
Liechtenstein
Luxembourg
Malta
Monaco
Netherlands
Norway
Poland
Portugal
Romania
Russia (USSR)
Spain
Sweden
Switzerland
United Kingdom (England, Scotland, Northern Ireland, Wales)
Yugoslavia

Canada and Mexico: There are no vaccination requirements for travel directly between the United States and either of these countries.

The Caribbean: There are no vaccination requirements for travel directly between the United States and any one of the Caribbean countries. For travel to more than one country in the Caribbean, check the individual country requirements.

Return to the United States: No vaccinations are required to return to the United States.

Health hints for the traveler

It is recommended that the traveler take an extra pair of glasses or lens prescription, and a card, tag or bracelet identifying any physical condition that may require emergency care.

If a physician is needed abroad, travel agents or the American embassy or consulate can usually provide names of physicians or hospitals. Prescription medications that the traveler must take should be accompanied by a letter from his physician. The letter should include a statement of major health problems and dosage of prescribed medications to provide information for medical authorities in case of emergency. The traveler should carry an adequate supply of such drugs.

Most patients who acquire viral, bacterial and parasitic infections abroad become ill within six weeks after returning home. However, some diseases such as malaria may not show symptoms for as long as six months to a year after the traveler returns to the United States. It is therefore a good idea for the traveler to advise his physician of any travel outside the United States within the 12 months preceding the onset of illness. Knowledge of the possibility of exposure to certain diseases abroad will help physician arrive at a diagnosis.

Water: Water may be safe in major urban hotels commonly used by American travelers; however, only chlorinated water sources afford significant protection against viral and bacterial waterborne diseases. Chlorine at the levels used in routine disinfection of water may not kill the parasitic organisms that cause giardiasis and amebiasis. In areas where chlorinated water is not available and where hygiene and sanitation are poor, travelers should be advised that only the following may be safe to drink:
- beverages such as tea and coffee, made with boiled water
- canned or bottled carbonated beverages, including carbonated bottled water and soft drinks
- beer and wine.

Where water is contaminated, ice also must be considered contaminated. It should also be emphasized that under these circumstances ice may contaminate containers used for drinking unless the containers have been thoroughly cleaned with soap and hot water after ice has been discarded. Water or ice on the outside of cans or bottles of beverages might be contaminated. Wet cans or bottles should be dried before being opened, and surfaces which are contacted directly by the mouth in drinking should first be wiped clean.

If no other source of safe drinking

HEALTH INFORMATION FOR INTERNATIONAL TRAVEL

Abbreviated Summary of Vaccinations Required by the Country and Information on Malaria Risk

Country	Vaccinations required by the country			Malaria risk
	Cholera	Yellow fever	Small-pox	
Afghanistan	None	II	II*	Yes*
Albania	II	II	I*	No
Algeria	None	II	III	Yes*
American Samoa	None	III	III	No
Angola	II	II	I	Yes*
Antigua	None	II	III*	No
Argentina	None	None	III	Yes*
Australia	None	II*	III	No
Austria	None	None	III	No
Azores	None	II*	II	No
Bahamas	None	II	III	No
Bahrain	None	II	III	Yes*
Bangladesh	None	II	I	Yes*
Barbados	None	II	III	No
Belgium	None	None	III	No
Belize	None	II	I	Yes*
Benin	None	I*	I*	Yes*
Bermuda	None	None	III	No
Bolivia	None	None	I	Yes*
Botswana	None	II	I	Yes*
Brazil	None	II*	I	Yes*
Brunei	II	II	I	No
Bulgaria	None	None	III	No
Burma	*	II*	III	Yes*
Burundi	None	II	I	Yes*
Cameroon	None	I*	I	Yes*
Canada	None	None	III	No
Canal Zone	None	None	III	No
Canary Islands	None	None	III	No
Cape Verde	II	II*	II*	Yes*
Cayman Islands	None	None	I*	No
Central African Empire	None	I	I	Yes*
Chad	None	II	I	Yes*
Chile	None	None	II	No
China, People's Republic of	II*	II*	I	?
China, Republic of (Taiwan)	II	II	II	No
Christmas Island	None	II*	III	No
Colombia	None	None	II	Yes*
Comoros	None	None	I	Yes*
Congo	None	I*	I	Yes*
Cook Islands	None	None	III	No
Costa Rica	None	None	II*	Yes*
Cuba	None	II*	III*	No
Czechoslovakia	None	None	III*	No
Democratic Kampuchea	None	II	I	Yes*
Denmark	None	None	III	No
Djibouti, Republic of	None	II	I	Yes
Dominica	None	II	III	No
Dominican Republic	None	None	III	Yes*
East Timor	None	I*	I	Yes*
Ecuador	None	II	II	Yes*
Egypt	II	II*	I	Yes*

EXPLANATION OF CODES
I   Vaccination certificate required of travelers arriving from ALL COUNTRIES.
II   Vaccination certificate required of travelers arriving from INFECTED AREAS.
III Vaccination certificate required of travelers arriving from a COUNTRY ANY PART OF WHICH IS INFECTED.
* Refer to U.S. Public Health Service booklet "Health Information for International Travel" (HEW Publication No. (CDC) 78-8280, Atlanta, GA 30333) for specific requirements and risks.
? = Information not available

water is available, tap water that is uncomfortably hot to the touch is usually safe, and after being allowed to cool at room temperature in a clean container can be used for brushing teeth as well as for drinking.

Water of uncertain purity may be made safe for drinking by the use of either chemicals or heat. If water is cloudy or not obtained directly from the tap, strain it through a clean cloth into a container to remove any sediment or floating matter; then treat with chemicals or heat as follows:

Chemicals (laundry bleach or tincture of iodine). Liquid chlorine laundry bleach can be purchased at grocery stores. Read the label to find the percentage of available chlorine and follow the directions in the table below. Liquid chlorine laundry bleach usually has 4 percent to 6 percent available chlorine.

Heat. Boil the water vigorously for at least 10 minutes. Allow to cool at room temperature. Do not add ice. Adding a pinch of salt to each quart of water and pouring the water from one clean container to another several times will improve the taste.

Food: Food should be selected with care to avoid illness. In areas of the world where hygiene and sanitation are poor, the traveler is advised to avoid unpastuerized milk and milk products, such as cheese, and to eat only what can be peeled or has been cooked and is still hot.

Prevention and treatment of diarrhea: The measures mentioned above under water and food are particularly helpful in preventing most serious intestinal infections. Unfortunately, even when people follow these general guidelines, they may still get diarrhea. If diarrhea occurs, drugs should be avoided, unless prescribed by a physician. If there is blood and/or mucus in the stool, if fever occurs with shaking chills, or if there is persistent diarrhea with dehydration, a physician should be consulted promptly. Most cases of diarrhea require only simple replacement of fluids and salts lost in diarrheal stools. Fluids that are readily available, such as canned fruit juices, hot tea, or carbonated drinks, may be used. Iced drinks and bottled noncarbonated fluids made from water of uncertain quality should be avoided. Here is a good formula for treating diarrhea.

HEALTH INFORMATION FOR INTERNATIONAL TRAVEL

Abbreviated Summary of Vaccinations Required by the Country and Information on Malaria Risk

Country	Cholera	Yellow fever	Small-pox	Malaria risk
El Salvador	None	II	III	Yes*
Equatorial Guinea	None	II	I	Yes*
Ethiopia	None	I	I	Yes*
Falkland (Malvinas) Islands	None	None	III	No
Faroe Islands	None	None	III	No
Fiji	II	II*	III*	No
Finland	None	None	III	No
France	None	None	III	No
French Guiana	None	I*	III	Yes*
French Polynesia (Tahiti)	None	II	III	No
Gabon	None	I*	III	Yes*
Gambia	None	II	III	Yes*
German Democratic Republic (East)	None	None	II*	No
Germany, Federal Republic of (West)	None	None	II*	No
Ghana	None	I	II	Yes*
Gibraltar	None	None	III	No
Gilbert Islands	None	II	III	No
Greece	None	II	III	No
Greenland	None	None	III	No
Grenada	None	None	I*	No
Guadeloupe	None	II	III	No
Guam	None	None	III	No
Guatemala	None	None	III	Yes*
Guernsey, Alderney, and Sark	None	None	III	No
Guinea	None	II	I	Yes*
Guinea-Bissau	None	I*	III	Yes*
Guyana	None	II*	II*	Yes*
Haiti	None	II	I*	Yes*
Honduras	None	II	III	Yes*
Hong Kong	None	None	III	No
Hungary	None	None	III	No
Iceland	None	None	I*	No
India	*	III*	III	Yes*
Indonesia	None	II	I	Yes*
Iran	II*	II*	I	Yes*
Iraq	II	II	I	Yes*
Ireland	None	None	III	No
Isle of Man	None	None	III	No
Israel	None	None	III*	No
Italy	None	None	II*	No
Ivory Coast	None	I	I	Yes*
Jamaica	None	II	II*	No
Japan	None	None	II*	No
Jersey	None	None	III	No
Jordan	None*	None*	III*	Yes*
Kenya	None	II*	I	Yes*
Korea, Republic of (South)	None	None	I	Yes*
Kuwait	None	II	I	No
Lao People's Democratic Republic	II	II	I	Yes*
Lebanon	None	II*	II	No
Lesotho	None	II	I	No

EXPLANATION OF CODES

  I   Vaccination certificate required of travelers arriving from ALL COUNTRIES.
 II   Vaccination certificate required of travelers arriving from INFECTED AREAS.
III   Vaccination certificate required of travelers arriving from a COUNTRY ANY PART OF WHICH IS INFECTED.
  * Refer to U.S. Public Health Service booklet "Health Information for International Travel" (HEW Publication No. (CDC) 78-8280, Atlanta, GA 30333) for specific requirements and risks.
  ? = Information not available

HEALTH INFORMATION FOR INTERNATIONAL TRAVEL

Abbreviated Summary of Vaccinations Required by the Country and Information on Malaria Risk

Country	Vaccinations required by the country			Malaria risk
	Cholera	Yellow fever	Small-pox	
Liberia	None	I	III	Yes*
Libyan Arab Jamahiriya	II	II	I	Yes*
Liechtenstein	None	None	III	No
Luxembourg	None	None	II	No
Macao	None	None	III	No
Madagascar	II	II	I	Yes*
Madeira	None	II*	II	No
Malawi	I	II	III	Yes*
Malaysia	None	II*	III	Yes*
Maldives	I	II	I	Yes*
Mali	II	I*	I	Yes*
Malta	None	II*	I*	No
Martinique	None	II	III	No
Mauritania	None	I*	I	Yes*
Mauritius	None	II*	III	No
Mexico	None	II	III	Yes*
Monaco	None	None	III	No
Mongolia	None	None	I	No
Montserrat	None	II	III	No
Morocco	None	None	III	Yes*
Mozambique	I	II	I	Yes*
Namibia	None	II*	I	Yes*
Nauru	II	II	III	No
Nepal	None	II	I	Yes*
Netherlands	None	None	III	No
Netherlands Antilles	None	II	III	No
New Caledonia and dependencies	None	II	III	No
New Hebrides	None	II	III	Yes*
New Zealand	None	None	III	No
Nicaragua	None	None	I	Yes*
Niger	None	I*	I	Yes*
Nigeria	*	I	I	Yes*
Niue	None	None	III	No
Norway	None	None	III	No
Oman	*	II	I*	Yes*
Pacific Islands, Trust Territory (USA)	None	None	III	No
Pakistan	II	II*	III	Yes*
Panama	II	None	II*	Yes*
Papua New Guinea	I*	II	I*	Yes*
Paraguay	None	II	III	Yes*
Peru	None	II	III	Yes*
Philippines	None	II*	I	Yes*
Pitcairn Island	II	II*	III*	No
Poland	None	None	III*	No
Portugal	None	II*	II	No
Puerto Rico	None	None	III	No
Qatar	II	II	I	Yes*
Reunion	None	II	III	No
Rhodesia	None	II	I	Yes*
Romania	None	None	I*	No
Rwanda	None	II	III	Yes*

EXPLANATION OF CODES
I   Vaccination certificate required of travelers arriving from ALL COUNTRIES.
II Vaccination certificate required of travelers arriving from INFECTED AREAS.
III Vaccination certificate required of travelers arriving from a COUNTRY ANY PART OF WHICH IS INFECTED.
* Refer to U.S. Public Health Service booklet "Health Information for International Travel" (HEW Publication No. (CDC) 78-8280, Atlanta, GA 30333) for specific requirements and risks.
? = Information not available

Prepare two separate glasses of the following:

Glass number 1
Orange, apple or
  other fruit juice . . . . 8 ounces
Honey or corn syrup . ½ teaspoon
Salt, table . . . . 1 pinch

Glass number 2
Water (carbonated
  or boiled) . . . . 8 ounces
Baking soda . . . . ¼ teaspoon

Drink alternately from each glass. Supplement with carbonated beverages or water and tea made with boiled or carbonated water as desired. Avoid solid foods and milk until recovery occurs. It is important that infants continue breast-feeding and receive plain water as desired while receiving these salt solutions. One commercial source of an oral anti-diarrhea preparation (glucose electrolyte) is available at this writing. It is called Stop Trot and is manufactured by Andwira, Inc., San Pedro, California 90732.

Swimming: Swimming in contaminated water may result in eye, ear and certain intestinal infections, particularly if the swimmer's head is submerged. Generally only chlorinated pools can be considered totally safe places to swim.

Insects: Insect bites are not only a source of discomfort but are also the method by which many infectious diseases are transmitted. Insect repellents, protective clothing and mosquito netting may be advisable in many parts of the world.

Health problems for pregnant women: Pregnant women might encounter basically the same problems as others during international travel. These have to do with exposure to infectious diseases and availability of good medical care. There is, however, the additional problem that air travel late in pregnancy might induce labor.

A pregnant woman should always check with her physician regarding vaccination. Because of the possible risk to the developing fetus, live, attenuated virus vaccines are not generally given to pregnant women.

Diseases to watch out for

Malaria: Although it has been eradicated in the United States, in

HEALTH INFORMATION FOR INTERNATIONAL TRAVEL
Abbreviated Summary of Vaccinations Required by the Country and Information on Malaria Risk

Country	Vaccinations required by the country			Malaria risk
	Cholera	Yellow fever	Small-pox	
Ryukyu Islands (Okinawa)	II*	II*	I*	No
Saint Helena	II	None	III	No
Saint Kitts-Nevis-Anguilla	None	II	III	No
Saint Lucia	None	II*	III	No
Saint Pierre and Miquelon	None	None	III	No
Saint Vincent	None	None	I*	No
Samoa	None	II	III	No
Sao Tome and Principe	None	I*	I	Yes*
Saudi Arabia	*	*	*	Yes*
Senegal	None	I*	III	Yes*
Seychelles	II	II	I	No
Sierra Leone	None	I	I	Yes*
Singapore	None	II	III	Yes*
Solomon Islands	None	II*	III	Yes*
Somalia	None	II	II*	Yes*
South Africa	None	II*	I	Yes*
Spain	None	None	III	No
Spanish Sahara	None	None	III	No
Sri Lanka	None	II	I	Yes*
Sudan	None	I	I	Yes*
Surinam	None	II	III	Yes*
Swaziland	II	II	III	Yes*
Sweden	None	None	III	No
Switzerland	None	None	III	No
Syrian Arab Republic	None	II	I	Yes*
Tanzania, United Republic of	None	II*	III	Yes*
Thailand	None	II	III	Yes*
Togo	None	I	I	Yes*
Tongo	None	II	III	No
Trinidad and Tobago	None	III	III	No
Tunisia	None	II	III	Yes*
Turkey	None	None	III	Yes*
Tuvalu	None	II	III	No
Uganda	None	I	I	Yes*
Union of Soviet Socialist Republics	None	None	III	No
United Arab Emirates	None	II	I	Yes*
United Kingdom	None	None	III	No
United States of America	None	None	None	No
Upper Volta	None	I	I	Yes*
Uruguay	None	None	II	No
Venezuela	None	None	II*	Yes*
Viet Nam	None	II*	I	Yes*
Virgin Islands (British)	None	None	III	No
Virgin Islands (USA)	None	None	III	No
Wake Island	None	None	III	No
Yemen	II	II	III	Yes*
Yemen, Democratic	None	II	III	Yes*
Yugoslavia	None	None	III	No
Zaire	None	II*	I	Yes
Zambia	II	II	III	Yes*

EXPLANATION OF CODES
I   Vaccination certificate required of travelers arriving from ALL COUNTRIES.
II Vaccination certificate required of travelers arriving from INFECTED AREAS.
III Vaccination certificate required of travelers arriving from a COUNTRY ANY PART OF WHICH IS INFECTED.
* Refer to U.S. Public Health Service booklet "Health Information for International Travel" (HEW Publication No. (CDC) 78-8280, Atlanta, GA 80333) for specific requirements and risks.
? = Information not available

many parts of the world more people suffer from malaria than from any other infectious disease. The disease is spread from human to human by the bites of female anopheles mosquitoes. If a female anopheles bites someone with malaria, the blood she sucks will contain malaria parasites. Within her body some of these parasites may develop over a two-week period. After this time, if she bites a well person, she will inject infective parasites into his blood. Some 10 to 14 days later, symptoms of malaria appear. These include a cycle of fever and chills, accompanied by headache, loss of appetite, nausea and vomiting.

There are two ways to combat malaria: by killing parasites in the blood of infected persons, and by killing mosquitoes that transmit the disease. For persons residing in areas where malaria is widespread, there are a number of drugs that will prevent illness following infection by most malaria parasites.

All travelers to areas where malaria transmission occurs should use prophylactic drugs. Well before departure they should obtain information from their state or local health department as to what areas on their itinerary may be malarious. If any are, they should see their physician and follow his recommendations on drugs to suppress or prevent the disease. When abroad they should also protect themselves from all kinds of biting insects as well as mosquitoes.

Any person who has been in an area where malaria is prevalent and later develops an illness with chills and fever should immediately call his physician and tell the physician where he has traveled. Physicians will notify appropriate public health officials of suspected or confirmed cases of malaria.

Typhoid fever: This infectious disease is caused by the typhoid bacillus (*Salmonella typhosa*). Typhoid victims or carriers discharge the organisms through their feces and, rarely, in their urine. If others consume water, milk or food that has become contaminated with these discharges, they may contract the disease.

Symptoms usually begin to appear one to three weeks after a person has ingested the organism, depending on the size of the infecting dose. The victim begins to feel tired and out of

TREATMENT OF WATER WITH CHLORINE

Available chlorine	Drops* to be added per quart or liter	
	Clean water	Cloudy water
1%	10	20
4% to 6%	2	4
7% to 10%	1	2
Unknown	10	20

* 1 drop = 0.05 ml

Mix thoroughly by stirring or shaking water in container. Let stand for 30 minutes. A slight chlorine odor should be detectable in the water; if not, repeat the dosage and let stand for an additional 15 minutes before using. Water is safe to use.

TREATMENT OF WATER WITH TINCTURE OF IODINE

Tincture of iodine	Drops* to be added per quart or liter	
	Clean water	Cloudy water
2%	5	10

* 1 drop = 0.05 ml

Let stand for 30 minutes. Water is safe to use.

sorts, with some fever and a headache, loss of appetite, and perhaps a cough. During the next ten days or so, the fever continues to rise, and the victim may suffer chills and a severe headache, and also feel weak and confused. Sometimes rose-colored spots appear on the trunk. Constipation is more common than diarrhea. As the fever subsides, the victim starts to feel better and to regain his appetite; but a weak feeling is apt to remain for some time.

The diagnosis of typhoid can usually be confirmed by laboratory tests during the first week after symptoms appear. If typhoid bacilli are present, antibiotics can then be started, shortening the spell of high fever and other severe symptoms. Hospital care is advisable for acutely ill patients and for carriers being treated intravenously with antibiotics.

Some people who have recovered from typhoid fever—and a few who have picked up typhoid bacilli but have never developed the disease—become typhoid carriers. People who know they are typhoid carriers should cooperate with public health officials to prevent others from becoming infected.

The spread of typhoid fever can be controlled through good community and home health practices. Unpasteurized milk and milk products can carry typhoid fever germs; shellfish that are taken from contaminated water may harbor typhoid germs; flies can carry typhoid bacilli and other disease organisms.

Because typhoid fever is only rarely contracted in the United States, people may forget that they can catch it when vacationing or traveling in other countries. In certain countries where hygiene and sanitation are poor, it is wise for the traveler to drink only beverages made from boiled water, canned or bottled carbonated beverages and usually beer and wine. Tap water that is uncomfortably hot to the touch is usually safe because it has been maintained at a high temperature for a sufficient length of time to be pasteurized. Ordinary liquid chlorine bleach or tincture of iodine can be used for purifying water (see above for directions).

Where water is contaminated, ice must also be considered contaminated, and it may contaminate containers used for drinking, even if the ice is discarded. In areas where this condition exists, the traveler should limit his cold drinks to those that can be chilled in the bottle or can.

Food is usually safe in large hotels and restaurants frequented by American travelers. Where hygiene and sanitation are poor, the traveler should eat only what can be peeled or has been cooked and kept hot.

Vaccination is advised for all travelers except infants under six months of age going to areas where typhoid fever is prevalent. The vaccine is given in two inoculations at least four weeks apart. If a person is continuously or repeatedly exposed, he should get a booster dose every three years. It is never necessary to repeat the original series of vaccinations.

If you need further information about typhoid fever, ask your local health officer or physician. If you become ill shortly after returning from foreign travel, consult your physician and inform him of your recent travel.

Yellow fever: This acute infectious disease is of short duration and varying severity. The mildest cases are characterized by sudden onset, fever, headache, backache, prostration, nausea and vomiting. As the disease progresses, the pulse slows and weakens, though the temperature may be elevated; liver and kidney failure may occur. Common hemorrhagic symptoms can occur. Jaundice is moderate early in the disease, but intensifies later.

Except for a few cases in Trinidad, W.I., in 1954, no urban outbreak of yellow fever has been transmitted in the Americas since 1942. Urban yellow fever outbreaks are still reported from Africa in areas contiguous to rain forest regions.

In urban and certain rural areas, the disease is transmitted by the bite of the infective *Aëdes aegypti* mosquito. In the forests of South America it is transmitted by the bite of several species of forest mosquitoes.

The incubation period is from three to six days.

The blood of patients is infective for mosquitoes shortly before onset of fever and for the first three to five days of illness. It is not communicable by contact.

Recovery from yellow fever is followed by lasting immunity; second attacks are unknown.

Preventive measures include vaccination for all persons who are going into areas where yellow fever does exist. Protective clothing, bed nets and repellents are advised for persons not immunized.

The International Certificate of Vaccination is valid, beginning 10 days after date of vaccination, for 10 years; if revaccinated within that period, for 10 years from date of revaccination.

Cholera: An acute intestinal disease, cholera is characterized by sudden onset, profuse watery stools, vomiting, rapid dehydration, and circulatory collapse. Death may occur within a few hours of onset. Fatality rates in untreated cases may exceed 50 percent; with proper treatment they are below 1 percent. Mild cases with only diarrhea are common, especially

91

in children.

The diagnosis is confirmed by culturing cholera vibrios from feces or vomit.

The transmission of the disease occurs through ingestion of water contaminated with feces or vomitus of patients and, to a lesser extent, feces of carriers, and food contaminated by water, soiled hands, or flies. Spreading from person to person by direct contact is rare.

The incubation period is from a few hours to five days, but usually two to three days.

There are a number of preventive measures: sanitary disposal of human feces, together with ready availability and use of hand-washing facilities; protection and purification of water supplies; boiling of milk or pasteurization of milk and dairy products; sanitary supervision of processing, preparation and serving of foods, especially those eaten moist and/or raw, and special attention to provision and use of hand-washing facilities by food handlers; destruction of flies, control of fly breeding, and screening to protect foods from fly contamination; education of the public in personal hygiene, especially thorough hand-washing before eating and after using the bathroom.

Hospitalization is desirable for patients experiencing acute symptoms, but strict isolation is not necessary.

Medical treatment includes prompt fluid therapy using adequate volumes of electrolyte solutions to correct dehydration and other symptoms. Some persons may go into shock.

Evidence of immunization is no longer recommended by the World Health Organization as a requirement for travel from country to country in any part of the world and is not required by the United States, although some individual countries may continue to require vaccinations. Travelers may be required to submit to a stool examination when they have come from an infected area within the incubation period of cholera.

Smallpox: The onset of this systemic viral disease is sudden, with fever, malaise, headache, severe backache, prostration and occasionally abdominal pain. Temperature falls and a deep-seated rash appears. The rash passes through successive stages and finally develops into scabs, which fall off at the end of the third or fourth week of the illness, and fever frequently intensifies in the later stages.

The last reported case of smallpox occurred in Somalia on October 26, 1977. With the demise of smallpox, international travelers do not have biological reasons for being vaccinated. It is indicated only for travelers to countries which require vaccination as a condition for entry, primarily those in Africa, Asia, and Central and South America and for the few laboratory workers who are likely to have contact with the smallpox virus. The United States no longer requires smallpox vaccination for any arriving international traveler.

30

LUNG DISEASES

The respiratory system, our breathing lifeline, may be temporarily congested by a cold, influenza or other infection. It may also become permanently clogged due to damage to the delicate tissues of the lungs by chronic diseases such as emphysema and bronchitis. A sudden, unexpected condition such as pulmonary edema or pulmonary embolism can also strike the lungs. All diseases of the lungs require immediate medical attention.

CHRONIC LUNG DISEASES

In the normal lung, the breathing passageways remain open for air traffic, and breathing is effortless. Healthy lung tissue is elastic and spongy, and the resilient alveoli—the tiny air sacs at the ends of the bronchioles in the lungs—suck in and expel air as a sponge does water. When the flow of air is blocked by an obstruction in the bronchial tree, trouble develops. A chronic lung disease is often the cause. The principal ones are emphysema and chronic bronchitis. Generally, these diseases develop so slowly that many victims are unaware of their problem until 50 percent or more of their lung function is destroyed. For this reason, early detection is essential.

Emphysema

Emphysema is a disease in which the thin walls of the air sacs, the alveoli, lose their elasticity, distend and then may tear. Groups of ruptured air sacs combine to form larger sacs, which trap stale or used air so that the lungs remain partially inflated all the time with air containing less than normal quantities of oxygen. The victim's greatest problem is to expel stale air so that he can inhale an adequate supply of fresh air. Gradually carbon dioxide accumulates. As a result, breathing becomes progressively more difficult, and death may follow from heart failure or suffocation.

The cause of emphysema is not known, although there is proof that tobacco smoking is related to it. Continued exposure to pollutants in the air, chest colds, influenza, asthma, bronchitis and other respiratory infections and ailments also contribute to the development and progress of the disease.

Signs/symptoms: Early symptoms include shortness of breath, persistent coughing and persistent fatigue.

Chronic bronchitis

Chronic bronchitis is characterized by inflammation and swelling of the linings of the bronchial airways and excessive production of mucus and other fluids that tend to block the airways, leading to irritative coughing and shortness of breath. As in emphysema, the principal known factors contributing to chronic bronchitis are smoking, air pollution and recurrent respiratory infections. The diseases frequently occur together.

Signs/symptoms: The onset of chronic bronchitis may be slow. Early symptoms, often shrugged off as "smoker's cough" or a "winter cold," include shortness of breath, persistent coughing and fatigue. By the time the condition is diagnosed, delicate lung tissue may be already irreversibly damaged.

Prevention of chronic lung diseases

See your doctor immediately if you have a persistent or recurring cough, a feeling of tightness or pain in the chest, shortness of breath, and a general weakness or tendency to tire easily. Avoid smoking and contact with other air pollutants.

Treatment of chronic lung diseases

A smoker must give up tobacco smoking. Other irritants, such as air pollutants and respiratory infections, should be avoided as far as possible. If infections do occur, they should be treated immediately.

A physician will often prescribe drugs to make breathing easier.

PULMONARY EMERGENCIES

Edema

Pulmonary edema is an emergency in which an abnormal amount of fluid fills the lungs.

Signs/symptoms: Some symptoms are an acute shortness of breath, frothing at the mouth, blue lips and blue fingertips, anxiety, and shock.

First-aid treatment

If shock develops, treat it immediately (see page 21). Secure oxygen for a victim who has difficulty breathing. Have the victim sit up rather than lie down, and take him immediately to a physician or hospital emergency room.

Embolism

A pulmonary embolism is the obstruction of a blood vessel in the lung by a blood clot that originated elsewhere in the circulatory system, such as in the leg, and migrated to a blood vessel in the lung.

Signs/symptoms: Some symptoms are rapid heartbeat and pulse, pain in the chest, acute shock, and sometimes bloody expectoration.

First-aid treatment

Treat a patient for shock if it develops (see page 21); secure oxygen for a patient who has trouble breathing; and get the patient to a physician or hospital emergency room immediately.

ASTHMA

Asthma is a noncontagious disease of the lungs. Nearly nine million Americans, young and old, are asthmatics. The repeated attacks of forced breathing they suffer may cause permanent damage to air passageways. With proper medical treatment, however, most asthmatics can live active lives.

Causes

The reasons for asthma include outside factors such as allergens, infection, climate and occupation. Emotional stress often can be a secondary factor.

Signs/symptoms: During an asthma attack the victim struggles to get air into and out of his lungs through the bronchial airways. The mucous lining of the bronchi becomes swollen with fluids; mucus blocks the small tubes; and spastic contractions of smooth muscles in the larger bronchi practically close down the passageways of the small bronchi called bronchioles. The result is a closing of the bronchial tubes, which traps the stale air in the alveoli and prevents fresh air from getting in. Breathing out becomes increasingly difficult. Forced breathing becomes necessary, and the rush of air through the narrowed passageways gives the wheezing sounds that are typical of an asthma patient.

First-aid treatment

In the long term the best treatment for asthma is to find out its causes and avoid them. Drugs are sometimes necessary to relieve asthmatic symptoms, including muscular spasms, swelling and mucus in bronchial tubes. The asthmatic who suffers an acute attack can gain relief from an injection of epinephrine (adrenalin), which is administered by a doctor. He may sometimes require hospitalization. Drugs can relieve symptoms, but they cannot cure asthma. Drugs should always be used under a physician's careful supervision.

If an asthmatic has an acute attack and cannot reach his physician or hospital emergency room, quiet the patient, loosen his collar and have him sit down. Removing any known offending allergies also helps. If victim has his medication with him—antihistamine tablets or cortisone—have him take it, or if he has an inhaler have him use it to ease his breathing. Try to secure oxygen also to ease breathing. If shock develops, treat it immediately (see page 21). Get victim to a physician or hospital as soon as possible.

TUBERCULOSIS

Tuberculosis (TB) is caused by a germ called the tubercle bacillus and affects mainly the lungs. When tubercle bacilli begin to multiply and spread, the body sets up a defense. Usually the defense is sufficient to stop the growth of the germs, and further progression of the disease is halted for the rest of the person's life. This is possible because the germ will hibernate without ever causing disease, and the damage done seldom has any effect on the person's well-being.

Signs/symptoms: Symptoms of TB in the early stages are mild and seldom noticed. This may result in postponing early detection and treatment. The early signs to look for are loss of weight, loss of strength and pep, irregular appetite and low-grade fever. As the disease progresses, a cough with thick mucus brought up from the lungs or blood-streaked sputum may develop. Sometimes, however, there are no symptoms.

Detection

A simple skin test called the Mantoux Tuberculin Test can show whether or not a person has been infected. If he has, the next step is for him to have a chest X ray. The chest X ray will reveal whether there is a disease in the lungs and show the general stage of the disease if present. If something is found on the X ray, a sputum sample is taken and examined in the laboratory to see if TB germs are present. Tuberculosis can develop in any part of the body, so other tests or specimens may also be needed.

First-aid treatment

TB is cured by chemotherapy, which is treatment with special antituberculosis drugs. Early diagnosis is essential.

Because tuberculosis is communicable, family members and others in close association with victims of the disease should be examined periodically.

93

31

MENINGITIS

Meningitis is an inflammation of the membranes (the meninges) covering the brain and spinal cord. Several distinct bacteria or viruses cause the disease. They enter the body through the nose and mouth, but just how they reach the central nervous system is not always clear. Droplets sprayed into the air by sneezing and coughing or direct contact spread the bacteria from person to person.

The fact that there are different types of meningococcal bacteria constitutes a serious problem for physicians and laboratory scientists who are attempting to develop better methods for preventing or treating the disease. Another problem in meningitis control is the ability of the meningococcus to be present in the body without causing illness. The disease most often strikes children, although adults too suffer from it.

Signs/symptoms

Meningitis usually begins suddenly with high fever; severe headache; and stiffness and pain in the neck, back and shoulders. Often nausea and vomiting are present. A skin rash of tiny bright-red spots frequently appears, and sometimes the rash resembles bruises.

If a physician suspects meningitis, he will examine the patient's spinal fluid, obtained by a procedure known as a spinal tap.

First-aid treatment

Prompt treatment of meningococcal meningitis is important. A doctor will usually give penicillin, and he may prescribe other antibiotics. With early treatment, most patients recover quickly.

32

POISONING

Poisoning can occur in different ways: from ingestion, inhaling, injections, skin contact or bites. If you discover a victim of poisoning, immediately call a doctor, hospital emergency room or poison-control center for instructions on how to treat the victim. When calling, give the approximate age of the victim, the suspected poison and amount taken, when the poison was probably taken, any first aid given, and if the victim has vomited. Then give first aid to maintain respiration and to preserve vital functions. Keep the victim warm, but be careful not to overheat him. Do not give any alcoholic or carbonated beverages or any drugs. (If another person is present, have that person do the calling while you take care of the victim.) Transport the patient to a doctor or hospital immediately.

INGESTED POISONS

Always try to locate the container from which the poison came. Bring the container and any vomitus to the doctor or hospital so that the poison can be identified. If you cannot reach a poison-control center, hospital emergency room or doctor, follow the instructions below.

Note. Antidotes listed on product labels are not always accurate; it is better to get help from a poison-control center.

If the victim is unconscious, is having convulsions, experiences a burning sensation in mouth or throat or has swallowed an acid, alkali or petroleum product (see the list on page 95), do not induce vomiting. Do not give any fluids. Administer artificial respiration and cardiopulmonary resuscitation (CPR) if necessary (see pages 17–19).

If the poison is known and is not an acid, alkali or petroleum product

If the poison is not an acid (bleach, toilet bowl cleaner, sulfuric acid, etc.), an alkali (lye, drain cleaner, etc.), or a petroleum product (gasoline, kerosene, benzene, lighter fluid, furniture polish, etc.), and *is* a noncorrosive substance (see list below), give water—three or four glasses for an adult and one or two glasses for a child. The poison-control center, hospital emergency room or doctor may tell you to induce vomiting. If so, give the victim syrup of ipecac. Give a child under a year two teaspoonfuls, give a child a year or older one tablespoonful (½ ounce), and give an adult two tablespoonfuls. Afterwards, give one cup of water. If the victim does not vomit in 20 minutes, repeat the dose.

Note. Never give activated charcoal along with syrup of ipecac.

If vomiting still does not occur, or if you do not have syrup of ipecac on hand, give water and then try to make person vomit by tickling back of throat with spoon or blunt object, or by placing finger down throat.

When the victim begins to vomit, keep his head down and turned sideways to prevent him from choking. Save a sample of the vomitus for the doctor.

The poison-control center or the doctor may tell you to give activated charcoal *after* vomiting occurs. Do not give unless a doctor recommends it, however.

The following common sources of poisoning are noncorrosive substances, for which vomiting should be induced if a poison-control center or doctor so recommends:

acetone
after-shave lotion
alcohol
antifreeze
arsenic
benzene
boric acid
bubble bath
camphor
carbon tetrachloride
cologne
cosmetics
cough medicine
DDT
deodorant
detergent
fabric softener
fingernail polish
    and remover
fluoride
hand and skin lotions
hair dye
hydrogen peroxide
ink
insecticides
iodine
mothballs, flakes
    and cakes
paint (lead)
perfume
pesticides

rat or mouse poison
roach poison
shampoo
sleeping pills
strychnine
suntan lotion
tranquilizers
turpentine
weed killer

If poison is an acid, alkali or petroleum product

The following common sources of poisoning are acids, alkalis or petroleum products, for which vomiting should *not* be induced:

battery acid
bleach
charcoal lighter
cleaning fluid
corn remover
dishwasher granules
drain cleaner
gasoline
grease remover
household ammonia
household cleaner
kerosene
lacquer thinner
laundry bleach
lye
metal cleaner
naphtha
oven cleaner
paint (liquid)
paint thinner
shoe polish
toilet bowl cleaner
typewriter cleaner
wax (floor or furniture)
wood preservative
zinc compounds

You can usually recognize acid or alkali poisoning by burns around the victim's mouth or lips, burning pain in his mouth or throat, cramplike or burning pain of the stomach, mental confusion and possibly shock. Petroleum poisoning symptoms include a burning irritation, coughing and possibly shock.

This type of poisoning should be treated by diluting and neutralizing the poison and not by inducing vomiting. If the victim is conscious and not having convulsions, give an adult one or two glasses of milk or water and a child under five years one glass. Always wash any acid off the skin with plenty of water. Remove contaminat-ed clothing. Treat any burns (see pages 38–40).

Get the victim to a hospital or doctor as quickly as possible. During transportation, keep victim's airway open. If victim begins to vomit, turn head to side to allow vomitus to drain out. Treat for convulsions (see pages 44–45) and possible shock (see page 21). Start artificial respiration at once if necessary (see pages 17–18). Keep victim warm, but do not overheat him.

INHALED POISONS

Poisonous gases such as carbon monoxide and vapors from volatile liquids like gasoline, turpentine and paints can cause poisoning by inhaling.

Symptoms: The victim will most likely experience irritation in the eyes, nose, throat or lungs. Headache, blurred vision, nausea, dizziness, unconsciousness and convulsions may follow. Death may result.

First-aid treatment

Get the victim away from the poison and into fresh, clean air. Loosen victim's clothing. If the victim is not breathing, begin artificial respiration promptly (see pages 17–18). Have someone else call a physician, hospital or poison-control center regarding treatment. Get victim to a physician or hospital as soon as possible. Also treat for chemical burns (see page 39) if necessary, removing any contaminated clothing and washing the skin with water.

Carbon monoxide

Each year hundreds of people die from carbon monoxide poisoning. Thousands of others suffer dizziness, nausea and convulsions. The major causes of carbon monoxide poisoning are:
● *lack of adequate ventilation in a car,* particularly while the car is in a closed garage with the motor running
● *charcoal grills used inside* a house, camping trailer or a mobile home
● *unvented space heaters,* including gas ranges
● *heating equipment which is in poor repair.*

Remember, when a generous supply of fresh air is available, and the fuel is burning properly, there is little danger of carbon monoxide poisoning.

Prevention of carbon monoxide poisoning: The U.S. Consumer Product Safety Commission offers the following suggestions to avoid carbon monoxide poisoning:
● All home fuel-burning equipment should be inspected yearly.
● All fuel-burning heaters used to warm the house should be vented to the outside. If you must use an unvented heater, be sure to leave a window open at least one inch. Unvented heaters should be turned off at night.
● Do not use a gas range or oven for heating a room.
● Never use a charcoal grill or hibachi inside, unless it is in a well-ventilated fireplace.
● Burning charcoal, whether it is glowing red or turning to gray ashes, gives off large amounts of carbon monoxide. Be sure it is in a well-ventilated area.
● Always leave all garage windows and doors open if you are running an automobile inside the garage. If you have an attached garage, be sure the fumes are not being vented into the house. Avoid running an engine inside for a long period of time.
● Have your car's muffler and tailpipes checked regularly. Carbon monoxide can leak into the car from a faulty exhaust system.
● Open your car windows when the car is stopped for any period of time with the motor running.

POISONOUS PLANTS

A number of plants are poisonous if touched, and others are poisonous if eaten. Learn to recognize poisonous plants (see Fig. 32-1) and to avoid them and any others you are not sure about. Never sample strange plants or their fruits.

Allergic skin reactions

Plants that affect the skin, causing an allergic reaction, include poison ivy, poison oak and poison sumac (see pages 31–32). The sticky sap of all three plants contains an active ingredient known as urushiol. Rubbing or crushing the plant or a leaf provides sufficient contact for an allergic reaction. Exposure can also occur when the plants are being burned, or from clothing or tools or pets that have touched the plants.

Signs/symptoms: The symptoms of the allergy usually develop within 12

95

POISONING

to 48 hours after contact. At first the area which touched the plant becomes red, and then bumps and blisters appear. This is usually accompanied by itching and sometimes by swelling. After reaching their peak in several days, the bumps and blisters begin to crust over and disappear. Extremely sensitive persons exposed to urushiol over large areas of the body may become quite ill.

First-aid treatment

First, make sure the skin and clothes are free of all sap. You can prevent spread of the lesions—the bumps and blisters—by sudsing the skin thoroughly with an alkali soap such as yellow laundry soap, or using 70 percent alcohol, and then washing any clothing that came into contact with the plants. Once the

source of urushiol is eliminated, very mild cases of rash require little or no further care; they usually clear up by themselves. Wet, cold compresses of water, boric acid or liquid aluminum acetate may relieve any inflammation during the oozing period. Calamine lotion is a good drying agent and helps relieve itching. For severe cases involving spreading rashes and swelling, a physician

Plant	Poisonous parts	Symptoms
Azalea	Entire plant	Vomiting, slow pulse, paralysis
Baneberry	Roots and berries	Vomiting, cramps, rapid heartbeat, dizziness
Bittersweet	Leaves and berries	Vomiting, diarrhea, convulsions
Black locust	Leaves, bark, pods, young sprouts	Nausea, weakness, depression
Bloodroot	Stems and roots	Diarrhea, vomiting
Buttercup	Entire plant	Irritant juices may severely injure digestive system, cause nausea and vomiting
Castor bean	Foliage and seeds	Nausea and vomiting, severe cramps; seeds can cause death
Daffodil, narcissus	Bulb	Nausea, vomiting, diarrhea; may be fatal
Daphne	Entire plant, especially berries	Diarrhea and internal bleeding; can be fatal
Dieffenbachia	Entire plant	Intense burning and irritation of mouth and tongue; can be fatal
Elderberry	Roots, stems, berries	Nausea, digestive upset
Foxglove	Leaves	In large doses, irregular heartbeat and pulse, digestive upset, mental confusion; can be fatal
Golden chain	Beanlike capsules in which seeds are suspended	Excitement, staggering, convulsions, coma; can be fatal
Hyacinth	Bulb	Nausea, vomiting, diarrhea; can be fatal
Iris	Leaves and roots	Digestive upset
Ivy	Leaves and black berries	Impaired breathing, coma
Jessamine	Berries	Digestive disturbance and nervous symptoms; can be fatal
Jimsonweed	Entire plant	Abnormal thirst, distorted sight, delirium, incoherence, coma; can be fatal
Lantana	Entire plant, especially berries	Affects lungs, kidneys, heart and nervous system; can be fatal
Larkspur	Young plant, seeds	Digestive upset, nervous excitement, depression; can be fatal
Lilly-of-the-valley	Leaves, flowers, roots	Mental confusion, irregular heartbeat, digestive upset
Mistletoe	Berries	Slow pulse, collapse; can be fatal
Monkshood	Fleshy roots	Digestive upset, nausea, nervous excitement
Moonseed	Berries	Abdominal pain, paralysis; can be fatal
Nightshade	Entire plant, especially berries	Intense disturbance of digestive and nervous systems; can be fatal
Oleander	Entire plant	Affects heart, produces digestive upset; can be fatal
Poison hemlock	Entire plant	Can be fatal
Pokeweed	Entire plant	Respiratory failure; can be fatal
Privet	Leaves and berries	Stomach upset
Rhododendron	Entire plant	Nausea, vomiting, depression, impaired breathing, coma; can be fatal
Rhubarb	Leaves	Stomach pain, nausea
Water hemlock	Entire plant, especially roots	Violent and painful convulsions; can be fatal
Wild cherries	Twigs, foliage	Excitement, prostration; can be fatal
Wisteria	Pods and seeds	Digestive upset
Yew	Entire plant; foliage more toxic than berries	Can be fatal

Note: People taking prescription drugs should avoid herbal teas. Herbal teas are really drugs, not foods, and can cause serious problems. Some herbal teas, such as sassafras tea, are also, in fact, too dangerous to be sold in food stores. Herbal remedies can pose a health risk.

96

YOURSELF

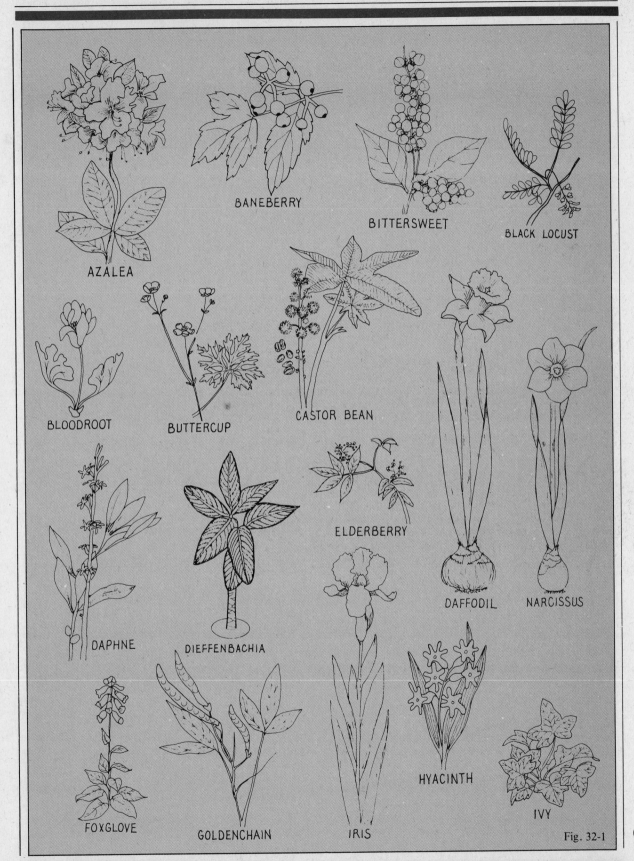

AZALEA

BANEBERRY

BITTERSWEET

BLACK LOCUST

BLOODROOT

BUTTERCUP

CASTOR BEAN

DAFFODIL

NARCISSUS

DAPHNE

DIEFFENBACHIA

ELDERBERRY

FOXGLOVE

GOLDENCHAIN

IRIS

HYACINTH

IVY

Fig. 32-1

97

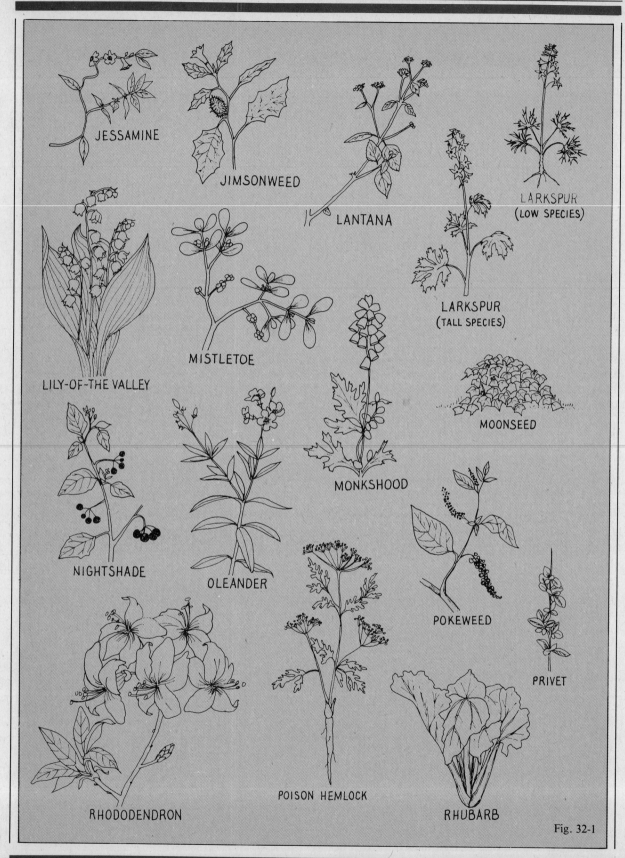

JESSAMINE

JIMSONWEED

LANTANA

LARKSPUR (LOW SPECIES)

LILY-OF-THE VALLEY

MISTLETOE

LARKSPUR (TALL SPECIES)

MOONSEED

MONKSHOOD

NIGHTSHADE

OLEANDER

POKEWEED

PRIVET

RHODODENDRON

POISON HEMLOCK

RHUBARB

Fig. 32-1

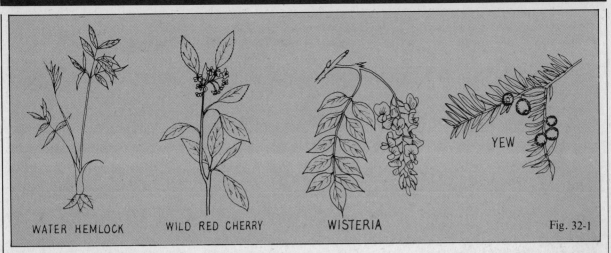

WATER HEMLOCK   WILD RED CHERRY   WISTERIA   YEW   Fig. 32-1

should be consulted immediately. Observe victim's breathing; if necessary give artificial resuscitation (see pages 17–18).

Prevention: The surest way to prevent poison ivy, poison oak and poison sumac is to avoid contact with the plants. Learn to identify these three plants (see drawings on page 32).

Ingestion of poisonous plants and herbs

If the plant or herb is poisonous, or if you think it may be, induce vomiting, using syrup of ipecac (see pages 94–95). Do this *only* if advised to by a poison-control center or doctor. Then take victim to the nearest hospital emergency room or doctor.

POISONOUS BITES

Snakebites

Nonpoisonous snakebites require no emergency treatment. Nonpoisonous snakes do not have fangs and have a double row of plates beneath the tail. But if you are in doubt about whether the snake was poisonous or nonpoisonous, treat the bite as poisonous.

There are four types of poisonous snakes responsible for biting approximately 8,000 people a year in the United States. Three of the snakes are known as pit vipers because of their vertical, elliptical pupils and heat-sensitive pits located between their eyes and nostrils. Pit vipers include rattlesnakes, copperheads, and cottonmouths. The venom of the pit viper affects the circulatory system. The fourth type of poisonous snake is the coral snake. Its venom affects the nervous system.

Treatment for a poisonous snakebite depends upon the type of snake, so it is essential to become familiar with the four types of snakes (see Fig. 32-2). Familiarize yourself in advance of an emergency with the first aid required in case of a poisonous bite.

Pit vipers:
1. *The rattlesnake* has a rattle composed of a series of long, interlocking segments at the end of the tail, which usually sounds a warning.
2. *The copperhead* has a brown to copper-red body marked with darker bands. The southern copperhead is paler and pinker than the northern copperhead. Most copperheads are found in the southeastern part of the United States.
3. *The cottonmouth,* also called a water moccasin, has olive, brown or black above with a lighter belly. The crossbands have dark borders; the centers are often lighter in color. Cottonmouth snakes are found in predominantly swampy areas of the southeast United States.
Signs/symptoms: Pit vipers have fangs that inject venom by puncturing the skin. Severe burning and pain result, with swelling spreading out from the area of the bite. These are often accompanied by nausea and vomiting, respiratory distress, weak pulse, dim vision, and shock.

First-aid treatment

Do not let the victim walk; keep him as quiet as possible. Immobilize the victim with the injured part lower than the rest of the body. Call a physician, hospital, or poison-control center and transport victim to a medical facility quickly. Call ahead so that antivenin, which counteracts venom, will be available. While awaiting transportation and en route, keep the victim warm.

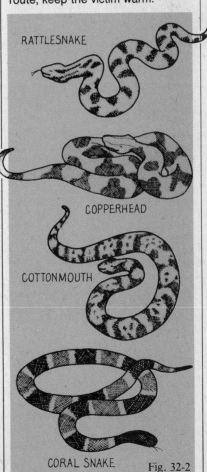

RATTLESNAKE

COPPERHEAD

COTTONMOUTH

CORAL SNAKE   Fig. 32-2

There has been much disagreement over the past few years regarding first aid for a poisonous-snakebite victim. According to one expert, a curator of herpetology at a major zoo, the old recommendations for cutting incisions above the bite, applying a constricting band, and suctioning the wound are of little help and can actually be dangerous. Making an incision can interrupt circulation to areas adjacent to the bite, applying a constricting band or tourniquet can reduce circulation to the area, and suctioning the wound can introduce bacteria into the bite. It can also poison the rescuer if he has cuts or wounds in his mouth. Instead, the best treatment is to get the victim to the hospital as quickly as possible. Most snakebite deaths occur 12 or more hours after the bite, so there is usually time to transport a victim. While awaiting help, do not give the victim any stimulants or alcohol. Watch for signs of shock and treat accordingly (see page 21). Perform artificial respiration if necessary (see pages 17–18).

Coral snakes: Coral snakes are found in the southeastern United States. They are usually brilliantly marked with bands of red, yellow and black encircling the body. They have erect fangs in the front of the upper jaw and teeth behind the fangs. Because of its small mouth and short fangs, the coral snake can usually bite only the fingers or toes of a person.

Signs/symptoms. Tiny puncture wounds which resemble scratch marks; slight burning; nausea or excessive salivation; paralysis of eyeballs; slurring speech; respiratory paralysis; coma and sometimes death.

First-aid treatment

Get victim to a doctor or hospital emergency room. While waiting for help, immobilize the victim.

Insect bites and stings

Hymenoptera (bees, wasps, hornets, yellow jackets, fire ants):
Signs/symptoms. Normal reactions involve pain, redness, swelling, itching, and warmth at the site of the sting. These symptoms last for a few hours and may be severe, but as long as they are confined to the area of the sting, they are considered normal. Toxic reactions usually are the result of multiple stings, which can cause muscle cramps, headache, fever and drowsiness. In severe reactions, the patient may develop a sudden lowering of blood pressure, collapse and have problems resulting from impairment of respiration, heart action and circulation. These reactions may lead to death if not promptly treated.

First-aid treatment

In the event of an insect sting or bite, any stinger (and any attached venom sac for a bee) should be removed. Gently scrape them out with a fingernail or knife; do not squeeze or press them. Then wash the affected area thoroughly. Ice applied to the spot may help lessen the pain and swelling. To relieve the itching and discomfort, apply calamine lotion or a paste made of baking soda and a small amount of water. Aspirin may relieve pain.

For a severe bite or for multiple bites, treat in the same manner as described above, but other medication and other procedures may be necessary. A doctor may prescribe antibiotics to control secondary infections. Apply a constricting band over the area of the bite if on the arm or leg. Do not make it so tight that victim's pulse disappears. Keep affected area lowered. If medical care will not be available quickly, leave the band in place, but remove it after 30 minutes or so. Apply ice to the site of the sting or bite. Observe victim closely to be sure that he does not stop breathing or go into shock. If he does, treat accordingly (see pages 17–19 and page 21).

Warning. Anyone who has a history of severe reactions to an insect sting or bite should take two precautionary steps. He should wear a bracelet or necklace and/or carry an identification card which states that he is allergic to specific insects and needs special treatment. In addition, he should always have an emergency insect-sting treatment kit available. He should be able to identify these insects (see Fig. 32-3).

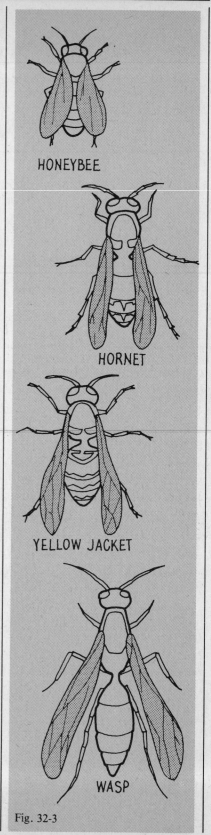

HONEYBEE

HORNET

YELLOW JACKET

WASP

Fig. 32-3

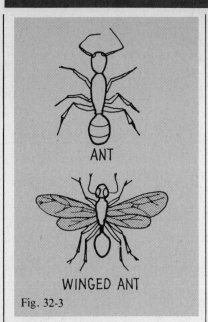

ANT

WINGED ANT

Fig. 32-3

Poisonous spiders

In the United States, most species of spiders are harmless. Two, however, can pose a serious problem: the black widow and the brown recluse, or violin, spider (see Fig. 32-4).

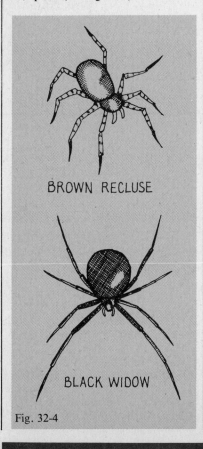

BROWN RECLUSE

BLACK WIDOW

Fig. 32-4

Black widow:

Signs/symptoms. The bite itself causes pain, and the spider injects a nerve toxin that produces swelling, sweating, cramps, nausea, dizziness and shortness of breath.

Brown recluse:

Signs/symptoms. The venom of this spider produces a severe local reaction. A rash may develop in a day or two. In a week or two, the bite may become an open sore that is slow to heal. The victim may experience chills, fever, joint pain, nausea and vomiting.

First-aid treatment for black widow and brown recluse

For a minor bite, use cold such as ice in a cloth, or a lotion such as calamine to relieve any itching or pain.

For a more severe bite, place a constricting band about two inches above the wound. Do not fix the band so tightly that you cannot slip your finger through. Keep the affected part of the body lowered. Remove band if medical help is not available after half an hour. Apply cold such as ice in a cloth. Observe closely to be sure victim is breathing and does not go into shock. If he does, treat accordingly (see pages 17–19 and 21).

Scorpions

The bite of a scorpion can be serious, even fatal, because of the venom injected through a stinger in the tail (see Fig. 32-5).

Signs/symptoms: The sting tingles or burns. Victim becomes dizzy and may feel like vomiting, have abdominal cramps and go into convulsions. Coma and even death may result.

First-aid treatment

Place a constricting band about two inches above the wound. Do not fix the band so tightly that you cannot slip your finger through it. Keep the affected part of the body lowered below the heart. Remove band if medical help is not available after half an hour. Apply cold to bite such as ice in a cloth. Observe closely to be sure victim is breathing and does not go into shock. If he does, use treatment on pages 17–19 and 21.

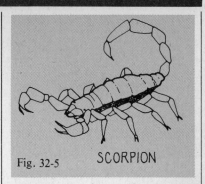

Fig. 32-5   SCORPION

Tarantula

The bite of the tarantula (see Fig. 32-6) can produce a severe local wound and can be fatal. Rare in the United States, tarantulas may appear in food shipped in from South America.

Signs/symptoms: The bite may resemble a small pinprick or it may be a severe wound.

First-aid treatment

Wash wound with soap and water. Cover with a sterile dressing. For severe reactions, get prompt medical help. Place a constricting band about two inches above the wound. Do not fix the band so tightly that you cannot slip your finger through it. Keep the affected part of the body lowered below the heart. Remove band if medical help is not available after half an hour. Apply cold such as ice wrapped in a cloth. Observe closely to be sure victim is breathing and does not go into shock. If he does, treat accordingly (see pages 17–19 and 21).

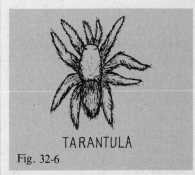

TARANTULA

Fig. 32-6

Tick

Ticks (see Fig. 32-7) feed entirely on blood—usually that of animals, but sometimes that of humans. While most tick bites are not painful and the victim may not even be aware of being

101

bitten, the wounds caused by the bites of some species are severe. Ticks carry spotted fever and a number of other diseases. In areas infested with ticks, it is unwise to sleep or sit on the ground. Clothing should be examined carefully at least once a day and ticks destroyed.

Signs/symptoms: The tick may be visible on skin as a dark area. Tick bites can lead to fever, chills, headache, muscle ache. Rash usually appears after one to three days of fever, usually on wrists and ankles. Later the rash may spread to the rest of the body.

BROWN DOG TICK
Fig. 32-7

First-aid treatment

Cover tick with oil and then detach with a clean tweezers, being careful to remove all parts. Clean the area with soap and water. Wash hands and tweezers with soap and water or rinse with alcohol.

Buy only insecticides and pesticides that come in containers with safety closures and store them safely out of children's reach. Do not spray insecticides and pesticides in areas that children or pets could touch or lick.

Mosquito

Some species carry dangerous diseases like malaria, encephalitis, yellow fever and dengue. The female mosquito (see Fig. 32-8) becomes infected by biting and feeding on the blood of infected animals and people. Under certain circumstances, she can later pass on this infection to other animals and humans.

Signs/symptoms: Itching, irritated skin, small red welts.

First-aid treatment

Wash with soap and water. Use cold compresses or a soothing lotion such as calamine lotion.

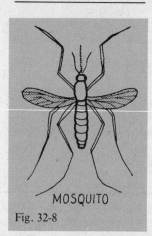

MOSQUITO
Fig. 32-8

POISONOUS MARINE ANIMALS

Certain marine animals can produce puncture wounds, and their stings or bites can result in a toxic reaction that requires emergency medical treatment. In addition, some shellfish are poisonous if eaten.

Stings or bites

Jellyfish and Portuguese man-of-war: Both have stinging cells on their tentacles that release venom (see Fig.32-9).

Signs/symptoms. Burning pain, rash, muscle cramps, nausea, vomiting, respiratory difficulty and possibly collapse.

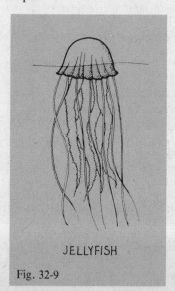

JELLYFISH
Fig. 32-9

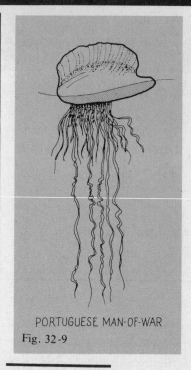

PORTUGUESE MAN-OF-WAR
Fig. 32-9

First-aid treatment

Remove tentacles with clean cloth. Wash wound with alcohol. For severe pain, take aspirin.

Stinging coral: Stinging cells (see Fig. 32-10) produce sharp, contaminated cuts and release venom.

Signs/symptoms. Burning, stinging pain.

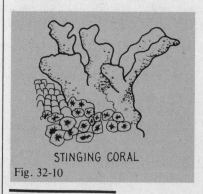

STINGING CORAL
Fig. 32-10

First-aid treatment

Clean with soap and water.

Cone shell: Venom is injected through a puncture wound (see Fig. 32-11).

Signs/symptoms. Numbness and tingling, impaired vision, paralysis, collapse and even death.

CONE SHELL
Fig. 32-11

First-aid treatment

Use a constricting band two inches above wound. Do not bind too tightly. Apply hot compresses for about half an hour and then remove band. Seek medical help.

Stingray: Stingrays can puncture the skin, injecting a toxic venom (see Fig. 32-12).
Signs/symptoms. Pain at site of cut, swelling, vomiting, muscular paralysis, convulsions, respiratory difficulty.

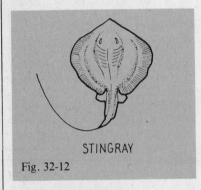
STINGRAY
Fig. 32-12

First-aid treatment

Remove stinger. Wash in hot water. Control bleeding and apply dressing. Apply a constricting band two inches above wound. Soak in hot water again or apply hot compresses for about half an hour. Remove band. If victim develops respiratory difficulty, apply artificial respiration (see pages 17–18).

SEA URCHIN
Fig. 32-13

Sea urchins: Their sharp spines and venom organs contain a nerve poison (see Fig. 32-13).
Signs/symptoms. Pain, muscular paralysis, dizziness.

First-aid treatment

Place constricting band two inches above wound. Soak in hot water or apply hot compresses for about half an hour. Remove band.

Ingestion of poisonous marine animals

Signs/symptoms: Numbness of face and mouth, general weakness, muscular paralysis, thirst, difficulty in swallowing.

First-aid treatment

Follow first aid as for noncorrosive poisoning. Dilute poison with water. Give an adult three or four glasses and a child one or two glasses. Physician may tell you to induce vomiting. If so, give one tablespoon (½ ounce) of syrup of ipecac to a child a year or older plus one cup of water, or two tablespoons for an adult. Follow with water. If victim does not vomit within 20 minutes, give one more dose.

If person has a severe allergic reaction, give him an antihistamine.

ANIMAL AND HUMAN BITES

Dog, cat, bat, skunk, rat and raccoon bites require prompt medical attention because they may be from a rabid animal. Human bites can also cause a serious infection.

Signs/symptoms: Bleeding, open wound, swelling and pain. If the animal was rabid, death can result.

First-aid treatment

Wash wound with soap and water. Flush wound and then control bleeding. Apply a sterile dressing and bandage (see pages 23–25). Consult a physician. If possible, try to catch or retain the animal and maintain alive for observation. Notify police.

Rabies

Rabies is an infectious disease that affects the nervous system, including the brain and spinal cord, of animals and man. Once it develops, it is nearly always fatal.

Cause: The disease is caused by a virus present in the saliva of infected animals, which is generally transmitted through a bite. There have been rare reports of persons developing rabies after "nonbite" exposures, such as from licks by rabid animals, the air in caves infested with rabid bats, and breathing aerosolized rabies virus in the laboratory. While not always the case, it must be assumed that an exposure will lead to death if the patient is not treated.

Occurrence: All the warm-blooded animals, including man, are susceptible to rabies. However, the disease is principally carried by dogs, cats, skunks, foxes, wolves, coyotes and raccoons. Bats also have become increasingly important as natural spreaders of rabies. Rabies is present in all parts of the continental United States. It occurs in animals during any season of the year. Many cases are reported in livestock, including cows, horses, hogs and sheep, which generally contract the disease from the bites of infected wild animals, such as skunks and foxes.

Incubation period: The interval between the moment the virus is introduced into the body and the time it reaches the brain and produces symptoms varies from 10 days to a year or more, the average being about 45 days. Bites on the head and neck are apt to produce symptoms sooner. Rabies in man is suspected if, weeks or months after exposure to the disease, an individual experiences an uneasy feeling, headache, fever, nausea, sore throat, or loss of appetite. Other early symptoms include unusual sensitivity to sound, light, and changes of temperature; muscle stiffness; dilation of pupils; and increased salivation. As the disease progresses, the patient usually experiences episodes of irrational excitement alternating with periods of alert calm. Convulsions are common. Extremely painful throat spasms may result on attempting to swallow. These lead to hydrophobia, or fear of water, which is characteristic of rabies victims. Death usually occurs from cardiac or respiratory failure within a week after symptoms appear.

Prevention: All owners of pets should have them vaccinated against rabies. Although there have been rare reports of recovery from clinical rabies, the disease is almost always fatal. Rabies may be prevented by prompt immunization. Immediate and thorough local treatment of all bite wounds and scratches is perhaps the most effective means of preventing rabies. Wounds produced by the bite of a rabid or possibly rabid animal should be thoroughly cleaned with copious amounts of soap and water. A physician should be consulted immediately. He will then decide on the type of immunization.

Management of biting animals: A healthy domestic dog or cat that bites a person should be captured, confined and observed by a veterinarian for 10 days. Any illness in the animal should be reported immediately to the local health department.

Early signs of rabies in wild or stray animals cannot be interpreted reliably; therefore, any such animal that bites or scratches a person should be killed at once and the brain examined for evidence of rabies. If examination of the brain at a competent laboratory is negative for rabies, the bitten person need not be treated.

LEAD PAINT POISONING

Lead poisoning is a serious crippler and killer of young children. The most common source of lead poisoning is peeling and chipped leaded paint found on the windowsills, doors and walls of older homes. The level of lead in paint sold today cannot exceed 0.06 percent. Some children apparently like to eat nonfood substances, including leaded paint—a tendency know as pica. If the poisoning is not diagnosed and treated early, it can lead to irreversible brain damage and even death.

Children are also exposed to lead paint poisoning by chewing objects covered with lead paint, such as furniture and playthings, and by inhaling lead dust during restoration or repair of homes. Adults are also susceptible to this type of lead poisoning.

Prevention

The U.S. Consumer Product Safety Commission offers the following suggestions to lessen the danger of lead paint poisoning:

1. Examine carefully the condition of your painted walls, ceilings, woodwork, windowsills, and doors, especially those areas within the reach of children.
2. If the paint is peeling or cracked, contact your physician or lead clinic and have your children's blood level checked. The physician can tell you what steps should be taken to correct the hazard.
3. If you recondition your home yourself, there are several steps you can take to rid it of lead paint. Scrape off chipped and cracking paint on windowsills, woodwork, doors, and porch railings. Then sand and repaint the area. Strip and sand walls, and plaster holes before repainting. Or instead of painting, cover walls with wallboard, plywood or paneling. Keep paint flakes and chips swept up. Dispose of them promptly so children won't eat them.
4. To prevent inhalation of lead when removing and sanding old paint, wear a face mask. Use a wet mop after cleaning up debris. Do not eat in the room where work is going on, and make sure plates and eating utensils are not exposed to dust.
5. Examine old toys and furniture for peeling paint. Take care to repaint toys, cribs and other furniture with lead-free paint.

Symptoms

Children who have lead poisoning may show the following symptoms: unusual irritability; poor appetite, stomach pains and vomiting; persistent constipation; sluggishness or drowsiness. Many victims, however, show no symptoms until it is too late. Only a doctor can diagnose lead paint poisoning.

PREVENTING POISON FROM BEING INGESTED

Since young children will eat and drink almost anything, keep all poisonous substances out of their reach. Ninety percent of all accidental poisonings involve children under five years of age. Medicines, household preparations, insect sprays, kerosene, lighter fluid, some furniture polishes, turpentine, paints, solvents and products containing lye and acids are frequent causes of accidental poisoning of children.

Poison-proof your house

1. Keep household products and medicines out of reach and out of sight of children, preferably in a locked cabinet or closet. Never leave a bottle of aspirin or other pills out; return it to a safe place immediately after using. Be especially careful when the telephone or doorbell rings not to rush off and leave a child alone with a potentially dangerous product.
2. Aspirin is the most common cause of accidental poisoning. Keep it out of sight and out of reach even if the bottle has a safety cap.
3. Read labels before using any household product and follow the directions carefully. These instructions have been written for your protection.
4. Keep all products in their original containers. The information on the label of the original container may be vital in case of a poisoning; it lists the hazardous ingredients. Antidotes listed on commercial product labels, however, are frequently worthless and sometimes harmful.
5. Clean out your medicine cabinet periodically. Pour contents down the drain or toilet, and rinse container with water before discarding. Do not put a container with its contents into a refuse can where a child may find it.
6. Keep foods and household products separated. Never place kerosene, antifreeze, paint or solvent in a cup, glass, milk or soft-drink bottle or other utensil customarily used for food or drink. Store cleaning fluids, detergents, lye, soap powders, insecticides and other everyday household products away from food and medications. Death could be the result of mistaken identification.
7. Avoid taking medicine in a child's presence. Children imitate adults, particularly parents.
8. Children should not be deceived by having flavored medicines called "candy." When left alone, they may locate the bottle and eat or drink its contents.
9. Always have the light on when giving or taking medicine. Read the label and instructions carefully.
10. Use a prescription drug only for the person for whom it was prescribed and in the dosage specified.
11. Wear rubber gloves and eye protection and provide adequate ventilation when using cleaning solvents and

104

insect and weed killers.

12. Ask for and use household substances which are available in child-resistant packaging. Always resecure safety caps after using. Remember that some children can open these containers, so make sure that all such items also are stored safely out of reach and sight of children.

33
STROKE

Stroke, also called a cerebrovascular accident or apoplectic stroke, ranks third among the causes of death in the United States, exceeded only by heart disease and cancer. A stroke interrupts the blood supply to some part of the brain, so that the nerve cells in the affected part cannot function. As a result, the part of the body controlled by those nerve cells suffers temporary or permanent damage. Common symptoms include loss of movement or weakness in a limb, a dangling arm, wobbly gait, a sagging face, incoherent speech or complete loss of speech.

A stroke is caused by one of the four following conditions: (1) a blood clot forming in a blood vessel of the brain, known as cerebral thrombosis; (2) a rupture of a cerebral blood-vessel wall, known as cerebral hemmorrhage; (3) a piece of clot or other material from another part of the vascular system which flows to the brain and obstructs a cerebral vessel, known as cerebral embolism; and (4) pressure on a blood vessel, as by a tumor.

RISK FACTORS

Major strokes occur without warning, but high-risk individuals can be identified.

Major risk factors

The major factors known to be associated with stroke are advanced age, hypertension, cardiovascular disease and diabetes.

Age: The risk of stroke rises sharply with increasing age, especially in the later years of life. Children, however, can experience a stroke as a result of a congenital defect in their blood vessels. Occasionally young women on contraceptive pills develop a stroke.

Hypertension: Strokes are more frequent in hypertensive persons, and the risk increases directly with the rise in blood pressure.

Cardiovascular disease: Atherosclerosis, or hardening of the arteries that feed the brain, can result in a stroke.

Diabetes: A stroke is more common in a diabetic than among nondiabetics, especially in younger age groups.

Other risk factors

Race: There is a trend toward a higher incidence, prevalence and mortality in nonwhites than in whites.

Sex: Males seem to be more susceptible to strokes than females.

Family history: The data are insufficient, but certain families seem predisposed to strokes.

Cigarette smoking: Some data indicate that cigarette smoking increases the risk of stroke, at least as a secondary factor.

Physical inactivity: Currently there is no documented evidence that lack of physical activity is a risk factor, but because there may be a greater incidence of heart disease in sedentary persons and because cardiac disorders are associated frequently with stroke, further study is essential.

Obesity: Obesity has not yet been documented as a definite risk factor, but in the presence of other risk factors, obesity may pose a threat.

Oral contraceptives: Numerous reports indicate a significantly greater occurrence of stroke in young women taking oral contraceptives than in those of a similar age not taking these drugs.

WARNING SIGNS

Although there may be no warning signs before a major stroke, a series of temporary brain disorders, known as transient cerebral ischemic attacks (TIA), can serve notice of an impending stroke if not treated promptly. A TIA attack is characterized by a sudden, marked reduction in blood flow to the brain or a partial obstruction of one or more of the major arteries that feed the brain. The frequency of the attacks varies. Attacks usually last about an hour, although they may last up to 24 hours. These attacks serve as a warning of potential death of brain tissue, but whether and when such attacks will occur is unpredictable. About one-third of the patients who eventually develop a major stroke suffer one or more episodes of TIA. If these attacks are recognized and properly treated with drugs, a stroke may be prevented. Symptoms to watch for include dizziness, loss of balance, ringing in the ears, double vision or loss of vision in one eye, speech disturbances, weakness or numbness on one side of the body, paralysis in a limb, loss of sensation. If you or somebody you know suffers from these symptoms, seek medical help at once. A stroke usually occurs anywhere from six to eighteen months after a TIA attack, but it can occur as little as a day after.

Signs/symptoms of a major stroke

1. Person usually unconscious.
2. Face flushed and warm but may sometimes appear ashen gray.
3. Pulse first slow and strong; later rapid and weak.
4. Respiration slow, with snoring.
5. Pupils unequal in size.
6. Paralysis on one side of the face and/or body, according to the part of the brain affected. (A doctor will be able to tell if victim has suffered a stroke by testing his reflexes.)
7. Loss of bladder and bowel control.
8. Inability to talk or slurring of speech.

Note: Sometimes it is difficult to distinguish a stroke victim from an epileptic or a drunk. Check the person's wallet or pockets for any tags or cards that may identify him as an epileptic.

First-aid treatment

The comatose stroke patient is best examined in a hospital, where facilities for resuscitation are available. Get medical help as quickly as possible. Call for a doctor, an ambulance, or a mobile life-support unit if your community has one.

Until help comes, if respiration is shallow or respiratory rate is less than eight breaths per minute, give mouth-to-mouth resuscitation (see pages 17–18). Turn patient to semi-prone position with head lowered so

105

tongue or saliva cannot block the air passage. Victim should not be placed on his back or have a pillow under his head; he may not be able to breathe easily. If it is necessary to move the victim, do so on a stretcher (see pages 22–23).

Keep victim warm with covers.

Keep victim quiet and reassure him if he is conscious.

Give him no fluids, unless the victim becomes fully conscious and can swallow. Discontinue giving fluids if victim vomits. Never give any alcohol.

If you must transport the victim yourself to a hospital or doctor, do so in a flat-bottomed vehicle such as a station wagon or truck. Two-door passenger cars are unsatisfactory. In transporting the victim, support his vital functions and keep the airway open. Transport him in a semiprone or lateral position. The semiprone position is better for drainage of secretions and vomitus, but the lateral position allows easier access to the airway for mouth-to-mouth resuscitation. Always cover the patient, but do not swaddle in blankets. It is important to keep the body temperature as near to normal as possible.

TREATMENT AND REHABILITATION

In making a diagnostic evaluation of a stroke, the doctor may use angiography—the injection of radiopaque dye into the neck arteries—for an X-ray examination of the brain.

Treatment varies according to the stage of the illness and the type of problems encountered. Sometimes surgery helps correct a blockage to the brain such as a clot or aneurysm. Drugs such as anticoagulants and blood-pressure–lowering agents are also included in most treatment of stroke victims.

Rehabilitation is a major part of recovery for stroke victims, offering them a means by which they can return to patterns of daily living that are as close to normal as possible under medical supervision. Rehabilitation includes physical therapy to help the patient recover as much use as possible of the parts of the body affected by the stroke, and speech therapy if the victim has suffered a speech impairment.

34

SUICIDE

REASONS FOR SUICIDE

Many people contemplate suicide at one time or another. According to Dr. Calvin J. Frederick of the George Washington University Medical School, the reasons for suicide and attempted suicide vary. Basically they are a combination of factors, principally loneliness followed by feelings of helplessness and hopelessness, such as in the case of a serious illness. "Everyone experiences one or two of these feelings occasionally," he notes, "but when all occur simultaneously the possibility of a suicide greatly increases."

"A potentially suicidal individual almost always considers himself or herself a failure," says Dr. Frederick. "Sometimes one's reasoning is based on fact; other times it is a matter of exaggeration. A sense of failure can stem from bad experiences like the loss of face, the loss of a job, the loss of a loved one. Unfortunately, such persons do not feel they have the inner resources to help themselves or to seek help, and so instead they decide to end their lives."

DANGER SIGNALS

The most common warning signs, according to Dr. Frederick, are perceived loss, prolonged depression, withdrawal from friends and normal activities, spells of crying, a change in eating habits (either loss of appetite or overeating), a change in sleeping habits (either insomnia or oversleeping), excessive drinking, use of drugs, and carelessness in dress.

A potential victim may also express a plan for death verbally, with veiled threats such as "I wish I were dead" or outright threats such as "I'm going to commit suicide."

Potential victims may, in addition, seek to settle their affairs and prepare themselves for death by giving away favorite possessions and/or making a will.

HOW TO HELP

According to Dr. Frederick, a person

considering suicide should always be taken seriously. "Listen to him or her very carefully, and try to evaluate the seriousness of what the person is saying. Some people can be very upset and not try to commit suicide while others may seem calm and be very suicidal, having already made the decision to end their life. In addition, remember that suicide is democratic. Young children, older people, rich and poor all attempt and do commit suicide."

If someone calls you and speaks directly about imminent suicide, Dr. Frederick advises trying to set up an immediate rescue. "Get the person's address, hang up the phone and call the nearest police or fire department. Do anything you can to save that person's life."

Some do's and don'ts

Never argue with a person contemplating suicide. It is an argument that cannot be won, and the potential victim may interpret your comments as a challenge or a dare. Instead, call for help and while waiting, reassure such persons that no matter how low they feel the feeling will pass and they must go on living. Tell them that their families and friends need to have them *alive*. Be patient and understanding and allow the person to fully vent feelings.

Make the environment safe and provocation-free by removing any medicines or dangerous objects.

Centers for help in a crisis

There are hundreds of suicide prevention and crisis intervention centers throughout the United States, many community-sponsored. These are places a person who is deeply troubled can call or go for emergency help. Trained volunteers or staff members will talk to the potential victim and/or get help to him or her.

To meet a National Institute of Mental Health recommended standard, a suicide prevention unit should have 24-hour telephone service and ought to provide professional backup and referral service.

Further reading. The following two pamphlets by Dr. Calvin J. Frederick provide additional information on preventing suicide: "Mental Health Trends," Stock No. 017-024-00529-1,

DHEW Publication No. (ADM) 78-365, available from the Superintendent of Documents, Washington, D.C. 20402; and "Dealing with the Crisis of Suicide," Revised 1978, a Public Affairs Pamphlet, No. 406A, available from the Public Affairs Committee for 50¢, 381 Park Avenue South, New York, New York 10016.

35

TOOTH PROBLEMS

Teeth have nerves and blood vessels, and are a living part of the body. When diseased or damaged, they can cause pain, or loosen and fall out. They can also be knocked out in an accident. By understanding what causes dental diseases and by taking proper care of the teeth, you have an excellent chance of keeping your natural teeth all your life. Good oral hygiene requires only a few minutes each day at home and a regular checkup by your dentist.

WHAT CAN GO WRONG WITH TEETH

Everyone has plaque, a sticky, transparent film of bacteria that is constantly forming on the teeth and around the gumline. The bacteria in plaque thrive on sugar and change it into decay-causing acids that break down the tooth's hard enamel and irritate the gums. If plaque is not removed with brushing or by a dentist or hygienist, it will eventually harden into calculus, where more plaque can hide and further attack the teeth and gums. The results are tooth decay and gum disease.

Tooth decay

If left unattended, the decay goes deeper and deeper into the tooth, eventually reaching the nerves and blood vessels of the tooth's inner pulp. By the time this happens, a deep cavity in the tooth or an infection at the root develops, causing a toothache.

First-aid treatment

If a toothache occurs during working hours, go to your dentist. If it occurs at night or on a weekend or holiday, you can try to ease the pain yourself. Look at your mouth in a well-lit mirror. If you see a cavity, clean it out with a cotton swab. Wet a small piece of cotton with oil of cloves, available at most drugstores, and pack it into the cavity with a toothpick. Try not to spill the oil of cloves on the tongue as it has a burny taste. If you do not see a cavity and if pain continues, put an ice pack against your jaw on the side where you feel the toothache. If this method is not effective either, try a hot-water bottle. Take an aspirin to relieve the pain. See a dentist as soon as possible.

Gum disease (periodontal disease)

Gum disease starts slowly and almost painlessly. Calculus also grows along the roots of the teeth and underneath the gums. At first the infection appears as a swelling and tenderness of the gums with occasional bleeding. This stage is known as gingivitis. Small pockets form around the teeth and trap more bacteria and food particles. Finally the bone supporting the teeth comes under attack and begins to shrink. The teeth become loose and may later fall out. Gum disease often occurs without any discomfort, so that often you cannot tell that periodontal disease is present. That is why a regular checkup with your dentist is essential.

Other factors that can contribute to gum disease include poor nutrition, cigarette smoking, hereditary lack of resistance, stress from uneven teeth or bad habits of chewing and tooth grinding, or systemic disease. Women who take oral contraceptives may be more susceptible to gum disease.

Bleeding gums

Bleeding gums often signify gum disease, but sometimes result from other conditions such as vitamin deficiency or blood disorders.

PREVENTIVE CLEANING CARE

Dental plaque diseases are easier to prevent than to cure.

Brushing

A good brushing twice a day, preferably in the morning after breakfast and at night after dinner and taking from three to five minutes, is good prevention. (If you cannot brush twice a day, rinse your mouth well after each meal.) The goal is to remove all the plaque from the teeth. Use a brush with soft or medium nylon or natural bristles rounded at the ends. Brush the inside of the front teeth with a gum-to-tooth motion. Then brush the inside of the back teeth and the chewing surfaces with short back-and-forth strokes. Brush where your teeth meet your gums, and brush the outside surfaces of all teeth with short back-and-forth strokes. In addition, gently brush the tongue, where bacteria can also collect. Rinse well.

Note. Too-vigorous brushing can injure teeth and gums.

Flossing

To remove germs and food particles on teeth surfaces, you should floss. Take an 18-inch length of dental floss, preferably unwaxed (although waxed floss may be easier to use), or dental tape and work it gently up and down between the teeth with a sawing motion. Be sure to clean the sides of each tooth, including the area below the gumline. Do not, however, cut into the gum. Clean between all the teeth, using a new length of floss or tape when necessary. When you finish, rinse your mouth with water to wash away debris dislodged by cleaning.

Fluoride

Fluoride, a chemical compound, makes teeth more resistant to decay and counteracts damage done by sugar and plaque buildup. Some communities with central water supplies have fluoridated their water. Another way of getting fluoride is to brush with a fluoride toothpaste. Rinsing with a fluoride mouthwash holds promise, and having a dentist apply a fluoride gel in a plastic mouthpiece is useful for children.

Staining teeth

You can temporarily stain teeth after brushing with disclosing tablets that contain vegetable coloring. Rinse your mouth with one of the tablets. It will stain any plaque that remains and show you what areas need to be brushed again. Rinse your mouth well when finished.

107

Diet control

Any between-meal snacks, particularly sweets, encourage the growth of disease-causing plaque. Limit consumption of sweets to times when you can brush, floss or at least rinse immediately.

REPLANTING A KNOCKED-OUT TOOTH

When a permanent tooth, including the root, is accidentally knocked out, it can often be replanted. The sooner the tooth is replanted into the jaw, the better the chances that it will take root. If possible, the tooth should be put back within 30 minutes. (This should not be confused with a weak tooth which has fallen out.)

If the tooth is not too dirty, rinse it thoroughly with cold water and gently wipe off any remaining specks with a clean, moist cloth or gauze. Be careful to preserve all the gum fibers still clinging to the tooth. Twist it back into place and go to the dentist *immediately*. He will splint the tooth and prescribe antibiotics as well as a tetanus injection to prevent infection. The tooth will probably need root canal treatment.

If the tooth is too dirty or you are squeamish, put it in eight ounces—about a glass—of iced water with ½ teaspoon of salt and go straight to the dentist with it.

Bleeding from a tooth socket can be controlled by direct pressure on the area with a small packet of gauze or with a clean cloth.

COMMON MOUTH SORES

Fever blisters, cold sores and canker sores range from one or two once in a while to weekly outbreaks of many painful blisters. They usually appear during an illness or period of physical or emotional stress. Medicines sometimes sooth the discomfort but do not necessarily provide cure. The sores heal naturally, usually within two weeks. If they do not, get prompt medical attention.

36
UNCONSCIOUSNESS

Because there are so many reasons why a person loses consciousness—shock, stroke, heart attack, diabetes, poisoning, among others—it is essential to call a physician at once. If you cannot reach a doctor, call for an ambulance or take the victim to a hospital emergency room, transporting him lying down on a stretcher (see pages 22–23).

First-aid treatment

Keep victim on his back. Turn head to side if possible to ease breathing. Loosen clothing around neck. Check breathing to be sure airway is open. If breathing stops, immediately give victim artificial respiration (see pages 17–18). Keep victim warm to prevent shock.

Try to determine the cause of unconsciousness. Look for such things as electrical shock, partly empty container of poison, or an emergency medical identification wallet card or bracelet indicating a hidden illness such as diabetes or epilepsy. (See pages 16–17 for securing emergency medication identification devices.)

Do not try to give the victim any food or liquid until he regains consciousness. Discontinue if victim vomits.

37
WOUNDS

A wound is an injury in which the skin or underlying tissues are broken, cut or torn. It can be anything from a small cut made by a razor blade to a large, open chest wound from an explosion. The wound may or may not bleed. There are two types of wounds, open and closed.

OPEN WOUNDS

Open wounds are those in which the skin is cut or torn and the wound is exposed. There are five major types of open wounds.

Types of wounds (see Fig. 37-1)

Abrasion: an irregular wound with spot or area of skin scraped off, such as a scraped knee.

Puncture: a hole in the skin made by a pointed object such as a knife, nail or bullet.

Laceration: a rough, jagged tear of tissue made by a blunt object such as a lawn mower.

Avulsion: a tearing away of tissue from the body such as that from an animal bite or explosion.

Incision: a single cut or gash made by a sharp object such as a piece of broken glass.

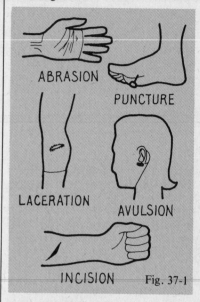

ABRASION
PUNCTURE
LACERATION
AVULSION
INCISION   Fig. 37-1

First-aid treatment

Stop bleeding (see pages 19–20). Cover wound with a clean cloth, preferably a sterile dressing, to prevent infection. Secure dressing with a bandage (see pages 23–25). For a severe, penetrating puncture wound, you may also have to treat for shock (see page 21). Consult a physician, who may recommend a tetanus shot to fight any possible tetanus infection (see page 85). An infection is indicated by swelling of the affected part, redness, pus, pain, and fever. Immobilize the infected area and elevate part if possible. Apply heat to the area and cover wound with a dressing.

For minor cuts which involve only a superficial wound and little bleeding, first wash your hands with soap and water and then wash the wound with soap and water. Apply a sterile dressing and secure with a bandage (see pages 23–25). Small cuts and scratches do not require a doctor's attention.

HEALTH INSURANCE

Removal of foreign objects: Foreign objects such as a wood splinter or fishhook require special attention.

Splinters. You can remove a wood splinter and similar small foreign objects by using a tweezers which you have sterilized over a flame, or using the tip of a needle sterilized in rubbing alcohol. Pull splinter out at same angle it entered the skin. If splinter is very deep, let a physician remove it. Wash wound with soap and water.

Fishhook. Do not remove a fishhook from the face or neck. To remove from an arm or leg, first push the shank through the skin until the point appears (see Fig. 37-2). Cut off barbed end with clippers. Remove shank from the wound. Wash with soap and water. Cover with a clean cloth. See a physician immediately.

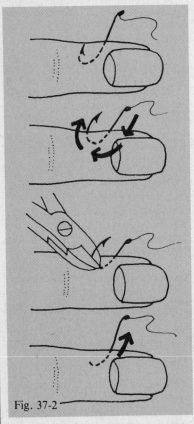

Fig. 37-2

Embedded objects. Do not move the victim. Do not remove embedded object, but cut off object a few inches from the wound. Cut clothing away from site of injury. Stabilize object with bulky dressing. Apply bandage to prevent movement (see pages 23–25). Treat for shock if necessary (see page 21). Get victim to a hospital emergency room or to a doctor.

Bullet wound: Stop bleeding (see pages 19–20). Treat for shock (see page 21). Splint any fracture where it lies (see page 70).

CLOSED WOUNDS

A closed wound is one in which there is no break in the skin but the tissues underneath are injured. A closed wound may be a minor bruise, such as a black eye in which small vessels of the skin are broken, or a crushing injury in which a fracture occurs.

Signs/symptoms: Common signs of closed wounds are pain and tenderness. With a bruise, there is swelling and discoloration of tissue; with a fracture there will be a deformity.

First-aid treatment

For a bruise, apply cold compresses or an ice bag. If pain persists, see a physician.

Some closed wounds may also cause severe bleeding, which can lead to shock. You must treat each emergency. (For bleeding, see pages 19–20; for shock, see page 21). Some closed wounds may impair breathing (see pages 17–18).

Internal injuries may be present. The signs are cold, clammy skin; rapid but weak pulse; pain and tenderness in the area of injury; vomiting or coughing up of blood. Seek prompt medical help.

SPECIAL CASES

Open chest wounds

Cover with an airtight material such as plastic wrap or aluminum foil after the victim has exhaled. Do not apply so tightly that victim's breathing is restrained. If no airtight material is available, use your hand. Place the victim on his injured side to allow room for the uninjured lung to expand. Get victim to a hospital or physician as soon as possible. Transport by stretcher, keeping victim in a lying-down position. Treat for shock if present (see page 21). If condition worsens, lung may have collapsed. Remove wrapping and listen for escape of air. Replace seal before air is sucked into wound.

Abdominal wounds

Abdominal wounds are serious. Have victim lie down with a pillow or pad under his knees to relax abdominal muscles. Treat for shock (see page 21). Keep victim warm. Get victim to a hospital or physician as quickly as possible. Transport on a stretcher (see pages 22–23). Give no fluids. Control bleeding by applying direct pressure on wound with a clean cloth (see page 19).

If intestines protrude, do not try to replace. Leave organ on the surface. Cover with a nonadherent material such as plastic wrap or aluminum foil which is dampened with cooled boiled water. Cover with outer dressing and bandage to hold in place. Again, keep victim on his back with a pillow or blanket under his knees.

Bites

Animal or human bites may involve puncture wounds, lacerations or avulsions.

For an animal bite, get quick medical aid. Wash wound with soap and water, and hold wound under water for a few minutes if bleeding is not profuse. Apply a sterile dressing and secure it in place with a bandage. Keep victim calm. If possible, catch or retain animal and maintain alive for observation regarding rabies.

For a human bite, first control bleeding and then cleanse wound with soap and water. Cover with a sterile dressing and secure in place with a bandage (see pages 23–25). Take victim to a physician or hospital emergency room.

38
HEALTH INSURANCE

Everyone needs health insurance. Most of us join a group plan through our company, fraternal organization, professional association, or church group—and then just stop thinking about it. But now that medical costs are skyrocketing, as good as your group health insurance plan may be, it probably does not give you as much protection as you need. Pull out your policy and compare its coverage to what some illnesses could cost you.

109

You may well find that you will have to reevaluate your coverage.

The basic health insurance that you get from your company or group is probably the best policy you can get for the money, providing more benefits for less cost than you could get by taking out a policy on your own. But it may not be enough. For example, the provisions "hospital room and board expenses" under most group plans do not usually cover the actual hospital bills. And the surgical schedules often are even more inadequate, generally paying only half the cost of an operation. Doctors' visits are not covered in many plans.

Because many basic group health insurance plans are either anemic in their coverage or have some gaps, you may want to consider supplementing your health insurance with a major medical policy. (Of course, some group plans are very comprehensive and include major medical coverage. Even so, you might need more.) If you don't have a group plan, you can purchase a major medical policy as a comprehensive medical insurance policy.

The first step is to find a good general insurance agent who can help you buy the kind of coverage you need at the best possible price. One way of finding an agent is to ask your friends, relatives and business colleagues for recommendations. And be sure to ask them *why* they like the insurance agent they are recommending. Generally, you want an agent who deals with more than one insurance company. The more lines your agent carries, the more flexibility he has in shopping around for a policy that fits your needs and your budget. The agent should also have a reputation for regularly reviewing his clients' insurance policies. He should be willing to explain everything in a policy to you. And finally, he should be able to revise portions of your existing policies, if that is possible. That is much less expensive than paying for a brand new one (new policies are expensive because of the commission costs).

What to look for in choosing your policy

1. If a policy you are considering has a "coordination of benefits" clause, make sure that the insurance company gives you something in re-turn—either lower premiums or increased benefits. A coordination of benefits clause lets the insurance company avoid duplicating benefits you might receive from another health insurance policy. Therefore it potentially saves them money. It works this way: The deductible on a major medical policy will rise automatically to match whatever you receive from another health insurance policy. (The deductible on an insurance policy is the amount that you have to take care of yourself. For example, if there is a $500 deductible for hospital costs, the insurance policy's coverage takes effect after the first $500 in expenses.) So, if the deductible on your major medical policy is $500, it will automatically rise to $700 under a coordination of benefits clause—if that is the deductible on your basic health insurance plan. You are, therefore, potentially liable for $200 more.

2. Take a good look at the accumulation period—the time you have to use up the deductible. It can range from as little as 30 days to as long as a year. The longer the accumulation period, the better off you will be. In other words, if the policy has a short accumulation period, you might have to go back and meet the deductible over and over again before coverage started again. For example, say the policy has a 30-day accumulation period. Assume that you become ill and run up hospital bills well above your $500 deductible. If you became ill again or had a relapse a month later, you would have to pay new bills under the $500 deductible all over again. If the accumulation period ran for a year, you would not have to worry.

3. If you have a family, the policy should also have a family deductible. If it does not, you could pay large amounts to the deductible for each member of your family should you all have a bad year. If you had a family deductible, it would probably be reached fairly quickly, and the insurance company would reimburse you for most of the medical bills your family ran up.

4. A trickier matter is figuring out how much of your medical costs you want to co-insure, or pay yourself. The more you feel you can afford to co-insure, the lower your insurance premiums will be. Generally, the insurance company will pay a percent-age of all covered medical bills after the deductible has been met. You pay the balance. In a typical policy, the company will pick up 80 percent of covered costs, leaving you responsible for 20 percent. If you think you can afford it, however, you can get a policy that makes you responsible for 25 percent or more of these costs. That is not as much of a risk as it seems at first glance, because the insurance company will pick up 100 percent of the costs (up to the policy's limit) after the bills reach a certain specified amount. For example, assume you have a policy that has a $500 deductible and pays 75 percent of all covered bills up to a specified limit—say $3,000—after which it picks up 100 percent of all costs to a total limit of $100,000. Thus, if your bills amounted to $8,000, you would pay only $1,125—the $500 deductible plus 25 percent of $2,500. The policy would cover everything else. And chances are that you would only have to pay $675, because your basic health insurance would probably take care of the first $500 of the bills.

5. Look for a policy whose benefit period runs for five years. The longer it runs, the more protection you will have if you are seriously ill, become the victim of a chronic disease, or are permanently disabled.

6. Avoid policies that have fixed schedules of benefits—a set dollar limit on the coverage for certain expenses, such as room and board. The limits may be way behind the times. You will be far better off with a policy that has limits which are based on what is "usual, customary, and reasonable" in your area. Note that the limits on the coverage for psychiatric care or private-duty nursing are usually lower than the limits on other costs, and the deductible is generally higher, because these are expenses that can be very long term.

7. Try to find a policy with a per-cause maximum, which places a limit on the coverage for a *particular* illness. If you exhaust the limit for one cause, say a heart attack, you will still be covered if something else, say a bronchial condition, befalls you. A lifetime maximum offers you less protection, because it could be quickly exhausted if you had a series of different accidents or illnesses.

8. The policy should be guaranteed

110

renewable. That means the company has to renew your policy, providing you have paid your premiums. What is more, it cannot raise your premiums unless it raises them for the entire group of people you are classed with.

9. Your children should be covered from birth until age 18. Some policies will cover them until they are 22, if they are single, dependent, and students. Avoid policies that cover children from 3 to 18. The very costly medical problems with children usually occur from birth to age three.

10. When you look over a policy, make sure it spells out exactly what the insurance company considers a "preexisting condition." Most policies will not cover you for a preexisting condition until a 2-year contestability period has elapsed. The catch is that you may have a preexisting medical problem that you were not even aware of. Hence, you want a policy that states any preexisting condition you know you have, and promises to pay for any other illnesses not listed in your policy as preexisting conditions.

To be prudent in this day of escalating medical costs, consider supplementing a major medical policy with an excess major medical policy. The cost of an excess major medical policy is inexpensive, considering the protection you will get. If you coordinate the deductible of the excess major medical policy with what you can receive from your major medical policy, you will get a large amount of coverage at a very low cost.

YOUR HOUSE

39

GETTING STARTED

Inspecting your home or apartment carefully once a year and making a routine check of appliances and fixtures is a good way to prevent problems from developing. Emergencies may still occur—a toilet becomes clogged, a fuse blows, the furnace goes out—even in the middle of the night and on weekends when a repairman is not readily available or available only at a higher rate. When an emergency happens around the house, first examine the problem, and then decide whether you can handle the repair yourself or should call in a professional repairman.

ASSUMING THE ROLE OF REPAIRMAN

If you are handy with tools and have the proper equipment (see the following pages for selecting tools), you can save on the high cost of materials and labor and avoid inconvenience by doing the repair work yourself.

In making repairs, never do them piecemeal. Make a plan and follow the instructions for specific problems in the following chapters. Avoid the cost and frustration of repeating the same repair on account of faulty materials or procedures. Always use the best materials you can afford.

For making plumbing, heating and electrical repairs, you should know your local building ordinances. You may have to use licensed people for part of the work. If you need specific tools and do not have them on hand, you can often rent them from a local hardware store, lumber yard, or retail tool store.

CHOOSING A REPAIRMAN

If you decide that a particular home emergency repair is too difficult or too time-consuming for you to handle, hire a professional.

Where to look for a repairman

Consult friends and neighbors, ask your banker, the local Chamber of Commerce, the National Home Im-

provement Council (11 East 44th Street, New York, NY 10017) and other sources that can verify credentials. Use the Yellow Pages only as a last resort. From your sources, compile a list of three or four repair people from which you select one person.

How to select a repairman

Ask each repairman for a list of past customers and check each reference to see if the work he did was satisfactory. Check the repairman's reliability with your local Better Business Bureau, or ask a bank or credit agency to check his credit rating. Check how long he has been in business, if he is a member of a trade association, if he is familiar with the area's local building codes—especially important whenever you are making structural changes, including altering the basic living area of your residence. Ask each repairman to give you a quote on the same job. Then select the one who offers you what you are looking for at the best price. Always beware, however, of special deals that promise unusually good prices.

After you have selected a repairman

Contracting for major repair work, having it done and getting satisfactory results can be a trying experience even with a reputable repairman. For your benefit and his, do not rely upon "reputation of honesty," "word of honor," or "verbal understanding." Instead, put an agreement between the two of you in writing. Make it specific and to the point. Agreements will vary slightly depending upon the nature of the repair.

Inspect the repair work with the repairman when the job is done. If there are questions, refer to the agreement. Give your *final* signature on the agreement and make the final payment only after all the work has been completed correctly and you are totally satisfied.

TOOLS AND EQUIPMENT

In order to handle both routine home maintenance tasks and emergency jobs, you will need a set of basic tools. These pages are a guide to selecting those tools. Know the specific purpose, correct use of and proper care for each tool you buy. A salesman at your local hardware store is a good

person to get advice from on what to buy. For expensive tools which you will need only occasionally, such as welding equipment, consider renting from a local hardware store, lumber yard, retail tool store, or rental agency. It is sometimes wise to buy a major specialized tool for a single large job. The savings in time, ease of operation and improvement of quality of work can be substantial. After completion of the project, you can keep the tool or sell it.

Whatever tools you decide upon, buy the best you can afford. High-quality tools can last many years and will help you avoid accidental injuries. Maintain your tools in good condition by keeping them sharp and clean. Know how to use each tool or piece of equipment. Always check a tool before and after you use it, and when finished store it safely in a tool box, on a tool rack or in a workbench. To add to your safety, always wear proper clothing and protective equipment. It is also a good precaution to keep a workroom locked so that children cannot get into equipment and hurt themselves.

Hand tools

Striking tools: Hammers, mallets and sledges are used to apply a striking force. Before using, make sure that the faces are free from oil or other substance that would cause the tool to glance off nails, spikes or stakes. Clean (and repair if necessary) all tools before storing them.

Hammers. You will need at least one hammer. Hammers are designated according to weight (without the handle) and style or shape. The shape will vary according to the intended work. The two main types are the carpenter's hammer and the machinist's hammer. The primary use of a carpenter's hammer is to drive or pull nails. It has either a curved or straight claw. The face may be bell-shaped or plain, and the handle may be made of wood or steel. The most common carpenter's hammer has a curved claw, bell face and wooden handle, sometimes with a rubber grip (see Fig. 39-1). A 16-ounce claw hammer is a good choice. Some people also find a machinist's hammer handy—for working with metal or around machinery. It has a variable-shaped peen, rather than a claw, at the opposite end of the

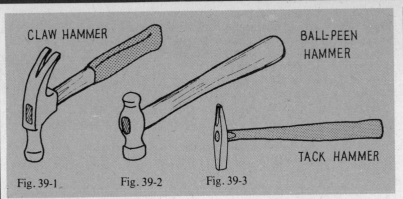

CLAW HAMMER

Fig. 39-1

BALL-PEEN HAMMER

Fig. 39-2

TACK HAMMER

Fig. 39-3

face. The ball-peen hammer is the most common type to own. It has a ball which is smaller in diameter than the face (see Fig. 39-2). You will also want to have a tack hammer on hand for tacking or driving small nails (see Fig. 39-3).

To use a hammer safely, hold it near the end of the handle for more hitting power. To start a nail, hold it in place and tap it gently a few times until it is firmly set. Hit it straight in. To avoid hammer marks on the wood, use a nail set—a small metal device (see Fig. 39-4)—or another nail to drive a nail the last one-eighth inch into the wood. Use putty or wood to fill the recess above the nail head. To remove a nail, use the claw end of the hammer. Place a small block of wood under the head of the hammer to avoid marking the wood.

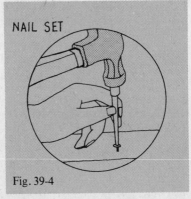

NAIL SET

Fig. 39-4

Do not strike one hammer against another because the two could chip and send pieces flying at you. Wear safety goggles to protect your eyes and heavy gloves to protect your hands. Never use a hammer with a loose head or cracked handle. Have loose heads tightened if possible. Discard hammers that are chipped or dented.

Mallets and sledges. The mallet is a short-handled tool (see Fig. 39-5) used to drive wooden-handled chisels, gouges, or wooden pins, or to form or shape sheet metal where hard-faced hammers would mark or injure the finished work. Never use a mallet to drive nails, screws, or any object that may cause damage to the face. The sledge is a steel-headed, heavy-duty driving tool (see Fig. 39-6) that can be used for a number of purposes. For example, short-handled sledges are used to drive bolts and large nails and to strike cold chisels.

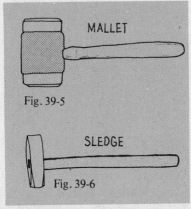

MALLET

Fig. 39-5

SLEDGE

Fig. 39-6

Turning tools (called wrenches): A wrench is a basic tool that is used to tighten and loosen a bolt head, nut, stud and pipe. The size of any wrench is determined by the size of the opening between its jaws. The opening of a wrench is made slightly larger than the bolt head or nut so that the wrench can slide on and off the nut or bolt with a minimum of play. If the wrench is too large, the points of the nut or bolt head will be rounded and destroyed. There are many types of wrenches, each designed for a specific use. Be sure to use one that fits the nut or bolt properly.

Open-end wrench. A solid, non-adjustable wrench with an opening in one or both ends is called an open-end wrench (see Fig. 39-7). This wrench cannot be varied in size. You will purchase open-end wrenches as part of a set.

Box wrench. The box wrench is safer than the open-end wrench because there is less likelihood it will slip off the work. With it you can completely surround a nut or bolt head (see Fig. 39-8).

Combination wrench. With the combination wrench, you can use the box end for breaking nuts loose or for snugging them down, and the open end for turning them quickly (see Fig. 39-9).

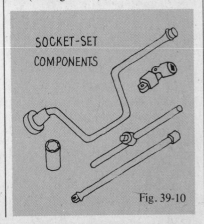

OPEN-END WRENCH

Fig. 39-7

BOX WRENCH

Fig. 39-8

COMBINATION WRENCH

Fig. 39-9

Socket wrench. The socket wrench consists of a handle and a socket-type wrench which can be attached to the handle. A complete socket wrench set consists of several types of handles along with bar extensions, adapters, and a variety of sockets (see Fig. 39-10).

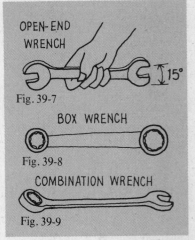

SOCKET-SET COMPONENTS

Fig. 39-10

113

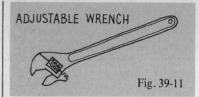

ADJUSTABLE WRENCH

Fig. 39-11

Adjustable wrench. A handy all-round wrench, the adjustable open-end wrench (see Fig. 39-11) is not intended to take the place of the regular, solid open-end wrench but is useful for fitting odd-sized nuts. By turning a thumbscrew, you can adjust the jaw opening to fit various sizes of nuts. The adjustable wrench is available in different sizes. It is helpful to purchase two, including a 12-inch one. The size of the wrench selected for a particular job depends on the size of the nut or bolt head. In using this wrench, adjust the jaws to fit snugly on the nut. *Note:* Do not use this type of wrench on items that are extremely hard to turn.

Pipe, or Stillson, wrench. When rotating or holding round work such as pipes, use an adjustable pipe wrench (see Fig. 39-12). Pivot the

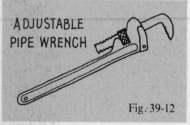

ADJUSTABLE PIPE WRENCH

Fig. 39-12

movable jaw on a pipe wrench to grip the work. The jaws in this tool are serrated and always make marks on the work unless you take adequate precautions. Adjust the jaws so that the bite on the work will be taken at about the center of the jaws. You should purchase two pipe wrenches in different sizes.

Keep wrenches clean and free of oil; otherwise they may slip and injure you or damage your work. Determine which way a nut should be turned before trying to loosen it. Most nuts are turned counterclockwise for removal. Provide some kind of kit or case for all your wrenches. *Note:* If a nut is hard to loosen, apply a few drops of penetrating oil or kerosene. Let it soak a couple of hours or overnight. If the wrench has a tendency to slip off, try turning it over.

Metal-cutting tools: You should have a variety of metal-cutting tools on hand, including snips and shears, hacksaw, chisels, files, and twist drills.

Snips and shears. You will use snips and shears for cutting sheet metal and steel of various thicknesses and shapes (see Fig. 39-13). Normally, you will use a shear to cut the heavier or thicker materials.

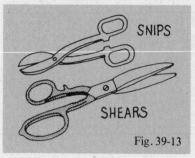

SNIPS

SHEARS

Fig. 39-13

Hacksaw. Use a hacksaw to cut metal that is too heavy for snips or boltcutters. There are two parts to a hacksaw: the frame and the blade. Common hacksaws have either an adjustable or a solid frame (see Fig. 39-14). The set in a saw refers to how

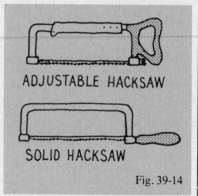

ADJUSTABLE HACKSAW

SOLID HACKSAW

Fig. 39-14

much the teeth are pushed out in opposite directions from the sides of the blade. The four different kinds of sets are alternate set, double alternate set, raker set and wave set.

To use a hacksaw correctly, you must select the proper blade. Coarse blades with fewer teeth per inch cut faster and are less likely to choke up with chips. Finer blades with more teeth per inch are necessary when thin sections are being cut. The selection should be made so that, as each tooth starts its cut, the tooth ahead of it will still be cutting. Place the material to be cut in a vise. A minimum of overhang will produce less vibration, give a better cut, and lengthen the life of

the blade. The proper way of using a hacksaw is shown below (see Fig. 39-15). The index finger of the right hand, pointed forward, aids in guiding

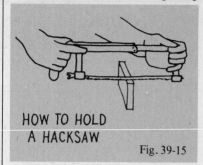

HOW TO HOLD A HACKSAW

Fig. 39-15

the frame. Apply pressure on the forward stroke, which is the cutting stroke, but not on the return stroke. Long, slow, steady strokes—40 to 50 per minute—are best.

The major danger in using a hacksaw is injury to your hand if the blade breaks. This accident can occur if you apply too much pressure, if you twist the saw, if you are cutting too fast, or if the blade becomes loose in the frame. Also, when the work is not tight in the vise, it will sometimes slip, twisting the blade enough to break it.

Chisels. Chisels are used for working with metal. A chisel will cut any metal that is softer than the material of which the chisel is made. The most common shapes of chisels are flat (known as cold chisel), cape, half round, round nose and diamond point—all named for the shape of their points (see Fig. 39-16).

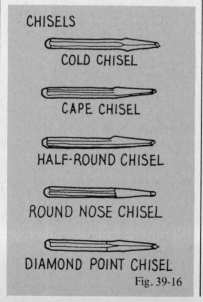

CHISELS

COLD CHISEL

CAPE CHISEL

HALF-ROUND CHISEL

ROUND NOSE CHISEL

DIAMOND POINT CHISEL

Fig. 39-16

Files. A file is a steel tool with a rough, ridged surface for smoothing or grinding away wood, metal or plastic and for sharpening other tools. You will need a variety of sizes (length), shapes (cross section) and coarseness of cut (teeth). Files are graded according to the degree of fineness and according to whether they have single- or double-cut teeth. Single-cut files have rows of teeth cut parallel to each other (see Fig. 39-17). You will use single-cut files for sharpening tools, finish filing, and drawfiling. They are also the best tools for smoothing the edges of sheet metal. Files with criss-crossed rows of teeth are double-cut files (see Fig. 39-18).

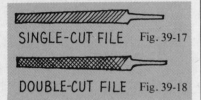

SINGLE-CUT FILE   Fig. 39-17

DOUBLE-CUT FILE   Fig. 39-18

The double cut forms teeth that are diamond shaped and fast cutting. You can use double-cut files for quick removal of metal and for rough work. Files are also graded according to the spacing and size of their teeth, that is, their coarseness or fineness (see Fig. 39-19). Files also come in different shapes. In selecting a file for a job, consider the shape of the finished work (see Fig. 39-20). A square file is

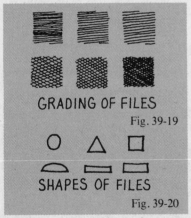

GRADING OF FILES
Fig. 39-19

SHAPES OF FILES
Fig. 39-20

tapered on all four sides. Use it to enlarge rectangular-shaped holes and slots. A triangular file is tapered on all three sides. Use it to file acute internal angles and to clear out square corners. Round files serve the same purpose as square files but for round openings. Half-round files are general-purpose

tools and are used for curved surfaces and the flat face on flat surfaces. When you file an inside curve, use a round or half-round file whose curve most nearly matches the curve of the work. A mill file is tapered in both width and thickness. One edge has no teeth and is known as the safe edge. Use it for smoothing lathe work, drawfiling and other precision work. A mill file is always single cut. Flat files are general-purpose files and may be single or double cut. They are tapered in width and thickness.

When you finish using a file, it may be necessary to finish the product with an abrasive cloth or paper, depending on how fine a finish you want on the work. Afterward clean the file teeth with a file card or brush to prevent the teeth from clogging up with metal filings and scratching your work, a condition known as pinning. Protect the file teeth by hanging your files in a rack when not in use, or by placing them in drawers with wooden partitions. Do not allow them to rust; keep them away from water and moisture. Avoid getting your files oily. Oil will cause a file to slide across the work and prevent fast, clean cutting. Never use a file for prying or pounding. Never use a file unless it is equipped with a tight-fitting handle.

Twist drills. Making a hole in a piece of metal is usually a simple operation. A large number of different tools and machines have been designed to make holes speedily, economically and accurately in all kinds of materials. But the most common tool for making holes in metal is the twist drill. One end of the cylindrical drill is pointed, while the other end is shaped so that it can be attached to a drilling machine (see Fig. 39-21).

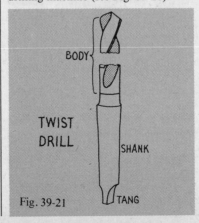

BODY

TWIST DRILL

SHANK

TANG

Fig. 39-21

Other tools that you may want to consider are countersinks, used to set the head of a screw or rivet flush with the material in which it is being placed; reamers, used to enlarge and true a hole; and punches, held in the hand and struck on one end with a hammer to make a hole.

Wood-cutting tools: If you work with wood, you will need a wide variety of hand tools.

Handsaws. The most common handsaw consists of a steel blade with a handle at one end (see Fig. 39-22).

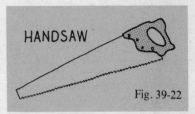

HANDSAW

Fig. 39-22

One edge of the blade has teeth, which act as two rows of cutters. When you use the saw, these teeth cut two parallel grooves close together. The number of teeth per inch, the size and shape of the teeth, and the amount of set depend on the use to be made of the saw and the material to be cut. Handsaws are described by the number of points per inch, with one more point than there are teeth per inch.
1. Crosscut saws and ripsaws. Ripsaws are used for cutting with the grain, and crosscut saws for cutting across the grain. The major difference between them is the shape of the teeth.
2. Special-purpose saws. The more common types of saws used for special purposes are shown in Fig. 39-23. The

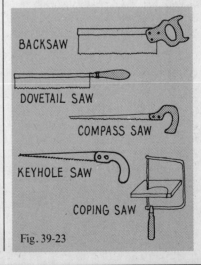

BACKSAW

DOVETAIL SAW

COMPASS SAW

KEYHOLE SAW

COPING SAW

Fig. 39-23

backsaw is a crosscut saw designed for sawing a perfectly straight line across the face of a piece of stock. A heavy steel backing along the top of the blade keeps the blade perfectly straight. A dovetail saw is a special type of backsaw with a thin, narrow blade and a chisel-type handle. The compass saw is a long, narrow, tapering ripsaw designed for cutting out circular or other nonrectangular sections from within the margins of a board or panel. A hole is bored near the cutting line to start the saw. A keyhole saw is simply a finer, narrower compass saw. A coping saw is used to cut along short, curved lines.

Planes. The plane (see Fig. 39-24) is the most extensively used of the hand shaving tools. Use it to trim wood to size and to bend wood. The

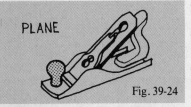

PLANE

Fig. 39-24

most common types of planes are the bench and the block plane, both designed for general surface smoothing and squaring. There are three types of bench planes: the smooth plane, the jack plane and the jointer plane. All are used primarily for shaving and smoothing with the grain, the chief difference being the length of the sole. The longer the sole of the plane is, the more uniformly flat and true the planed surface will be. The block plane, which is usually held at an angle to the work, is used chiefly for cross-grain squaring of end-stock. It is also useful, however, for smoothing all plane surfaces on very small work.

Boring tools. When working with wood, you will often have to bore holes. You can do this with auger bits, braces or drills (see Fig. 39-25).

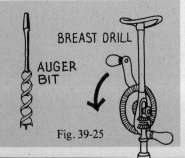

BREAST DRILL

AUGER BIT

Fig. 39-25

1. Auger bits. Use bits for boring holes for screws, dowels, and hardware, as an aid in mortising, and in shaping curves. Bits vary in shape and structure with the type of job to be done.

2. Braces and drills. The auger bit is the tool that does the cutting in the wood, but another tool must be used to hold the auger bit and give you enough leverage to turn the bit. The tools that most often are used for holding the bit are the carpenter's brace, the breast drill and the push drill.

Wood chisels. A wood chisel is a steel tool fitted with a wooden or plastic handle. It has a single beveled cutting edge on the end of the steel part, or blade. The shapes of the more common types of chisels are socket firmer, tang paring, mortising and butt (see Fig. 39-26). The firmer chisel has a

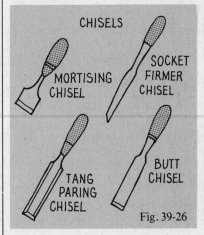

CHISELS

MORTISING CHISEL

SOCKET FIRMER CHISEL

TANG PARING CHISEL

BUTT CHISEL

Fig. 39-26

strong, rectangular cross-section blade designed for heavy and light work. The blade of the paring chisel is relatively thin and is beveled along the sides for fine paring work. The butt chisel has a short blade designed for work in hard-to-get-at places.

A wood chisel should always be held with the flat side or back of the chisel against the work for smoothing and finishing cuts. Whenever possible, it should not be pushed straight through an opening, but should be moved laterally at the same time that it is pushed forward. This will give a smooth and even surface. Wherever possible, other tools such as saws and planes should be used to remove as much of the waste as possible, and the chisel then used for finishing purposes only.

Screwdrivers: A screwdriver is designed to drive and remove screws. It should never be used as a pry bar, scraper, chisel, or punch. There are two main types of screwdrivers: a standard, or straight, screwdriver and a recessed screwdriver. Standard screwdrivers (see Fig. 39-27) are classified by size, according to the combined length of the shank and the blade. Recessed screws have a cavity in the head and require a specially

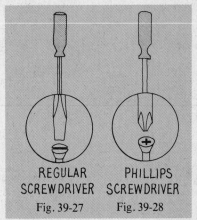

REGULAR SCREWDRIVER

PHILLIPS SCREWDRIVER

Fig. 39-27   Fig. 39-28

shaped screwdriver. The most common type is the Phillips head screwdriver. Five standard-size Phillips screwdrivers handle a wide range of screw sizes. The screws all have a four-way slot, called a Phillips head, into which the screwdriver fits (see Fig. 39-28). This prevents the screwdriver from slipping. In addition, for fast, easy work there is the ratchet screwdriver. It can be used one-handed and does not require the bit to be lifted out of the slot after each turn. It may be fitted with either a standard bit or a special bit for recessed heads. It is most commonly used for driving screws into soft wood.

When using a screwdriver, select the proper size so that the blade fits the screw slot properly. This prevents burring the slot and reduces the force required to hold the driver in the slot. It is easier to put a screw into wood if you have made a shallow hole first with a nail or drill. Rub wax or soap into the screw threads to make the screw go in easier. When using the screwdriver, push against the head of the screw as you turn it. Never use a screwdriver to check an electrical circuit. Never try to turn a screwdriver with a pair of pliers. Do not work in your hand while using a screwdriver;

if the point slips it can cause a bad cut. Hold the work in a vise, with a clamp, or on a solid surface. If that is impossible, be careful never to get any part of your body in front of the screwdriver blade tip. Choose an assortment of slotted and Phillips screwdrivers.

Pliers: Pliers, small pincers for handling small objects and for cutting wire, are made in many styles and sizes. Always try to buy pliers with rubber grips, which insulate the handles so that you can use them for electrical repair work. If necessary, wrap tape or cloth around a nut to avoid scratching it.

The following are the most common types of pliers you will need around the house: combination pliers, handy for holding or bending flat or round stock; long-nosed pliers, less rugged and easily breakable if used on heavy jobs, but good for holding small objects in tight places and for making delicate adjustments; round-nosed pliers, handy when you need to crimp sheet metal or form a loop in a wire; diagonal cutting pliers, designed for cutting wire and cotter pins close to a flat surface; slip-joint pliers (see Fig. 39-29), with straight, serrated jaws

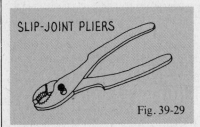

SLIP-JOINT PLIERS

Fig. 39-29

and a screw or pivot holding the jaws in either of two positions in order to grasp small or large objects; slip-joint combination pliers, similar to slip-joint pliers, but with the additional feature of a side cutter at the junction of the jaws which can cut material such as soft wire and nails.

Vises and clamps: Vises are used for holding work when it is being planed, sawed, drilled, shaped, sharpened or riveted, or when wood is being glued. Clamps are used for holding work which, because of its shape and size, cannot be satisfactorily held in a vise, or when a vise is not available. Clamps are generally used for light work. There are many types of vises and clamps. Some of the most common include a machinist's bench

vise, a bench and pipe vise, a clamp base vise, a blacksmith's vise, a pipe vise, a C-clamp (see Fig. 39-30), and a hand-screw clamp.

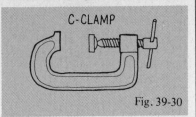

C-CLAMP

Fig. 39-30

Keep vises clean at all times. You should clean and wipe a vise with a light oil after using it.

Sharpening stones: All sharpening stones are divided into two groups, natural and artificial. Natural stones have very fine grains and are excellent for putting razorlike edges on fine cutting tools. Most sharpening stones have one coarse and one fine face. Some of these stones are mounted, and the working face of some of the sharpening stones is a combination of coarse and fine grains. Stones are available in a variety of shapes. Use a coarse stone to sharpen large and very dull or nicked tools. Use a medium-grain stone to sharpen tools not requiring a finished edge, such as tools for working soft wood, cloth, leather and rubber. Use a fine stone and an oilstone to sharpen and hone tools requiring a razorlike edge. If the stones become uneven from improper use, true the uneven surfaces on an old grinding wheel or on a grinding stone. Stones must be carefully stored in boxes or on special racks when not in use. Never lay them down on uneven surfaces or place them where they may be knocked off a table or bench or where heavy objects may fall on them. Do not store sharpening stones in a hot place.

Power tools

Power tools offer an efficient and economical means of building or repairing items around the home, but some of the same features—sharp, rapidly moving parts and electric current—that make these tools useful also can make them dangerous. Never operate power equipment unless you are familiar with the controls and operating procedures. Inspect all tools before using to see that they are clean and functioning. Be sure you have good illumination when working.

Safe use of power tools: Most injuries associated with electrical home tools are due to contact with the cutting surface, electrocution and shock, fire, and flying pieces of wood and other stock. The need for caution in using power tools cannot be overemphasized. Be especially mindful of the above safety points, which are described in more detail on the following pages.

Contact with the cutting surface. A leading cause of injuries involving power tools is contact with the blade, bit, or other sharp revolving surface on drills and sanders. A blade guard should be provided on tools that can be equipped with them, such as jointers, planers and automatic lathes, and it should be kept in good working order.

On portable tools, look for a "deadman" switch that shuts off power when hand pressure is released, and dynamic braking that makes the blade, bit or other attachment stop immediately after you turn off the power.

When there is binding between the cutter and the board or other stock, the stock is violently ejected, exposing the hands to the blade or bit. This kickback can be caused by cutting too deeply or quickly or cutting stock with knots, embedded nails or screws. Keep blades, bits, wheels and other attachments sharp, clean and lubricated and cutters securely fastened in place to help prevent kickback and broken attachments. When feasible, move portable tools away from hands and body instead of toward them.

Blades, bits and other attachments can shatter and cut the user as they break when too much pressure is exerted on a tool with defective parts or with unevenly attached pieces. To avoid broken parts, don't use attachments that are intended for a larger or smaller tool or a higher-speed tool. When practical, don't start the motor when the bit or blade is in contact with the work. Finally, don't exert undue pressure on the tool when it is in operation.

Users of tools can be cut when repairing or carrying a tool without first turning it off and unplugging it, or from not following other safety precautions. Many children are injured when playing with tools that have been left within their reach.

To help avoid accidents involving contact with cutting surfaces:

1. Look for comfortable, securely attached handles on tools.

2. Look for an on/off switch located where it cannot be turned on accidentally.

3. Read the instruction manual thoroughly before using a new, borrowed or rented tool to better understand its capabilities and hazards.

4. Dress appropriately; wear closed, sturdy shoes and safety glasses. Don't wear loose clothing, ties or jewelry that may catch in moving parts. Roll up loose shirt sleeves.

5. To avoid falling onto or dropping a portable tool, don't overextend your reach.

6. Don't work when tired, rushed or anxious.

7. Keep the work area clear of loose material. Move electric cables and extension cords out of the way so you won't trip on them.

8. Wait until the motor is off, all parts are stopped, and the tool is unplugged and cool before repairing it, cleaning it or carrying it to another spot.

9. Keep children away from the work area at all times. Never allow them to operate tools.

10. Store tools in a high or locked place, away from children.

11. Failure to use a vise or clamps, when appropriate, to hold the work in place also can contribute to injuries. If the hand or tool slips or kickback occurs, the hand and fingers can be exposed to the cutting surface.

Electrocutions and shocks. To reduce the risk of electrocution, choose tools carefully. Some appliances you use (such as power tools) can have double insulation or provision for connecting the metal housing to ground through the third conductor in the flexible cord supplying the appliance.

In general, to avoid electrocutions and shocks from the use of power tools, observe the following precautions:

1. Install a ground fault circuit interrupter in the housing circuit to prevent potential shocks from power tools or any other electrical appliance.

2. Do not use tools in a damp area.

3. Have a double-insulated tool tested by a qualified electrician if it turns

very hot. The insulation could be deteriorating.

4. Wear special welder's gloves or heavy leather gloves as protection against mild electrical shock as well as sparks and hot metal.

5. Do not use metal ladders, which can conduct electricity, when making electrical repairs.

6. Avoid using an extension cord. If you must use one, choose an extension cord of a suitable gauge, or wire size, for its length and with the same ampere rating as the tool. General lightweight extension cords are not adequate. Also, with an extension cord, always connect the end of a portable electric power tool into the extension cord before you insert the extension cord into an outlet.

7. Keep tools and cords away from heat, oil and sharp edges that can damage electrical insulation.

8. Disconnect tools by pulling on the plug, not the cord.

9. Repair immediately any tool that is damaged or that gives off minor shocks. Have electrical cables checked for breaks, loose connections, bare wires. Check that all prongs on plugs are secure.

Fires. Fires can break out when sparks from power tools ignite nearby flammable liquids, such as paint, varnish, gasoline and kerosene. The best way to prevent such fires is to keep all flammable liquids away from the work area when you operate a power tool or electrical accessory. In addition, potentially dangerous household liquids should always be tightly closed after use and placed out of the reach of children.

Sparks can ignite a cloth wrapped around a hot tool. Instead of using a cloth, wait until the tool cools before putting it away.

Flying materials. Another cause of injuries is contact with flying particles, sawdust, wood blocks and other materials being cut. The stock should be held with a clamp or vise, and the operator should wear eye shields or goggles to protect the eyes from fragments. Under all circumstances, the operator should be aware of the potential dangers in operating a power tool and should exercise caution.

Specific power tools: The following are some of the most common power tools used around the house. Portable

power tools are especially handy.

Power saws (excluding chain saws). The power saw, while extremely helpful, is one of the most dangerous power tools, and therefore requires great care. Major accidents occur for the following reasons:

1. Contact with the blade. This usually happens because a blade guard either was not provided for the saw, had been removed or was malfunctioning. The blade guard on portable circular saws can malfunction by staying in a retracted position after completion of the cut. Kickback can occur when the blade jams or binds in the wood and throws the saw toward the operator of portable circular saws, or propels the wood toward the operator of stationary equipment. Binding can be caused by a dull blade, warped or knotted wood, or forcing the cut. The blade continues rotating after the power is turned off.

Floors that become slippery, sometimes because sawdust or scrap has accumulated, can lead to a fall onto the blade.

2. Electric shock. Saws should be double insulated or have a three-prong grounded plug.

3. Carelessness or inexperience of the operator. Both of these reasons also account for many accidental contacts with the blade.

The U.S. Consumer Product Safety Commission offers the following suggestions for the purchase, safe use and maintenance of power saws.

Selecting the saw

● A blade guard is a necessity. Buy a saw with the guard you feel most comfortable using, and keep it on the saw. Some types of saws, such as sabre saws, cannot be designed with a guard; be especially careful to avoid contact with the blade.

● Ask a salesman for antikickback fingers on saws.

● Test the saw to see if the blade stops as soon as possible after power is turned off. Dynamic braking is an added safety feature.

● Make sure your saw is protected against shock by double insulation or a three-prong grounded plug. Three-prong plugs must be used with a three-prong socket.

Using the saw

• Read the instruction manual carefully before use.
• A ground fault circuit interrupter installed in the electrical circuit supplying power for the saw also reduces potential shocks from saws and other electrical tools and appliances by cutting off all electrical power in the circuit when it senses abnormal circuit flow.
• Keep the blade guard and other safety devices in place at all times.
• Use a push stick during ripping cuts with stationary saws to keep the hands away from the blade.
• Do not force the cut; let the saw operate at its own speed.
• Never let the saw run unattended.
• Wait until the motor is off, blade stopped, and saw unplugged or locked before repairing or cleaning around the saw.
• Keep children away from the work area at all times. Never allow them to operate power saws.
• Use an appropriate socket for three-prong plug or use a properly grounded adapter. Don't remove the third prong.
• Dress sensibly. Wear closed, sturdy shoes and safety glasses, and avoid loose clothing or jewelry that may catch in moving parts.
ing parts.
• To help prevent shock, don't use a saw in a damp or wet area.
• Put rubber or other nonslip matting around the work area. Keep the floor clean.
• Have good overall lighting in the work area.
• Keep the electric cord out of the way of cutting when using a portable saw.
• Keep the widest, heaviest part of a portable saw's base on the supported part of the material being cut.

Maintaining and storing the saw

• When repairing or replacing a three-prong grounded plug, be certain the wires are connected correctly; otherwise, the saw could become a shock hazard. Qualified electricians should repair plugs.
• Keep the blade sharp, clean and lubricated.
• Remove gum buildup on blade which could cause binding, by rubbing blade with steel wool saturated with ammonia.
• Frequently inspect and, if necessary, replace the carbon brushes on brush-type motors before they wear down.
• Inspect blade for cracks and replace promptly. A cracked blade may indicate a problem in the saw's operation.
• Store saws in a high or locked place, away from children.
• Lock motor switches of table saws when finished working, to prevent children from turning on saws.

Drills. Although it is especially designed for making holes, you can adapt a drill for different jobs by adding accessories for sanding, sawing, buffing, polishing, screwdriving, wire brushing, and paint mixing. For your first drill, select a 3/8-inch variable-speed reversible electric model.

Sanders. Sanders are tools designed to hold and operate abrasives for sanding wood, plastics and metals.

Grinders. These are tools used for rough grinding and finishing of metallic surfaces.

Measuring tools

There are many kinds of tools for making accurate measurements, necessary in executing home repairs.

Rules and tapes: There are many variations of the common rule. Sometimes the graduations are on the side only, sometimes a set of graduations is added across one end for measuring in narrow spaces.

FOLDING RULE
Fig. 39-31

STEEL TAPE
Fig. 39-32

RIGID TAPE
Fig. 39-33

A metal or wood folding rule (see Fig. 39-31) is sometimes useful, but it cannot be relied on for extremely accurate measurements because a certain amount of play develops at the joints after they have been used for a while.

Steel tapes are usually made from six to 300 feet in length (see Fig. 39-32). The shorter lengths are frequently made with a curved cross section so that they are flexible enough to roll up, but remain rigid when extended. Long, flat tapes require support over their full length when measuring, or the natural sag will cause an error in reading. A 12-foot steel tape is a handy length to select.

A flexible-rigid tape usually comes in a metal case and winds itself into the case when a button is pressed, or when the tape is pushed (see Fig. 39-33). A hook at one end slips over the object being measured so one person can handle it.

Calipers. Simple calipers (see Fig. 39-34) are used in conjunction with a scale to measure diameters. Calipers are adjusted by pulling or pushing the legs to open or close them. Fine adjustment is made by tapping one leg lightly on a hard surface to close them. Do not use them as screwdrivers or pry bars.

CALIPER
Fig. 39-34

Squares. Squares are primarily used for checking the trueness of an angle or for laying out lines on materials. Most squares have a rule marked on their edge. As a result they may also be used for measuring. There are several types of squares that you will find useful around the house:
1. Carpenter's square. The most common uses for this square (see Fig. 39-35) are laying out and squaring up

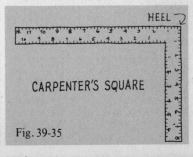

HEEL
CARPENTER'S SQUARE
Fig. 39-35

large patterns, and for testing the flatness and squareness of large surfaces. Squaring is done by placing the square at right angles to adjacent surfaces and seeing if light shows between the work and the square.

2. Try square. The try square consists of two parts at right angles to each other: a thick wood or iron stock and a thin, steel blade (see Fig. 39-36).

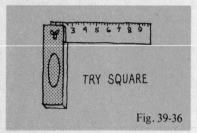

TRY SQUARE

Fig. 39-36

Most try squares are made with the blades graduated in inches and fractions of an inch. This square is used for setting or checking lines or surfaces which have to be at right angles to each other.

Levels: Levels are tools designed to determine whether a plane or surface is true horizontal or true vertical. Some precision levels are calibrated so that they will indicate, in degrees, minutes, and seconds, the angle of inclination of a surface in relation to a horizontal or vertical surface.

The level is a simple instrument consisting of a liquid, such as alcohol or chloroform, partially filling a glass tube so that a bubble remains (see Fig. 39-37). The tube is mounted in a

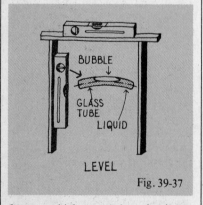

LEVEL

Fig. 39-37

frame, which may be aluminum, wood or iron. Levels are equipped with one, two or more tubes. One tube is built in the frame at right angles to another. The tube indicated in the diagram is slightly curved, causing the bubble to seek the highest point in the

tube. On the outside of the tube are two sets of graduation lines separated by a space. Leveling is accomplished when the air bubble is centered between the graduation lines.

Levels must be checked for accuracy. You can do this by placing the level on a true horizontal surface and noting the tube marking. Reverse the level end for end. If the bubble appears on one side of the graduations with reference to the operator on the first reading and on the other side for the second reading, the level is out of true and must be adjusted. Do not drop a level or handle it roughly. To prevent damage, store it in a rack or other suitable place when not in use.

Buy a 24-inch level.

Fastening components

All fasteners are designed for one purpose—to attach components together securely. Some are used best in woodworking. Others have special applications for fastening metal parts. Still others are used to accelerate fastening and unfastening panels.

Woodworking fasteners:

Nails. Nails are available in a wide range of lengths and sizes (gauges). Holding power is determined by the length of the nail, diameter and shape of the shank, and the size of the head. The usual type of shank is round, but there are various special-purpose nails with other types of shanks. Nails with square, triangular, longitudinally grooved and spirally grooved shanks have a much greater holding power than smooth, round wire nails of the same size.

The lengths of the most commonly used nails are designated by the "penny system," which originally stood for the price per pound of nails. The abbreviation of the Latin word for "penny" is the letter *d.* Thus the expression "a 2d nail" means a two-penny nail. The higher the penny, the longer and thicker the nail. Nails larger than 20d are called spikes and are generally designated by their length in inches (such as 5 inches or 6½ inches); nails smaller than 2d are designated in fractions of an inch instead of in the penny system. (Some nails are not sized according to the penny system but according to length. Ask a hardware salesperson for help.)

You will need to find the right type and size of nail for the repair work

you are doing (see Fig. 39-38). The brad and finish nails both have a deep

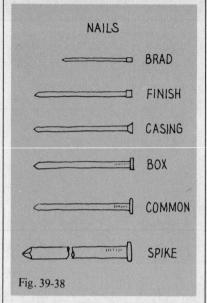

NAILS

BRAD
FINISH
CASING
BOX
COMMON
SPIKE

Fig. 39-38

countersink head that is designed to be set below the surface of the work. These nails are used for interior and exterior trim work where the nails are set and puttied to conceal their location. The casing nail is used for the same purpose, but because of its flat countersink head it may be driven flush and left that way. One of the most widely used and strongest nails is one with a flat head without countersink, known as the common nail. It is used in general wood construction. Other nails are box nails, a skinny version of the common nail, for rough, light work when appearance does not matter. Thinner in gauge than common nails and not as strong, roofing nails with large heads hold down roof shingles and asphalt roll roofs.

Wood screws. Screws have several advantages over nails. You can easily withdraw them at any time without injuring the material. They hold the wood more securely, can be easily tightened, and generally are neater in appearance. They come in seemingly limitless shapes and sizes. The screw most people are familiar with is the wood screw, usually made of common steel.

The size of an ordinary wood screw is indicated by the length and body diameter (unthreaded part) of the screw. The three most common types of wood screws are flat head, round head, and oval head (see Fig. 39-39). Body diameters are designated by gauge numbers, running from 0 (for about a $\frac{1}{16}$-inch diameter) to 24 (for about a $\frac{3}{8}$-inch diameter). The designation of length and gauge number would appear, for example, as "1$\frac{1}{4}$-9" to mean a No. 9 screw 1$\frac{1}{4}$ inches long. In general, the length of a screw for holding two pieces of wood together should be such that after the body extends through the piece being screwed down, the threaded portion (about two-thirds of the screw) will take hold in the other piece.

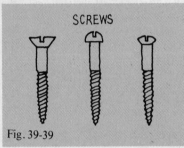

SCREWS

Fig. 39-39

It is a good practice to drill a pilot hole whenever you are planning to insert a screw in wood. Never use a hammer to force it—there will be no surface left for the threads to grab. Choose the proper drill bit for the pilot hole—the same as the inside diameter of the spiral thread (the root diameter). It is better to drill a hole too small rather than too big; it can always be enlarged. If the pilot hole is the proper size and the screw is still difficult to drive in, withdraw it and coat the threads of the screw with soap, beeswax, or paraffin.

Bolts. A bolt is distinguished from a wood screw by the fact that it does not thread into the wood, but goes through and is held by a nut threaded onto the end of the bolt. The three most common types of bolts used in woodworking are stove bolts, machine bolts and carriage bolts.

Metal-fastening devices: You can fasten metal parts together with various fastening devices such as rivets, bolts, and screws. Rivets provide a more permanent type of fastening, whereas bolts and screws are used to fasten together parts that may have to be taken apart later. Use molly screws or toggle bolts on a plastered wall where strength is needed to hold heavy pictures, mirrors, or towel bars, for example.

Miscellaneous supplies

There are, in addition, other tools, equipment and supplies you should have on hand to be properly equipped for making home repairs.

Sharpening tools: To keep hand tools in the best usable condition, cutting edges must be sharpened frequently and certain other tools trued or shaped for special purposes. Shape or sharpen chisels, punches, drills, tinships, screwdrivers and other hand tools on an abrasive grinding wheel. Too much grinding, however, shortens the useful life of a tool. You should also have on hand sandpaper in a number of finishes from coarse to very fine.

Adhesives: You will need a variety of adhesives for both indoor and outdoor jobs. Use any glue carefully, according to instructions on the container.

Plumber's tools: Be sure to have a rubber suction cup, also known as a plumber's friend or plunger, to unclog a toilet or drain; a seat-grinding tool for refacing a faucet seat; a toilet (closet) auger and an auger or snake for removing obstructions. Additional tools and supplies are listed in "Plumbing" chapter, pages 130–138.

Ladders

Whether using a stepladder to paint a ceiling or an extension ladder to clean out gutters, it pays to take extra precautions. A fall from the height of even a low ladder can mean a painful and incapacitating injury.

Selecting a ladder: Taking proper precautions with ladders begins with the selection of a ladder. The major considerations are the type of work the ladder will be used for, the weight the ladder will have to carry, and the construction of the ladder.

The majority of ladders sold for household use are Type III light-duty ladders, rated for a maximum load of 200 pounds (the user plus materials). If the ladder will have to carry more weight than this, select a Type II medium-duty ladder for a maximum load of 225 pounds or a Type I heavy-duty ladder for a maximum load of 250 pounds. Most ladders will be labeled with their duty rating.

Buy a ladder long enough for any use to which you might put it. Keep in mind that the length of a ladder is

not the same thing as its usable length. You should not stand on the top step or the top of a stepladder. The top three rungs of a straight or extension ladder are not meant to be stood on either, and the height these ladders can safely reach is further reduced by the angle at which they are used.

On metal ladders, check for sharp edges, dents, and bent steps, rungs or rails. Wooden ladders should be free of splits, cracks, chips and all but small, tight knots. No ladder should have loose rungs or steps.

Steps on wooden stepladders should be reinforced underneath with metal rods or metal angle braces that are securely attached to the step and side rail. The bottom step of all stepladders should have metal angle braces.

The construction of an individual stepladder can be checked by standing on the first step from the bottom and trying to twist the ladder. If it feels unsteady, choose another ladder.

All metal ladders should have slip-resistant rubber or plastic feet. Metal stepladders should have slip-resistant steps. Some wooden stepladders also have this desirable feature.

Metal ladders will conduct electricity. Therefore a wooden or fiberglass ladder is preferable if the ladder will be used in the vicinity of power lines or electrical equipment.

Using a ladder safely: Even a rigidly constructed ladder can be involved in an accident if the proper precautions are not taken in its use. Critical factors in safe use include reading all instructions accompanying the ladder, setting up the ladder properly and using good sense while working on the ladder. You will usually use a straight or extension ladder for outdoor work and a stepladder for indoor work. Never leave any raised ladder unattended.

Straight and extension ladders. To raise a straight ladder, brace the lower end against a wall and then grasp the top rung with both hands (see Fig. 39-40). Raise the top end and walk underneath the ladder, moving down the rungs until the ladder is vertical. To use an extension ladder, raise it to the desired height, being sure the locks on both sides of the ladder engage securely.

To position the ladder properly, place the top of the ladder against the

Fig. 39-40

wall so that the distance between the wall and the base of the ladder is one quarter of its working length. Since the rungs on ladders are normally one foot apart, the approximate distance is easy to compute (see Fig. 39-41).

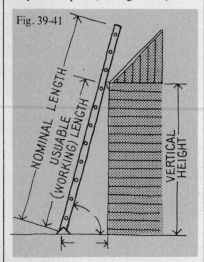
Fig. 39-41

If the ladder is to be used for getting onto a roof, there should be three feet of ladder—at least three rungs—extending beyond the edge of the roof.

The ground under the ladder should be level and firm. Large, flat wooden boards placed under the ladder can level a ladder on uneven ground or give a ladder better footing on soft ground. If possible, secure the ladder in place. A good practice is to have a helper hold the bottom of the ladder.

Other points to remember when raising and positioning the ladder: Never use a ladder in a strong wind; the point where the ladder rests against the wall should be flat and firm; a ladder should not be placed in front of a door that is not locked, blocked or guarded; and before positioning the ladder, check for nests under the eaves—the top of a ladder is no place to discover a wasp nest.

Face the ladder when climbing or descending and use both hands. Mount the ladder from the center, not from the side. Tools should be carried in the pockets, in a bag attached to the belt, or raised and lowered by rope. Be sure that the soles of your shoes, preferably rubber, are clean and dry.

Work facing the ladder, holding on with one hand. If it is ever necessary to work with both hands, hook one leg over a rung. A good general guide is to keep your body centered between the rails of the ladder at all times. If you find that you must reach far to the side to get to the work area, get down and move the ladder.

In case of sudden dizziness or a panicky feeling, bow your head, drape both arms over the rung in front of you, close your eyes, and wait until the feeling passes.

Do not use a ladder as a scaffold or for any purpose other than that for which it was intended.

Be very careful about using a metal ladder around electrical wires or equipment. Many fatalities occur when a metal ladder brushes against power lines. Use only double-insulated or properly grounded electrical tools on a metal ladder; even better, use such equipment only on a dry wooden or nonconductive fiberglass ladder.

Stepladders. Many of the suggestions for using straight and extension ladders apply equally to a stepladder. In addition, follow the rules below when using a stepladder.

Erect a stepladder on a flat, level surface. Do not place it on a table or any similar platform for added height. Never use a stepladder as a straight ladder.

Before climbing a stepladder, make sure that its legs are fully extended and the spreader locked. The locking device on some ladders can pinch, so keep the fingers clear when setting up the ladder.

Do not step on the top platform or top step (see Fig. 39-42).

Do not step on the bucket shelf or attempt to climb or stand on the rear section.

Fig. 39-42

Storing and maintaining your ladder: To keep your ladder in good condition, store and maintain it properly.

Inspect a ladder before each use for wear and damage. This is particularly important after a long period of storage or after a ladder has fallen.

Never use a damaged ladder. Have repair work done only by a competent repair shop. If the damage is major, discard the ladder. Do not attempt to straighten a bent metal ladder.

Periodically tighten the reinforcing rods under the steps of a stepladder, the spreaders and other hardware.

Ladders should be stored in a sheltered area. Wooden ladders suffer from exposure to heat and dampness and need a dry, well-ventilated storage area. A wooden ladder used outdoors should be shellacked, varnished or given two coats of linseed oil as a protective coating. Never paint a wooden ladder; the paint can hide defects.

Store straight or extension ladders horizontally on racks or hooks with support points at the top, middle and bottom of the ladder to prevent sagging and warping.

Emergency supplies

Be sure to keep on hand the following articles in case of a home emergency: flashlight, in good working order plus extra batteries; portable radio, in good working order plus extra batteries; candles in case of a power failure; large matches, for lighting candles and relighting pilot lights on gas appliances; spare fuses; fire extinguishers (see "Fire Safety," pages 138–150); a variety of knives, including a good pocket knife; and a 25-foot, three-prong extension cord.

122

40

ELECTRICAL EMERGENCIES

Most of us take electricity for granted. Our homes are filled with electrical appliances which keep us warm, cook our food, give us light, and provide entertainment. But electricity is also a source of potential problems. For example, if a person operates a radio while in the bathtub, stands on wet ground while using power tools or sticks a fork in a toaster to dislodge a piece of toast, he can receive an electrical shock which may be fatal. An overloaded circuit or a poor electrical connection can start a fire.

This chapter will help you to use electricity safely, and to deal with common electrical emergencies around the house. For major repairs, it may be better to call in a qualified electrician.

WHAT IS ELECTRICITY?

Electricity is a form of energy generated by friction, induction, or chemical change. It is distributed to a house through individual circuits from the household's local power center, either from fuses in a fuse box or circuit breakers in a circuit breaker box. Electricity is described in the following terms:

Ampere is a measure of the amount of current which flows through a wire. It is the current which can hurt or kill you.

Volt is a measure of the force which pushes the current along the wire. High voltage is generated at the power plant and is transformed down to approximately 120 volts for most home circuits.

Ohm is a measure of the resistance to the flow of current. The human body, especially when wet, has low resistance and therefore can conduct electric current.

Watt is a measure of electrical power, or the rate of using a certain number of amperes pushed by a certain number of volts (watts = volts × amperes).

To understand these terms better, consider this example. Suppose that an electric frying pan uses 1200 watts when it is operated. Since the normal house voltage is 120 volts, the amount of current (amperes) flowing through the frying pan is 10 amperes. A lethal dose of current in the human body is much less than one ampere, so if even a small fraction of the current in the frying pan leaks and runs through your body you can receive a fatal electrical shock. If the shock does not kill you immediately, it can cause convulsive heart action which may lead to death.

Consider another example. The normal wall outlet is capable of carrying 15 amperes (most fuses and circuit breakers will safeguard your home by breaking the circuit if the current is more than 15 amperes). If you overload a wall outlet with a 10-ampere frying pan, a 5-ampere coffeemaker, and a 4-ampere blender, either a circuit breaker will trip or a fuse will blow. However, if you have used a high-amperage fuse, the current will continue to flow; and the overloaded outlet and the house wiring will heat up, most likely causing an electrical fire.

USING ELECTRICITY SAFELY

To use electricity safely, you should be sure the appliances and tools you use have been tested for safety by an independent testing agency such as Underwriters Laboratories Inc., and have been evaluated for electrical, fire and mechanical hazards. Know when and how to use extension and appliance cords, how to use receptacles, what codes should be complied with, and how to avoid an electrical shock.

Grounding

Electricity is ground seeking and will force its way through anything grounded. Accidents occur when, because of faulty equipment, a circuit shorts out or when the amount of current is more than the wires, appliances and other circuit components can handle safely.

The human body is a good conductor of electrical current. Therefore, you should choose appliances carefully. Some appliances you use (such as power tools) can have double insulation or have provisions for connecting the outside metal enclosure to ground through a third conductor in the flexible cord supplying the appliance. If there is a current leak in the normal circuit (which uses the two regular prongs in a plug), the current can be carried directly to the ground by a third wire (the third prong in a plug). While some current could still pass through your body if you touch an appliance which has a fault in the normal circuit, most of the current will be carried to the ground by the third wire (provided it is used and does not have a loose, corroded or poor connection). Some outlets have a provision for the third prong. You should always use the third prong when it is found on your appliance; do not break or cut it off. It is also safer to have your wall outlets rewired to accept three-prong plugs than to use two-prong adapters. However, if you must use an adapter, be sure to attach the pigtail third wire to the screw holding the faceplate to the wall receptacle. If the screw itself is properly grounded (which can be determined by an electrician), this should provide a line to carry any leaking current directly to the ground. If it is not grounded, you must install a wire from the ground to the outlet box.

Ground fault circuit interrupters: Until recently, there was no positive way to protect against fault currents (accidental electrical paths to ground) that were too small to actuate fuses or circuit breakers in your home. Now, a device has been developed which senses ground faults in circuits and immediately cuts off all electrical power in that circuit. This device is called a "ground fault circuit interrupter," or GFCI. Many building codes now require installation of one or more GFCIs in new construction. Most circuits in existing houses do not have GFCIs, but it is a good idea to have them installed, by a qualified electrician. The GFCI provides protection against electrical shock, especially in circuits servicing bathrooms, kitchens, laundry facilities, exterior receptacles and swimming pools.

Using extension and appliance cords safely

Each year many people are injured using extension and appliance cords incorrectly. Follow these suggestions for purchasing and using them correctly.
● Use extension cords only as a temporary convenience.
● When buying an extension cord, test the receptacle to be sure the appliance plug fits properly.

● Look for extension cords with self-closing outlets to cover unused receptacles, or with only a single outlet if that is all that is required. (At present these are difficult to find on the market, but are especially good if children are around.) Or, cover unused extension cord receptacles with electricians' tape or plastic safety caps, to prevent, for example, a child from making mouth contact with the current.

● Be sure that no plug prongs are exposed when the extension cord receptacle is being used.

● Use special extension cords with at least 15 amps to carry the load for high-wattage appliances such as air conditioners and freezers.

● Never overload a wall receptacle with too many appliances by using multireceptacle adapters or cords.

● Instruct children not to go near plugs and outlets, and not to attempt to unplug cords.

● Have extension and appliance cords replaced at the first sign of wear, so you avoid electrocution, electrical burns, shock or short circuits.

● Use only three-wire extension cords for appliances with three-prong plugs. Never snip off the third prong.

● Use outdoor extension cords with outdoor appliances.

The National Electrical Code requires that wall outlets be no more than six feet apart; this short distance usually eliminates the need for extension cords.

Wall outlets

The insertion of foreign metallic objects into wall outlets, most often by small children, is a common cause of electrical accidents. When an object of low resistance, such as a hairpin, completes the circuit, a short circuit develops that will normally trip the circuit breaker or blow the fuse because of the high current flow. The object will then become hot and most likely cause burns or perhaps ignite a fire. When two objects are inserted simultaneously and the circuit is completed through an individual's hand or body, the only chance for protection is if the shock knocks the person or object free, or if the power is shut off. If a GFCI is used in the circuit, it will detect the unequal flow of current and open the circuit in time to prevent a fatal shock.

There are several types of caps de-

signed to cover an unused outlet in order to reduce the hazard of shocks and to deter children from inserting a foreign object. You can insert into the outlet a plastic safety cap, which can be purchased at most drug or hardware stores, or you can use outlets with rotary caps that must be rotated 90 degrees to expose the plugs. Another possible solution is to raise outlets from the present standard of 12 to 16 inches above the floor to a height beyond the reach of small children. In children's bedrooms, you can place all convenience outlets on a circuit controlled by one switch. Outlets would then be deenergized except when the switch is thrown.

Always be sure a plug is completely inserted in a wall outlet with none of its prongs exposed, because a poor contact at the wall outlet may overheat both the plug and the outlet and cause an accident.

The same hazards which exist with indoor receptacles also exist with outdoor receptacles.

Avoiding electrical shock

Electrical shock can be caused by equipment failure, negligence, or both. To avoid electrical shock, always be sure equipment is deenergized before working on it, avoid making unauthorized modifications on equipment, and always repair equipment that has caused shocks. Test the insulation resistance and the completion of the ground connection after repairing the equipment.

You can make sure you have turned off the electricity in an outlet by plugging in a lamp which you know is working properly. If the lamp goes on, you probably shut off the wrong circuit breaker or removed the wrong fuse. Switch on the circuit breaker you turned off or replace the fuse you removed. Then turn off the power in another fuse or circuit breaker. Test again. When the lamp goes off, you know the power in that circuit is also off.

You should also know about testers. Use a voltage tester to check that the current is off before you begin an electrical job. It lights up when its probes are touched to anything that is charged with electricity. Or you can use it with the power on to test for proper grounding. Use a continuity tester only with the power off to find

the malfunction in a wiring component, such as checking to see if a cartridge fuse has blown.

Be sure your body never forms part of a closed circuit through which current can flow.

If you feel even a slight shock when you touch an appliance, stop using it. Unplug it, and have it checked. Always repair all broken insulation or other defects immediately.

Receiving an electrical shock can be an emergency. To treat a victim, see page 52.

Note. Electrical contractors are required to follow either the National Electrical Code or the Uniform Building Code to insure safety in making electrical repairs and changes. Be sure if you have a repair made by a contractor that he complies with the code.

COMMON ELECTRICAL REPAIRS

If you are not experienced in making electrical repairs, do not attempt any major jobs. Instead call in a qualified electrician. If minor problems are involved, however—replacing a blown fuse or fixing the circuit breaker or rewiring a lamp—you can master these repairs yourself by following the instructions on the following pages.

When making any electrical repairs, insulate yourself: Wear dry shoes, rubber gloves, and stand on a rubber mat. Use just one hand and keep your other hand free. Do not use metal ladders, which can conduct electricity. When changing light bulbs, disconnect the lamp first.

If you smell gas from a gas range or other gas appliance, don't turn any electrical switches on or off because a spark could ignite the gas. Extinguish all open flames and pilots. Open all windows and doors, and then call the gas company immediately and have the gas shut off. Do not hunt for a gas leak yourself.

Follow all directions on labels or instruction booklets, especially regarding heavy-duty extension cords or special circuits, which some appliances require. Remember that the UL (Underwriters Laboratories) label is not a complete guarantee of safety. It means that Underwriters Laboratories, a nonprofit organization, has tested samples of the product and found them in compliance with volun-

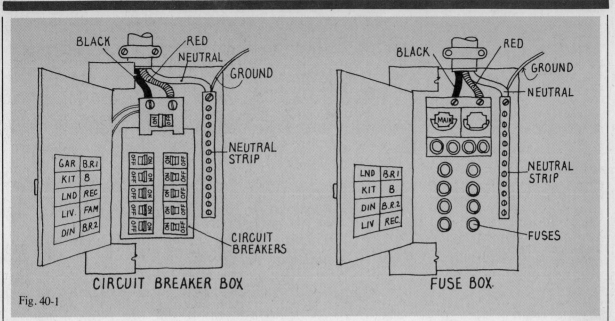

Fig. 40-1

tary safety standards. Use the electrical troubleshooting guide on page 148 of "Fire Safety" for adding up the wattages of common household appliances and for taking corrective action when an electrical problem develops.

Note. If your house is wired with 15-20-amp aluminum wire, a fire hazard may exist. Call in an electrician to check the wiring and possibly repair or replace it.

Replacing a fuse or circuit breaker

The electrical system of your house is protected by the fuses of a fuse box or the circuit breakers in a circuit breaker box (see Fig. 40-1). When a current exceeds a safe amount, either a fuse will blow or a circuit breaker will trip, stopping the flow of electricity in that circuit. By noting on your fuse box or circuit breaker box which branch circuit of the house each fuse or circuit breaker controls, you isolate future problems. It is wise to label the box when you first move into your house. Working with another person, discover by trial and error which fuse or circuit breaker controls which appliance(s) or outlet(s). One person stands at the box removing the fuses or flipping the switches while the other person writes down the results.

When the current stops in your house, first determine the problem. For example, check to make sure you are not operating a defective appliance

or too many appliances on one circuit. Restoring the electricity will depend on which type of protection you have. If you have a fuse box, unplug or unscrew (usually counterclockwise) the fuse that blew, using a fuse puller (if you have one) for additional safety. There are different types of fuses, and with some—the screw-in plug and time-delay fuses—it is easy to recognize a blown fuse by the melted metal strip behind the fuse window. If the fuse blew because of a short circuit, the melted metal piece will leave the window discolored. If, however, the fuse blew because of an overload, the metal piece will have melted but the window will remain clear. With a cartridge fuse, there will be no evidence of damage when the fuse blows. You should then remove the fuse and check it by touching a continuity tester to the metal and caps. If the tester bulb lights, the fuse is good and an appliance (or appliances) you were using is at fault. If the bulb does not light, the fuse has probably blown and you must replace it. If that still does not correct the problem, call an electrician for help. When installing any fuse, turn off all lights and devices on the circuit controlled by that fuse for safety. Then install a new fuse of the same ampere rating as the one that blew. Installing a larger fuse than that recommended for the circuit can expose the house to the possibility of electrical fire. Always keep a supply of the types and sizes of fuses you

need next to your fuse box to avoid delay and inconvenience in making the repair. Never replace a fuse by a penny or any other metal object.

Many people find it worthwhile to replace a fuse box with a circuit breaker. With a circuit breaker, you will merely set the switch that tripped to the "on" position, or in some cases to the "off" and then to the "on" position. Many new homes come equipped with a circuit breaker box rather than a fuse box.

If a fuse blows or a circuit breaker trips frequently and you cannot locate a short circuit, an overload, or a problem in the wiring, a switch or an outlet, call in a qualified electrician.

Never test any circuit with your fingers or with tools.

Some people feel safer if they shut down the power for the entire house before making repairs. Do this at the main switch on the fuse or circuit breaker box. Then proceed with the repair. Afterward turn the power back on.

Repairing or replacing electrical plugs

If your lamps or appliances do not work right, the problem may be the electrical plugs. If your old plug cannot be used, buy a new plug with a UL label. A damaged plug can cause a fire or a shock. For repairing a damaged plug, see Figs. 40-2 through 40-9. Using a knife, cut the cord to remove the damaged part. Slip the

125

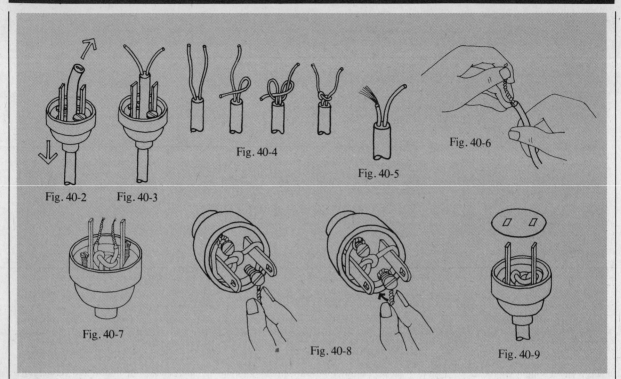

Fig. 40-4

Fig. 40-5

Fig. 40-6

Fig. 40-2   Fig. 40-3

Fig. 40-7

Fig. 40-8

Fig. 40-9

new plug on the cord. Clip and separate the cord. Tie Underwriters knot. Remove a half inch of insulation from the end of the wires. Do not cut any of the small wires. Twist small wires together, clockwise. Pull knot down firmly in the plug. Wrap the wire around the screw, clockwise. Tighten the screw with a screwdriver. Insulation should come to the screw but not under it. Place insulation cover back over the plug.

Replacing an electrical switch

A switch is a device used to connect an electrical circuit with the source of power. When a light flickers, it may be necessary to replace an electrical switch. You can purchase one of the many types available—an ordinary toggle switch, a silent mercury switch, or one of the attractive decorator switches that have been marketed recently. Although the one you choose may not be identical with the old unit, it is installed in basically the same way. Be sure to obtain a three-way switch as a replacement when two switches located on different walls control a single fixture—for example, when a switch on the wall at the bottom of the stairs and another one at the head of the stairs control the same ceiling light.

To insure your safety, shut off the current that leads to the device you are going to replace, by either tripping the circuit breaker to the "off" position or removing the fuse. If you are afraid to work with electricity, do not attempt to install a new unit—call in a professional electrician.

Once the current is turned off, remove the faceplate that covers the device, and then the two screws that secure the switch to the metal wall box. Pull the unit a few inches out of the box. You may meet slight resistance—the wires attached to the instrument are a little stiff. Loosen the terminal screws. For the absent-minded: Make a diagram noting where each wire was secured as it is detached. There may be only one black and one white wire; two black wires; or in the three-way switch one black, one white, and one red wire. There also may be a green wire included with any of these combinations. Note, too, that there are colored screws—brass coated for the black and red wires, zinc coated for the white wires, and green coated for the green wire. You want to rewire the new switch exactly as the old one.

To install the device correctly, the top of the switch must be placed in the upright position. Loosen a screw,

hold the hook of the wire facing clockwise, and situate it underneath the screw head. With the screwdriver turning to the right, tighten the screw down upon the wire. Return the newly wired unit to the box and replace the screws that hold it firmly against the wall. Resecure the switch plate and flip the switch to "off."

Turn the current back on and the switch will work. If the main house power was tripped, remember to reset any electrical clocks or lamp-timers and any thermostat timers.

Rewiring a lamp

An erratically functioning lamp is annoying. The light may flicker or periodically remain unlit when the switch is turned on. Check that the bulb is secure in the socket and the plug firm in the outlet. If there are no problems in either case, find the source of the trouble by dismantling the unit. It may be that the switch is broken, the cord is worn, or the terminal connections in either plug or socket are loose. If the unit is old, it's a good idea to replace socket and cord.

Step 1: Set the unplugged fixture on a table. All lamps have three components—socket, cord and plug (see Fig. 40-10). Diagram the assembly as you take it apart. The socket is at-

126

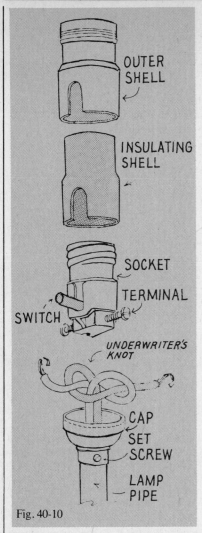

Fig. 40-10

tached to the tube in the center of the fixture and holds the whole lamp together. The cord is secured to the socket by small screws, then goes through the tube, out of the base, and into the plug.

Step 2: To replace the socket, unscrew the old socket from the pipe. Separate replacement socket, taking off outer shell and cardboard shell. (The word *press* is stamped on the outside of the shell, but if it does not come apart easily, wedge in a screwdriver to unlock the little notches at the press point). Screw the new cap onto the tube and tighten the set-screw. (Check diagram for fitting.)

Step 3: To rewire, feed fresh wire from the end of the tube up into the cap. Pull a few inches of cord out and make a small cut at the division area of the wires. Grasp each wire and pull

apart until there is a 2-inch to 2½-inch separation. Make a cut in each piece of insulation ¾ inch from the end. Take care to slice insulation and not wire. Twist insulation until it slips off wires. Make an Underwriters knot. Loosen the terminal screws, wrap the bare wires clockwise around screws, and tighten securely with a screwdriver. Reassemble socket and then remaining parts of the lamp.

Step 4: Add a contact-type plug to the end of the cord, following directions printed on the package.

Step 5: Insert bulb, plug in lamp, turn switch and—light.

What to do when the power goes off

If the power in your home goes off completely, check to see if neighboring houses have power.

If the power is off only in your house, it may be due to an overloaded or short circuit. Turn off lights and unplug all appliances. Replace one fuse at a time or switch on one circuit breaker at a time to locate the problem. Plug in each appliance and turn each light switch one at a time. If power fails again after an appliance is plugged back in or a light is turned on, you know that is where the problem exists. Have that appliance checked or the outlet or wiring repaired.

If neighboring houses also do not have power, there may be trouble in the outside lines. If so, report the power failure to the power company. For these occasions, known commonly as "blackouts," you should have on hand such emergency supplies as candles, a flashlight with good working batteries, a battery-powered radio, food that does not require cooking, paper plates and plastic utensils, and wood if you have a fireplace. Check these supplies periodically, and whenever you know a storm is approaching. In case of a storm, unplug major appliances, but leave one light switch on so you know when the electricity comes back on. By unplugging appliances you will avoid a sudden surge of power that can cause fuses to blow or circuit breakers to trip when electricity returns.

If the electricity goes off in cold weather, turn off the water supply at the main inlet water valve and drain

the water from the rest of the plumbing so your pipes do not freeze and burst. For other suggestions on coping with a power failure, including keeping food on hand, see Chapter 57, "Natural Disasters."

USING APPLIANCES SAFELY

The Association of Home Appliance Manufacturers advises consumers to read and carefully follow the instructions that come with an appliance. Do not rely on your experience with an older, slightly different appliance or on the experience of friends or neighbors who may have a product that is similar but not quite the same. The basic rule is to keep an appliance clean and in good repair. Following are guidelines from the association on using appliances wisely.

When installing a new appliance or moving appliances to a new location, have a qualified electrician verify the following facts: that adequate electrical service is available to the home; that the addition of the appliance will not overload the individual household circuit on which it is used; that appliance circuits have adequately grounded, three-prong receptacles; and that grounded outlets are properly polarized.

Most individual circuits can supply up to a maximum of 15 amps, and therefore should supply only one major appliance having a rating of no more than 12 amps or several smaller appliances having ratings of no more than 7.5 amps. It should be remembered that there is usually more than one outlet per circuit. The total amps needed by a number of appliances in use simultaneously should not exceed the limitation of the circuit fuse. Overloading electric outlets can cause a short circuit or even a fire.

A three-prong (grounding) plug is provided on many major appliances for protection against shock hazards, and should be plugged directly into a properly grounded three-prong receptacle. Where a two-prong wall receptacle is encountered, replace it with a properly grounded three-prong receptacle in accordance with the National Electrical Code and local codes and ordinances. Have a qualified electrician do the work.

The use of an extension cord is not recommended. If you do use one, be sure the conductor is large enough to

127

handle the load of the appliances. Do not use a cord with wire smaller than 16 gauge, and be sure it has a three-prong (grounding) electrical plug.

General recommendations

- Learn the correct use of the appliance by reading the instruction book.
- Do not overload.
- Use appliances only for intended purposes.
- Do not use any appliance when your body is grounded better than that appliance—for example, when you are in the bathtub, when your hands are in water, or when you are standing on wet grass. Do not use electrical appliances outside when they can get wet because the water can cause a short circuit and possibly fatal electric shock.
- Be sure the appliance fits the setting in which it is used. Many appliances such as refrigerators also require ventilation around them to carry away heat.
- Keep appliances in good repair. Worn cords and loose plugs should be correctly replaced.
- Always grasp the plug—not the cord—when disconnecting an appliance from an outlet.
- Do not operate an appliance that is partially disassembled, or when some part is missing or broken.
- If you feel even a slight shock when you touch an appliance, stop using it immediately. Unplug it and have an electrician check it. Repair all broken insulation or other defects.
- If an appliance starts smoking, if it feels unusually hot, or if it is producing an odor, pull the plug or otherwise shut off the electricity. Do not use it again until it has been carefully checked and any fault corrected. To avoid what could be a fatal shock, do not pour water on an appliance while it is plugged in. If the appliance is on fire, follow the instructions for extinguishing Class C fires, page 141 in "Fire Safety."
- Do not ignore or disconnect the safety devices. They indicate that something is wrong and requires proper servicing.
- Keep children away from a machine that is in operation. Unplug and close or lock appliances not in use.

Specific appliances

Observe these recommendations in using the following appliances.

Dehumidifiers: Unplug the unit before removing cabinet or before servicing. Always replace the cabinet before operating the unit to avoid contact with rotating fan blades or live electrical parts. Unplug the unit before correcting an overflow. Empty water regularly if this is required for proper functioning. Be sure the air inlet and outlet are not blocked.

Dishwashers: Use a separate, properly rated and fused circuit. For built-in units, follow manufacturer's recommendations for installation of an air gap in the drain line. Follow the manufacturer's instructions for grounding. Do not touch the heating element if the dry cycle is interrupted or at the end of the cycle. The heating element might still be hot enough to burn you. When interrupting the wash cycle, be sure that the water action has stopped before opening the door or lid. The following box tells how to cope with some common dishwasher problems.

What to do when . . .

—*pump motor won't run.* Check fuses, circuit breakers, motor brushes, or something inside pump causing impellor to be jammed.
—*final rinse won't shut off.* Check rinse valve or valve stem that is jammed, dirt or pipe scale that is under the valve seat, or a valve plunger that is jammed inside the valve body. If the machine is automatically timed, have the timer checked by maintenance people.
—*pump running but very poor or no wash action.* Check the pump intake and/or pump housing for blockage. Also, a leaking pump seal or packing gland will cause a loss of wash action. Articles frequently get into the pump intake. take.
—*no final rinse.* Check for closed valve upstream from the rinse valve. If these are electric solenoid valves, check for burned-out valve coil, broken connection, timer relay defect, defective operating switch, or blown fuse.
—*wash arms not revolving.* Check for plugged end sprays, or improper end-spray angle adjustment.

The wash spray driving out through the angled end sprays is the only force which causes the arm to revolve.
—*rinse arms not revolving.* Check for plugged rinse sprays or poor rinse pressure.

Disposers: Turn off the power switch before unjamming or removing objects from the disposer. Never put fingers in a disposer. Use a wooden spoon or the wooden handle of a spatula to loosen a jam, and tongs to remove objects from the disposer. Leave deflector in place during grinding to keep foreign objects from dropping into or being ejected by the disposer. Drain cleaners may be harmful to the disposer. Allow the unit to completely dispose of waste to prevent unnecessary jams during subsequent use. If a dishwasher drains into the disposer, be sure that the disposer has been cleaned before starting the dishwasher.

Microwave ovens: Do not use the microwave feature if the door is damaged—for example, a tear or gap in the closure seal, broken hinge, or warped door. Do not attempt to operate the microwave oven with the door open. Keep the door closure seals clean; dirt can build up and produce gaps in the closure. Do not defeat the safety features of your oven by poking objects into the viewing screen, door seals or other openings. Also, do not allow an object to protrude from any part of the oven during operation. Attempts to repair this oven by unqualified persons could result in damage or hazard. Have a qualified repairman make repairs.

Ranges: Know where your main range electrical disconnect or gas shutoff valve is located. In gas ovens, turn off pilots when using spray oven cleaners. Fasten long hair and loose clothing when working with or near an operating range. Do not leave small children unattended near a range when the range is in use. Turn pot handles away from outer edges. Be careful of flammable substances in cooking and baking areas. Do not store combustibles in ovens. Do not use water on grease fires. Smother with nonflammable lid or use dry chemical- or foam-type extinguisher. Keep hoods and grease filters clean.

128

If a fire does occur, do not throw water on it. First turn off and unplug the appliance. Then:

—carefully toss a handful of baking soda on the fire;
—slide a lid over the appliance; or
—use a dry-chemical fire extinguisher.

Refrigerators and freezers: Disconnect power cord from electrical outlet before attempting any repair work, light bulb replacement or cleaning. After the refrigerator/freezer is in operation, do not touch the refrigerating coils or surfaces, particularly with damp or wet hands. Keep fingers and hands out of automatic ice-making mechanism. Because your refrigerator or freezer is grounded (as are your sink and range), you must keep all other electrical devices nearby in good electrical repair.

Room air conditioners: Be sure to turn off and then unplug unit before removing decorative front panel for filter replacement or cleaning. Use the recommended size fuse or circuit breaker and branch circuit wire for proper and safe operation. Turn the unit off if the fan motor fails to operate. Wait for at least two minutes before restarting after the unit (compressor) has been shut off or the temperature control setting has been changed. Quick restarts may blow fuses or trip circuit breakers.

Laundry equipment: Disconnect the electric supply cord when cleaning or servicing. Wipe tubs and drums after washing and/or drying fiberglass fabrics. Keep clear of moving parts.

Automatic washers. Do not add or remove any article, or reach into the tub, unless the washer is stopped. Do not use dry-cleaning solutions or flammable or combustible products in the washer.

Automatic dryers. Only items washed in water should be put in automatic dryers. Do not dry items containing foam rubber or similarly textured rubberlike materials. Dryer heat can restart the curing process in the rubber, thus generating heat and causing fires. Clean lint filter after each load. Do not exhaust dryer into a chimney. Exhaust dryer outdoors with flameproof vent tubing. Turn main gas valve off before servicing.

Wringer washers. Keep hands away from wringer rolls and turn wringer off when not in use. Disconnect the electric supply cord and release the wringer when you leave the machine, or when cleaning or servicing. Do not use dry-cleaning solutions or flammable or combustible products in the washer.

Portable appliances: Don't leave portable appliances plugged in unless they are in actual use regardless of whether they are turned off. Don't overload electrical circuits. Be certain that proper ampere fuses are used in fuse boxes. Don't plug two heat-producing appliances into the same circuit at the same time; otherwise, these high-wattage appliances could blow a fuse or, even worse, start a fire. Unplug electrical appliances before filling with water, if water is called for. Do not use extension cords unless the wire is the right size for the wattage of the appliance. Do not tinker with the inner workings of portable-appliance thermostats; they are too delicate for anyone except an expert to try to repair. Immediately replace any frayed electrical cords or damaged plugs. Clean according to manufacturer's instructions. Don't immerse the appliance when cleaning unless the instructions clearly state that it is safe to do so. Immediately repair or take to a repair shop all damaged appliances or ones that give you an electrical shock. If they cannot be repaired, dispose of them at once.

● Unplug toasters if you must use a utensil to remove a piece of toast.
● Unplug an electric knife when not in use. Keep safety catch on. Remove blades from knife before cleaning.
● Disconnect a percolator cord when a coffee pot is empty.
● When using bonnet hair dryers, do not step into a tub of water with the bonnet on.

Televisions: Be aware that the "instant-on" feature has been suspected of causing some TV fires. If you do not desire this feature, don't buy a TV set with "instant-on," or buy one with an "instant-on defeat switch" that switches off the current.

Follow all operating instructions and safety precautions that may have been furnished with your TV. Always turn the TV off if you leave the room for more than a short time. Never leave a TV on in an empty house. Un-plug the TV from the wall outlet and disconnect the external antenna lead-in wires at the TV set when you leave on vacation. It is not recommended to routinely unplug the TV from the wall outlet after each viewing session because this can cause the stranded wires within the cord to break and develop a fire hazard, or you could be seriously shocked if the plug is carelessly removed or inserted into the wall outlet. Warn children never to drop or push objects into the TV cabinet because they could contact a part carrying hazardous voltage and receive an electrical shock. Don't cover the ventilation openings in the TV with cloth or papers, or by placing the set close to a wall or piece of furniture; this can cause the heat inside the TV cabinet to build up and start a fire. Never expose the set to rain or water. If the TV becomes damp or wet, pull the plug and have it inspected by a service technician before further use. Rain or excessive moisture may cause electrical shorts.

If abnormally loud snapping or popping noises are made by the TV set, unplug it and consult your dealer or service technician. Have dealer or technician verify that replacement parts have the same safety characteristics as original parts.

If a fire does start, pull the plug immediately to disconnect the electrical circuit. If the fire is small, and if you have a dry-chemical fire extinguisher, attempt to put out the fire. Don't use water to extinguish the fire because you could get an electrical shock. Get everyone out of the house if fire is large, and call the fire department.

If your wiring system has not been overhauled recently and your house is not new, you probably do not have enough energy to handle the requirements of modern electric living. The result is that you probably are overloading your circuits and, even worse, overworking the motors in your appliances to an extent that certainly will shorten their lives and may mean a fire hazard. Similarly, old wires if overused may dry out, causing the insulation to fall away and leave live wires dangerously exposed inside the structure, with the hazard of a fire-causing short circuit. Obsolete wiring is always dangerous.

41

PLUMBING, HEATING AND COOLING EMERGENCIES

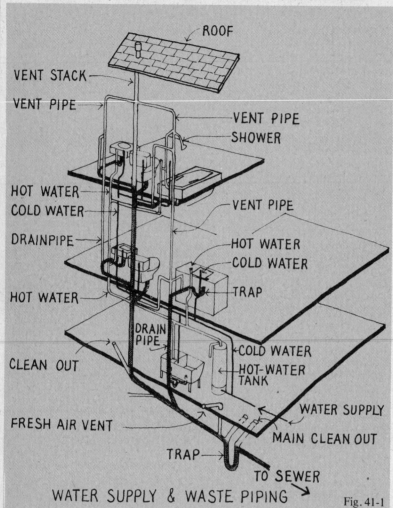

ROOF
VENT STACK
VENT PIPE
VENT PIPE
SHOWER
HOT WATER
COLD WATER
VENT PIPE
DRAINPIPE
HOT WATER
COLD WATER
TRAP
HOT WATER
DRAIN PIPE
COLD WATER
HOT-WATER TANK
CLEAN OUT
WATER SUPPLY
FRESH AIR VENT
MAIN CLEAN OUT
TRAP
TO SEWER

WATER SUPPLY & WASTE PIPING

Fig. 41-1

valve (see Fig. 41-2) that controls the flow. When the pipes branch out to lead to other parts of the house, additional valves control the water pressure to the various arms of the system. In addition, each plumbing fixture (toilet, dishwasher, lavatory, etc.) should also have its own shut-off valve, called a supply stop.

The wastes from the household running from all plumbing fixtures, except the toilets, empty by means of gravity through 1½- or 2-inch pipes, then into 3- or 4-inch drainpipes, and finally flow out into the sewer, cesspool, or septic tank. Drainage is assisted by pipes that rise up and funnel through the roof. Called vents, these pipes contain only air—no water runs through them. The vents prevent the buildup of sewer gases within the system by providing a continual inflow of fresh air. They also prevent backup of wastes. Without vents, water and waste would not flow properly through the drain system.

Another necessary part of the waste system is the trap, which supplies a water seal between each plumbing fixture and the sewage line. A trap always has water sitting in it if it is functioning correctly (see Fig. 41-3). (An exception would be if evaporation had taken place because water had not drained in that particular line for a long period of time.) There is also a large trap located at the end of the main house drainpipe before the pipe connects to the sewer or septic line. Traps for kitchen sinks and lavatories are made in two shapes: the "P" trap (see Fig. 41-4) and the "S" trap (see Fig. 41-5). The P empties through an outlet tube protruding from the wall, while the S drains through a longer

The plumbing in your house forms a system consisting of two parts: One, the intake, draws fresh water into the premises; the other, the outlet, drains wastes, assisted by that water.

All water coming into a house is supplied through a single pipe called the main supply line. The water enters under pressure from the utility. Once in the building, it branches out to form the cold and then in turn the hot systems (see Fig. 41-1). Cold water travels through the water heater in the house to produce the hot water. At the point where the main line enters the house is located the main shut-off

MAIN SHUT-OFF VALVE

Fig. 41-2

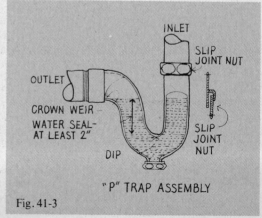

INLET
SLIP JOINT NUT
OUTLET
CROWN WEIR
WATER SEAL AT LEAST 2"
SLIP JOINT NUT
DIP

"P" TRAP ASSEMBLY

Fig. 41-3

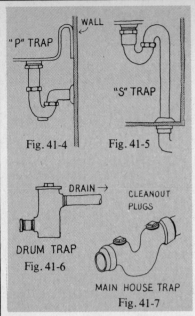

"P" TRAP
WALL
Fig. 41-4

"S" TRAP
Fig. 41-5

DRAIN →
DRUM TRAP
Fig. 41-6

CLEANOUT PLUGS
MAIN HOUSE TRAP
Fig. 41-7

outlet tube running through the floor to the drain connection. Both of these traps have as a component the "J" bend pipe, which is secured to the sink tailpiece and to the outlet tube with large slip nuts. The J bend is easily replaced when it cracks or corrodes. Most bathtubs and shower stalls have a P trap. In some houses built before World War II, however, there is a drum trap instead, running off of these fixtures (see Fig. 41-6). The main house trap usually is a one-piece affair with two clean-out plugs (see Fig. 41-7).

Introductory tips

1. Identify all shut-off valves with labels. This includes valves on the boiler and water heater.
2. Be sure all family members know the location of the main shut-off valve.
3. In an emergency, if a supply stop valve does not shut off the water supply running to a fixture and a valve further down the line feeding this line fails, turn off the main valve.
4. Vent pipe openings at the roof must be kept clear at all times to insure proper drainage and air ventilation within the waste system.

SLUGGISH AND CLOGGED DRAINS

Slow or clogged drains are the most common plumbing headache a home-

owner encounters. Traps and the small fittings connecting pipes are usually the places where debris, residue, and dropped objects get caught and cause a blockage. Bends in pipes have a small radius and are notorious for catching silverware, combs and toothbrushes, dropped most often by children.

Sink drains

If you have been remiss in keeping the strainer in the kitchen sink in place, garbage will have collected in the trap. The pipe that follows the trap and any pipe further down the line can also become blocked from the continual addition of cooking fats and coffee grinds to the drain. Grease tends to build up in the line, and grinds in turn stick to the grease. If this happens repeatedly, the drain quickly becomes stuffed.

Nothing is more frustrating than having a clogged sink drain, especially when you are in the midst of preparing dinner. If the drain is merely sluggish, waste is the probable cause. Remove any vegetable peels, utensils, etc., that are sitting in the sink. Also lift out the strainer covering the trap. Wait until the water remaining in the sink empties. If the drain is still clogged, sometimes all that is needed to open it up is to add boiling water. Bring several kettles of water to the boiling point and then pour the steaming liquid into the sink. If the blockage was not severe, the heat will dissolve some of the coagulated material, loosen it from the pipes, and permit water to run freely through the drain. If this method proves successful, follow with hot running tap water for ten minutes.

If the line is still sluggish after the water has seeped out of the sink, use a homemade chemical drain cleaner: Pour equal amounts ($\frac{1}{2}$ to 1 cup) of baking soda and vinegar, in that order, into the drain. Immediately replace the strainer fixed in the closed position. The bicarbonate of soda/acetic acid mixture will set up a bubbly chemical reaction. This formula is safe and noncaustic. Leave the drain tightly closed for 15 to 20 minutes and then flush the line with water. If the drain is now free of its blockage, let hot water run for ten minutes.

A commercially produced household drain cleaner can be employed

instead of the above, but you must be sure to follow all directions on the label. Choose a granular drain cleaner packaged in a sturdy container. (Liquid cleaner tends to burn on contact with the skin more quickly than the granular type.) Store the cleaner in a dry area of a locked cabinet so that it is well out of reach of children. If the cleaner does not clear the line, *never* use a plunger, also known as a plumber's friend or rubber suction cup (see Fig. 41-8). Instead call a plumber. Be

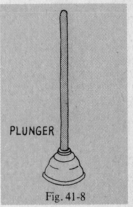

PLUNGER
Fig. 41-8

sure to tell him that a caustic material was poured down the drain. A skin burn can result from the corrosive chemicals in the trap if they should splash or drip out.

A completely clogged line requires the use of a plunger if you have not used a commercially produced household drain cleaner. Clear the sink of all but a couple of inches of cold water. Lift out the strainer. Set the plunger cup over the trap opening, and with both hands on the handle, pump up and down several times. The obstruction should become free and permit the water to flow into the pipe. Follow by running hot water into the sink.

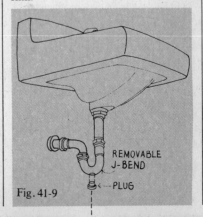

REMOVABLE J-BEND
PLUG
Fig. 41-9

When none of the above measures works, the J bend must be removed unless it has a clean-out plug. Place a bucket on the floor beneath the fixture to catch the water sitting in the trap (see Fig. 41-9). Remove the plug with a wrench. Use a hanger wire to work around inside of the bend to try to dislodge the obstruction. When there is no plug, use a 12-inch adjustable wrench or a monkey wrench to loosen the large slip nuts holding the bend to the sink tailpiece and outlet tube (see Fig. 41-10). Remember to work counterclockwise. At this point, if the preceding directions were followed, the trap will probably become clear, and the obstruction will be in the line past the J bend. Slip a plumber's snake, also known as an auger or wire (see Fig. 41-11), into the outlet tube and

dle with one hand and slowly rotate the flexible wire in a circular direction.) Getting around elbows in pipes with this tool can be very frustrating, and you may need help. If so, it will be less expensive in the long run if you call a drain and sewer service rather than a plumber because many times the stoppage is so far down in the line that the plumber will find it necessary to call in the service anyway, and then you will have to pay two service charges.

If you met with success in cleaning the line yourself by removing the plug or trap, then you will have to replace the fittings. To insure a watertight fit, wrap a layer of Teflon pipe-joint tape over the threaded portions of the J bend. Replace the washers and hand-tighten the plug or the nuts. Then

has been dropped into a sink or lavatory trap, do not attempt any of the above methods other than removal of the trap.

When a piece of jewelry falls into a drain, it can be retrieved sometimes if you act quickly enough. Do not turn on the water, or, if it is running, turn it off immediately. Remove the plug or J bend. Pour the water from the pipe into a bucket, and if you are in luck, the jewel will come tumbling out. If not, try the same procedure on the main waste trap.

Bathtub drains

Bathtub drains are similar to lavatory drains (see Fig. 41-14). They too, of course, have stoppers. Treat them as described above. When using the plunger, lift out the stopper and seal the overflow tube. If a plunger does not clear the line, try a snake. Remove the stopper mechanism and run the snake into the overflow tube (see Fig. 41-15) and down into the trap. If you find this does not work, do not attempt opening the trap unless it is easily accessible. Know your limitations. Call a plumber.

Shower drains

A shower stall drain is like a kitchen sink drain and is treated accordingly. Remove the strainer and clean it periodically.

Main line stoppage

When water from several plumbing fixtures in the house does not drain, the main line has a stoppage in it. Remove the cover of the main waste trap with a wrench. It may take a bit of coaxing to loosen it. Once the cover is off, see if the trap is clear of waste and residue. Too much toilet paper at one time can suddenly clog the trap. Scoop out the sludge. (This is a messy job, so wear rubber gloves.) Replace the cover and tap in place if necessary to reengage the threads, then tighten. Try flushing water through several fixtures other than toilets to see if the line has cleared. If not, call in a professional sewer and drain service. In no time, the service will root out the line with an electric auger.

Too much paper thrown into the bowl at once can produce a temporarily stuffed-up toilet. Toys, combs, diapers, etc., can also clog the bowl. If the draining action of the water sud-

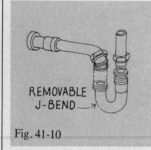

REMOVABLE J-BEND

Fig. 41-10

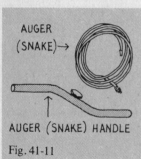

AUGER (SNAKE) →

AUGER (SNAKE) HANDLE

Fig. 41-11

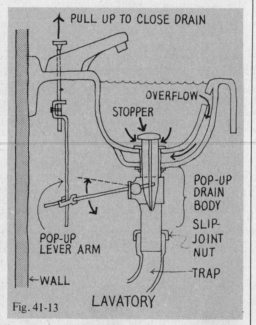

↑ PULL UP TO CLOSE DRAIN

OVERFLOW

STOPPER

POP-UP DRAIN BODY

SLIP-JOINT NUT

POP-UP LEVER ARM

←WALL

TRAP

LAVATORY

Fig. 41-13

work it slowly down into the line. (It is possible, but difficult, to work a snake into the line without removing the trap; see Fig. 41-12. Hold the han-

tighten (clockwise) with the wrench.

Lavatory drains

Lavatory drains are similar to kitchen drains, and can be handled in much the same way, with a few exceptions. The pop-up drain has a stopper that closes or opens the trap when a vertical rod is pulled up or pushed down (see Fig. 41-13). Some stoppers lift out easily for cleaning, while others require the disconnecting of a horizontal rod. When a plunger is used, the stopper needs to be lifted out and the overflow holes sealed with a wet rag.

Needless to say, if you know an object too large to pass through the line

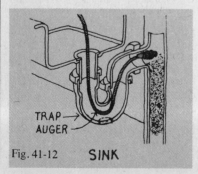

TRAP

AUGER

Fig. 41-12   SINK

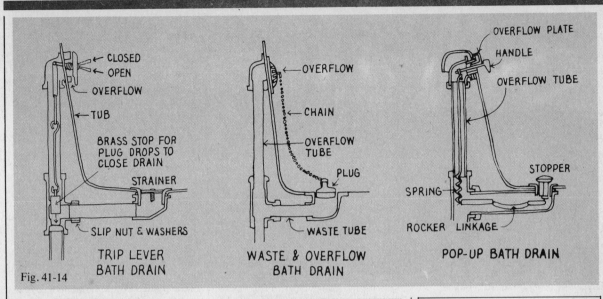

Fig. 41-14

TRIP LEVER BATH DRAIN

CLOSED
OPEN
OVERFLOW
TUB
BRASS STOP FOR PLUG DROPS TO CLOSE DRAIN
STRAINER
SLIP NUT & WASHERS

WASTE & OVERFLOW BATH DRAIN

OVERFLOW
CHAIN
OVERFLOW TUBE
PLUG
WASTE TUBE

POP-UP BATH DRAIN

OVERFLOW PLATE
HANDLE
OVERFLOW TUBE
STOPPER
SPRING
ROCKER LINKAGE

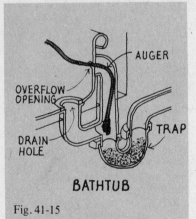

AUGER
OVERFLOW OPENING
DRAIN HOLE
TRAP

BATHTUB

Fig. 41-15

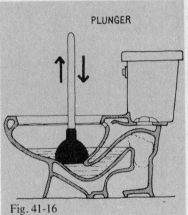

PLUNGER

Fig. 41-16

Fig. 41-17

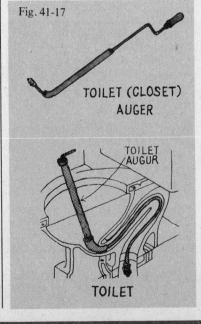

TOILET (CLOSET) AUGER

TOILET AUGUR

TOILET

denly slows down, a second flush may clear the bowl. However, if the water level begins climbing, you have to act quickly to stop the fresh water from the refill tube from causing the bowl to overflow. Shut off the toilet supply stop valve. Set a plunger over the outlet opening and work it up and down. If the plunger does not clear the blockage (see Fig. 41-16), try using a toilet (closet) auger (see Fig. 41-17). Slip the end of the tool into the bowl opening and slowly work it into the curve of the trap. Crank the handle until the movement tightens, then withdraw the auger without turning the handle. If nothing is clinging to the auger's end, repeat the process. Some materials such as plastic will break up with the threading motion of the end of the turning auger. If this attempt proves fruitless, then call a plumber, who will remove the bowl from the floor.

Kitchen sink tips

1. Do not pour coffee grinds, small bits of food, or grease down the drain.
2. When washing greasy pots and pans, wipe with paper towel and then run a heavy stream of cold water over the utensil to help dislodge the fats and wash them away in a congealed state.
3. If disposal unit empties into the sink line, always use cold water to completely grind the garbage. Only then can hot water be flushed through the unit.
4. Always keep the strainer cover over the trap opening.
5. To use a plunger on a double sink, seal off one side to insure a vacuum.
6. To keep the drain clear, use the soda-vinegar treatment (see page 131) monthly.

Bathroom tips

1. When lavatory or toilet lines suddenly do not drain well, always question any children in the house before attempting to clear the line. They may have thrown something down the drain.
2. Use the soda-vinegar treatment (page 131) monthly in each drain.
3. Always keep a hair strainer screen over the bathtub and shower stall drains.

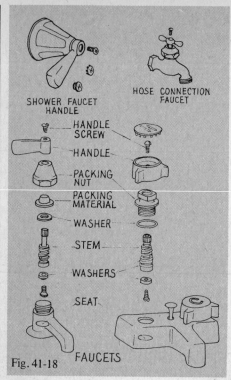

SHOWER FAUCET HANDLE

HOSE CONNECTION FAUCET

HANDLE SCREW
HANDLE
PACKING NUT
PACKING MATERIAL
WASHER
STEM
WASHERS
SEAT

FAUCETS

Fig. 41-18

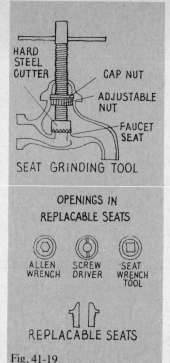

HARD STEEL CUTTER
CAP NUT
ADJUSTABLE NUT
FAUCET SEAT

SEAT GRINDING TOOL

OPENINGS IN REPLACABLE SEATS

ALLEN WRENCH
SCREW DRIVER
SEAT WRENCH TOOL

REPLACABLE SEATS

Fig. 41-19

LEAKY FAUCETS

Faucets, too, work on the intake-outlet principle. The water feeds through the supply line pipe into the opening of the seat of the faucet. It then is released or stopped by a turn or twist of the handle. It moves through the spout and out the aerator if there is one.

Ignoring a leaky faucet is throwing money as well as water down the drain. In the course of a year, gallons of water are wasted needlessly. Replacing a washer and other parts in an ordinary faucet is an easy job that can be done in just a few minutes. The necessary parts and tools are readily available at most hardware stores.

Turn off the water at the nearest supply stop valve. Open the faucet handle so that the residual water sitting in the line will spill out of the spigot. If the water keeps dripping, the shut-off valve is faulty, so you will need to close a valve farther down the line. Again, let the residual fluid escape.

Dual-handle faucets

Most dual-handle (compression) faucets consist of the same components, although their sizes differ considerably (see Fig. 41-18). Some of this plumbing hardware has additional parts such as an escutcheon and an extra washer or two of varying designs. If you are attempting to fix a leaky faucet for the first time, diagram the assembly as you take it apart, to become familiar with the parts and to insure that you can return each piece to its original spot in the correct sequence.

Before removing the handle, look for a small snap-on button placed in the center. Pry it off. Many handles are secured to the spindle by means of a small set screw. Some set screws can be loosened only by using a hexagonal Allen wrench. The handle also may need a little persuasion to be separated from the spindle. Do not force it; a little tapping from beneath will help. With an adjustable wrench or monkey wrench (not with a pipe or Stillson wrench), unscrew the stem packing nut. If the nut is chrome plated, cover it with tape or leather to prevent it from being scratched by the jaws of the wrench. Set the handle back on the spindle and use it to back off and lift out the stem.

The interior assembly is the same whether the valve is part of the spigot or simply one handle of a mixing faucet that controls the hot and cold water but leads into a common spot.

Wipe out the inside of the faucet with a paper towel. Examine the seat. If it is chipped, nicked, or roughened, it should be replaced or refaced until smooth with an inexpensive seat-grinding tool (see Fig. 41-19). A slotted, square, or hexagonal opening in the center will indicate if the seat can be replaced. The slot takes a regular blade screwdriver, the square opening takes a seat wrench tool, and the hexagonal one requires an Allen wrench or seat wrench tool to loosen and extract the seat.

Remove the screw from the end of the stem and peel off the old washer. Be sure to purchase a washer that is the same size as the one being replaced. If the screw threads are stripped, replace the fastener, but remember that a new screw must be made of brass to prevent corrosion. Stems also are replaceable if necessary.

Reassemble the unit. Do not, however, turn down the handle so that the water sits tight against the seat to shut off the water. Open the supply stop valve and water will instantly flow. Then close the tap. The handle position will probably need adjusting to the proper shut-off point.

Water leaking from under the handle also needs to be stopped. Try tightening the packing (stem) nut. If the leak does not cease, then again turn off the supply valve and lift out the stem. Depending on the design of the spindle, there are three things that can be done: (1) Replace the "O" ring near the lower end of the stem; (2) replace the packing washer; (3) use self-

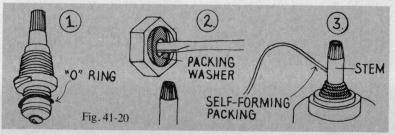

1. "O" RING
2. PACKING WASHER
3. STEM
SELF-FORMING PACKING

Fig. 41-20

forming wicking around the part of the stem that sits directly under the stem nut (see Fig. 41-20).

Sometimes a faucet becomes noisy once water is flowing through it. The stem seems to vibrate. The screw securing the washer to the stem may not be tight, or the threads on the stem and receiving portion of the housing itself may be worn. To check for worn threads, press down on the handle while the water is running. If the noise stops, it probably is the threads. Replace the stem. A loose screw will be obvious on inspection. Of course, remember to shut off the water supply before examining the stem. If neither of the above halts the noise, it is time for a new fitting.

The continual drip, drip, drip of water from a leaky spout onto the body of a plumbing fixture will, with time, leave a water stain. Usually a bluish-green color, it is almost impossible to remove. Saturate a rag with vinegar and set it over the stained area for 15 minutes. The color should be bleached out by the acetic acid and the accompanying lime buildup loosened. Now scrub with cleanser sprinkled in a wet sponge or rag. Never scrub any plumbing fixture with steel wool.

Wall-mounted shower faucets

Wall-mounted shower faucets are similar to those on a sink or lavatory (see Fig. 41-21). On older fittings, for

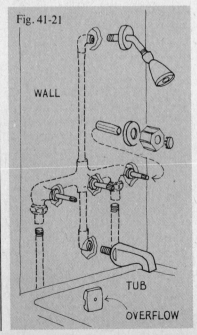

Fig. 41-21

WALL

TUB

OVERFLOW

removal of the stem nut, the use of a large socket wrench may be required. The stems on these particular fixtures are usually quite long.

Showers are plagued with the same internal faucet problems that sinks and lavatories face. To find the source of a dripping shower head, examine the faucet innards.

If a tub with a shower has one set of faucets, the shower water is controlled by diverting the water that would have led into the tub spout up through the pipe that travels to the shower head. The diverter switch is pushed, lifted or turned. When the diverter is engaged and water drips out of both the spigot and the shower head, the diverter needs to be replaced.

Leaky single-handle faucets

The design of single-handle (non-compression) faucets varies considerably (see Fig. 41-22). Some have a

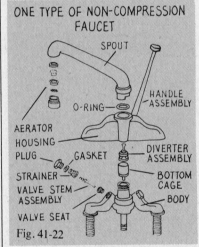

ONE TYPE OF NON-COMPRESSION FAUCET

SPOUT

HANDLE ASSEMBLY

O-RING

AERATOR HOUSING PLUG

GASKET

DIVERTER ASSEMBLY

STRAINER

BOTTOM CAGE

VALVE STEM ASSEMBLY

BODY

VALVE SEAT

Fig. 41-22

lever arm that swings from the top of the unit; on others the lever attaches to a pin exiting from the back of the body. Still others have a knob-type handle that is pushed for "off," pulled for "on," and rotated for water temperature settings. The arm may control a ball-and-cam mechanism, a valve-and-cam assembly, or a cartridge. The lever arm design operates when hollows in a ball make contact with the opening in small rubber seats; by a tapered cam moving the valve stems out of the seats; by alignment of two perforations in the cartridge with a sleeve; and by the matching up of holes in discs within a cartridge.

Repair on these faucets is simple.

Instead of changing washers, you usually replace the seat or cartridge (see Fig. 41-23). Parts for the units are

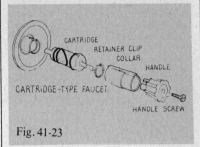

CARTRIDGE

RETAINER CLIP

COLLAR

HANDLE

CARTRIDGE-TYPE FAUCET

HANDLE SCREW

Fig. 41-23

packed in kits, which include diagrams and instructions for installation. Tell the person waiting on you the particular plumbing problem (e.g., dripping spout, water leaking from under the collar, movement of the handle is too tight). You must know the type of faucet and the manufacturer, and sketch it if the model number is not stamped on the fixture.

Sink sprays

Sink sprays, like shower heads running from tub faucets, are controlled by diverters that sit under the spigot. To replace the hose and spray head, turn off the supply valve. Set a bucket under the sink to catch the water that is sitting in the hose. Loosen the nut that secures the hose to the threaded stud which protrudes from under the faucet. Pull the spray head out of the hole in the sink; the hose should follow. If the nut is too large to pass through the hole, the spray will have to be removed. Unscrew the bottom section (see Fig. 41-24), remove the washer or washers, pry off the spring ring, and the hose will drop out of the coupling and fall through the sink hole.

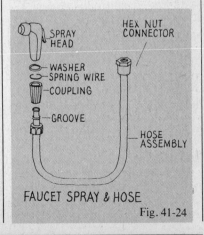

SPRAY HEAD

HEX NUT CONNECTOR

WASHER

SPRING WIRE

COUPLING

GROOVE

HOSE ASSEMBLY

FAUCET SPRAY & HOSE

Fig. 41-24

Faucet tips

1. To unclog the holes in shower heads and sink spray nozzles, boil them in vinegar for a few minutes and then brush off any remaining lime deposits.
2. When water does not come out of the faucet in a steady stream, remove the aerator and clean the screens.
3. To keep the area where the faucet housing meets the sink clean, use a toothpick to remove hardened residue.
4. Use baking soda instead of cleanser to clean gold-plated bathroom fixtures.

TOILETS

The flushing mechanism of the toilet is not mysterious. When the handle is pushed (see Fig. 41-25), the lift arm rises, pulling up the connecting rod and the lift wire that is attached to the stopper ball. The stopper ball, which previously was sitting in the valve seat, is then hoisted upward. Since the valve seat is open, the water rushes down into the bowl.

The float ball is buoyant and hovers near the surface of the water. When the water level begins to drop as the stopper ball is unseated, another chain of events takes place. The float arm connecting the float ball to the ballcock (the part that controls new water entering the tank; see Fig. 41-26) becomes a lever arm as the float ball lowers in the dropping water. The float arm pulls the valve plunger in the ballcock upward. At the base of the plunger is a washer that sits on a seat and reacts like any faucet washer when it is lifted. Fresh water is fed up the supply pipe and runs in two directions—through the tank filler tube and through the refill tube into the overflow tube. The overflow tube water then runs into the bowl.

In the meantime, the water level has dropped to the top of the flush valve seat, and the tank stopper ball reseats itself and makes a seal. Fresh water is now flowing into the tank and the float ball starts to rise. As the water and the float ball rise to the previous level, the valve plunger again closes down over the seat, and the cycle is completed as the flow of water is shut off.

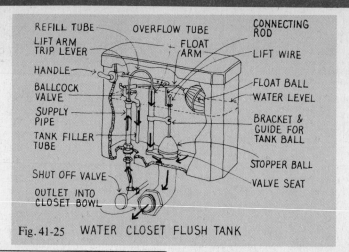

Fig. 41-25   WATER CLOSET FLUSH TANK

Toilet tips

If the toilet keeps running, check the following:

1. Does the stopper ball sit tightly in the valve seat? The ball and the seat must line up to mesh properly. The bracket and guide may need adjusting. The seat and the ball also wear out. If they become mushy, replace them.
2. Does the float have water in it? Metal floats corrode, take in water, and then do not rise to the proper height to completely close the plunger valve. Replace the float with one made of foam.
3. Is the float arm set too high? If the water level rises above the overflow tube, water will constantly run into the tube. Bend the float arm slightly downward.

If the toilet fills too slowly, the supply shut-off valve may not be opened wide enough or the water level height may be too low. Bend the float arm so that the float ball level allows the water to rise.

If water creeps out from under the tank lid, the refill tube may not be pointed so that the tube water completely runs into the overflow tube. The water may be hitting the edge of the tube at the wrong angle, glancing off of it and up onto the lid. Reposition it by bending slightly. Also, it may have a break in its wall, and will then need replacing.

When the parts of the ballcock valve start to corrode and break, replace the entire valve setup with one of the newer designs that have fewer parts.

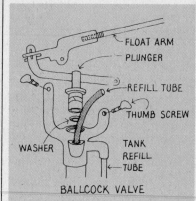

Fig. 41-26

PIPE PROBLEMS

Houses with galvanized pipe have more pipe problems than those with copper piping. Eventually the galvanized pipes just give out and have to be replaced. Even the main line running into the house eventually becomes so corroded that the inside diameter begins to close in and the water pressure slowly drops. This pipe, too, needs replacing.

Once a leak is noticed in the house plumbing, more will surely follow. Until a plumber is called, stopgap measures can be used for a short period of time. Turn off the flow of water. Dry the pipe. Fill a pinhole with a round toothpick. When the wood swells, the drip should stop. Use bathtub caulking to seal a leaky area. Let the adhesive set, then wrap strong tape around the caulked area. Cut a small disc from an inner tube or plastic coffee can lid, place the disc over the pipe hole, and secure it with a C clamp. Turn the water back on.

136

Leaks at joints such as elbows can sometimes be stopped by using epoxy glue. Once the adhesive is cured, the water can be turned back on.

A two-part epoxy putty can be employed to close leaks in waste-pipe joints. Knead the putty together and use a screwdriver to force the material deeply into the joint opening. Follow directions included in the putty package for curing time before the line is used.

Leaks around the area where the supply tube meets the supply valve usually can be cleared up by tightening the nut that holds the two together. If this does not work, the nut and ferrule (compression ring) need replacing.

Frozen pipes are the main reason copper piping begins to leak. Once a pipe bursts, the section or the entire pipe needs to be replaced.

Excessively cold weather causes pipes to freeze if they are not protected, especially those located in exterior walls or in unheated areas such as crawl cellars. Try to insulate these pipes if at all possible. Electric heating cable wrapped around the pipe will help prevent freezing.

Before the first frost, turn off the supply valve leading to the hose faucet located on the outside of your home. The outside faucet itself should be left open during the winter months to prevent freezing of any water that may seep into the line.

If the weather has been very cold for a few days and you think that the pipes located in exterior walls will freeze, open both the Hot and Cold faucets that are fed by these specific pipes to allow a slight drip for the duration of the severe cold. This will prevent the water from expanding and bursting the pipes.

When subfreezing temperatures are predicted and your heating system is not functioning, first turn off the emergency switch leading to the boiler. Then turn off the main house line valve, open all faucets and flush the toilets. Open the faucet situated at the lowest point in the system (usually in the basement sink or in the furnace room). Under such severe conditions, it is a good idea to pour antifreeze into toilet bowls and sink, lavatory and tub traps. Turn off the emergency switch to both the boiler and the water heater—a toggle switch for oil-fired systems and a petcock for gas. A valve is located near the floor on each of these units. If there is no drain in the floor, then attach a hose to the valve and run it to the nearest sink or to the outside. Call in a plumber to turn on both the water and the heat.

Noisy plumbing can be quite annoying. A condition known as water hammer occurs sometimes when a faucet is closed quickly. It is most noticeable when washing machine valves close—a kind of "klonk" sound is heard. The rushing water is suddenly stopped (it is like running into a wall at high speed). The noise can be alleviated or stopped by having a plumber install an antihammer device such as an air chamber or a coiled pipe.

If your entire water system vibrates when water runs through it, some of the pipes are probably not well secured. The addition of more pipe strapping, a block of wood or a wedge behind a joint or a pipe will help secure the pipes and stop them from rattling.

HEATING SYSTEMS

Home heating systems break down into four groups: (1) steam, (2) hot-water, (3) forced-air, and (4) electric.

Steam (found in older homes) is the most inefficient and noisy. Pipes bang and radiator valves hiss. The steam is generated in the boiler and moves up to the radiator through riser pipes. Keep the water-gauge vial on the boiler filled up to the indicated line or at least half full at all times. When the boiler is cool, turn off the system and remove the steam valves to clean them. Boil them in vinegar and blow air through the stem to remove entrapped air and to prevent rattling when the system is on. Thread them back into place. If the threads in the radiator and on the valve do not fit snugly when the valve is put back in place, they are worn and should be re-threaded with a tapping tool. To prevent knocking in the line, raise the end of the radiator that contains the steam valve (use an IX2). The radiator should pitch slightly toward the shut-off valve. Always keep it completely open. If the valve leaks, tighten the appropriate nut.

In the *hot-water* system, the water heat originates in the boiler. It is electrically pumped through pipes into radiators, or convectors, and then back into the boiler to be recycled. Once the thermostat setting is raised, the heat rises quickly and evenly, especially when baseboard radiation is used. Vacuum the radiators and fins on the convectors frequently to keep them dust free. Radiators in this system occasionally do not heat up completely; they become air locked and have to be "bled." When the pump is circulating the water, hold a pan under the small vent valves that sit near the top of the radiators. With a radiator key or with a screwdriver (depending on which tool controls the valve), open the valve until water just starts to flow, then close the valve immediately. Convector valves are located near the fins (in baseboards under a corner cover) and are bled with pliers or a screwdriver. Wrap a rag around the pipe under the valve before it is bled. Take care not to burn yourself with the escaping hot water.

Forced-air heat is the most common system installed in modern houses. The furnace produces heat in the form of hot air, which is blown through ducts and registers throughout the house. The air is dry, and many units have a humidifier and also an electronic air cleaner incorporated within the unit. Maintenance is minimal; the air runs through filters, which must be kept clean (some are washable), or must be replaced periodically. Keep register passages free of furniture and drapery. Air-flow direction can be controlled on some registers.

Call in a reputable heating maintenance service to keep your system in order. Have it inspected and vacuumed yearly. A few minor parts may need replacement. (Gas-fired burners are maintained by most utilities; contact the customer service department for a maintenance check prior to the heating season. Also, have a chimney sweep clean both the furnace flue and the fireplace flue every few years.)

Electric heat is the most efficient. It is clean and quiet. No precious fuel goes up the chimney, and a single room at a time can be heated. Keep the registers free from blockage. An electrician maintains this type of heating system.

If your heat does not go on, depending on your type of system, ask some of the following questions before you call a serviceman: Has anyone ac-

137

cidentally shut off the boiler emergency switch? Is the fuse or circuit breaker switch controlling the boiler off? Is there fuel in the oil tank? Does the thermostat make electrical contact with the circulating pumps? Is the water gauge vial filled to the necessary level? If there is nothing apparently wrong after these questions have been answered, try depressing the small reset button (if there is one) on a box located on the side of the boiler. If nothing happens when the button is pressed, it is time to call a serviceman. As a safety factor, flip the boiler emergency switch until the serviceman arrives.

Heating tips

1. Know the location of the boiler emergency switch. Located near the basement or boiler room door, it usually has a red switch plate cover.
2. Know the location of the main shut-off valve for the gas line.
3. Know the location of the gas petcock valve on the gas boiler and/or the gas water heater.
4. If a strong gas odor hits you when you enter a house, open doors and windows. Do *not* turn on a light switch or strike a match. Leave the house immediately. Go to a neighbor's house and call your utility's emergency service.

FIREPLACES

Fireplaces play a large role in houses today. They are no longer just decorative; people use them for warmth. Many even have a blower installed in them to help return some of the escaping heat to the room. Otherwise it would have gone up and out the chimney. When the damper is open, heat from the house, whether a fire is burning or not, goes up the chimney. To save fuel, install a glass screen.

The front hearth should extend at least 12 inches past each side of the opening and 20 inches or more in front of the opening to protect the adjacent area of the floor from sparks.

Cracks in the chimney, firebrick lining, and accompanying mortar must be sealed. Use furnace cement. Clean the surface and brush out debris. Dampen the area with water, apply the cement and let it harden 24 hours before you light a fire.

Fireplace tips

1. Do not burn unseasoned wood; it causes creosote to build up in the flue lining.
2. Do not use flammable liquids to kindle a fire.
3. Always keep the damper open when a fire is burning, and that includes the embers.
4. Never burn more than one artificial log at a time.
5. Always cover the opening to the fireplace with a screen when a fire is burning.
6. Keep the damper closed when there is no fire burning.

TOOLS AND SPARE PARTS

Basic tools that you should have on hand to make simple plumbing repairs include the following:

- wrenches, including a 12-inch adjustable wrench and a 12-inch Stilson wrench
- toilet (closet) auger
- screwdrivers in a range of sizes to fit the faucets, valves, and other parts of the system
- plunger, also known as a rubber force cup or plumber's friend
- auger, also known as a snake or wire
- Teflon pipe-joint tape adjustable pliers.
- baking soda and vinegar for cleaning clogged drains, or a commercially produced household drain cleaner of the granular type
- seat grinding tool.

Additional tools required for more extensive plumbing repairs include:

- hacksaw and blades (blades should have 32 teeth per inch)
- tapered reamer or half-round file
- set of wood bits.

Always use the proper-size wrench or screwdriver. Do not use pipe wrenches on nuts with flat surfaces; use an adjustable or open-end wrench. Do not use pipe wrenches on polished surface tubings or fittings, such as are found on plumbing fixtures. Use an adjustable wrench. Tight nuts or fittings can sometimes be loosened by tapping the handle of the wrench lightly with a hammer or mallet.

It should not be necessary to stock a large number of spare parts. Past plumbing troubles may give some indication as to the kinds of parts most likely to be needed. Spare parts should include faucet washers and packing.

DAMP BASEMENTS

Damp basement walls may require a major repair, especially if the basement space is to be used. The dampness may come from many sources—clogged drain tile, clogged or broken downspouts, cracks in walls, lack of slope of the finished grade away from the house foundation, or a high water table. Check for dampness by examining the basement a few hours after a heavy rain.

The most common source of dampness is from surface water flowing against the foundation wall. This might be from downspouts or surface drainage. Keeping water away from the foundation can best be accomplished by proper grading.

Cement water paints and cement grouts, available commercially, are sometimes effective for damp-proofing if leaks are small and the water that penetrates the wall is not under pressure.

A high water table is a more serious problem. There is little possibility of achieving a dry basement if water comes in at various times of the year. Heavy foundation waterproofing or footing drains may help, but it is unlikely that will do more than minimize the problem. Have a plumber install a sump pump.

42

FIRE SAFETY

Every year over 6,000 persons die as a result of fire in the home, and many more are injured. In addition, fire causes millions of dollars in property losses. Among the measures that can be taken to reduce fire losses, none is more important than educating people about fire. The difference between minor fire damage and total destruction of the home, including loss of life, depends on how well we prepare for and deal with fire. This chapter contains suggestions for everyone, including guidance on what to do in case of a fire, ideas for safeguarding the home from fire and for lessening the likelihood of a destructive fire, and recommendations on smoke and heat detectors. Although specific instructions follow on fire fighting, it is of the utmost importance to notify the fire department in case of fire.

In case of fire

There is no time for doubt or indecision. Especially at night when people are sleeping, the first few minutes are critical. A fire can spread much more rapidly than you think. Evacuate if you see flames, smell smoke, or even hear the sound of fire. Alert everyone in the home. Scream and shout. Help out those who cannot help themselves, including infants, the elderly, and disabled persons. Make sure all people are evacuated. Notify your local fire department immediately.

ORGANIZING A HOME FIRE DRILL

The time to plan for a fire emergency is before it happens, when everyone is calm and rational. Organize a family conference and emphasize the most important idea: *Saving people always comes first.* Then rehearse the evacuation.

Knowing ahead of time how to get out during a fire can save precious seconds. While the best exit is the normal way out, an alternate escape route should be preselected in case the normal route is blocked by fire or smoke.

Take each person to his room and describe what to do in case of fire. Give everyone a responsibility. Older children should look out for the younger ones. Special plans should be made for those who cannot escape by themselves. Have them sleep where it will be easier for them to get out. Adults who cannot walk should sleep on the first floor of a house. Small children should sleep near older persons who can provide help. Only the most agile should sleep in a hard-to-evacuate basement or attic bedroom.

Practice your emergency escape plan at night. Keep a flashlight in each bedroom to help escape during the dark. Make sure children can actually open and escape from the window you expect them to use in case the normal way out is blocked. Have

children practice opening the window periodically. Do not expect too much of children, but at least teach them to close their bedroom doors and wait by an open window until someone can reach them from outside.

Emphasize to children that adults are sometimes difficult to awaken, particularly if the adult has been drinking or has taken medicine. Make sure the children understand that they must leave by themselves if an adult cannot be roused.

Tell family members to try to remember to close doors to rooms and close the door to your home or apartment to slow the spread of the fire. Select a meeting place outside so you can be certain that everyone is safely out of the building. After everyone has been alerted and is safely out of the house, call the fire department from a place where you will not be trapped by flames or smoke, such as a neighbor's home or street fire alarm box. Children should know how to use the telephone so that they too can report a fire. Do not return to rescue property.

ESCAPING SAFELY
Getting out of a house

In the typical two-story single-family house, the hallway close to the bedrooms on the second floor is the most vulnerable. Because smoke and hot gases will rise, a downstairs fire can quickly block the only way out.

If fire breaks out when you are in your bedroom and the door is closed, test before opening it. Look for seeping smoke and feel the upper edge of the door. If you do not see smoke and the upper edge of the door is not hot to the touch, open the door slowly, but be prepared to close it again fast. If the hallway is passable, act quickly. Get everyone up and out without delay. Do not stop to dress or to get valuables. Close doors behind you to slow the spread of the fire. The fastest, safest way to get out—whether you live in a one- or a two-story house—is to use the normal exits. If heavy smoke and flames are blocking hallway and stairs, you may have to use a window or other emergency exit (see Fig. 42-1 for exiting from windows).

In exiting, stay low. The best air is near the floor. Hot gases and smoke collect near the ceiling first, then

Fig. 42-1

move toward the floor as the smoke layer gets thicker. Take short breaths; breathe through your nose. Smoke is the greatest danger in a fire. Most people die because smoke either blocks their escape or disables them. Not only are the gases from a fire poisonous, but the stress of an emergency makes you breathe harder, so you tend to take in more of these poisonous gases. Young children and elderly people are affected more quickly by smoke than are healthy young adults.

If you are in your bedroom with the door closed and smoke is pouring in around the bottom, or if the door feels hot along the top edges, it is already too late to escape through the hallway and down the stairs. Shout to wake other people, but keep your door closed. Use a window for escape or to get fresh air while awaiting rescue.

Getting out of a high-rise apartment

High-rise apartment buildings are usually built of materials that will not burn and will not collapse even in a severe fire. A fire in such a building, called a fire-resistive building, will normally be confined to the apartment where it started—provided the apartment door is closed. In most cases, if the fire is not in your apartment, you can stay there in complete safety. The only case in which you

FIRE SAFETY

should think about getting out is if smoke is beginning to fill your apartment, but the corridor is still clear of smoke. Head for the stairway, not the elevator. A bad fire can cut off power to elevators or make them act erratically and you may get trapped. If you get out of your apartment and there is a panic rush for the main exit, get away from the crowd. Try to find another way out. Once you are out, do not go back in. Call the fire department. Use an alarm box or telephone.

If the corridor is smoke-filled and you cannot reach a stairway, go back to your apartment. Close all the doors between you and the fire. Vents through which the smoke could reach you should be closed or blocked. Open a window, but not one directly over the fire. Break one if necessary; you must have fresh air. Call the fire department from your apartment. Stay near the floor, where the air is better.

If the fire is in your apartment and you cannot get out, stay behind a closed door. Pick a room with a window and a telephone. Open the window at the top and the bottom. Heat and smoke will go out the top. You can breathe out the bottom. Feel the door of the room you are in with your hand. If it is hot, do not open it. If the door is cool, open it slowly but stay behind it. If you feel heat or pressure coming through the open door, slam it shut. Call the fire department from your telephone. Do not panic and do not jump from a window. Many people have jumped and died without realizing rescue was minutes away.

If you live in an apartment, familiarize yourself with whatever fire alarm there is in the building. (Many smaller or older apartment buildings do not have one.) Know where the "pull box" is located and how it is operated. Your family should know what the fire alarm bell or horn sounds like, and what to do when they hear it. Try to get the other families in your building together to have fire drills. Often the local fire department will assist with such drills. Always have the number of the local fire department handy in case of an emergency.

Escaping through windows

From most houses and from the lower floor of apartment buildings, emer-

gency escape through windows is a good possibility. A folding escape ladder securely hooked over the inside sill of a building is a good way to exit, but such ladders should never be used from very high floors because of the possibility of injury.

If you do not have a collapsible metal or rope ladder when fire breaks out, you can proceed (as shown in Fig. 42-1) for escaping by climbing out a window. The second-floor windowsill is usually not more than 13 feet from the ground. A person of average height, hanging by the hands, will have a drop of about six feet to the ground. Often the second-floor window opens onto a porch roof or balcony from which it is possible to drop to the ground or await rescue. Dropping onto concrete walks or pavement is most likely to result in injury, while bushes, soft earth and grass will soften a fall.

Windows are also useful when you are waiting for help. Often you can stay in the room for several minutes—provided you keep the doors closed and a window open. Otherwise, smoke and fire may be drawn in. Keep your head low in the window to be sure you breathe fresh air rather than smoke or gases that may have leaked into the room. Shout for help.

For the babysitter

Tell your babysitter what to do in case of a fire. Tell him or her about alternate escape routes, where children are sleeping, the priority of saving lives over saving property, the location of the telephone and telephone extensions, and where you can be reached. You should have the telephone number of the fire department taped to the receiver of each telephone, along with other important phone numbers for everyone in the household to use. The instructions to the babysitter should be written and posted in a convenient location. Do not leave the babysitter out of your plans.

Helping others who are trapped

If people are trapped in a burning house before help arrives and you are in the vicinity, help them if you can do it safely. A rescue attempt by an untrained person through heavy smoke and flames is nearly always hopeless. Wait for the fire department. Equipped with special clothing

and breathing apparatus, fire fighters have a much better chance for rescuing those who are trapped.

FIRE-FIGHTING TOOLS

Every home should include some basic fire-fighting tools: a garden hose, preferably already connected; a ladder; buckets filled with sand; containers filled with water; fire extinguishers (see below); and a collapsible metal or rope ladder. Every apartment should have fire extinguishers.

Buying and using fire extinguishers

Every house and apartment should have a multipurpose fire extinguisher or several types of fire extinguishers to put out different classes of fires. Be sure you know how to use the extinguishers. An extinguisher is useful in the workshop or garage for small fires that you can put out yourself without endangering lives. Hang it near the door through which you would escape. Also keep a fire extinguisher in your kitchen.

Classes of fires: There are three classes of fires that occur in the home. Your ability to identify the type of fire quickly may save your home—or your life. The reason is that most extinguishers are designed to fight particular classes of fires. Some fight only one class; some fight two classes. Only one home-type extinguisher fights all three classes of fires. (There is a fourth class of fire—Class D—which involves combustible metal. These fires are not common in the home and will therefore not be discussed in this chapter.)

Selecting a fire extinguisher: Fire extinguisher labels indicate by letters (e.g., A:B:C) the classes of fires they fight and by numbers in front of the letters (e.g., 2-A:10-B:C) the approximate size of the fire they can extinguish. The numerical ratings are established by Underwriters Laboratories, Inc. The actual size of fires indicated by each numerical rating is not listed here because too many variables are involved. Rather, we suggest particular fire extinguisher sizes for particular fire hazard areas.

The numerical code starts with 1 and increases by whole numbers. The higher the number, the larger the fire the extinguisher can put out. For example, an extinguisher with a 10-B:C

140

YOUR HOUSE

on its label will extinguish a fire approximately twice the size of one that an extinguisher marked 5-B:C will. The numerical code does not apply to Class C extinguishers. The only requirement of a Class C extinguisher is that it contain an extinguishing agent which is not a conductor of electricity.

Certain extinguishers for home use have not only multiple alphabetical ratings (A:B:C or B:C) but multiple numerical ratings as well (2-A:10-B:C). This means that the extinguisher can be used against any Class A fire, Class B fire, or Class C fire of a size that you would attempt to combat in your home.

Match the extinguisher to your need: Before you invest in fire extinguishers for your home, ask yourself: What are the hazard areas where fires are likely to start? What class of fire would be most likely to occur in each area?

You can approach the problem of selection in three ways. You can buy all-purpose extinguishers which are effective against all types of fires; you can buy extinguishers especially designed for specific types of fires likely to occur in particular areas; or you can buy both kinds.

For example, in areas where you are likely to have only ordinary combustible materials such as wood, paper, cloth or plastics, select a water-type extinguisher with a minimum 2-A rating. In areas where flammable liquids, gases, grease or electrical apparatus are stored or used, select an extinguisher with a minimum 5-B:C rating.

If you decide to buy fire extinguishers to match your home hazard areas, consider the following suggestions:

● In the utility room or workshop where old paint cans and solvents are stored, and in the laundry and furnace area where fire might start in electrical equipment, a B:C hazard area extinguisher is recommended, with at least a 5-B:C rating.

● In the kitchen, because of the possibility of grease fires or fires in electrical appliances, a B:C hazard area extinguisher is recommended, having at least a 5-B:C rating.

● In the living room, where fire might break out in an upholstered chair or a rug, or in live electrical equipment such as the TV, an all-purpose extinguisher is recommended. It should have a rating of at least 2-A:10-B:C.

● In the bedroom where fire might break out in such readily combustible materials as bedding and clothing, or in electrical equipment, an all-purpose extinguisher is recommended. It should have at least a 2-A:10-B:C rating.

● In the garage, a B:C hazard area extinguisher with at least a 5-B:C rating is recommended to fight a fire in flammable liquids and gases, and fire in electrical equipment. Because attics usually have only one entrance/exit door, you should not attempt to fight an attic fire. Place the extinguisher away from the hazard area but convenient to it and to an escape route. If you do not intend to mount the unit, remove the mounting brackets. Brackets on an unmounted extinguisher make it awkward to use and may cause injuries.

Using the fire extinguisher: After you buy a fire extinguisher and install it in a good location, learn how to use it. Because extinguishers vary in their operation, we will not attempt to cover the instructions for each type, but general remarks on the use of water and dry-chemical extinguishers are listed below. Read the owner's manual which comes with your extinguisher, as well as the operating instructions which appear on the extinguisher label. Explain how to use the extinguisher to everyone in the family who is mature enough to cope with a fire.

Class A fires. In using a water-type extinguisher, direct the stream of water at the base of the fire, using a side-to-side motion to wet the burning surface. Separate and soak the burning material. The water will cool and saturate the burning material to quench the fire. *Caution:* Do not use water on flammable liquids, gases or grease (Class B fires) or on fires in live electrical equipment (Class C fires).

In using a multipurpose dry-chemical-type extinguisher, aim the nozzle directly at the base of the burning material from a distance of about six feet. Coat the burning material with the chemical. The chemical will smother the fire.

Class B fires. Using a dry-chemical extinguisher, direct the discharge at the base of the flames, moving the dry-chemical extinguisher or its noz-zle from side to side so that the discharge sweeps in front of the fire area. Stand back at least six feet; otherwise, the force of the discharge will "splash" the fire into other areas.

Class C fires. Before using dry-chemical extinguishers, shut off electrical power. If possible, pull the plug. Direct the discharge at the base of the flames.

In fighting a home fire that is spreading, keep near a door for quick escape, stay low, and if the fire gets too big get out, closing the door behind you.

Maintenance: Follow all the directions in the owner's manual and on the label of the fire extinguisher regarding its maintenance. The gauge on a pressurized unit should be checked regularly to see that its pressure is maintained. Have the extinguisher recharged promptly after each use according to the directions on the label. You can do this by calling an authorized fire-extinguisher service center listed in the telephone directory, or by calling or writing the manufacturer for information about your closest service center. A dry-chemical extinguisher should be recharged with the same kind of chemical agent as shown on the nameplate. Some extinguishers come with disposable cylinders so no recharging is necessary. For this type, you need buy only a replacement unit. Never attempt to use a physically damaged extinguisher until it has been tested by an approved fire-extinguisher service center.

HOME FIRE ALARM SYSTEMS

Special devices which you can buy for the house, apartment or mobile home can detect small amounts of smoke, invisible combustion gases and flames, and sound an alarm while there is still time to get out. Home fire alarms are needed primarily to alert occupants to a fire that starts while they are asleep since most fire-related deaths in this country are caused by inhalation of smoke and toxic gases during nighttime hours. There are now several brands of these detectors on the market, and you can buy them from any number of nearby sources, such as hardware stores. Many of them are good, reliable and inexpensive. Some of the more sophisticated systems can even call the fire department and perform security functions.

141

Smoke detectors

The best systems are smoke detectors, tested and labeled by Underwriters Laboratories (UL) or Factory Mutual (FM). The United States Department of Housing and Urban Development requires a smoke detector to be installed in each new home or apartment built under its Minimum Property Standards.

Home fire alarm systems can range from a single smoke detector outside the bedrooms to a complete system covering all rooms. The single-station detector is available for easy installation by the homeowner in compact units containing both a detector and loud alarm bell or buzzer. It can be electrically operated by either household current or batteries. The battery-operated unit is very easy to install and requires only periodic checking, but must have its batteries replaced once a year. It sounds a trouble signal when the battery needs to be replaced. This signal usually lasts seven days. If you are away from home for an extended period, it is advisable when you return to check your detector to make sure the batteries have not lost power. Smoke detectors that operate on household current can be powered in two ways. The detector, equipped with an electrical cord, can be plugged into an existing wall outlet, or it can be wired permanently into your home's electrical system.

For a more extensive system, two or more single-station units can be used; but where several units are desired, it is customary to install a special control panel to which all the detectors and alarm bells needed are wired. These panels are normally installed by a professional alarm firm.

Smoke detectors operate on either a photoelectric or an ionization principle. The photoelectric smoke detector contains a small light source and a photocell. When smoke enters the detector, light is reflected from smoke particles onto the photocell and an alarm is triggered.

The ionization chamber smoke detector contains a small radiation source that produces electrically charged molecules called ions. The presence of these ions allows a small electric current to flow in the chamber. When smoke particles enter the chamber, they attach themselves to these ions, reducing the flow of electric current. The change in the current sets off the alarm.

Both types of detectors are equally effective. Ionization detectors will respond more quickly to flaming fires. Photoelectric detectors generally respond faster to smoldering fires. These differences are not critical.

Heat detectors

There are also heat detectors. They can be either the "rate-of-rise" type, which senses a rapid rise in temperature, or the fixed-temperature type, which is activated when it is heated to a preset temperature—usually 135° F. Rate-of-rise heat detectors operate faster than the fixed-temperature type, but neither gives early warning of a smoldering fire. They sense the temperature of the fire after it has already reached the flaming stage. They may be cheaper, but they will not give the protection you need. Heat detectors can be useful as supplements to smoke detectors, and may be installed in attic spaces, garages, and other areas where fires will not immediately block safe escapes.

Location of devices

Because smoke rises, the best place to install a smoke detector is on the ceiling or on an inside wall just below the ceiling. If the ceiling is below an uninsulated attic or in a mobile home, the detector should be placed on the wall 6 to 12 inches below the ceiling. In a multilevel, air-conditioned home, a detector is needed on each level so that one is near each sleeping area (see Fig. 42-2). On the first floor, the detector should be placed on the ceiling at the base of the stairwell.

Consider these other areas as possible locations for smoke detectors: (1) at the top of the basement stairway in a house or small apartment building; (2) in the living room, family room or study if the entrance to the room or group of rooms is more than 15 feet from the bedroom or hallway smoke detector; (3) in the bedroom of the person who insists on smoking in bed or the person who likes to sleep with the door closed.

Do not install a detector within three feet of an air supply register that might blow smoke away from the detector, and do not install a detector between the air return to the furnace and the sleeping areas, as the smoke will be recirculated and diluted, re-

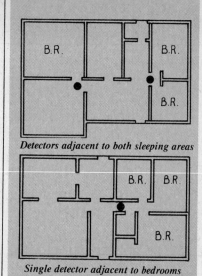

Detectors adjacent to both sleeping areas

Single detector adjacent to bedrooms

Proper locations for smoke detectors outside bedrooms

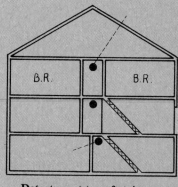

Detectors at top of stairway on each floor

Fig. 42-2

sulting in a delayed, or even a false, alarm.

Maintenance of devices

Whatever system you choose, be sure it is easy to test, is designed to minimize false alarms, and gives an unmistakable warning sound to alert a household, whether asleep or awake.

Dirt, extreme change in temperature, and cooking exhaust smoke can cause a false alarm or a malfunction of a smoke detector. Keep the grillwork of the detector free of dirt by dusting or vacuuming regularly. To prevent false alarms, locate the detector away from air vents, air conditioners and fans. Check and replace batteries periodically. Test detectors every 30 days.

142

FIRE FIGHTING BY THE HOUSEHOLDER

Some situations producing fire and smoke involve little likelihood of immediate fire spread, and the householder may safely take action to put out the fire. Remember never to fight a fire if there is a chance of being trapped. If you are in any doubt about putting out the fire, call the fire department before doing anything.

Clothing fires

When a person's clothing catches fire, it must be put out immediately. Children and the elderly are particularly vulnerable to such fires.

What to do: If it is *your* clothing, do not run. It fans the flames. Lie down and roll over and over. Remove the clothing if you can do so without pulling it over your head. Act fast.

If it is someone else's clothing, do not let the person run. Get the victim on the ground—grab and push if necessary. Roll the victim over and over. Use anything handy to smother the flames—rug, coat, blanket, draperies, towel, bedspread or jacket. If the person is outside, use sand, dirt, snow or anything else handy. Do not wrap the victim's face, only the body. Try to remove the burned clothing, but do not pull it over the victim's head. If injury results, get medical attention as fast as possible. See pages 38–40 for treatment of burns.

Preventing clothing fires: Avoid getting close to open flames or red-hot surfaces. Check your kitchen for hazards. Store only baking and storage dishes in cabinets over the stove, never food, which can tempt a child who might be wearing loose, flowing garments. Teach children the danger of playing with matches or lighted candles. Make or buy costumes made of flame-retardant materials for Halloween and other festivities.

Flame-retardant sleepwear: Manufacturers are required to make infants' and children's sleepwear flame retardant through size 14. While still combustible, clothing that has been treated or that uses special fabrics does not ignite as easily as other clothing.

Before washing the sleepwear, be sure to read the instructions on the label. Some sleepwear should be laundered before being worn. However, improper laundering can destroy the special flame-retardant qualities. Wash only with a good-quality phosphate detergent. Do not use soap, low- or non-phosphate detergent or liquid bleaches. Avoid powder bleaches. Flame-retardant clothing should not be sent to a commercial laundry.

Indoor cooking fires

All of the ingredients for dangerous fires are found in the kitchen. In fact, kitchen fires involving cooking constitute 40 percent of all household fires. Noncooking kitchen fires account for another 25 percent of the total number of household fires. The things that burn include cooking oil, grease, paper towels, napkins, garbage, clothing, even food. The things that start fires include the burners on the stove and in the oven, the toaster, the electric grill, and the deep-fat fryer. Most cooking fires involving cooking oil and grease are Class B fires, and can best be extinguished with dry-chemical, carbon dioxide or halogenated hydrocarbon fire extinguishers (see chart below). Never use water for these or electrically initiated fires. In addition, many people put food on the stove or in the oven and forget about it. Keep your mind on your cooking.

What to do: In a fire in the kitchen, it is always best to eliminate the source of heat, whether it be gas or electricity. (1) For *food in the oven,* close oven door and turn off heat. (2) For *smoke from an electric appliance,* pull the plug or otherwise turn off electricity. If flaming, do not use water but other types of extinguishers. This is a Class C fire. (3) For *small pan fire on stove,* cover with a lid or plate. Turn off heat. (4) For *deep-fat fryer,* turn off heat and cover with metal lid if you can approach it. Do not attempt to move appliance. This is a Class B fire.

Preventing cooking fires: Normal precautions are all it takes to keep cooking fires from starting. Oil and grease will not easily catch fire at room temperature, but can burst into flame after being heated. Once in flames, they will burn fiercely and are difficult to extinguish. Prompt evacuation of the home is usually essential in this case. Small kitchen fires—those that are confined to a pan, for instance—can be extinguished by covering the utensil with a lid or plate, or smothering it with table salt or baking soda. An oven fire usually will go out

---

FIRE EXTINGUISHERS FOR THE HOME

	Water	Dry Chemical			Carbon Dioxide	Halogenated Hydrocarbons	
	Pressurized Water	Ordinary Sodium Bicarbonate	Multipurpose	Potassium Bicarb. ("Purple K")		"Halon" 1301	"Halon" 1211
SUITABLE FOR USE ON:							
Class A fires: paper, wood, cloth, rubber, plastics, etc.	Yes	*	Yes	*	*	*	*
Class B fires: oil, gasoline, solvents, paint, cooking oil, grease, etc.	No	Yes	Yes	Yes	Yes	Yes	Yes
Class C fires: energized electrical wiring, equipment and appliances	No	Yes	Yes	Yes	Yes	Yes	Yes
Usual size or capacity designation for extinguishers in the home	2½ gal.		2½ to 10 pounds		10–15 lbs.	2–3 lbs.	

* Can be used to contain a fire, but may not extinguish it.

within a minute once the heat is turned off and the oven door is closed. Be sure kitchen exhaust hoods are clean and free of grease.

Note. Never use a gas range or an oven to heat your kitchen. An unvented fuel-burning appliance can produce potentially deadly levels of carbon monoxide. Do not leave the door of a hot oven open. Children could burn themselves on the heating elements.

The barbecue grill

Because of the danger of carbon monoxide poisoning, charcoal cooking should always be done out of doors unless you have an adequate exhaust hood. The charcoal fire is not a hazard by itself out of doors, but it becomes dangerous when someone comes too close to the grill.

The common fire incidents involving barbecue grills occur when the user ignites the charcoal with a flammable liquid or freshens it by pouring a combustible liquid over smoldering coals. Even if the fluid does not ignite when it strikes the charcoal, it will be heated, producing vapors that are as explosive as gasoline. Never use charcoal lighter fluid, kerosene, or any other combustible or flammable liquids to freshen a fire. Instead, to freshen your charcoal fire, moisten a few pieces of charcoal separately with lighter fluid, then carefully add them one at a time to the grill. Never use gasoline, gasoline lantern fuel, or similar flammable liquids to start a fire.

Rubbish and trash fires

Rubbish and trash ignite easily, burn rapidly, and spread fire quickly. The best way to deal with trash is to dispose of it weekly. Good housekeeping reduces the chance of fire because it gets the unwanted materials out of the home. The most common places for storing rubbish and trash are in the kitchen and basement. Rubbish and trash fires occur more often in these areas because the devices that start fires—heater, furnace, electrical appliances, flammable liquids—are also found there.

In an apartment, if you must store most of your rubbish in the kitchen, keep it in a metal can with a cover. In a house, also keep rubbish in a metal can with cover, preferably in the back-

yard. If a rubbish or trash fire begins and you can get to it before it spreads, extinguish with water. Once fire spreads, call the fire department.

Keeping a home clean: Be a spring housecleaner all year.
- Wastebaskets should not be larger than necessary. Metal baskets are preferable to cardboard or plastic. Empty all wastebaskets often. Do not let them overflow.
- Rubbish containers and garbage cans should be steel, with steel covers, if stored inside the home or attached garage.
- Rubbish and trash, wastebaskets, and rubbish containers should be kept away from the range, water heater, furnace and other ignition sources.
- Get rid of old clothes, toys, boxes and rags.
- Keep storage areas neat. Cardboard boxes and other combustibles are best stored on steel shelves off the floor.

Match and smoking fires

Matches are neither toys nor flashlights. Teach your children to understand that clothing and other materials in the home will burn, and that a match can ignite them. Keep matches out of youngsters' reach. Store one or more flashlights or lanterns where you can easily find them in an emergency, so you can avoid the temptation to use matches or candles to light the way.

An elderly person with slow reflexes or with arthritis may have difficulty grasping a match or trying to pick one up if it has been dropped. Give him an easy-to-operate lighter that will go out by itself if dropped. Keep matches away from the mentally depressed or severely retarded.

Cigarettes and other smoking materials are among the most common causes of fires. Everyone knows that smoking in bed is dangerous, yet every year hundreds of people die after falling asleep with lighted cigarettes in their hands. The best advice about smoking in bed is DON'T. Dispose of cigarettes and other smoking materials in ashtrays, and empty the ashtrays into a covered metal can, the toilet or the garbage disposer before retiring at night. Look for smoldering smoking materials in chairs and couches. Hot ashes in between the cushion and the side of upholstered furniture can smolder for hours before

suddenly bursting into flames in the middle of the night.

POTENTIALLY HAZARDOUS MATERIALS

Liquids that burn

Flammable liquids: Flammable liquids, being heavier than air, will flow along the ground for considerable distances, produce invisible explosive fumes, burn along the surface with extreme rapidity, and burst into flames from a small spark at some distance from the liquid. The fires that flammable liquids start are Class B fires and need to be put out by smothering with a dry chemical, carbon dioxide or halogenated hydrocarbon from an extinguisher.

Gasoline, if needed at all, should be stored in a tightly capped metal can and kept in quantities of not more than one gallon in the garage or shed. If there is no other place and it must be stored inside, always use a good-quality safety can that carries the Underwriters Laboratories or Factory Mutual approval label. Always take the can outside to fill a lawn mower, snowblower, lantern or other equipment; never do it inside the house, garage, apartment or mobile home.

Acetone and benzene are almost as dangerous as gasoline and should be handled in the same manner. Lacquer thinner, methyl ethyl ketone and toluene are other common flammable liquids. If they are used inside, be sure the area is well ventilated. Extinguish all flames, including pilot lights. Use only ½ cup at a time. Read the label. If it says "Extremely flammable," using the liquid indoors would be highly dangerous and should be avoided.

Other liquids such as turpentine and alcohols emit only a small quantity of fumes at room temperature and are less dangerous, but nevertheless should be used with care. Once ignited, they will burn vigorously. Keep these fluids away from heat sources and open flames.

Combustible liquids: Combustible liquids, such as paint thinner, kerosene, charcoal lighter fluid, cigarette lighter fluid, cleaning fluid, and turpentine, do not produce flammable or explosive vapors under ordinary conditions. Combustible liquids are dangerous and flammable, however, when heated, when in a spray or when spread in a thin layer over a large area. Never attempt to heat such liquids. Use caution even with hot cooking oil and melted grease, which also burn rapidly. Never spray or pour a combustible liquid over a flame or hot surface. If it spills on your clothing, promptly take off the garment and let it dry in a safe place. The combustible liquid becomes flammable as it evaporates over a large surface area.

When using combustible liquids to clean rugs, walls, floors or any large piece of fabric, remember that a match or flame can ignite the fumes and start a fire over the entire area of the cleaning surface. Use a water-base cleaner whenever possible. When it is necessary to use a combustible cleaning fluid indoors, open the windows and extinguish all pilot lights and other flames. Clean only three or four square feet at a time, using a small amount of cleaner. Let dry for 30 minutes. Clean away from the door first, then work towards the door, so that if a fire starts it will be easier to leave the room. Keep the containers tightly closed when not in use.

Always read the label. Avoid buying liquids labeled "Extremely flammable." In any case, purchase only the amount you need. Once opened, store in the container you purchased it in, in a well-ventilated location. Glass can break and plastic containers can dissolve, so do not substitute these for the original container.

Combustible liquids cause Class B fires (see page 141).

Gas dangers

Natural gas ordinarily is used in urban areas, while liquid propane (LP) gas is the most common fuel gas used in rural areas. Both types have an added odorizing agent making it possible to smell a leak. Both gases are flammable and highly explosive.

If you smell a slight gas odor, look immediately for the source of the leak. *Never use a lighted match or candle for this purpose.* If you need extra light, use a flashlight. To check for gas leaks, first examine all pilot lights and stove or heater burners. Use a soap solution to test for a leak in gas piping. Wipe it on the pipe; bubbles will identify any leak. In checking leaks, remember that natural gas is lighter than air and will rise to the ceiling. The opposite is true of leaking LP gas; it will collect near the floor or in the basement—places it is difficult to vent. If you are unable to determine the source of the leak, call the gas company.

If the odor is strong, get everyone out at once and leave the door open. Do not operate any electric switches or use the telephone. Call the fire department from a neighbor's home. Do not shut off the gas supply unless the gas shut-off valve is outside the building.

When igniting gas appliances, have the match lit before turning on the gas. Keep your face turned away to avoid the flashback of an unsuspected gas buildup. If you move or if you buy a new gas appliance, be sure the label is marked for use with the type of gas you have available, natural or LP.

Portable stoves, torches and small LP-gas cylinders contain enough gas to cause explosions in confined areas. Observe all safety precautions on the label.

If you live in a mobile home, the gas connections can be loosened or detached by highway vibrations during a move. Be sure that all fittings are tight before connecting the gas supply. Gas fires are Class B fires; for fighting them, see page 141.

Contact cements

Extremely flammable, contact cements are frequently used to lay carpet and to apply wall and ceiling decorating materials. Use only very small quantities at a time. Open the windows and extinguish all flames, including pilot lights. Do not use electrical tools in the same room.

To extinguish a fire started because of contact cement, see Class B fires, page 141.

Hair sprays

Many hair sprays can be ignited before and after using, particularly with long, loose hair near open flames. Never use matches or lighters while spraying. Stay away from the cooking range until the spray is completely dry.

To extinguish a fire begun because of hair spray, use a good volume of water.

Oil-base materials

Linseed oil, turpentine, oil-base paint and other oils of fish, animal or plant origin may ignite spontaneously on soaked rags or papers. Store rags and papers in a covered metal can, or thoroughly soak with water before placing in the garbage.

To extinguish an oil-base material fire, refer to Class B fires, page 141.

HOME-CONSTRUCTION, DECORATING, AND REMODELING SAFETY

Wall and ceiling materials

Survival during a fire depends to some extent on the type of wall and ceiling materials exposed in your home. Commonly used plaster and gypsum wallboards are considered safe building materials.

If your home has plastic laminates on the walls, acoustic tile on the ceilings, exposed insulating materials or wood paneling, a fire can develop more rapidly, to the point where your chances of getting out safely are seriously reduced.

While manufacturers of ceiling tiles and panels now generally market only products with reduced flame-spread characteristics, wall paneling commonly sold today for use in the home may cause fire to spread quickly. Paneling in many older mobile homes, as well as thin (less than $\frac{1}{4}$ inch) prefinished plywood paneling, plastic laminates on plywood or hardboard, corkboard, particle board, and rigid urethane insulation all contribute to the rapid spread of a fire. Some of these materials can be specially treated to reduce their flammability, but the typical product sold for home use in lumberyards, discount stores and home centers is likely to have dangerous flame-spread characteristics. In a fire, these substances not only can cause flames to spread rapidly from the point of origin, but they can also give off thick, suffocating smoke. The greatest danger occurs when these materials are used in large quantities.

Most of these fires are Class A fires and can be extinguished with water.

There are corrective measures. Cover the dangerous material with gypsum wallboard. Install an automatic smoke detector in the area to give early fire warning. Special intumescent paints and varnishes are available that will puff out on the surface of the paneling to form a temporary heat shield, thereby retarding the

145

spread of fire. Low-density, unfinished fiberboard can be made safer by applying a generous coat of ordinary latex paint.

Carpeting and wallpaper

Carpeting purchased today must pass a low-flammability test when it is used as floor covering; but if it is used in large quantities on the walls, it can produce the same hazards as flammable paneling. Thin wall coverings, such as wallpaper and vinyl applied to plaster or gypsum wallboard, create no significant hazard and should be of no concern to the houseowner.

Extinguish carpet-related fires with water; they are considered Class A fires.

Holiday and party decorations

Fire is an unwelcome guest during the holiday seasons and at parties. Follow the precautions listed below:
1. Costumes and party dresses worn at children's parties are especially dangerous around lighted candles and other flames. Use candles sparingly and keep paper hats, dresses or long hair away from them. Do not leave candles burning unattended while you are away or asleep.
2. Christmas trees that are artificial and flame-retardant are the safest. Metal trees present no fire hazard, but they can be the source of a serious shock if electric lights are attached to the tree. Sharp metal edges may cut the cord insulation; the metal needles might touch an electrically charged component. Anyone touching the tree and a grounded object at the same time could receive a severe shock. The only way to illuminate a metal tree safely is to use colored floodlights in different areas of the room.

Natural trees will burn extremely fast, especially when dry, so always buy a fresh one. Brittle branches and shedding needles are a sign of dryness; fresh needles bent between the fingers will not break. Do not depend on a nice green color; trees may be sprayed green to improve their appearance. When using a natural tree, buy a wide, stable base to put the tree in. Fill the base with water until the tree's cut line is covered, and keep the water at that level for as long as you use the tree.

Place the tree away from sources of heat, which accelerate its drying out.

Turn off radiators and close hot-air registers near the tree. Place your tree so that it does not block an exit if it catches fire.
3. Use only UL-labeled Christmas tree lights. Before putting them on the tree, check the lights for loose connections, broken or cracked sockets, and spots where bare wire is exposed. Remember that a bare wire or bad connection can start a fire without blowing a fuse.

A damaged socket will not effectively insulate a person from electric shock. Do not use sets with cracked or broken sockets. Check the plug or connector for loose or missing plastic inserts, which are used in some designs to plug in additional strings of lights. If loose or missing, they can expose bare metal conductors. Push the prongs on the connector against a hard surface to simulate plugging in the set, or plug the connector into a disconnected extension cord five times. The prongs should remain fixed, neither becoming loose nor causing an insert to push out from the other end. If the prongs or the insert move, be safe and do not use the set.

Spread the wires where they enter bulb sockets and connectors. Check for exposed wires where insulation may have pulled back. To avoid shock hazards, do not use sets with exposed bare wire. With the bulb in place, check between the bulb holder and the socket for exposed hairlike wires. These wires may be filament wires (which serve as the contact between the bulb and the socket) that have been improperly trimmed. Remove the bulb and trim the wires so they are not exposed outside of the socket. When reinserting, make sure the bulb leads touch the contacts inside the socket. Do not use sets with exposed filament wires.

When inserting and removing the bulb and its holder from the socket, the contact in the socket should not slide out of the socket. To avoid a shock hazard, do not remove the bulb and its holder with the set plugged in, and do not use a set if the contacts are not fixed in the recessed part of the socket.

Before beginning to decorate, place the light set on a nonflammable surface and plug it in for 10 to 15 minutes. Check for smoking and melting.

Remember that lights should never

be attached to metal trees.

Do not overload extension cords or light strings. Do not connect more than 200 midget lights or more than 50 larger lamps together through one string or cord. Do not connect large lamp sets through miniature light sets.

Any set to be used outdoors should be specifically constructed and labeled for outdoor use. Do not use indoor lights for outside lighting. Remove outdoor lights as soon as the season is over.

Be sure all lights are off when you leave the house or go to bed. Unplug lights from the wall outlet. Always disconnect any electrical appliance by grasping the plug, not by pulling on the cord.
4. Never use wax candles in or near a tree or pine boughs.
5. Buy only materials for decoration that are labeled as flame-retardant or noncombustible. Do not use plastic blocks as a candle base, or use a spray on decorative materials unless it is marked as flame-retardant. Gift wrappings and packing materials should be promptly discarded in the garbage can.

Remodeling hints

When you remodel your home is a good time to make some changes that can increase your chances for getting out alive in case of a fire.

Emergency exits: From bedrooms on lower stories and from basement recreation rooms, windows are usually an emergency, second way out. To be acceptable for emergency escape, they should open easily to at least 18 inches wide by 24 inches high. Basement windows just above the ground outside can be 24 inches wide by 18 inches high as a minimum. The sill should be not over 4 feet above the floor and preferably less. Jalousie and hopper windows usually are not suitable for escape.

Electrical wiring: Avoid aluminum wiring unless copper clad. Even the experienced do-it-yourself wiring installer should first buy one of the books on electrical wiring sold by the major mail-order retailers. These books will both simplify the work and provide guidance on safe installation.

Doors: Fire and life safety can be improved by installing a steel or heavy wood door—not a hollow-core door—between the hall to the bedrooms and the rest of the house, and another one at the top of the basement stairs. Put a lock on the door and you also will have improved security.

Interior finish: The following materials are sufficiently fire safe for general use on the walls and ceiling of your home: (1) any ceiling tiles or prefinished wood paneling that is UL labeled with a flame-spread of 200 or less; (2) plaster; (3) gypsum wallboard; (4) wallpaper, canvas or thin plastic under $\frac{1}{16}$ inch, on plaster or gypsum wallboard; (5) fiberglass; (6) ceramic tile; (7) metal tile; (8) mineral-fiber ceiling tiles.

Other types of wall finish materials should be used only in small quantities, such as partial wall covering in a small room like a bathroom.

Security: If a window needed for emergency fire escape is an invitation to intruders, there are several solutions:
1. Glaze the window with an impact-resistant glazing material such as tempered glass, heavy plastic sheet, or wired glass.
2. Install a metal gate or grille over the inside of the window which can be released easily from the inside without the use of a key.
3. Install an alarm system on that window. Locks requiring a key to open a door from the inside and multiple locks that must be opened in a certain order can prevent escape in case of fire. A single deadbolt lock that does not require an inside key provides good security if any glass panes in the door are protected as described above.

HEATING EQUIPMENT FIRE PROTECTION

Follow the manufacturer's maintenance instructions. Kerosene- and oil-burning appliances usually need cleaning and adjusting annually. Motors, blowers and pumps need periodic oiling.

Carefully follow the instructions provided for lighting of gas-, oil- or gasoline-burning devices. Never bypass any of the safety controls. Use only the fuel for which the appliance was designed. Keep boxes, trash and other combustibles at least three feet away from any heating appliance.

Portable heaters should be placed where they will not tip over, and where curtains and bedding will not fall on them. Make sure there is a guard over electric heating coils to prevent the coils from coming into contact with things that burn, especially clothing. All room heaters need frequent checkups and cleaning. A dirty heater is a fire hazard. Turn heater off or to low before going to bed. When using a fuel-burning heater in the bedroom, open the window. Ventilation prevents suffocation that can be caused by a heater consuming oxygen.

Give burners the fresh air they need for most efficient combustion by adjusting as recommended in the manufacturer's specifications. Dirty, yellow flames produce soot accumulations that can ignite or cause a burner to malfunction.

Check and clean your furnace regularly. Be sure all furnace automatic controls and emergency shutoffs are in good condition. Check flue pipes. Keep trash and combustible storage away from the heating system. If heater or any other heating appliance is not working properly, it should be repaired immediately.

Heating fires are Class B fires. See page 141 for fighting them.

Fireplace safety

Check your fireplace and chimney for safety before you begin to use them. Wood fires send soot up the chimney, where it forms a layer that can build up and become a fire hazard. As a safety measure, call in a chimney sweep to clean out the sooty lining about every two years. Check chimneys annually for cracks, loose bricks and mortar, and excessive soot accumulation—especially if you burn coal or wood.

Always be sure that the damper is open before a fire is started, and do not close it again until the embers are completely out. Make certain the fire is out when you go to bed. If you are in doubt whether the fire is dead, spray the ashes with water.

To make ash removal easier in the future, line the fireplace floor with aluminum foil, and then put in the log grate. Protect the area around the hearth from sparks by using a metal screen. Keep the area around the fireplace clear of anything that burns, and do not hang anything flammable from the mantel.

Never use flammable or combustible liquids, including gasoline, gasoline lantern fuel, kerosene or naphtha, to start or freshen a fire. Never use excessive amounts of paper to build a roaring fire. Never burn charcoal in your fireplace or in a charcoal broiler or hibachi unit inside the house; it can give off deadly amounts of carbon monoxide. Never burn locust wood; it is a very hard wood and can actually create a fire hot enough to melt the fireplace grate.

Use chimney guards. Squirrel and bird nests can stop up chimneys.

ELECTRICAL FIRES AND PROTECTION FROM THEM

Electricity is dangerous. It kills directly by shock, and it kills indirectly by starting fires in four different ways:
1. *Overcurrent:* Too much electricity passing through wiring heats it to the extent that insulation and surrounding material begin to burn.
2. *High-resistance fault:* This is produced by an imperfect electrical path. Examples are poor contact points or frayed wiring, where localized heating occurs and fire starts.
3. *Arcing:* An arc—where a spark leaps across a gap—is a normal occurrence in electrical devices. Usually the tiny, glowing particles are confined within the device, but a short circuit in an extension cord can start a fire. Even a tiny spark in an ordinary switch can cause gasoline vapors to explode.
4. *Hot surfaces:* The outsides of many electrical devices and appliances get hot enough to ignite paper, wood, and cloth. Examples are light bulbs, heaters, irons and toasters.

Prevention of electrical fires

1. *Do not overload the circuits:* If a fuse keeps blowing or if a circuit breaker frequently trips, the circuit is probably being overloaded.
2. *Never replace a fuse with one having a higher ampere rating:* Circuits in most older homes should use 15-amp fuses; in newer homes, 20-amp fuses. Special heavy-duty circuits for electric stoves and other appliances may utilize 25- or 30-amp or heavier fuses.
3. *Keep appliance cords and extension cords in good condition:* Replace rather than repair if the insulation is frayed or brittle. Do not tack extension cords to walls as substitutes for permanent wiring, and do not lay them under rugs and carpets.

147

4. *Do not use an ordinary extension cord for any appliance which uses a great deal of electricity:* An appliance which uses more than 600 watts (5 amps) should be equipped with special heavy-duty cord with 14- or 16-gauge wires. Sometimes extension cords may be labeled heavy duty when their insulation is thicker than normal, but their wiring is only 18 gauge—which is dangerous when used with high-wattage appliances.

5. *Do not use an appliance which is not working properly:* Get it repaired immediately.

6. *Keep appliances with hot surfaces away from things that can be ignited:* Check the undersides of coffee and hot-water pots, deep-fat fryers and similar heating devices. They can become hot enough to set fire to the counter or table.

7. *Keep paper and cloth away from light bulbs:* Do not dry clothing by laying it over a lamp. Do not shield the light by covering it with material that burns.

8. *Provide a ground connection for the outside TV antenna:* Special fixtures and instructions are readily available from TV or hardware stores.

If an appliance starts smoking, if it feels unusually hot, or if it is producing an odor, pull the plug or otherwise shut off the electricity. Do not use it again until it has been carefully checked and any fault corrected. To avoid what could be a fatal shock, do not pour water on an appliance while it is plugged in. If the appliance is on fire, follow the instructions for extinguishing Class C fires, page 141.

Television sets

Television sets with the instant-on feature stay energized even when switched off and have been suspected of causing fires. To be safe, use the instant-on defeat switch if the set is equipped with it, or plug the set into a wall outlet controlled by a switch. Television sets need ventilation. Do not cover ventilation openings with cloth or papers, and do not place the set against walls, radiators, or furniture. Spilling liquids into the TV cabinet can also cause a short circuit and start a fire. Never leave a TV on when leaving a room or the house. Unplug the TV from the wall outlet when you leave on vacation. If a television set begins to smoke, keep clear because the picture tube may burst. Shut off power to the circuit. If fire begins, ex-

---

ELECTRICAL TROUBLESHOOTING GUIDE

Symptom	Possible causes/Corrective action
Fuse blows or circuit breaker trips frequently	*Fuses only: temporary overload caused by starting current in motors/*Replace fuses with dual-element, time-delay type. *Overloaded circuit/*Check wattage of lights and appliances on circuit (1800 watts maximum for 15-amp circuit and 2400 watts maximum for 20-amp). *Short circuit/*Turn off all lights and unplug all appliances. If fuses still blow or circuit breakers trip, the trouble is in the wiring, a switch, receptacle or other built-in device. A qualified electrician is needed. Check all plugs for evidence of burning or sparking. Repair or replace. If trouble is still not found, turn on lights and plug in appliances one by one. When defective device is found, disconnect until repaired or replaced.
Air conditioner runs slowly	*Excessive voltage drop in home wiring/*Have new separate circuit installed for air conditioner. *Use of improper extension cord/*Put in new circuit or use a 14-gauge extension cord.
Shock from electrical appliance	*Defective wiring or loose connection/*Unplug until repaired.
Cover plates over outlets, switch receptacles or lighting assemblies hot, particularly when not in use	*Loose wiring connection/*Shut off power and tighten connections.
Odor of burning insulation	*Defective ballast in fluorescent light/*Replace ballast. *Overloaded or defective extension cord or power cord/*Replace with proper-size cord. *High-resistance fault in electrical appliance or lighting assembly/*Check each appliance or light assembly for odor or excessive heat. Replace or repair. *Loose connection and high-resistance fault at receptacle, switch or fixture/*Shut off power and tighten connections.
TV picture shrinks	*Refrigerator or other motor starting/*Switch appliance to another circuit.
Lights flicker or dim periodically	*Temporary overload caused by motor starting/*Not harmful; put motor on separate circuit if trouble is annoying. *Wiring inadequate/*Install heavy-duty wiring for high-amperage appliances; use No. 10 or No. 12 wiring to outlying buildings. *Inadequate electric service/*Add wattage of all lights, appliances and motors you use at the same time. If they exceed rating of electrical service in your home, a larger service must be installed. *Loose connections with aluminum wiring/*Shut off power and tighten connections. (It is better not to use aluminum wiring.) *Power supply or service entrance problems/*Contact utility company.

Appliance	Typical Wattage
Television, Hi-fi, Mixer, Blender	250–350
Coffee Pot, Disposal	600–900
Toaster, Waffle Iron, Fry-Pan, Deep Fryer, Iron	1000–1500
Electric Room Heater, Hot Plates, Dishwashers	1500–1650
Refrigerator, Freezer, Sump Pump, Vacuum Cleaner (high momentary starting current and two-element fuses) may require	300–400

tinguish it according to Class C fire instructions, page 141. If necessary, call the fire department.

Aluminum house wiring

Aluminum house wiring has been blamed for many electrical fires. Over a period of time, aluminum-to-copper connections at switches and outlets may become loose and a high-resistance fault can occur. Inspect outlets and switch covers periodically. If they feel hot to the touch, the connections should be immediately checked, and tightened if necessary. To check for loose wiring, first disconnect all electrical power by shutting off the circuit breaker or removing the fuse. If in doubt, consult an electrician.

Electrically initiated fires are Class C fires and should be treated according to the instructions on page 141.

Overloading circuits

To determine if the circuits in your home are being overloaded, add up the wattages of all the lights and appliances on each circuit. If the wattages of the appliances used at the same time exceed 1800 watts for a 16-ampere circuit or 2400 watts for a 20-ampere circuit, the circuit is overloaded. Wattages are shown on the nameplate of all appliances, or can be estimated from the table below.

Warning. Never make repairs to any electrical wiring unless the power is disconnected by opening the circuit breaker or removing the fuses.

OUTDOOR FIRE SAFETY TIPS

Keep your fire safe

1. Select a site on level ground sheltered from high wind, and away from heavy brush, logs, tree trunks, overhanging branches, and other fuel.
2. Clear the ground down to mineral soil in a circle 10 feet across.
3. Keep your fire small.
4. Never leave your fire unattended.
5. When you break camp, put your fire out. Drown it with water, stir the coals, and drown it again.

Note. In some regions, and at certain times of the year, open fires may be prohibited. It is a good idea to check before going into the forest.

Take care if you smoke

1. Stop, sit down, relax. Do not smoke while riding or hiking.
2. Use a flat rock as your ashtray or dig down to mineral soil with your heel.
3. Crush out your smoke before you move on.

Making a fire

Conserve your matches. Carry a candle as a fire starter. Be sure you have dry deadwood. If the forest is wet, find dry wood by splitting dead timber that is well off the ground. For tinder, make shavings of dry center wood. Build your fire out of the wind if possible. Start with small twigs. Lay twigs so air can circulate. Add larger twigs and branches as fire grows.

For a signal fire, add wet leaves or green branches for more smoke.

HOUSEHOLD FIRE SAFETY CHECKLIST

To see how fire safe your home or apartment is, answer the questions in this checklist. Do it once a year. Skip questions that do not apply. Five or more "no" answers and you are in trouble. Three or four "no" answers indicates that improvement is needed. One or two "no" answers says your home is in good shape but it can still do better. Zero "no" answers means that your home is fire safe.

DATE _____   _____   _____

Escape

	YES	NO	YES	NO	YES	NO
1. Does everyone in your household recognize the importance of getting out immediately if they even suspect the existence of a fire?	☐	☐	☐	☐	☐	☐
2. Does everyone in your household know that life safety is the first consideration and that no actions (even calling the fire department) should be taken until after everyone has been alerted?	☐	☐	☐	☐	☐	☐
3. Have you shown everyone in your household the ways they can get out in case of fire? Do they know more than one way out?	☐	☐	☐	☐	☐	☐
4. Can all windows and doors needed for emergency escape be opened easily from the inside?	☐	☐	☐	☐	☐	☐
5. Does everyone in your household know which fire department to call if you live in a suburb or rural area?	☐	☐	☐	☐	☐	☐
6. Do you make it a regular practice to let your baby-sitters know what to do in case of fire?	☐	☐	☐	☐	☐	☐

(continued on next page)

HOUSEHOLD FIRE SAFETY CHECKLIST (continued)

	DATE						
		YES	NO	YES	NO	YES	NO

Hazardous materials

7. Is gasoline always opened, poured and used only outdoors? ☐ ☐ ☐ ☐ ☐ ☐

8. Is all gasoline stored in either a UL-labeled safety can or a capped metal can in a shed or garage? ☐ ☐ ☐ ☐ ☐ ☐

9. If you have more than one gallon of gasoline stored, is it in a safety can? ☐ ☐ ☐ ☐ ☐ ☐

10. Are other flammable liquids and combustible liquids either in their original containers or in tightly capped metal cans? ☐ ☐ ☐ ☐ ☐ ☐

11. Do you take precautions never to use a combustible liquid to "freshen" any fire or to start a fire in a stove not designed for liquid fuel? ☐ ☐ ☐ ☐ ☐ ☐

Fire equipment

12. Are smoke detectors tested regularly as recommended by the manufacturer (monthly, unless otherwise indicated)? ☐ ☐ ☐ ☐ ☐ ☐

13. Have new batteries been installed in battery-operated smoke detectors within the past year? ☐ ☐ ☐ ☐ ☐ ☐

14. Have all fire extinguishers been checked and recharged according to instructions on the nameplate? ☐ ☐ ☐ ☐ ☐ ☐

Electrical

15. Are all the fuses in your home the proper size (15 or 20 amp on general circuits except special stove, dryer or air conditioner circuits)? ☐ ☐ ☐ ☐ ☐ ☐

16. Have you operated circuit breakers in your home several times each year to be sure they don't stick? ☐ ☐ ☐ ☐ ☐ ☐

17. Does the insulation on all electric cords appear to be in good condition? ☐ ☐ ☐ ☐ ☐ ☐

18. Are the plugs and receptacles on all electric cords attached tightly and in good condition? ☐ ☐ ☐ ☐ ☐ ☐

19. Have all electric outlet and switch plates been checked within the past six months to determine whether they are hot to the touch? ☐ ☐ ☐ ☐ ☐ ☐

Heating equipment

20. Have you inspected the chimney this year to be sure there are no cracks or loose bricks? Are metal chimneys well supported with tight connections? ☐ ☐ ☐ ☐ ☐ ☐

21. Are the smoke pipes on all furnaces and heaters well supported, tightly connected and clear of combustibles? ☐ ☐ ☐ ☐ ☐ ☐

22. Is combustible material kept at least three feet from your furnace, heaters and stoves unless instructions permit less clearance? ☐ ☐ ☐ ☐ ☐ ☐

23. Do you oil, clean, adjust, and perform other needed maintenance on heating equipment as required by the manufacturer's instructions? ☐ ☐ ☐ ☐ ☐ ☐

Housekeeping

24. Are filled wastebaskets regularly emptied? ☐ ☐ ☐ ☐ ☐ ☐

25. Do you keep matches and lighters away from small children? ☐ ☐ ☐ ☐ ☐ ☐

26. Are ashes from smoking materials emptied into the toilet, the garbage disposer or into a covered metal can? ☐ ☐ ☐ ☐ ☐ ☐

27. Do you use ashtrays only on solid surfaces instead of on arms or seats of upholstered furniture? ☐ ☐ ☐ ☐ ☐ ☐

28. Do you make a fire-safety walk-through of your home before going to bed? ☐ ☐ ☐ ☐ ☐ ☐

43

HOUSEHOLD SECURITY

With the increasing rate of residential burglary, homeowners are becoming more and more concerned for the security of their homes and belongings. Although no house can be totally burglar proof, you can make it so difficult for burglars to enter that they will decide to try elsewhere. A well-designed security system is one in which the various components are related: restrictive barriers (either real or symbolic); hardware; electronic security devices; neighbors; and security personnel (if the residence is located in an apartment house).

DEFENSIBLE SPACE

Defensible space describes the result of a series of design characteristics aimed at maximizing control of crime within a residential community. Under this program, all areas are designed as either public, semiprivate, or private. The design determines who has the right to be in each space, and allows residents to be confident in responding to any questionable activity or persons within the particular space.

Real and symbolic barriers

Boundaries can be marked with real or symbolic barriers. Real (or physical) barriers can prevent a person from entering a certain area by requiring him to have a key, answer through an intercom, show his face through a peephole or use some other means of identification to gain entry. While no barrier is impregnable, real barriers can be relatively difficult to overcome.

Symbolic barriers define passage between different areas without physically preventing entrance. For example, such barriers include low walls, changes in levels of landings, and planters. By employing a combination of symbolic barriers along a route, it is possible to indicate to an entrant that he is crossing a series of boundaries (see Fig. 43-1).

Creating territorial areas

Housing sites larger than a city block are best subdivided by through streets.

Through streets bring safety in that they:

— facilitate direct access to all buildings in the area by car and bus;
— bring vehicular and pedestrian traffic into the complex and so provide an important measure of safety that comes with the presence of people;
— facilitate patrolling by police, provide easy access, and act as a means for identifying building locations.

Established neighborhoods of private homes can be subdivided into smaller areas by streets. New homes can be built in small clusters.

Controlling grounds

Fencing can be a very effective means of limiting access. The fencing surrounding most single-family houses does not have locked gates, and it is intended primarily to protect children, pets and gardens, and to define the area around the house as private outdoor space. Any intrusion into the area within the fence is therefore noticeable. Such fencing is of minimal value against premeditated crime, but it does make criminal intent visible and so is an important deterrent.

A conventional use of fencing in multifamily complexes is to limit access to secondary exits, ground-level dwellings, and large semiprivate areas such as a front or back yard.

Controlling interior public spaces

The most vulnerable locations in multifamily buildings are the interior public spaces, including lobbies, elevators, stairwells, and corridors. These are areas open to the public but without the attending surveillance given a street by passersby and police. The crimes that occur in these interior public spaces are the most feared types of crimes against persons, such as robbery, assault, and rape. Limiting access to these spaces through the use of a doorman or intercom/door-lock system can be of substantial benefit.

The lobby: Improving visibility is the most important ingredient in providing a naturally secure lobby. It is crucial that a tenant entering a building be able to see what is going on in the lobby from the outside. Entry doors should be constructed of a transparent material covering as large an area as possible. In vandalism-prone areas, the main entry doors should be made of unbreakable glass or a similar sturdy, transparent material. Hidden nooks and blind curves provide perfect hiding places. Where such features cannot be removed structurally, the use of mirrors, windows and improved lighting may ease the situation. A lobby with clear lines of sight discourages lingering by strangers.

Fire doors and fire stairs: Secondary exit doors are the weakest link in

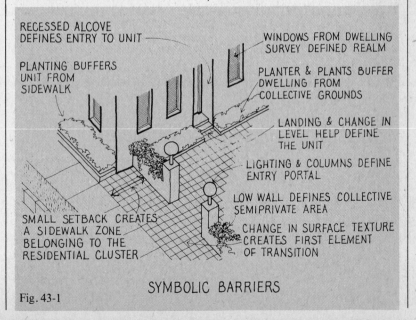

RECESSED ALCOVE DEFINES ENTRY TO UNIT

PLANTING BUFFERS UNIT FROM SIDEWALK

WINDOWS FROM DWELLING SURVEY DEFINED REALM

PLANTER & PLANTS BUFFER DWELLING FROM COLLECTIVE GROUNDS

LANDING & CHANGE IN LEVEL HELP DEFINE THE UNIT

LIGHTING & COLUMNS DEFINE ENTRY PORTAL

LOW WALL DEFINES COLLECTIVE SEMIPRIVATE AREA

CHANGE IN SURFACE TEXTURE CREATES FIRST ELEMENT OF TRANSITION

SMALL SETBACK CREATES A SIDEWALK ZONE BELONGING TO THE RESIDENTIAL CLUSTER

SYMBOLIC BARRIERS

Fig. 43-1

the security of multifamily buildings. An ideal secondary exit door would be one that allows exit but not entrance. Unfortunately, there is no acceptable emergency exit system that allows egress only. Fire doors are frequently used by criminals for entry and exit. Installation of "panic" hardware and the absence of exterior hardware sometimes prevent criminal use. Unfortunately, a securely designed building is one in which the fire door exits to an area that is less convenient or desirable for tenants than the area outside the main door. One solution is to have all fire doors exit into an area secured by a high fence around the building. Other mechanisms can be used to limit access through the emergency exit system. A fire exit passageway, for example, can be modified by installing a second door inside the building a short distance from the existing exterior door. Both doors should be equipped with hardware that lets them be opened only from the inside. In addition, the fire door on each floor above ground level should be capable of being opened from the corridor only. Thus, once someone has gone into a stairwell, he can exit only at the ground level. In a well-designed building, the doorman can see the fire doors from his position at the main entry.

Elevators: There are virtually no structural modifications that can improve security within elevators, although mirrors, communication devices, emergency buttons, or an electronic surveillance system can help. The safety of the elevator is dependent on the general security of the building. Security modifications to other areas of a building improve security within the elevator. If the elevator waiting area and the elevator cab are a visible extension of the lobby, the residents are afforded some protection. Similarly, if the fire door and fire stairs are secure, there is less chance of a criminal entering the elevator on an upper floor.

Securing the dwelling

Illegal entry into dwelling units is traditionally prevented by use of proper doors, windows, locks and lighting (see pages 152–159). These are building design features that in themselves limit access, improve surveillance and promote neighbor recognition.

Windows: Ground-level windows are generally most vulnerable to illegal entry and breakage. There are three ways to discourage illegal entry through ground-floor windows:
- Design ground-floor areas with few windows.
- House items on the ground floor that hold no interest to a burglar.
- Assign the grounds adjacent to the building for the use of the neighboring residents and fence off the grounds for their protection.

Elaborate architectural details—protruding ledges, for example—often increase the vulnerability of lower windows. Fences, garbage containers, and parked cars, when located near windows, are used as stepping stones to an otherwise inaccessible window. Care should be taken to prevent this type of situation.

Most windows above the ground floor are relatively inaccessible—with some very important exceptions. Fire escapes make windows accessible. Because of fire safety and fire codes, little can be done to modify fire escapes, except in terms of hardware. One solution is to ensure that the ladder from the lowest fire escape be at least 12 feet above the ground and that the ground area under the fire escape be highly visible. Another point of entry to the fire escape is the roof, which can be secured with panic hardware and possibly can be patrolled. The roof also provides possible entry to windows or balconies on the top floor. Other accessible windows are those located diagonally across from a stairwell window, and those above or near door canopies.

Doors: Security of doors, beyond the hardware aspect, depends on surveillance and neighbor recognition. An experienced burglar needs just a few seconds to open a locked apartment door equipped with minimal hardware. Within this interval, the crucial factors are: Will the intruder be seen or heard by tenants? Will the viewer perceive the person as an intruder? Will the viewer respond by calling authorities or in some way challenging the criminal?

In multifamily dwellings, physical design can directly influence the opportunity for surveillance of doors. Apartment doors located on interior corridors are generally difficult to keep under surveillance. Any windows, mirrors or lighting that allow someone inside an apartment or outside the building to view the hallway and doors can be helpful.

In most single-family houses where the entrance is on a public sidewalk, the only means of improving surveillance is to avoid placing trees, shrubs, and statuary where they hide the doors and windows and from which a burglar could climb to an upper window. Locate lighting where it provides visibility around doors, windows and walkways (see page 159).

Additional factors: In multifamily dwellings, it is also helpful if the superintendent or building manager lives on the premises. He will then be concerned about his own family's safety as well as that of the tenants.

Active tenant associations in apartment houses and block associations in neighborhoods have also been found to increase safety.

DOORS, WINDOWS, LOCKS AND LIGHTING

Good doors, windows, locks and lighting help secure a house or apartment from intruders. Much of this material is intended to prevent burglary. Some of the measures, particularly those suited for multifamily dwellings, will also deter forcible entry, robbery and vandalism.

The residential dwelling

Doors: If you want to protect your home against burglary, the place to start is your door. Almost all intruders will try to get through the doors before resorting to the windows. If you have the right kind of doors, locks, frames and hinges, you can increase your chance of keeping burglars out and your valuables in.

Door materials. The major security test of door material is its ability to withstand efforts to force entry by brute strength and its ability to retain securely the locking devices attached. Materials most commonly used for doors are wood, aluminum, steel, and glass, often in combination with hardboard, fiberboard, asbestos, and plastic. The two most common door designs are panel and flush doors.

Panel doors consist of vertical and horizontal members framing rectangular areas in which opaque panels, panes of glass or louvers are located (see Fig. 43-2). Flush doors consist of

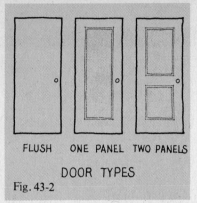

FLUSH   ONE PANEL   TWO PANELS

DOOR TYPES

Fig. 43-2

flat panels running the full height and width of the door (see Fig. 43-2). Solid-steel flush doors, although most secure, are rarely used except in very high-security areas such as banks and prisons. Steel-clad doors, which are flush doors constructed of 24-gauge sheet-metal facing bonded to a nonresinous, kiln-dried wood interior, provide the optimum weight-strength ratio for ordinary residential use. Hollow steel doors (1¾-inch flush type) are satisfactory in multiple dwellings. Aluminum doors can provide sufficient protection but may be comparatively expensive.

While less strong than steel-clad doors, wood doors can offer good protection. All exterior wood doors should be of solid-core construction and at least 1¾ inches thick. Although flush doors provide better security, if panel doors are desired for aesthetic reasons, the panels should have a minimum ½-inch thickness (see Fig. 43-3). Both hollow-core wood doors and thin-wood panel doors are unacceptable where security is a major factor.

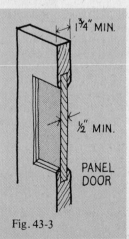

1¾" MIN.

½" MIN.

PANEL DOOR

Fig. 43-3

Door frames. The sides and top of a doorway form a frame that holds the door in place. The side members of the door frame are called jambs; the top member is called the head (see Fig. 43-4). The strike is the portion of the jamb that is cut out or drilled out to allow installation of the metal plate that accepts the latch or bolt from the door lock (see Fig. 43-5).

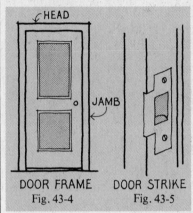

HEAD

JAMB

DOOR FRAME   DOOR STRIKE
Fig. 43-4   Fig. 43-5

Wood frames do not provide much security unless they are at least 2 inches thick. Metal-covered wood frames make a good security investment when used in combination with metal-covered wood doors. If a hollow steel frame is used, the residual air space behind the frame should be filled with a crush-resistant material such as cement grout, especially in the area of the strike (see Fig. 43-6). This will prevent an intruder from wedging a crowbar between the door and the frame and crushing the frame to free the lock.

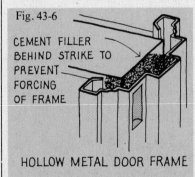

Fig. 43-6

CEMENT FILLER BEHIND STRIKE TO PREVENT FORCING OF FRAME

HOLLOW METAL DOOR FRAME

For doors swinging in, rabbeted jambs should be used. These are jambs containing a metal extension that protrudes beyond the edges of the closed door, thus preventing tampering in the area of the strike (see Fig. 43-7). For doors without rabbeted

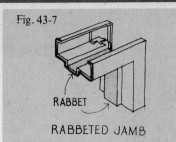

Fig. 43-7

RABBET

RABBETED JAMB

jambs, an L-shaped piece of angle iron at least 2 feet long, mounted in the area of the strike, gives extra protection (see Fig. 43-8). The iron acts as a lip protecting the strike from attack.

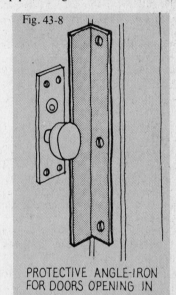

Fig. 43-8

PROTECTIVE ANGLE-IRON FOR DOORS OPENING IN

For doors opening out, a flat metal plate, called an escutcheon plate, can be mounted on the face of the door in the area of the lock. This plate, which extends beyond the edge of the door and fits flush with the jamb when the door is closed, will protect the lock from attack in the area of the strike (see Fig. 43-9). All plates located on

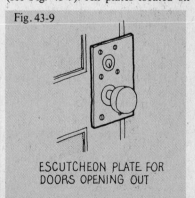

Fig. 43-9

ESCUTCHEON PLATE FOR DOORS OPENING OUT

153

the outsides of doors should be attached with tamper-resistant connectors such as round-headed carriage bolts or one-way screws.

Door hinges and closers. Spring hinges close the door automatically by using spring force. A spring hinge prevents a criminal from slipping in behind a resident who has neglected to close the door immediately upon entering. Spring hinges also prevent a door from staying open after a resident has passed through. Door closers (see Fig. 43-10) serve the same purpose. These are for more heavy-duty doors and are commonly used in lobbies and commercial facilities.

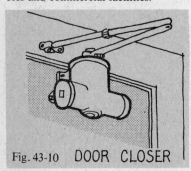

Fig. 43-10 **DOOR CLOSER**

Hinges should be mounted on the inside of a door so that burglars cannot remove the door from the hinges. If hinges must be placed on the outside, they should have nonremovable pins. Pins can be made nonremovable by peening the straight end or by drilling and tapping a machine screw into the middle of each pin from the inside of the open hinge (see Fig. 43-11). Doors with outside hinge pins

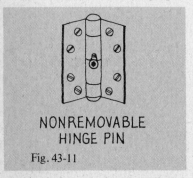

NONREMOVABLE HINGE PIN

Fig. 43-11

can also be protected by putting two screws halfway into the jamb edge of the door. One screw is placed near each hinge, and a receiving hole is drilled into the jamb for each screw. These protruding screws hold the door when it is closed, even if the hinge pins are removed.

Door locks. Locks must withstand or seriously delay not only a simple forced entry but also sophisticated criminal attack. Locks may also guard against window entry–door exit crimes. The parts of a lock include the following.

1. *Cylinder:* the part into which the key is inserted. If the proper key is used, the cylinder will allow the key to turn, thus moving a bolt or latch.

2. *Deadbolt:* a heavy metal bar that moves horizontally into the strike of the door jamb, thus locking the two together. It is called a deadbolt because it cannot be pushed back unless the knob is set free by insertion of the correct key.

3. *Latch:* the part of the lock that keeps the door in a closed position by extending into the strike automatically when the door is closed. The latch is most often operated by the doorknob; most can be pushed back by external pressure without having to turn the doorknob.

4. *Strike:* the portion of the jamb where a metal plate has been placed to receive the deadbolt and/or latch.

5. *Stopworks:* two buttons located under the latch. Pressing the top button in allows the doorknob to turn freely and operate the latch from both inside and out. Pressing the lower button in allows the inside doorknob to operate the latch, but freezes the outside doorknob.

6. *Throw:* the length in inches that the deadbolt extends beyond the face of the lock.

7. *Deadlatch:* a kind of latch held in the projected position by an automatic mechanism that is depressed against the strike plate (see Fig. 43-12).

Fig. 43-12

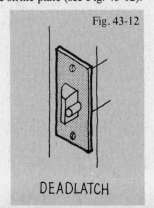

DEADLATCH

Note. No lock is good if left unlocked. Make locking your door a habit.

Primary locks. Primary locks operate in conjunction with the latch. There are two major types: mortise locks and cylindrical or bore-in tubular locks (commonly called key-in-the-knob locks).

Mortise locks (see Fig. 43-13) are more common than key-in-the-knob locks and will provide good security. All mortise locks with latches should contain a deadbolt with at least a 1-inch throw constructed of case-hard-

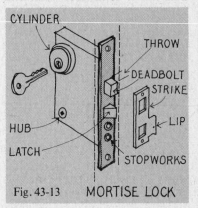

Fig. 43-13 **MORTISE LOCK**

ened steel, brass or zinc alloy, or bronze. The deadbolt and latch should be key operated from the outside and operate from the inside by a device not requiring a key. Mortise locks with latches used in residences should not contain an automatic spring latch with stopworks. Although stopworks prevent the outside knob from being turned, they leave the premises open to easy entry because they do not prevent the latch from being pushed back. An intruder need only insert a plastic card into the strike area, push back the spring latch and open the door (called "shimming" or "loiding" the lock). In locks without stopworks, the deadbolt (which cannot be loided) must be thrown by the key of the resident. Eliminating the stopworks prevents the resident from relying on the stopwork and latch mechanism alone.

Key-in-the-knob locks (see Fig. 43-14) are less secure than mortise locks.

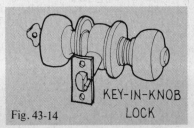

Fig. 43-14 **KEY-IN-KNOB LOCK**

They can be easily gripped by a tool and twisted until they break. A key-in-the-knob lock can include a deadbolt, at a price comparable to or slightly higher than that of a mortise lock.

Secondary locks. A secondary lock (also called a rim lock) operates independently of the latch. It is usually mounted above the primary lock at shoulder level and is operated by a key from the outside and by a turnbolt from the inside. It will increase the protection of your house. Both mortise and secondary locks may require keys to open them from inside and outside. A secondary lock is useful where access to premises may be gained through a small opening other than the door, such as a window transom, because it will prevent the thief from using the door to remove large objects or to escape.

There are three major types of secondary locks: a spring bolt, a horizontal deadbolt and a vertical deadbolt. The spring bolt operates much the same as a primary door latch does, and it can be easily opened (see Fig. 43-15). A button may be set to dead-

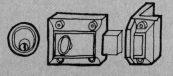

Fig. 43-15   SPRING BOLT

lock the bolt. However, the button must be set from the inside and can only be used when another means of egress is available. It is not recommended as a secondary lock. A horizontal deadbolt operates much the same as a deadbolt on a primary lock. It can also be easily overcome. By inserting a crowbar between the door and the jamb, the intruder can pry them apart to release the bolt from the strike. For this reason, the longer the throw of the deadbolt, the greater the protection it affords. The recommended minimum throw is 1 inch (see Fig. 43-16). A vertical bolt deadlock

Fig. 43-16   HORIZONTAL BOLT

should be used as a secondary lock wherever possible. It utilizes two deadbolts that fit vertically into eye-holes or sockets attached to the jamb. This creates a firm bond between the door and the jamb. The vertical bolt deadlock made by Segal is highly recommended, both for its pressed-steel construction and for its ability to hold up under heavy use (see Fig. 43-17). For additional security, a pick-resistant cylinder should be installed in a good vertical deadbolt body.

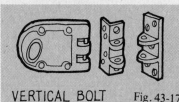

VERTICAL BOLT   Fig. 43-17

The locks discussed so far rely on the rigidity of an existing door frame to resist attacks on the lock. In older apartment buildings that contain weak door frames, a buttress-type door lock is advisable. Locks of this type include a bar set against a plate on the door and into a receptacle in the floor, thus forming a triangular buttress (see Fig. 43-18). Most of these locks can be operated only by a key from the outside.

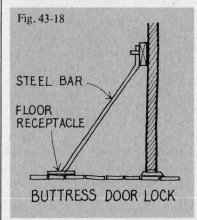

Fig. 43-18

STEEL BAR

FLOOR RECEPTACLE

BUTTRESS DOOR LOCK

The double-bar lock may also be used to increase the strength of a door. It has two steel bars that extend up to 2½ inches into each side of the jamb (see Fig. 43-19). The cylinder is protected on the outside by an escutcheon plate to prevent forcible removal. A pick-resistant cylinder can be installed for added protection.

Cylinders. Regardless of the type of lock purchased, the cylinder is critical

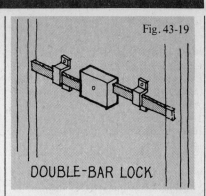

Fig. 43-19

DOUBLE-BAR LOCK

in providing protection. It must withstand efforts by sophisticated criminals such as lock pick experts. The most common type of cylinder is the pin tumbler, which operates as follows: As the key is inserted, spring-loaded pins are raised to the proper position to allow the barrel and the key to turn. The turning causes the bolt or latch, or both, to move. If the wrong key is used, the pins will line up incorrectly and prevent the barrel from turning (see Fig. 43-20). Cylinders have recently become available that utilize special keyways and keys to make the cylinder pick proof or pick resistant. Medeco, Illinois Duo, Sargent, Keso, Eagle Three Star, Mela, Fitchet, and Miracle Magnetic are highly pick resistant. Such cylinders provide improved security, but may require registered keys that can be duplicated only at the factory upon receipt of a signed request. Medeco has proven most difficult to overcome because it uses twisting tumblers operated by a key with angular or criss-cross cuts. Only if the proper key is inserted will the pins twist the exact

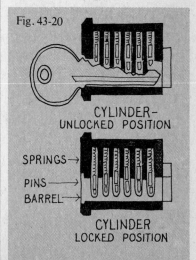

Fig. 43-20

CYLINDER-
UNLOCKED POSITION

SPRINGS →
PINS →
BARREL →

CYLINDER
LOCKED POSITION

amount needed to allow the barrel to turn. From a security standpoint, a cylinder should have at least six pins. This often results in the cylinder being longer than the thickness of the door. Protruding cylinders should be protected by one of the following devices:

1. *Spinner ring:* a hardened steel ring that forms a collar around the cylinder when gripped (see Fig. 43-21).

SPINNER RING

Fig. 43-21

2. *Bevelled ring cylinder guard:* a case-hardened steel ring that prevents the cylinder from being gripped by a tool because of its bevelled shape (see Fig. 43-22).

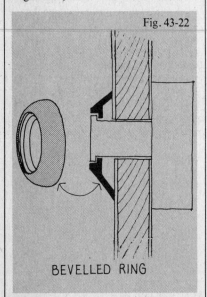

Fig. 43-22

BEVELLED RING

3. *Escutcheon plate:* a metal plate mounted to the door that covers all of the cylinder except the core, the part where the key is inserted. The plate therefore protects the cylinder from attack. The plate should be of malleable cast iron and attached to the door with one-way screws. Machine bolts should not be used to mount escutcheon plates on mortise locks because

the increased pressure can have an adverse effect on the mechanism (see Fig. 43-23).

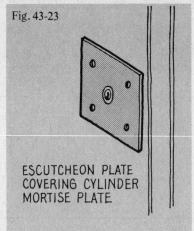

Fig. 43-23

ESCUTCHEON PLATE COVERING CYLINDER MORTISE PLATE

Maintenance of locks. A good lock can become dirty or worn and should therefore be checked several times a year. One sign of age is a new key jiggling in the lock. In that case, consider replacing your lock for better protection. If the lock is dirty and the key does not slide into it easily, squirt powdered graphite, a graphite oil, or silicone spray directly into the keyhole. You can also coat your key with any of these substances before using it. If the key still does not slide into the lock, call a locksmith. *Note:* Never use grease or oil on a lock; it can become clogged.

Caution. Too many locking devices can interfere with your escape during an emergency. If you have a double-cylinder lock, as a safety precaution be sure the key is accessible to the entire family.

Doors with large glass panels. Since burglars often break through the glass in and around doors to reach in and open the door from the inside, exterior doors containing large panes of glass are not recommended for security. French doors that open out should have hinges with nonremovable pins. The vertical stile incorporating the lock should be able to withstand a concentrated horizontal load of 300 pounds. The doors should contain a mortise-type lock that is key operated from the inside and outside. The lock should contain a pin-tumbler cylinder with at least six pins or a pick-resistant cylinder. Even when fitted with key-operated locks inside and

outside, doors with large panes of glass are a security problem. Use of break-resistant glass is one good modification. Bars or metal grilles can also provide good security, but may be aesthetically unacceptable. Alarms can also be used on these vulnerable doors.

Double doors. On double doors, the active leaf should be equipped with a mortise-type lock. The inactive leaf should be equipped with flush bolts with at least a ¾-inch throw at head and foot (see Fig. 43-24).

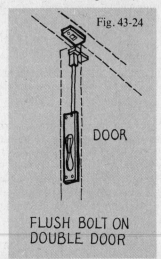

Fig. 43-24

DOOR

FLUSH BOLT ON DOUBLE DOOR

Sliding glass doors. Sliding glass doors opening onto a ground-level patio or accessible balcony are particularly vulnerable. The doors can be removed by lifting them from the outside off their tracks. The doors should be constructed instead so that the movable sections of the door slide on the inside of the fixed portion. Sliding doors should be break resistant, made of plate glass, and equipped with a vertical-bolt Segal lock (see Fig. 43-25) that uses a hook-type bolt to grip

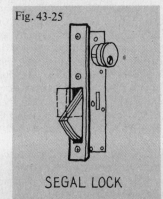

Fig. 43-25

SEGAL LOCK

the door and frame together, or a Loxem Sli-door lock that hooks at top and bottom (see Fig. 43-26). A steel

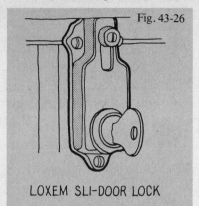

Fig. 43-26

LOXEM SLI-DOOR LOCK

rod can also be placed in the bottom track of each sliding door frame so the doors cannot be pushed open.

Private garage doors. Many rolling overhead doors operated by electric motors offer adequate security because the motors are controlled by a key switch inside the garage or by a low-power radio transmitter. Manually operated doors should be provided with slide bolts on the bottom bar (see Fig. 43-27). Chain-operated doors

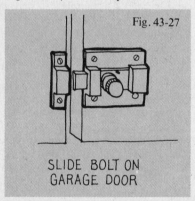

Fig. 43-27

SLIDE BOLT ON GARAGE DOOR

should be provided with a cast-iron keeper and pin for securing the hardened steel chain.

Door interviewer or peephole. Interviewers are devices installed on an opaque door to allow residents to see and hear who is outside the door without opening it. An optical interviewer should be installed on each door that provides entry into private dwellings. Optics of the interviewer include one-way glass, plastic and wide-angle glass. Interviewers with openings of over ¼ inch are not recommended because they can easily be punched out to allow insertion of

tools to open the door from the inside. Someone may also stick a knife, wire or gun through the hole while you are looking through it. Interviewers are located approximately 4 feet 9 inches from the floor. Wide-angle glass allows maximum visibility. Although a wide-angle lens does produce a curved, fisheye image, clarity of the image is not impaired. If wide-angle glass is not used, the person outside cannot be seen unless he is standing in a direct line with the interviewer (see Fig. 43-28).

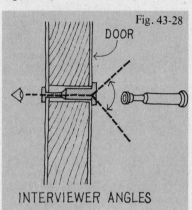

Fig. 43-28

DOOR

INTERVIEWER ANGLES

Chain lock. A case-hardened steel chain that fits into a horizontally mounted slide track on one end of the door jamb may be installed instead of an optical interviewer (see Fig. 43-29).

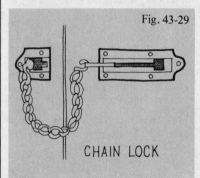

Fig. 43-29

CHAIN LOCK

The chain allows the door to open slightly, preferably not more than 2 inches, to permit easy conversation without fully unlocking the door. The chain should be used for interviewing only—not to protect a locked door; it can be too readily overcome by simple tools and brute force.

Windows:

Window materials. Because windows contain large sections of glass, they naturally pose a security prob-

lem. Windows most vulnerable are those accessible from the ground and those leading to fire escapes. Less vulnerable are windows over a canopy, as above a main entrance; windows adjacent to stairwell windows; and windows on the top floor.

Normal windowpane glass is approximately one-eighth of an inch thick, extremely brittle, and easily breakable. Plate glass is usually one-quarter of an inch thick and tempered to withstand an accidental knock. Plate glass is used for larger areas because of its greater strength and because its higher initial cost is worth the extra protection it affords. Tempered glass has a thin, hardened coating; and while no stronger than plate glass, it will not cut someone who breaks it. Several companies have developed unbreakable transparent polycarbonate materials that look like glass but are very difficult to break. Another type of durable glass is fabricated much like the safety glass used in automobiles. It has two layers of high-quality glass bonded together with a layer of tough vinyl in between. While this type of glass can be broken, the trouble required to do so and the resulting noise are considerable deterrents to burglars.

Oversized glazed areas should be avoided. Anything beyond standard size—6 feet by 8 feet—is expensive and may be difficult to obtain.

Window locks. All windows to which a burglar can gain access, including many at second-story level, should have key locks (see Fig. 43-30). A set of keys should be conve-

Fig. 43-30

KEYED WINDOW LOCK

157

nient to the window for use in emergencies, but should be far enough away so that a burglar cannot find them.

Among the common window locks that are easy for intruders to break—especially if an intruder is willing to risk the noise of breaking a small section of the glass—are the crescent sash lock (see Fig. 43-31); various fric-

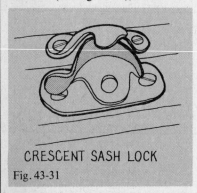

CRESCENT SASH LOCK
Fig. 43-31

tion or pressure devices such as the thumbscrew latch; pin-type latches such as the simple steel pin-in-the-hole device; and the slide-bolt latch (see Figs. 43-32, 33, 34).

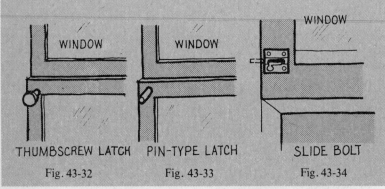

THUMBSCREW LATCH   PIN-TYPE LATCH   SLIDE BOLT
Fig. 43-32   Fig. 43-33   Fig. 43-34

Window bars, grilles and gates. Where tighter security is desired and appearance is of secondary importance, metal bars, grilles and gates have proven most reliable. If a wire mesh grille is used, the metal should be at least ⅛ inch in diameter and the openings should not exceed 2 inches (see Fig. 43-35). The grille should be attached to the window frame with machine or roundhead bolts that cannot be removed from the outside. If bars are used, they should be placed not more than 5 inches apart. The bars should have a diameter of at least ¾ inch and be set at least 3 inches into the masonry.

MESH
WINDOW GRILLE
Fig. 43-35

Sliding gates afford excellent protection and can be pushed inside or opened for emergency exit. Tracks should be used on the tops and bottoms of gates to prevent them from being pulled or pried away from the window (see Fig. 43-36).

All of these devices should be installed inside the window for maximum security. Be sure grilles and gates can be opened from the inside so that they do not present a fire hazard.

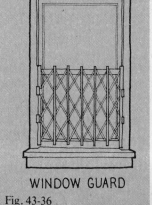

WINDOW GUARD
Fig. 43-36

Skylights. The best protection for skylights is installation of metal bars, grilles or mesh. Bars should be made of steel not less than ¾ inch in diameter and should be placed not more than 5 inches apart (see Fig. 43-37). If mesh is used, it should be at

SKYLIGHT PROTECTION
Fig. 43-37

least ⅛ inch thick, and the spaces should not be greater than 2 inches. Mesh should be secured firmly by machine or roundhead bolts that cannot be removed from the outside. If metal is undesirable, a securely fastened hasp and padlock will discourage entry and exit through the roof if the glass is not removed. Both hook-and-eye and sliding-bolt devices are unacceptable security measures for skylights.

Multifamily dwellings

Lobby doors and walls: All lobby entrance doors should provide maximum visibility of the lobby so that a tenant entering a building can see what is going on in the lobby from the outside. This often requires that the lobby doors include large glass areas. Glazed areas should be divided so that sheets larger than 6 by 8 feet are not needed. The door frame should be constructed of heavy-duty metal, and the door should have a key-operated lock with a pin-tumbler cylinder containing at least six pins. The key for this lock should not open any other door. An antifriction latch (see Fig. 43-38) and a sturdy door closer

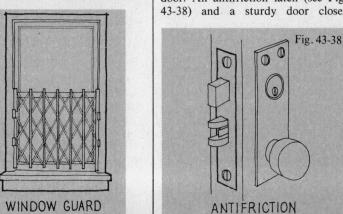

Fig. 43-38

ANTIFRICTION
LATCH BOLT

should be used in conjunction with the lock. Lobby doors, especially if locked or equipped with intercoms, should open out for fire safety and protection against vandalism.

Secondary exits: Exit doors leading to fire stairwells on each landing should have self-locking deadlatches to allow free egress while prohibiting entry. The stairside surface of the door should be free of hardware to prevent access to one floor from another via the stairwell. Hardware should limit access to the roof or ground floor exits via the stairwell. Panic hardware, if required, should be in the form of vertical-bolt latches on the top and bottom of the door. This hardware makes the door more sturdy and makes entry from the outside difficult (see Fig. 43-39).

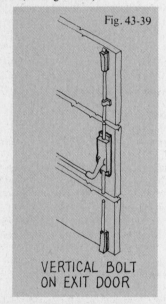

Fig. 43-39

VERTICAL BOLT ON EXIT DOOR

Doors leading into buildings from garage areas should have self-locking deadlatches that allow free egress but require a key for entry into the building. The door should be protected in the area of the strike. All exit doors should be equipped with a self-closing apparatus that can be adjusted to the desired tension.

Elevators: Every elevator should have an unbreakable light fixture for safety. It is difficult to prevent crime by modifying elevator equipment. The safety of the elevator is dependent upon the general security of the building. Restricted access to the building through the use of a buzzer-reply system, tenant patrol groups, or doormen

is more likely to be effective. Closed-circuit television and audio-intercom systems inside elevators are other possible crime-control devices. A common device used to increase visibility in an elevator is a convex mirror placed in an upper back corner of the elevator. This allows a person to see if anyone is waiting inside the elevator before walking into a possibly dangerous situation.

Garage doors and secondary entrances: If access to a building is to be limited, entry through the garage door must be carefully controlled. The most practical solution is to have an attendant, or a locked door which only tenants can open and which automatically closes behind them, usually within 15 seconds. The garage door should be monitored by tenants, security personnel, or electronic equipment if a building is to retain a high level of security.

A door leading directly from a parking area to the building interior must be treated the same as a main entry. Such a door will be used continually, and requires equivalent security measures.

Mailbox rooms: The bank of mailboxes should be in the most secure and easily surveyed space available. Ideally, mailboxes should be located in a locked room, lighted 24 hours a day, to discourage muggings and other crimes. The door to a mailbox room should have sturdy, self-locking hardware.

Lighting

Good lighting permits adequate visibility and surveillance. The higher the lighting level, the better the security. The light should be without excessive glare and should generate no heavy shadows. The lighting should be resistant to vandalism and easy to maintain.

Interior lighting: Lobbies, elevators, stairwells and corridors of a multifamily dwelling must be well lit. Interior lighting normally requires only conventional incandescent bulbs, but low-glare or frosted incandescent or fluorescent luminaries are preferable. It is usually desirable to install low-wattage fixtures at close intervals to minimize shadows and glare.

Leaving on a few lights at staggered intervals in a single-family home can

serve as a deterrent to potential criminals when no one is home.

Exterior lighting: All heavily used spaces in a multifamily dwelling such as paths, entry doors and parking areas should be lit by 5 to 10 footcandles (a measure of illumination). Higher fixture locations have a variety of advantages. As a rule, the useful ground coverage of an elevated light fixture is roughly twice the height of the fixture. Higher luminaries are safer from vandals. A variety of specialized, high-intensity light sources can illuminate large outdoor areas such as recreation facilities and parking lots. Mercury-vapor and sodium-vapor lamps are available in sizes up to 1500 watts. It is best to provide an appropriate level of light without creating too much glare or too many shadows. To control lamp and fixture breakage, fixtures of tough, break-resistant plastic should be installed.

Each single-family house should contain several outdoor lights: by the walkway to the front door, by the garage, in the backyard, by a porch or terrace. Floodlights to illuminate dense shrubbery serve as extra protection, making it harder for a potential burglar to hide in a clump of trees. Homeowners should form the habit of turning on outdoor lights at night whether or not they are at home.

ELECTRONIC SECURITY SYSTEMS

Electronic security equipment includes alarms designed to detect unauthorized entrance; closed-circuit television systems, apartment-to-lobby intercom locks, and various audio devices.

Alarms

Alarm systems range from simple equipment that protects a single door or window to sophisticated systems that cover the entire house and automatically alert the police or a private protective service. An alarm should perform the two functions of detecting and reporting the presence of an intruder. All alarms are made up of three basic parts: the detectors or sensors, the central control unit and the actual alarm. A wide range of devices detects intrusion of a criminal into a building. The detectors or sensors fall roughly into two categories—contact devices and motion-detection devices.

159

Contact devices: Contact devices are mechanical switches that detect movement or perhaps the breakage of glass, operating on their own wiring, house-current wiring or batteries. A common type consists of a contact on the door or window and a contact on the frame. When the door or window is closed, the two contacts form part of an electrical circuit. When the door or window is opened, the contact is broken, the circuit is opened, and the alarm circuit is activated (see Fig. 43-40). A similar device, called a string-

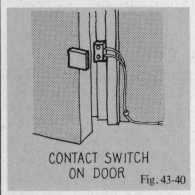

CONTACT SWITCH
ON DOOR   Fig. 43-40

pull alarm, employs a slight variation in that the opening of the door pulls a string which closes a switch that trips the alarm. Many contact devices are purely mechanical, as described above, while others include magnetic and mercury switches.

The usefulness of a contact depends upon its sensitivity—how much the device can be jarred without its being activated—and upon its reliability.

Foil strips are a related mechanism used primarily to detect breakage of glass in windows and doors. A delicate strip of metal foil is glued or taped to the glass. The foil strip acts as one long, continuous electrical circuit. If the glass is broken, the foil is broken, which interrupts the circuit and activates the alarm. Foil can be circumvented if it is possible to break the glass or release a lock without breaking the foil.

Contact devices can be made with a lock mechanism (see Fig. 43-41). This type of alarm is set off whenever an attempt is made to force or pick the lock.

Each contact device can protect only one opening; therefore, even a single-family house requires several devices to protect all points of entry. Contacts may be hidden so criminals

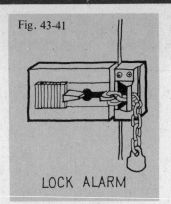

Fig. 43-41

LOCK ALARM

cannot locate them easily.

Heat-sensitive devices are sometimes combined with contact switches to provide an inexpensive fire-security alarm system.

Motion-detection devices: These devices can detect an intruder's movements in a protected space. Detection can be accomplished in a variety of ways. Seismographic devices are triggered by vibrations or weight on a floor. Photoelectric cells use a beam of light to detect any motion across a protected span. Ultrasonic devices send inaudible sound waves through a room. Movement by an intruder changes the pattern of reflected sound waves and triggers an alarm. Increased sensitivity improves the effectiveness of each of these systems, but also adds to their cost.

Motion detectors are far more expensive than contact devices, but one motion device can protect an entire area, regardless of the number of points of entry. Installation costs are often minimal, as the detection device need not be connected to any part of the structure. Motion detectors are most useful in spaces temporarily unoccupied, such as houses left empty during vacation. More expensive motion-detection devices can protect limited areas, such as a single door or window.

Alarm reporting systems: There exist two kinds of alarm reporting systems. Intrusion is reported either by a loud alarm on the premises (called a local alarm) or via wires to a security force that is prepared to respond when notified (called a central alarm or silent alarm).

A local alarm has a bell or buzzer connected to the intrusion device to produce a loud signal on the premises. This type of alarm can be installed

readily. The deterrent effect is dependent on the burglar's being intimidated and driven off by the noise, or by neighbors calling the police. Local alarms are often operated by batteries. Instead of an alarm being sounded, lights in the building can be turned on by an alarm system, or lights and alarm can both be activated. This local system also protects people sleeping in a house by alerting them that a break-in is being attempted. Generally, keys are required to shut off local alarms.

A central alarm-reporting system sounds an alarm at a remote point usually connected to the detection device by wires (telephone lines are used in many cases). The terminal is usually located in the local police station or station of a private protective agency. The alarm system's usefulness depends on the speed and reliability of the response by police or agency personnel.

A local alarm signal is often activated at the same time as a central alarm, thus simultaneously frightening the criminal and alerting the authorities. If only a central alarm-reporting system is activated, the criminal is not warned that an alarm has been sent. This system, called a silent alarm, increases the chances of apprehending the intruder, although it eliminates the possibility of driving the intruder off with noise.

A telephone-dialer alarm automatically calls a number the homeowner has specified, and plays a recording saying a burglary is in progress in the home.

Two good optional features include a key-operated switch that allows the homeowner to turn the system on and off from outside the home with a key or a control panel (operated by pushing a sequence of buttons), or by devices called panic buttons that, when connected to the control unit, allow the homeowner to activate the alarm manually as a signal for help. Panic buttons are usually placed by the front door and in the bedroom.

The single major problem of all alarm systems is the possibility of false alarms. False alarms can be caused by defects in the intrusion-detection device, in the reporting system, or by improper operation. False alarms diminish the credibility of the entire system.

Related to the false alarm problem is the question of how the alarm can be turned off if activated. Most alarms operate on a 20-second delay basis; that is, the alarm will not sound for 20 seconds after a contact is broken or motion detected. This allows the resident, if he knows the alarm has been tripped accidentally, a brief period to switch off the system. The switch can be a button located in a hidden place. A key-operated switch is more secure, but the possibility of false alarms increases because residents often forget or cannot locate their keys. The turn-off mechanism should not be so simple or accessible, however, that the criminal can activate it.

Selecting alarm systems: The security alarm business is large and complex, and it is therefore impossible to specify manufacturers or even types of alarm systems. The quality of installation and the maintenance program that backs up the system are crucial elements that should outweigh initial price in the selection of equipment. The best advice is to deal with firms that have a verifiable history of quality installations, a reliable guarantee record, and an established repair and maintenance program.

The concept of a consistent level of security avoids excessive expenditures for one piece of equipment while other means of entry are unprotected. Equipment characteristics should fit specific installation situations. For example, it is often difficult to install contact switches in older houses because window frames often have warped or buckled. String-pull devices have to be set from the inside and therefore cannot be used for a normal exit door.

Selection of alarm equipment should be based on the specific characteristics desired: Should the system be visible to deter attempted burglary, or should it be hidden to increase the likelihood of apprehending a burglar?

The system you purchase should conform to local ordinances, e.g., noise level and licensing of installers. Two good optional features are a test switch that allows you to check all sensors without sending an alarm, and battery-powered backup that allows the system to continue to operate during a power failure or when electrical lines are cut. Whatever system you choose, display the sticker of the alarm company to announce that your house or apartment is protected.

Closed-circuit television

When used in residential settings, closed-circuit television (known as CCTV) provides surveillance where physical design precludes unaided oversight. While initially costly, CCTV often reduces security personnel requirements or obviates the need for expensive redesign of existing structures. Electronically aided surveillance is not as good as personal surveillance, however.

Camera locations: The locations of CCTV cameras and the light level in that area are key factors in determining cost and effectiveness. The camera must be able to view an area that is significant in terms of crime control, but the camera itself must be protected from theft and vandalism. This means that the body and lens of the camera should be in an inaccessible place. A mirror is often used to reflect the image into the lens, so that the expensive lens will not be broken by pointed instruments, thrown objects, or bullets. All interior cameras should be placed inside sturdy housings which are equipped with tamperproof connectors. Cameras must be accessible for maintenance and repair, however.

A number of locations meet all of these requirements. Elevators in high-rise buildings are often protected by CCTV. Building lobbies are another common location. Outdoor locations usually depend upon inaccessibility to protect equipment from theft and vandalism.

Lighting: Lighting plays a key role in the cost and effectiveness of a CCTV system. While increasing lighting levels is expensive, well-designed extra lighting has an intrinsic value as a crime deterrent.

Monitoring of CCTV systems: The effectiveness of CCTV depends on the nature and quality of monitoring. Many people may be used as monitors: city police, project security personnel, members of organized tenant patrols and individual tenants.

Intercom systems

Most urban multifamily dwellings are equipped with buzzer-reply systems to limit access to the building to tenants and their recognized guests. A typical buzzer-reply intercom system in an apartment functions as follows:

A panel located outside the lobby entrance door lists the names and apartment numbers of all tenants in the building. Next to each tenant's name is a call button that when pressed rings a bell or buzzer within that tenant's apartment. The tenant responds to the call by walking to a panel mounted on the wall of his apartment and speaking via an intercom system to the person outside the door. When identification is established, the tenant pushes a button on the panel, which momentarily allows the entrance door to be opened without a key. Because the costs involved in installing wiring for such a system in an existing building are very high, buzzer-reply systems are usually installed in new buildings during the construction phase.

Elevator audio systems

Use of audio systems in elevators is rapidly increasing. An elevator audio system is an uncomplicated sound-transmission installation consisting of a microphone and speaker located in the elevator cab and connected to similar devices near the elevator doors on each floor. The system allows someone inside the elevator to communicate with anyone standing in the elevator waiting area in case of an emergency. An additional connection can be made so that a doorman, guard, or maintenance man can respond to persons inside the elevator.

PRIVATE SECURITY PERSONNEL

The function of private security personnel

In a residential situation, deterrence is the major goal. Most private housing security personnel have no greater authority to arrest than do other citizens. Residential security personnel should be highly visible, screen entrants and keep the peace within a particular neighborhood. While the ability of private security personnel to respond to an emergency and to apprehend a criminal is a decided plus, these functions are best left to the police.

Doormen in apartments: A doorman is assigned to a particular building or cluster of buildings with a single entry. He screens all persons entering the complex. A doorman should have absolute control of all access to a building, including the main door at which he is stationed, the rear and/or fire exits, and any garage or service entrances. From this single post, he can extend his control through the use of electronic or other surveillance devices to protect secondary and garage entries. A doorman will quickly learn to recognize residents of the building and their frequent guests. An intercom system that allows the doorman to communicate with tenants in their apartments is essential in enabling him to confirm the identity of guests and make further inquiries concerning strangers. The major inhibiting factor in the use of doormen is the high ratio of men to apartments served. A single doorman cannot intelligently serve many more than 200 dwelling units. During rush hour—5:30 to 6:30 p.m.—when people are returning home, a virtual tieup of people will occur if the doorman is unable to recognize all tenants and their guests easily. The effectiveness of a doorman system depends on the presence of a doorman 24 hours a day. If a doorman must leave his post to perform other duties such as carrying packages for a tenant, this can interfere with his primary function of guarding the door. Instead, an assistant should be available during hours when service requests are greatest and during lunch hours and breaks. A variation on the doorman system is the use of a concierge at a desk in the front of the lobby.

Stationary guards: These security personnel are assigned to a specific location, such as the lobby of a building, a location between two building entrances, or a hut centrally located in an apartment complex or in a residential neighborhood. This type of guard helps deter crime just by his presence. Rather than screening each entrant, he enforces a code of acceptable behavior within the confines of the complex, and he responds to emergencies. Guards are generally uniformed and may or may not be armed. The deterrence capability of such a guard is similar to that of a doorman, but is somewhat heightened by his training and additional authority, as displayed by police-type uniform, gun, handcuffs and nightstick. The success of this system depends largely on the

ability and commitment of the guard, but his physical presence makes residents feel safer.

SAFEKEEPING YOUR VALUABLES
You only encourage criminal activity by leaving valuables—silver, jewelry, antiques, money—by an open or uncurtained window. Instead, hide your valuables. That way, if a burglar does penetrate your outer security system, he will have to search for your valuables; and the longer it takes, the more likely it is that he will leave or be discovered. The best place to conceal valuables is in closets protected with a deadbolt lock or an electronic security alarm, or in a home vault.

You should always keep an up-to-date list of your most valuable items. Mark them with your name, Social Security number and driver's license number. Police in many communities participate in Project Safeguard, whereby you can borrow an electric engraver from them to etch identification onto your valuables. A burglar will probably not hesitate to take a marked valuable from your home, but it will be easier for the police to recover it and return it to you.

If your home is burglarized, make a detailed list of the missing items for the police and for your insurance agent. Let the police see the condition of your home after a burglary—*before* you clean up. There may be clues to help police catch the intruders.

SUSPICIOUS PERSONS
Always report people who appear suspicious to the police: people driving cars that seem to be cruising, possibly looking for a target; salesmen without proper credentials; people who call and announce that they have the wrong number who may actually be trying to check if an owner is at home (never respond to a supposed wrong telephone number with your number); people who ask to use your telephone because of an emergency (make the call for them but don't let them inside your home).

Confrontations on the street
When you walk assertively, with a brisk pace and a confident expression, you are less likely to be a victim. Always know where you are going; carry a map if necessary. It is always safest to walk near the curb on a well-lit and

busy street. That way you can run into the street and stop a car if necessary. Also, avoid passing close to shrubbery and dark doorways. If you think you are being followed, turn around and look. If you are, quickly cross the street. If necessary, cross back and forth from one side to the other. Do not be afraid to run. If a car approaches you and you are threatened, scream and run in the direction opposite that of the car. The driver will have to turn around to pursue you. Go into the nearest public place and tell the owner. Then call the police if the person following you does not cease doing so. If you are nervous about returning home at night, ask a friend to accompany you and wait until you are safely in your apartment or house. There is safety in numbers. Have your key ready in hand so your house door can be opened quickly.

If you are confronted on the street and cannot escape, try to remain calm. Yell "Fire!" or blow a whistle to draw attention. If no one comes to your rescue and the thief demands money and valuables, give them up. Carry money in a little change purse or envelope within your purse or pocket so you will not have to give up your entire purse. In a criminal encounter, the odds are against you if you respond in a violent way. Make a mental picture of the criminal, noting the sex, height, build, color of eyes and hair, hair style, skin color, and unusual markings, including scars, clothing, jewelry, speech patterns.

Confrontations while traveling
Never hitchhike at any time of the day. When traveling at night, take a cab or bus over a subway. Always wait for a cab, bus, or subway where someone is present in case you need help.

If you are driving your own car, travel on well-lighted, populated streets. Keep windows shut and doors locked. Keep your car in gear while halted at traffic lights and stop signs. If your safety is threatened, hold down on the horn and drive away as soon as possible. Check your rearview mirror. If you believe you are being followed by another car, do not drive into your driveway or park in a deserted area. Pull over to the curb at a spot where there are people, and let the car pass you. If the car continues to follow you, drive to the nearest place where you can get help, such as a gas station. If you should be followed into your driveway at night, stay in your car with the doors locked. Sound your horn to get the attention of neighbors or scare the other driver off. When parking at night, select a place that will be lighted when you return. Check for loiterers before leaving your car. Never leave your car keys in the ignition, even if you are only going to be parked for a short time. Take them with you, and make sure you lock your car.

Confrontations in elevators

If you live in an apartment where you know the other residents and find yourself by elevators with a stranger, it is wise to let him take the first car and wait for another. This also applies if you are visiting in a building and feel the person waiting with you by the elevator is suspicious-looking.

If you are on the elevator and someone gets on whose presence makes you uneasy, get off at the next floor. Always stand near the control panel. If attacked, hit the alarm button and press as many of the other buttons as you can reach with your arm or elbow, making the door open on several floors. Scream for help. Run to the nearest apartment.

Confrontations in your home

If you are in your house or apartment when an intruder bursts in, stay out of his way. If you have an alarm button, use it to alert the police. Common sense is best and there are very few good rules to follow. The intruder is more likely to hurt you if confronted. If you can, lock yourself in your bedroom and call the police, giving your name, address, the details of what is happening, and your hiding place. If you cannot escape from the intruder, try to remain calm. Again, the odds are against you if you respond in a violent way. Make a mental picture of the criminal, noting sex, height, color of eyes and hair, hair style, skin color, and unusual markings, including scars, clothing, jewelry and speech patterns.

SPECIAL CRIMES

Sexual assaults

The following advice comes from the pamphlet "Protective Measures to Prevent Rape" put out by the Sex Crimes Analysis Unit of the New York City Police Department.

Most sexual attacks occur in the privacy of a home or apartment. Women who live alone should list only their last names and initials in phone directories and on mailboxes. Secure your home well, and never let a stranger in. Require any caller to identify himself or herself satisfactorily; this includes repairmen, delivery men, and policemen as well. If a window or door has been forced or broken while you were absent, do not enter or call out. Use a neighbor's phone immediately to call the police and wait outside until they arrive.

If you are assaulted, try to remain calm. You may be able to talk the offender out of proceeding. If you are not successful in talking him out of the attack, try to resist physically by striking violently. Get out of the home or apartment quickly. If you cannot resist, call the police as soon as the offender has left. Many communities have special police numbers for sexual assaults. It is important that you press charges. If you wish to speak to a female officer, inform the officer who responds to the call. Do not wash or douche. Have a medical exam and an internal gynecological exam as soon as possible, preferably accompanied by a police officer. Inform the doctor of the exact acts committed upon you and have him note any medical evidence of them. Semen smears must be taken by the doctor. Doctors should note any bruises or injuries, external or internal. Have doctor test for venereal diseases. Inform police of all details of attack and of anything unusual you may have noted about the attacker. Show police any external bruises or injuries, however minor, resulting from the attack. Also show them to a friend who might be available as a witness at the trial. Give your undergarments to the police for semen analysis. Give any torn or stained clothing to the police. When calm, make note of the events of the attack and any unusual details.

Kidnapping

If you ever receive a telephone call from a person announcing that a family member or friend has been kidnapped, ask to speak to the victim. Afterwards, report the crime to the police.

Parents should always know the whereabouts of their children and should teach them never to speak to or go anywhere with strangers.

LEAVING YOUR HOME

Short absences

The majority of intruders are unwilling to enter a house when someone is in it. Therefore, any steps you can take to create the illusion that the house or apartment is occupied will help to prevent a crime. One way to suggest that someone is home is to leave your radio on. A dog that barks when strangers approach can also be an asset.

Adjust the window shades or blinds the way you would if you were at home. A house with all the shades drawn in the middle of the day is an indication that the owners are away.

Never leave your garage door open revealing an empty garage.

Never leave your entrance door unlocked, even if you are "just out for a few minutes."

Be sure you have secured all doors and windows before departing. If you have an alarm system, be sure that it is in working order and that you turn it on before you leave.

Never leave a note on your door telling a friend you will be returning soon.

Going on vacation

Keep your vacation plans private. The more people who know them, the more chance that the information will get into the wrong hands.

If possible, pack belongings in the car in the rear of the house, out of sight of anyone passing by your street.

Ask a neighbor to look in on your house or apartment from time to time. Inform the local police that you are going away so that they too can check your home. Stop mail, newspaper and milk deliveries. Pay utility and telephone bills so that no person need call or visit during your absence. Arrange for lawn care and snow removal if you live in a house; if you live in an apartment, ask a neighbor to pick up leaflets that may be left at your door. Adjust your thermostat to 55° F in winter and to 80° F for air conditioning in summer.

Before leaving, be sure you have locked all doors and windows and turned on any electronic security de-

HOUSEHOLD SECURITY/CHILDPROOFING YOUR HOUSE

vices you may own. Be sure all water faucets are turned completely off. Leave a few lights on with timers so that the house appears lived in.

If there are signs of burglary upon your return, such as a broken window, do not enter your house. Instead, call the police from a neighbor's home. Wait for the police to arrive before you enter.

New home/new apartment

Whenever you move, have the keying changed on all your locks. That does not mean that you have to have new locks installed—only that the tumblers in the locks have to be reset.

Lost keys

If you lose your keys along with some identification indicating your address, it is best to change the cylinders on your locks. Always keep house keys separate from other keys you may have. Do not give out keys to anybody.

44

CHILDPROOFING YOUR HOUSE

All young children get their share of cuts, bruises and even sprains in the course of growing up. Minor injuries can usually be treated with a gentle swab of antiseptic and a bandage. Serious accidents, however, are another matter. No child should experience even one such accident. The results can be tragic—brain damage, an ugly permanent scar, amputation, or even death. Parents and people who care for children want to give them all the love and protection possible. Yet the leading cause of death and injury to young children today is accidents in the home. These happen because many persons simply do not know about situations in the home that can be dangerous to young children. They do not know how to avoid accidents, or how to act quickly and do the right thing when an emergency occurs.

Can you prevent a serious home accident from happening to your child?

Take this quiz.

Yes No

1. Household cleaners—detergents, furniture polish, oven cleaners, bleach—can be safely stored under the sink if you warn your toddler *never* to touch or play with them. — —
2. If the phone or doorbell rings while you're busy with your baby, a safe place to leave him is on your bed because you will be gone for *just a moment.* — —
3. When you're cooking or serving meals, a good play-spot for your toddler is the kitchen floor—where you can keep an eye on him. — —
4. A normal child will never drink bleach, bug killers, or kerosene because they taste awful. — —
5. You accidentally add salt instead of sugar to the baby's formula. The formula may not taste good, but at least it won't hurt the baby. — —
6. When your child refuses to take aspirin or medicine your doctor has prescribed, tell the child it is "candy" to encourage him to take the medicine. — —
7. Toddlers can be left alone in the bathtub or wading pool if you are careful to put in no more than one or two inches of water. — —
8. Toddlers will not try to touch the flames in a barbecue or a fireplace because the heat will frighten them away. — —

If you checked "yes" to even one of the statements in the quiz, you are taking risks with your child's safety. Even if you made a perfect score, you should read this chapter to learn the many do's and don'ts about preventing accidents that happen to children every day.

Children's accidents fall into five basic groupings: (1) severe falls, blows, cuts and animal bites; (2) suffocation and strangulation; (3) poisoning; (4) drowning; and (5) fires, burns and electric shock.

FALLS, BLOWS, CUTS AND ANIMAL BITES

Guarding against falls

Severe falls are the most common form of injury to infants. Following are some ways to make your home fall-safe.

Total protection for babies: A baby is completely helpless and requires total protection. He wiggles and rolls. His crib—with the sides pulled up—and his playpen are the only safe places for the child to be left alone. Never let him lie unguarded on a couch, bed, changing table or any other high place from which he might fall. If you have to answer the door or the telephone while you are in the middle of a diaper change, wrap the baby up and take him with you or put him back into the crib. Make it a habit to take him with you if you must reach for anything that prevents you from keeping at least one protective hand on him. Turning your back even for a second can be risky.

When your baby learns to crawl, barricade the tops and bottoms of any staircases. One of the most frequent accidents that happens to babies at the crawling stage is falling down stairs.

When your child begins to walk and climb, you will have to be extra watchful of him. Along with protecting him, you should then begin to teach him about possible dangers. Because the toddler wants to investigate everything, do not leave windows and doors open; this is an invitation to disaster.

Do away with stair and floor hazards: Keep stairs free of objects that can cause you to fall while carrying the baby. Tack down extension cords and scatter rugs on the floors. Always keep one hand free to hold the handrail on staircases. People frequently fall because they cannot see where they are going. Be certain your hallways are well lighted and that your stairways have a light switch that can be operated from both the bottom and top floors. All rooms should have a switch near the door so a light can be put on without stumbling in the dark. Night lights in hallways, bedrooms and bathrooms are also excellent safeguards.

Fall-proof the bathtub: A baby is more safely bathed in something smaller than the bathtub, such as a

164

YOUR HOUSE

washbasin or kitchen sink. Use only a small amount of water at first until you get the knack of holding the baby securely. A basin or tub lined with a diaper is less slippery. Never leave a baby alone in a bath for any reason.

Bathtubs for the older child should have a nonskid bottom. You can buy inexpensive rubber mats with suction discs or adhesive on the underside. Or you can buy strips of nonskid material that can be stuck in a pattern on the bottom of the tub. Young children should never be left unsupervised in the tub for even an instant.

Guarding against blows

Sharp-edged furniture, open drawers, and easily overturned items such as lamps and flower pots are the frequent cause of severe blows to young children. Eliminate these hazards when possible. Otherwise, keep a watchful eye on your child until he is old enough to use care in avoiding accidents.

If you have playground equipment in your yard or home, watch your child as you would at a public playground to ensure he does not get in the way of other children's active play on swings, seesaws and slides.

Guarding against severe cuts

Check around the house in order to remove sharp objects such as scissors, knives, razor blades, tools, sharp-pointed toys and breakable objects from places readily accessible to children. Do not allow a child to be in the yard with you if you are using a power mower. A mower can throw off missiles like cans, stones, broken glass, and even its own blades.

Guarding against animal bites

Family pets, even puppies, can be dangerous around very young children. Teach your child to play gently with pets and to avoid strange animals. Have your own pets properly immunized against rabies by your veterinarian.

Never leave food in bed with children. This may attract rodents.

SUFFOCATION AND STRANGULATION

Precautions in the crib and playpen

The crib and playpen sometimes can be a source of grave danger to an in-fant. Choose furniture carefully (see pages 169–172). Be certain that slats are spaced no more than $2\frac{3}{8}$ inches apart so the baby cannot catch his head between them. Also be careful of loose slats that could come out, leaving a dangerous gap in which the baby's head could get caught.

A young baby who cannot raise his head should never sleep on a pillow. He might bury his head in it and suffocate. Thin plastic, such as the kind from a dry cleaner, is a very dangerous item in a baby's world. It should never be used to cover a crib mattress, nor should it be left where a baby could grab it and pull it over his face.

Dangerous toys and objects in the home

Every household has a large number of objects that are tempting to a baby. Before putting an infant in the playpen or on the floor to play, check the area carefully. Keep buttons, beads, pins, screws—anything small enough to fit into the baby's mouth—safely out of reach. Small objects can get lodged in the throat and cut off a child's air supply, or can puncture a vital organ if swallowed.

The most dangerous toys for a child under three years of age are also those small enough to swallow. Do not let a young child play with marbles, small plastic toys, toys with detachable pieces or stuffed animals and dolls with tiny button eyes that he can pull off. Never let your child chew on balloons; he might accidentally bite off a piece and choke.

Abandoned refrigerators and trunks are also very dangerous. Children love to play and hide in them, and suffocation easily results. Remove doors from refrigerators and remove lids from trunks.

POISONING

Fatal poisonings are most frequent in children between the ages of one and three. Children often explore by tasting things and may eat or drink anything they find, no matter how bad it tastes. To protect your child against possible poisoning, know which substances in and around your home are poisonous and keep them out of your child's reach at all times. Never underestimate your child's cleverness and skill in getting to poisons.

Substances that are poisonous

Common household chemicals and drugs: Nearly all household chemicals and drugs contain poisonous elements. Watch for manufacturers' warnings on the labels of products you bring home which may read: "Poison," "Caution: Harmful If Swallowed," "Keep Out of Reach of Children." Inspect your home carefully and be certain such clearly marked poisons are kept out of your child's reach at all times. Here are some poisonous items found in most households:

Insect and rat poisons
Kerosene, gasoline, benzene, turpentine, cleaning fluid
Liquid furniture and auto polish
Lye, alkalies used for cleaning drains, bowls and ovens
Oil of wintergreen
Plant sprays
Bleach, ammonia, washing soda, detergents
Mothballs
Aspirin and other medication

Unmarked poisons: You cannot always rely on a product label to give you the proper warning. Items such as nail polish, perfume, cosmetics and hair tonics may offer no clue to the hazards of accidental swallowing. Prescription drugs and some over-the-counter medicines do not carry warnings about the dangers of overdose or accidental swallowing. Alcoholic beverages contain no cautionary words as to the harm they can cause your child if he drinks large quantities of them. Your best line of defense is to suspect anything that is not a known and healthful food item, and to keep it out of the child's reach.

Poisonous plants: A surprising number of plants are capable of poisoning. Diefenbachia and mistletoe are two common examples. Teach your child never to eat any part of a plant not commonly used as food, especially unknown berries or mushrooms. Even nibbling on leaves, sucking on plant stalks, or drinking water in which plants have been soaking may cause poisoning. See the list and diagrams in "Poisoning" chapter, pages 96–99.

Food poisoning: Proper sterilization of a baby's formula and prompt refrigeration of milk and opened jars of baby food are extremely important

165

in preventing the growth of harmful bacteria that cause food poisoning.

Some nonpoisonous foods can be just as dangerous as poisonous ones when given to an infant by mistake. For example, putting salt instead of sugar into a baby's formula can be dangerous.

Too much medicine: When giving any medication, always follow the directions for dosage on the label or, in the case of prescription drugs, the doctor's instructions. Do not make the mistake of thinking, "If a little medicine is good, a lot is better."

An overdose of good-tasting medicine such as candy-flavored baby aspirin and vitamins is one of the leading causes of poisoning in young children. Children love the taste of these medicines and will climb to great heights in search of them, especially when they are hungry. It is best to lock up aspirin and vitamins. Never encourage your child to take medicine by telling him it is candy.

Lead poisoning: In the home the main source of lead poisoning is dried, peeling paint on walls, woodwork, repainted furniture, and repainted toys. Children suck and chew on toys and furniture all the time. They pick at peeling paint and loose plaster until they pull off a piece and then put it into their mouths. If you repaint any surface inside your house, use only unaltered lead-free paint. Even if you do use a lead-free paint, there may be layers of old paint underneath that have a high lead content. Scrape off all the layers of old or peeling paint, and dispose of the paint outside the house in a covered container. When your child is outdoors, keep a watchful eye. Most outdoor paints have a high lead content. Do not let your child bite on window sills, porch steps, or bars on iron gates. Some children display an unusual appetite for nonfood substances such as paint chips, plaster, crayons, chalk, wallpaper, dirt and cigarettes. This abnormal craving is called pica. A child with this malady must be well protected, for persistent pica can cause lead poisoning. If you suspect lead poisoning, get prompt medical attention; the child's blood level will be checked to determine if lead poisoning has occurred. Children who have lead poisoning may show the following symptoms: unusual irritability; poor appetite; stomach pains and vomiting; persistent constipation, sluggishness or drowsiness.

Rules to follow in storing poisonous substances

1. Never keep household cleaners and chemicals under the sink or on low-lying shelves where a crawling child can easily find them and be tempted to sample their contents. Store these items in a high cabinet, preferably one that can be locked.
2. Dispose of empty poison containers in a safe receptacle outside the house where a child cannot fish them out and play with them.
3. Put medicine and household chemicals away immediately after using them. Store them in a high cabinet, preferably one that can be locked. If the phone rings or you go to answer the door while you are using one of these items, take the bottle with you. Do not turn your back on a child while a poisonous substance is within his reach.
4. Do not underestimate a child's cleverness and skill in getting to poisons and being able to open the "child-proof" safety caps.
5. Do not transfer potential poisons into food containers such as bowls, jars, soft drink or milk bottles. Many people do this, especially when using kerosene, turpentine, spot remover, or bleach. Children innocently identify the container with a familiar drink and sometimes swallow its contents before parents can stop them.
6. Poisonous substances should never be stored around food. Adults have also mistaken poisons like roach powder and boric acid solution for food, resulting in fatal poisoning.

DROWNING

Never leave your child alone in the bathtub, wading pool, or around open frozen bodies of water. Drowning takes only seconds, and even shallow water is dangerous. Do not leave your bathtub filled or tubs of water around where a baby can fall into them. Make certain any swimming pools or wading pools are securely fenced off or supervised.

FIRES, BURNS AND ELECTRIC SHOCK

Every year a startling number of babies and young children die or are injured in fires. Careless smoking and children playing with matches and lighters cause one out of every five fires. Do not leave matches and lighters around a room; they are a temptation to children. Never leave a child alone in a house. In minutes, he could kindle a fire or one could occur and trap him. Children panic easily in fires, and when parents are not there to rescue them, they have been known to hide under beds or in closets. Home fire drills are an excellent safety measure. The best way not to panic in case of fire is to know what you are going to do *before* a fire ever breaks out. Your first impulse in a fire should always be escape. If the fire is very small and has just started, you can possibly extinguish it yourself with the proper equipment (see chapter on "Fire Safety," pages 140–141). Always send the children outside first. Smoke—not flames—is the real killer in a fire.

Preventing burns

Burns are another hazard to children. Fireplaces, open heaters, hot registers, floor furnaces, and radiators have all caused horrible burns to young children. Because you cannot watch your children all the time, you should screen fireplaces and put guards around heaters, furnaces, registers and radiators.

Sometimes you may have to use a vaporizer or portable heater in a child's room. Place it beyond the child's hand reach, far enough away so that its heat cannot ignite the child's bedclothes.

Use caution in the bathroom. Check bath water temperature to avoid scalding. Place rough-surfaced adhesive strips in bathtubs to keep children from slipping.

Use caution in the kitchen. It is unsafe to let an infant crawl or a small child walk around the kitchen while you are cooking or serving meals. There is danger of your tripping and spilling something hot on the baby, or of your splattering grease on him, or even of the child pulling a hot pot off the stove onto himself. If you spill grease or water on the floor, mop it up right away to prevent anyone from skidding and falling. Place the child, instead, in a playpen or high chair. Be certain the chair or playpen is well away from the range. Turn pot handles inward toward the back of the range and never leave the oven door open. Avoid tablecloths that hang over the table's edge. The child may grasp the cloth and pull hot foods down on himself. Keep matches in a high place. Keep electrical appliances, mixers, blenders, food processors and slicers away from children's reach.

Preventing electric shock

To a child, an electric outlet is a fascinating hole in the wall, just right for poking. Use childproof covers or heavy electric tape on unused electric outlets to keep out the baby's fingers and toys or other objects. Have damaged appliances and frayed cords repaired promptly, for a defect can produce a lethal jolt. Never let a child chew on an electric cord.

All electrical toys for children must have labels that tell you the earliest age at which most children can use them safely. Read the instruction book that comes with the toy to the child. Use the toy a few times with the child to make sure he understands how the toy operates. Use common sense about supervision. For example, a nine-year-old using a toy oven will need a great deal of supervision. Be sure the plug of an electrical toy fits snugly into wall outlets or extension cords. No prongs should be exposed. Teach children to disconnect the toy by pulling on the plug, not the cord. Keep infants and toddlers away from where older children are using an electrical toy. Check electrical toys regularly for broken parts, frayed cords, and damage to compartments that enclose wiring. The older the toy, the more often you should check it. Immediately after use, electrical toys should be put away in a dry storage area out of the reach of younger children. Only an adult or responsible older child should replace a light bulb on an electrical toy. Be sure the replacement bulb is the proper wattage and that the plug is disconnected when the bulb is changed. If any toy is so badly damaged that it cannot be repaired, throw it away immediately. Electrical toys with heating elements are recommended only for children over eight years old.

If your child receives an electric shock, first see if he is in contact with the live wire. If the child is still touching the live wire, trying to pull him away with your bare hands will not help him or you. In fact, you might get a severe shock yourself. First, shut off the current, preferably by pulling the main switch. If you do not know where the switch is, take out the extension cord. If you cannot do either, then pull the live wire away from your child, but not with your bare hands. Use a dry stick, rubber gloves or a piece of cloth or newspaper. If you have to pull the child away, do not touch the child with your bare hands either. Use folds of cloth or newspaper, heavy gloves or a pole or board—anything that is dry and is not metal. Then give the child artificial respiration and first aid immediately (see pages 17–18), and call a doctor.

If your child is not in contact with the live wire, remember that an electric shock can stop the victim's respiration and sometimes his heart. Usually an electric spark can cause a severe burn. Give him artificial respiration immediately if necessary (see pages 17–18) and CPR (see pages 18–19), and treat his burns as soon as possible. Then call a doctor.

PREPARATION FOR EMERGENCIES

Even after you have done everything you can think of to protect your child from accidents, they can still happen. In an emergency, the most important advice can also be the most difficult to follow if you are not prepared: Keep calm and do not panic. It helps greatly if you plan for an emergency before one ever happens:
1. Tape a list of important telephone numbers on a wall by the telephone.
2. Take a first-aid course and familiarize yourself with first-aid emergency measures.
3. Have on hand in the medicine cabinet the items needed for any emergency (see page 25 for stocking your cabinet).
4. If you are alone with a sick child, first administer any urgently needed first aid, then telephone for help.
5. If your own doctor is not available, dial the all-emergency code for your city that is published in any telephone book, and be sure to add it to your emergency telephone list.

FIRST AID AND EMERGENCY TREATMENT

Even when you are careful about safety, accidents and illness will occur. You should know what to do.

Choking, drowning, electric shock, bad bleeding, burns, poisoning, fainting and convulsions and shock require immediate action to save a life. You cannot wait for help or advice. The following guide provides quick tips for common childhood emergencies. Also refer to the specific chapters on first aid.

Choking

Check to see if the child can still move air in and out. If so, wait for child to cough up foreign object. If not, apply the Heimlich Maneuver. There are two ways to apply the maneuver to an infant. You can hold the child in your lap and place the index and middle fingers of both hands against the abdomen above the navel and below the rib cage (see Fig. 44-1), then press into the abdomen with a quick upward thrust. Or you can place the infant face upward on a firm surface and perform the maneuver while facing him (see Fig. 44-2).

Fig. 44-1

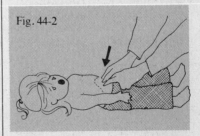
Fig. 44-2

If the maneuver is not successful or if the child can breathe but keeps choking, rush him to a hospital.

CHILDPROOFING YOUR HOUSE

Drowning or electric shock

For an electric shock victim, turn off power if possible. Do not touch victim until contact is broken. Pull from contact using dry rope, wooden pole or loop of cloth.

Use mouth-to-mouth rescue breathing until child breathes on his own or until you reach a doctor:
1. Clear the mouth with your finger, quickly removing any mucus, vomit, food or object.
2. Place child on his back on the floor, table or other firm surface.
3. Tilt his head back with his chin up.
4. Cover his mouth and nose with your mouth and blow gently until you see his chest rise.
5. Remove your mouth and let his lungs empty.
6. Take a quick breath yourself.
7. Repeat at a rate of about 20 times a minute.

If air is not moving, quickly check the position of the child's head and try again. If still no movement, hold the child upside down, slap him firmly between his shoulders, check his mouth for blocking, and try again. DO NOT STOP!

Bad bleeding

Stop the bleeding by pressing with your hand directly on the bleeding spot. Get a cloth or piece of clothing under your hand and press firmly. Continue to press. If bleeding continues, add more cloth and continue to press. Direct pressure from your hand will stop almost any bleeding. Even if an arm or leg is nearly cut off, you can usually stop the bleeding with pressure. If bleeding continues, try applying pressure to pressure point (see pages 19–20). Use a tourniquet *only* as a last resort when other methods fail (see page 20).

Chemical burns

If lye, oven cleaner, pesticides or other strong chemical comes in contact with child's skin or eyes, wash it off with large amounts of water for a long time. Remove any contaminated clothing. Place the affected area directly under a faucet, garden hose or shower and keep rinsing for five minutes. Use a bottle, cup or gentle faucet to wash out eyes. Keep the eyelids open as much as possible.

For 2nd- and 3rd-degree heat burns, cut away loose clothing, but not clothing that adheres to the skin. Cover with layers of clean, moist dressings. Treat for shock (see page 21). Never break blisters; they may become infected.

Poisoning

Poisoning from swallowed medicines or products:
1. Immediately have child drink several glasses of milk or water unless he is having convulsions.
2. Call a physician, hospital, poison-control center or rescue squad. Tell them the name and brand of the substance that was swallowed. Keep the container, the label and anything left in the container. Describe the condition of the child—whether he is vomiting, unconscious, drowsy, cold.
3. If a doctor advises it, make him vomit. Make child vomit even if you cannot reach a doctor unless:
   —he is unconscious or having a convulsion;
   —the substance swallowed was a strong alkali or acid (lye, ammonia, drain cleaner, oven cleaner);
   —the substance swallowed was a petroleum product such as kerosene, gasoline, turpentine, lighter fluid, insecticide or furniture polish. If any of these is swallowed, go directly to a hospital emergency room, clinic or doctor's office.
4. Make child vomit by giving one tablespoon, or ½ ounce, of syrup of ipecac if he is over one year old. Give an accompanying glass of water, about one cup. Give an infant just two teaspoons of syrup of ipecac. Activated charcoal can be used if you do not have syrup of ipecac on hand. If you do not have either, and have a long trip to the doctor or hospital, stop at a pharmacy, get some ipecac syrup and give it on the way to the doctor or hospital. When a child is vomiting, keep his face down and head lower than the hips to avoid his choking on the vomit.

Poisoning from smoke or fumes: Remove the child to a place where there is fresh air. Use mouth-to-mouth resuscitation if the child is not breathing.

Poisoning from a snakebite: Do not let the victim walk; keep him as quiet as possible. Immobilize the victim with the injured part lower than the rest of the body. Call a physician, hospital, or poison-control center and transport victim to a medical facility quickly. Call ahead so that antivenin, which counteracts venom, will be available. While awaiting transportation and en route, keep the victim warm. Do not give the victim any stimulants or alcohol. Watch for signs of shock and treat accordingly. Perform artificial respiration if necessary (see pages 17–18).

Fainting, unconsciousness and convulsions

For fainting and unconsciousness, loosen clothing around the neck. Keep mouth clear. Give nothing to the child. Do not splash water on the face. Summon aid.

For convulsions, keep calm. Do not restrain victim. Prevent child from hurting himself, however, by clearing the area of any objects that may be hazardous. Loosen tight clothing around the neck. Once convulsive movements stop, get child to lie down, and have him lie on his side. Allow him to rest or sleep. Summon aid.

Shock

After any severe injury, burn or bleeding, the child may become pale, clammy and cold. Keep child lying flat and warm with blankets (unless child has suffered head and chest injuries and then he should be placed in a semireclining position). Get child to a medical facility immediately. Maintain an open airway. Give nothing by mouth, especially stimulants. If victim is conscious and not vomiting, however, and if medical help cannot arrive for an hour or more, give victim "shock solution." Mix one teaspoon salt and ½ teaspoon baking soda in one quart of water. Give a child over one year two ounces every 15 minutes over a period of one hour; give an infant one ounce every 15 minutes over a period of one hour.

MINOR FIRST AID

Cuts: Stop the bleeding by pressing area with a clean cloth. Wash well with soap and water. Pat dry. Cover with sterile gauze pad or adhesive bandage. Do not use iodine, mercurochrome or first-aid ointment. Soap and water will take care of germs. If the skin does not fall back into place neatly, or if the wound is as much as ¼ inch deep, stitches or a special bandage may have to be applied to speed healing and prevent scarring. Protec-

168

tion against tetanus should be considered whenever skin is broken and cut is dirty. See tetanus immunization schedule, page 85.

Scrapes: Wash thoroughly with soap and water. Use a wet gauze to remove all dirt particles. Cover with a sterile gauze pad or adhesive bandage.

Bruises: Apply cold compresses for half an hour. If the skin is broken, treat as a cut.

Burns: Rinse with cold water. Cover with sterile dressing or clean cloth. Do not use ointments or greases. Cold compresses may relieve the pain of a fresh burn. Do not break blisters.

Falls: If your baby falls, do not pick him up right away. If he cries loudly immediately, he probably does not have a serious head or neck injury. Look to see whether he moves both arms and legs and whether they look broken. If you think anything is broken, leave him where he is and call for help. If he is crying and moving his arms and legs, you can pick him up and comfort him.

If he is unconscious after a fall, call immediately for medical advice. If child cries loudly, run your hand over his head to be sure there are no lumps or depressions. Let him rest or play quietly. If he stays well and active, you probably have nothing to worry about. Check child frequently, and if he becomes very sleepy or vomits more than once, get medical advice quickly.

Insect bites and stings: Remove the stinger if present. Apply cold compresses and then calamine lotion to reduce itching. Tell the child to avoid scratching.

Animal bites: Wash with clean water and soap. If bite is not bleeding profusely, apply sterile dressing. If possible, catch or retain animal and keep alive for observation by police.

Nosebleed: Have child sit down. Blow out from the nose all blood and clot. Apply pressure on outside of nostril for at least five minutes with a cold compress. If bleeding continues, insert a wedge of cotton moistened with cold water into bleeding nostril. If bleeding stops, leave packing in place for another five minutes. If bleeding continues, secure medical help immediately.

TIPS FOR BABY-SITTERS

There are certain do's and don'ts for all people sitting for a child.

1. Before the parents depart, be sure they have left the following numbers by a telephone:
- Where parents will be
- Nearby friend or relative
- Children's doctor
- Fire department
- Police department
- Poison-control center
- Hospital
- Ambulance service.

2. Have the parents show you through the house or apartment and point out where the items you will need are located, such as children's clothing, electricity and gas turnoffs, fire extinguishers, first-aid supplies.

3. Know where the emergency exits are located. In case of fire, get the children out of the house without stopping to telephone fire department. Take children to a neighbor's home. Call fire department from there, and then call the parents to let them know where you and the children are.

4. Keep the youngsters safe by preventing accidents. Know where the potential hazards, such as electrical outlets, appliances, and exposed heating elements, are.

5. Stairs can be dangerous for children. Keep a curious child from playing on or around them. Remember, too, that stairs are not meant to be a storage area. Anything placed on the stairs can become an obstacle to fall over.

6. Babies in carriages, walkers or strollers should never be left unattended in an area around stairs or ramps.

7. Caution children about the dangers of glass doors or windows. To prevent injuries, keep doors and windows locked at all times.

8. Never open the door to strangers. If there is a question about someone at the door, call the parents to check with them. If you cannot reach them, call the police if the stranger does not leave.

9. In case of accident or illness, do not try to be a doctor. Treat only minor cuts and bruises. Call the parents for instructions. If they cannot be reached, call your own parents or go to a neighbor for help. If the parents ask you to give a child medication, be sure they leave instructions.

10. Never leave children in the house alone, even for a minute. Never leave a baby in the care of a young child.

11. Stay awake; study, read, or watch television.

12. Do not have friends over, unless the parents have agreed.

Playing with children

Whether you are actually playing with the children or supervising them, keep them within safe play areas, preferably within your sight. Keep them away from potential danger areas in the home such as the kitchen, bathroom, workshop and storage areas.

Teach children to play safely by showing them how to use their toys in a safe manner, if they do not know how. Be sure they put their toys away after play.

Daytime sitting may include playing outdoors with the children. Outdoor play equipment—swings, seesaws and slides—are fun, but can be dangerous too. Be sure children understand the hazards of standing in a swing, walking in front or in back of a swing, climbing up the front of a slide. Do not let children climb trees or play in the street or driveway. Do not let them play in the garage or in a toolshed.

BUYING AND MAINTAINING CHILDREN'S FURNITURE AND OTHER EQUIPMENT

Carefully select all furniture and equipment (see Fig. 44-3). Be suspicious of so-called safety products and "doctors'" endorsements. Although a product may be advertised as safe, it may not be. Use furniture and equipment only for the purpose for which they are intended. Remember that there is no substitute for close parental supervision.

Baby walkers

Walkers provide exercise for a baby, and may help to protect the child who is learning to walk. Select a walker that is stable. The wheel base should be both wider and longer than the frame of the walker itself. Small, flimsy wheels or a narrow base can contribute to tipping. Be sure the seat is made of sturdy materials—unbreakable plastic or tough fabric with heavy-duty stitching or rugged snaps.

Look for protective covers for coiled springs and hinges. Locking devices and screws should have no sharp

169

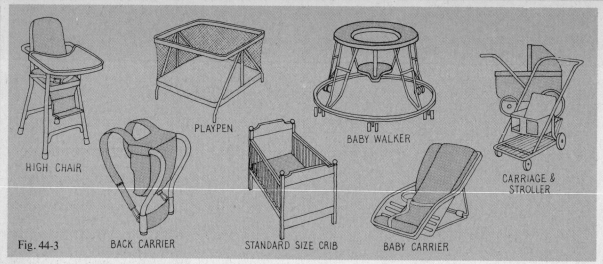

HIGH CHAIR

PLAYPEN

BABY WALKER

CARRIAGE & STROLLER

Fig. 44-3 BACK CARRIER STANDARD SIZE CRIB BABY CARRIER

edges or points. When the baby walker is in use, assist the child in maneuvering on and off carpets, across thresholds and around furniture. Remove throw rugs. Loose rug fibers can become entangled in the wheels. Place guards at the top of all stairs or keep stairway doors closed to prevent falls. Be aware of what the child is doing. The unattended child is too often an accident victim. Prevent the child from running or leaning too far when using the walker.

Cribs

Whether you buy a standard- or nonstandard-size crib, there are certain safety features to check for. It must have no more than $2\frac{3}{8}$ inches between slats—about three adult fingers' width. It should have a snug-fitting mattress. If you can fit two fingers between mattress and sides, the mattress is too small. The crib sides must lock at maximum height, and there must be no rough edges or exposed bolts. The latching device should not be able to be released easily. The finish should be a safe material such as nonlead paint.

Bumper pads are extra protection in a crib when the slat distances are too wide. Make sure bumpers run around the entire crib, tie or snap in place and have at least six straps. To prevent an infant from chewing on the straps and swallowing them, trim off any excess length.

Remove and destroy all plastic wrapping materials. Before throwing the materials away, tie them in knots. Children have suffocated while playing with plastic bags.

As soon as the child can stand up, lock the crib's side rail at the maximum height and adjust the mattress to the lowest position. Remove bumper pads, large toys and boxes. An active child will use anything for climbing out of the crib. If the height of the crib side is less than three-quarters of the child's height, the child has outgrown it and should sleep in a bed.

If dangling toys are left hanging from crib sides, make sure the cord is not long enough to wrap around the child's neck. It should be less than 12 inches.

Fixing an old or antique crib: If you paint or refinish an old or antique crib, use only high-quality household enamel paint. Do not use paints made prior to 1972 when 0.5% lead limitation became effective; they may contain a higher percentage of lead.

Bumper pads are very important on older cribs. Many of the older cribs have too much space between the slats, and the pads help to prevent a baby's head getting caught.

High chairs

When selecting a high chair, choose one that has a wide base for stability. Always place the high chair on a level surface so that it remains stable. The high chair should include safety straps not attached to the tray. Avoid models with hardware that is rough or pointed.

When settling a child in the high chair, always use the seat belts and any other restraining straps provided. Do not allow the child to climb into the chair on his own. Check the tray each time it is used to see that it is properly latched to both sides. Supervise the child closely, and instruct other children not to pull on the high chair or climb up on it. Use the high chair only in an area free of traffic—away from doorways, refrigerators, ranges and other large kitchen appliances. If the seat is slippery, attach rough-surfaced adhesive strips to it.

Strollers and carriages

Take your child with you when you go to buy a stroller or carriage so that he or she can try it out for comfort. Test strollers and carriages for stability. The base should be wide enough to prevent tipping, even when the baby leans over the side. If it can be adjusted to a reclining position, be sure it does not tip backward when the baby lies down. Wheels should be large enough in diameter to provide stability. Do not overlook canopies and shopping baskets attached to strollers. They can affect stability. The canopy should lock in a forward horizontal position. When it is unlocked, it should rotate to a downward position in the rear of the stroller. The shopping basket for carrying packages should be low on the back of the stroller and located so that its center is in front of or directly over the axle of the rear wheels.

When using the stroller or carriage, always do the following: Check that the latching devices are securely fastened; be sure the brake operates properly; use seat belts or harness; do not allow another child to stand in the basket; supervise the child.

170

Back carriers

Do not use a frame back carrier until a baby is four to five months old, when the neck is usually strong enough to withstand normal jolts. Buy a carrier to match a baby's size and weight. Try it on with the baby in it and check for enough depth to support the baby's back and leg openings small enough to prevent the baby from slipping out but big enough to prevent chafing of the baby's legs. Restraining straps are essential. Children may stand up and try to climb out of frame carriers. Look for sturdy materials with strong stitching or large, heavy-duty snaps to prevent the baby from slipping out. Avoid joints that may accidentally close and pinch or cut the baby. Avoid sharp points, edges or rough surfaces. Look for a back carrier with soft, padded covering over the metal frame near the baby's face. Bumping against the frame may cause injury to the head or face. Check the carrier periodically for ripped seams, missing or loose snaps and frayed seats or straps. Repair promptly.

When leaning over or stopping, bend from the knees rather than the waist to minimize the chances of the baby falling out of the back carrier. Use a seat belt on the baby at all times.

Playpens

Buy a playpen large enough so that the baby is unable to crawl over the side or cause the pen to tip over by leaning his weight against it. Mesh playpens with large open weave can be used as a toehold for climbing. Instead, the playpen should have a small weave, approximately ¼ inch in size.

There should be no protruding bolts or rough edges. Hinges should lock tightly. Leave no large toys in the playpen that can be used for climbing out of it. Slats on the playpen should be no more than 2⅜ inches apart. If slats are too far apart, interweave sheeting among the slats and fasten securely. If toys are hung from the sides, be sure the cord is short enough not to wrap around the baby's neck. It should be no more than 12 inches long. Always bring a playpen indoors after it has been used outdoors. Rainwater and sun can damage it. Do not let a child use a playpen once he is able to climb over the sides.

Baby or infant carriers

The carrier is designed for feeding time, for carrying a baby from place to place, or keeping a young baby in a room with you without having to hold him. Do not use it as a car seat. Never buy one with a narrow base or slippery bottom surface. Instead, the carrier should have a stable base, be made of sturdy materials, and have a safety strap. It should have a supporting device that locks firmly in place.

When using a carrier, always stay with the baby and always use safety straps. If bottom is slippery, attach rough-surfaced adhesive strips. When using carrier on high surfaces, make sure the child is within arm's reach and clear of dangerous objects.

Dressing or changing tables

Always strap child in place on a changing table. Remember that even the straps do not always prevent a child from falling off. A table with guard rails offers some additional protection against infant falls, as does a table with a recessed rather than a flat top.

Car seats

It is essential to buckle infants and toddlers into crash-tested car restraints for every trip in a car. Seat belts and harnesses that come as standard equipment in new cars are not suitable for children under four, or for children weighing less than 40 pounds. More than 20 different models that meet crash-testing standards are now sold. When shopping for an approved crash-tested device, keep in mind that they fall into five groups (see Fig. 44-4).

Infant: Baby rides backwards in a semireclining position. This type of restraint is suitable for infants up to 20 pounds.

Birth to 40 pounds: This restraint can be used for both infants and young children. For infants, it should be placed in a backward-riding position as the seat above is (the design varies slightly). For the toddler and older child up to 40 pounds, it should be tilted up and placed so that the child rides facing forward.

Harness in a seat: The chair-type restraint must have a 5-point harness—one that comes across the lap, over both shoulders and through the crotch. This type is suitable for children who are able to sit up unaided and who weigh at least 15 pounds. They can be used until four years or 40 pounds.

Harness alone: This is a 5-point harness which is secured by a strap around the seat back and is bolted to the floor or to the rear window shelf. It will fit a child who can sit up unaided and weighs 15 to 50 pounds.

Shield type: Children weighing over 20 pounds can use a restraint featuring a C-shaped shield which is secured by the standard safety belt. Some infant restraints have their own individually designed shields which snap on when the restraint is faced forward for use by an older child.

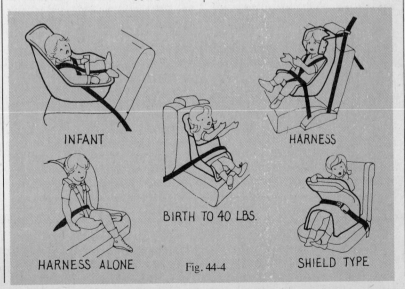

INFANT

HARNESS

HARNESS ALONE

BIRTH TO 40 LBS.

SHIELD TYPE

Fig. 44-4

171

Bunk beds

Select bunk beds that are made of wood or metal with rounded edges, and have a mattress that fits tightly to prevent exposure of hard edges; a ladder that grips the bed frame firmly and does not slip when you climb on it; a guard rail that can be secured into position and does not have open spaces through which a child could fall. Consider purchasing bunk beds that can be taken down to form two single (twin) beds if you later decide you do not want the bunk bed style.

When possible, place the bunk beds in the corner of a room so that there are walls on two sides. Keep the guard rail securely in place at all times, no matter what the age of the child. Do not permit very young children to sleep in the top bunk because they have greater difficulty climbing the ladder, especially if they have to get up at night. Consider keeping a low-watt night light on so that children will be able to see the ladder if they have to get up at night.

Replace any loose or missing rungs on the ladder. Keep the guard rails in good repair. Cover any sharp edges with heavy tape, rubber padding or towels to prevent cuts.

Toy boxes and toy chests

If you are buying a chest or box with a hinged lid, be sure that the lid is lightweight and has a flat inner surface and a device that will hold it open in a raised position so that it will not slam shut of its own weight. Make sure that the device to hold the lid open is not able to pinch the child. There is some evidence that a lid with protrusions or recessed areas on the inner side may make it more difficult for a child to get free should the lid close on the head accidentally.

Check for rough or sharp edges on all metal components and for splinters and other rough areas on wooden boxes.

The toy box or chest should be well ventilated, with ventilation holes in the lid and near the top on two opposite sides. Or the toy box can feature a lid that does not close completely.

Always buy a toy chest that does not lock. If you own a box with a lid that may be hazardous—one that is heavy, has a recessed inner surface, or one that will not remain open or has poor ventilation—the hazard can be eliminated simply by removing the lid.

There is now available an excellent source catalog that reveals hard-to-find products to protect your child from accidents. Items included are Kinderguard latches to keep children out of cabinets containing dangerous chemicals and poisons, safety window locks, safety caps for electrical wall outlets, and many more. Called the "Child Safety Catalog," it can be obtained free by writing to Safety Now Co., Inc., P.O. Drawer 567, Jenkintown, Pa. 19046.

45

CONTROLLING HOUSEHOLD PESTS

You can rid your home of practically all pests, and keep it free of them, by a combination of good housekeeping and the right presticide used at the right time.

It is easier to prevent pests from infesting your home than it is to get rid of them after they have entered. Household pests seek food, water and places where they may hide and breed. If you eliminate these attractions from your home, the pests will go elsewhere.

Some basic rules

1. Practice good sanitation. Many household pests live on spilled food that has not been completely cleaned up. They breed, multiply and hide in small areas where food is left available to them, and in seldom-used storage cabinets and around water pipes and toilets. Keep these places clean. Frequent scrubbings with hot water and soap or detergent will do the job. Throw away or put in storage items that are not used.
2. Promptly dispose of garbage, crumbs, scraps of fabrics, lint and other waste materials that pests may eat or in which they may breed. Garbage left open during the night is always appealing to pests, which are active in the dark.
3. Keep all foods in tightly closed, clean containers. Before purchasing dry foods, examine packages carefully for evidence of breaks and resultant insect infestation. Use up packaged products before insect eggs can hatch and develop.
4. Do not permit insect pests to hitch-hike into your home. Cockroaches and silverfish often enter the house in the crevices of cardboard cartons used in transporting groceries or other materials.
5. Permanently seal up places where pests may enter. Caulk openings and cracks around wash basins, toilet bowls and water pipes. Fill in the cracks around baseboards and between floorboards. Cover openings where rats or mice may enter. See that windows and doors are tight-fitting.
6. Pesticides may be needed to supplement good housekeeping. Follow the directions and heed all precautions on pesticide labels for use and storage. *Note:* Many pests are becoming resistant to pesticides, and we will soon need to employ alternative methods of control.

PESTICIDES AND THEIR APPLICATION

There are many kinds of pesticides, and they may be applied in different forms to serve various purposes. In order to select the right form and apply it properly, study the following explanations.

Surface sprays

These sprays are applied to surfaces in the home where insects are likely to crawl. The spray particles are coarse, and they dampen or wet the surfaces. When the spray dries, a thin deposit of insecticide remains. For several weeks, the deposit kills insects that crawl over it. You may buy these sprays in pressurized containers or in garden-type compressed-air sprayers, or you may buy a liquid insecticide and apply it with a household hand sprayer that produces a coarse spray. You have less control, however, over pressurized sprays than you have with hand sprayers.

Caution. Do not spray oil-base insecticides on asphalt-tile floors because they may dissolve the asphalt. They may also soften and discolor some linoleums and some plastic materials. If in doubt about spraying such surfaces, test the spray on a small, inconspicuous place. If you use an oil-base insecticide for the cracks in a parquet floor, apply it lightly; a heavy amount may dissolve the underlying adhesive, which in turn may stain the floor.

Space sprays and aerosols

Space sprays and aerosols are designed to be used in the air. They are especially effective against mosquitoes, houseflies, and other flying insects. They may also be used to penetrate the hiding places of other insects such as roaches, and drive them into the open where they may be killed with a surface spray or dust.

The particles of a space spray are much finer than those of a surface spray, and float in the air for a time. The particles of an aerosol are finer still, and stay in the air longer.

Space sprays leave little residue, and generally should not be used on surfaces. Aerosols are entirely too fine for surface application.

You may buy space sprays in pressurized containers, or you may buy liquid insecticide and apply it as a space spray with a household hand sprayer having a nozzle that produces very fine particles. Household aerosols are available in pressurized containers.

Some sprays sold in pressurized containers may be labeled for both surface and space applications. If you use one of these products for spraying in the kitchen or pantry, first place cooking and eating utensils, and food, where they will not be contaminated by falling particles.

Before using a space spray or aerosol, close all windows and doors tight. Spray the chemical into the air as directed on the container label. Breathe as little of it as possible. Some people may be allergic to the materials in space sprays or aerosols. After using, leave the room, close the door and do not reenter for half an hour or longer. Before occupying the room, air it thoroughly.

Dusts

Insecticidal dusts usually contain the same active ingredients as sprays. They are used for surface applications, and may be blown by a household hand duster, available in hardware stores, into cracks, corners, and other places difficult to reach with sprays.

Paintbrush application

Insecticide may be applied to surfaces in liquid, cream or paste form with a paintbrush. This method often permits a more accurate placement of the material than does spraying or dusting. It is particularly good where only spot treatments are needed.

Poisoned bait

Poisoned bait is matter on which a pest will feed that has been impregnated with a pesticide. In the home, poisoned baits may be used to control rodents and some other pests. Frequently they are more hazardous to humans and pets than other forms of pesticide. If you use a poisoned bait, handle it with extreme care; follow the directions and observe all precautions on the container label.

Note. You may find that the labels on some pesticide containers in retail stores call the active ingredients by their chemical names. The accompanying table (see Fig. 45-1) gives examples of common and chemical names of pesticides.

USE PESTICIDES SAFELY

If not handled and applied properly, many household pesticides can injure humans or household pets.

Read the label

Always buy pesticides that have a U.S. Environmental Protection Agency (EPA) federal registration number, indicating that they have met certain safety guidelines. The first rule of safety in using any pesticide is to read and follow the directions and precautions on the container label. Make sure it lists the name of the pest you want to control. Many pesticides can injure and some can even kill wildlife, fish, honeybees, domestic animals and humans. Reread the label each time you use a pesticide; do not depend on your memory. Many pesticide manufacturers include instruction leaflets with their products. Carefully read these also.

Store pesticides safely

Always leave pesticides in their original containers with the original labels. Store them as directed on their labels, tightly closed, where children and pets cannot reach them. Do not place them near food. Do not store them under the sink, in the pantry, or in the medicine cabinet. Store away from heat. If a pesticide is marked "POISON," there will be an antidote statement on the label. Read it. In case of accident, take the container with you when seeking medical assistance. Do not save or reuse empty containers. Rinse with water and dispose of the containers properly. Most pesticide-related accidents are due to children having access to the containers.

Apply pesticides safely

Determine the right amount of pesticide. Use an unbreakable plastic measuring cup. (Never use the same cup in the kitchen for cooking.) Be careful not to get the pesticide on food, dishes, or cooking utensils. Remove aquariums, birds, cats, dogs and other pets and their food and water pans before applying pesticide. Keep children away from application areas. Also, place poison baits out of reach of children and pets. Do not smoke while handling a pesticide. When the label warns against breathing pesticidal mists or dusts, open windows and doors while applying them.

Handle oil-base sprays as though they were flammable. Avoid spilling an insecticide on the skin and keep it out of the nose, eyes and mouth. If you spill any on the skin or clothing, remove contaminated clothing immediately and wash the skin thoroughly with soap and water. Launder clothing before wearing it again. Wash your face and hands after every use.

If you accidentally swallow some

COMMON AND CHEMICAL NAMES OF PESTICIDES

Common name	Chemical name*
Diazinon	0,0-diethyl 0-(2-isopropyl-4-methyl-6-pyrmidinyl) phosphorothioate
Malathion	S-[1,2-bis (ethoxycarbonyl) ethyl] 0,0-dimethyl phosphorodithioate
Pyrethrin	Pyrethrin or pyrethrum
Ronnel	0,0-dimethyl 0-(2,4,5-trichlorophenyl) phosphorothioate
Strobane	Terpene polychlorinates (65-percent chlorine)

*The chemical name shown on the label may not always be exactly as shown here; variation is possible in the arrangement and inclusion of numbers.

Fig. 45-1

pesticide or if you feel ill effects after using it, call a physician at once. Read the label to him, naming the active chemical ingredient. If you cannot immediately reach a physician or your poison-control center, call your fire or police department. These agencies can help you get to a hospital. Follow directions on pages 94–95 of "Poisoning" chapter for removing poison.

Remember to clean all spraying equipment after each use. Use separate equipment for insecticides and weedicides.

HOUSEHOLD PESTS

Many pests that invade homes are present at all times in all parts of the United States. Some occur only at certain times or in certain areas. The following pages describe several kinds of pests. To control a pest you must know what it looks like. The information also tells what the pests do, and how they may be controlled. *Note:* The illustrations are greatly enlarged for the most part.

Ants

Several species of ants, similar in appearance, invade homes. And because some ants have wings, and termites readily shed their wings soon after emerging in buildings, ants are sometimes mistaken for termites. The two insects, however, may be readily distinguished if examined carefully. Ants are pinched in at the waistline (see Fig. 45-2); termites are not (see Fig. 45-3). Also, the rear wings of an ant are considerably smaller than the front wings, while there is little difference in size between the rear and front wings of a termite.

Habits and damage: Ants crawl over any food they can reach, spoiling it and carrying bits of it to their nests. They usually do not attack fabrics, leather or similar materials found in homes. They seldom infest sound wood; but some species, notably carpenter ants, do damage wood, preferring to establish their nests in decaying or water-damaged structures.

How to control ants: Locate the ants' nest, if possible. It may be outdoors, or it may be in the house— within a wall or partition, under flooring, under a pile of papers, or in an out-of-the-way corner. You may be

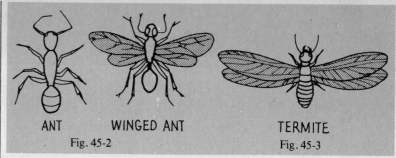

ANT   WINGED ANT
Fig. 45-2

TERMITE
Fig. 45-3

able to trace the ants' line of march from the food source to the approximate location of the nest. If you find the nest or nest entrance, treat it with an insecticide. If the nest is outdoors, try to seal off all cracks and openings into the house through which the ants may be able to enter. Control the ants on shrubs with pesticides labeled for use on plants.

Inside, use a liquid household insecticide containing baygon, diazinon or malathion. To treat most places, apply the insecticide as a surface spray. For kitchen treatments, you may prefer to apply the liquid with a small paintbrush to place it exactly where you want it. Apply insecticide to surfaces over which the ants are crawling in their line of march. Treat all cracks, openings, or runways they may be using to enter the house or to enter a room. These may include:
- the lower part of window frames, and around doors;
- supports, posts, pillars or pipes;
- cracks in baseboards, walls and floors, and around sinks, bathtubs, toilets and kitchen cupboards;
- openings around electrical outlets and plumbing or heating pipes.

Allow a few days for the ants to reach the insecticide deposits. If the pests continue to appear, they probably are entering over surfaces you have not treated. In this event, find and treat those surfaces.

Carpenter ants: These ants are large and reddish brown to black. Workers are from $\frac{1}{4}$ to $\frac{1}{2}$ inch long. Indoors these ants feed on sweets and other foodstuffs. They do not eat wood, but they do nest in it. Insecticide applied to the nest will eliminate the colony. Wood that may have become damp should be inspected. Carpenter ants nest in wood damaged by roof leaks, overflowing gutters, leaking air-conditioners, and leaking drains.

Bats

Sometimes bats (see Fig. 45-4) enter a home and establish their roost in the attic, in a space between the walls, or in an unused part of an upper story. When this occurs, the bats should be gotten rid of as soon as possible.

Habits and damage: These flying mammals stay in their roosts during the day, and fly at night in search of insects on which to feed. Normally bats are harmless, but they are subject to rabies. A bat infected with this often-fatal disease can transmit it to humans. Bats are also objectionable because of the noises they make and the bad odor that emanates from their droppings and urine. This odor persists long after a roost is broken up, and may attract a new colony of bats unless thorough sanitary measures are taken.

BAT
Fig. 45-4

How to control bats: First make sure all bats are out of the house. Then cover openings through which they might enter with sheet metal or $\frac{1}{4}$-inch-mesh hardware cloth. Leave no opening larger than $\frac{1}{4}$ inch.

It may be necessary to fumigate the infested areas. This operation is dangerous. Do not attempt it yourself. Employ a professional exterminator; he has the experience and equipment needed to control bats. Never handle live bats; you may be exposed to rabies. Also, wear rubber gloves when picking up and disposing of dead bats.

174

Bedbugs

The mature bedbug is brown, flattish and between ¼ inch and ⅜ inch long (see Fig. 45-5). When engorged with food (blood), the body becomes elongated and swollen, and the color changes from brown to dull red. The change in size, shape and color is so great that bugs in different degrees of distention may appear to be of different species. These pests are no longer common in the United States, but they do occur occasionally.

Bedbugs may be carried into the home from theatres, hotels, rooming houses, or park cabins. They may hitchhike into your home in bundles of laundry.

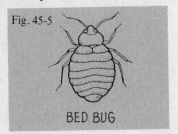
Fig. 45-5

BED BUG

Habits and damage: A female bedbug lays her eggs in cracks and crevices. These may be where parts of a bed are joined together, around the tufts of a mattress, or in a suitcase touching the end of a bed. The bugs hide in these places during the day and move out at night to feed.

Bedbugs feed on blood—usually human blood—and their bites may cause severe itching. They avoid the light, and are seldom seen. Often the only evidence of bedbug infestation, other than itching bites, is black or brown spots on bed sheets or on other surfaces where the bugs have been resting; these spots are digested blood. There usually is an offensive smell in rooms where bedbugs are numerous.

Bedbugs are also objectionable because they soil bed linens and mattresses. It never has been proven that they are disease carriers.

How to control bedbugs: Once the pests have entered an occupied house, only the application of insecticide will remove them. Household surface sprays containing malathion, ronnel or pyrethrin are usually effective against bedbugs. Ronnel or malathion may require only one application; pyrethrin must be applied several times at intervals of one week.

Spray the slats, springs and frames of beds, enough to wet them thoroughly. Cover the mattresses completely with spray, but do not soak them; be sure to get the spray into seams and tufts. (Sprays containing more than 0.1 percent of malathion are not safe to use on mattresses.) Allow a mattress to dry before using it.

Spray bedside furniture, baseboards and the openings or cracks in walls and between floorboards. If some bedbugs are present several weeks after treatment, spray again. Wash sheets and dry-clean blankets.

Carpenter bees

They occasionally nest in wood in buildings in many parts of the United States. They can be recognized by their bare, shiny abdomens (see Fig. 45-6). The abdomens of bumble bees, on the other hand, are covered with rows of dense yellow hair.

Fig. 45-6

CARPENTER BEE

Habits and damage: Relatively soft wood and unpainted wood are far more likely to be attacked than hard or painted wood. The bees cut an entrance hole about ⅝ inch in diameter across the grain of the wood and construct galleries with the grain.

How to control carpenter bees: The only practical method is to apply insecticide to the nest galleries. Dusts are usually the best. Dust the nest at night when bees are less active. If you do not have the right equipment, call a pest-control operator. Fill all nail holes. Carpenter bees often start their galleries from nail holes.

Centipedes

House centipedes (see Fig. 45-7) do not damage food supplies or household furnishings and do not have a poisonous bite. They feed on household pests. But these insects are annoying and may frighten some people.

Habits: Most centipedes normally live outdoors. In some areas, however, one species of long-legged centipede

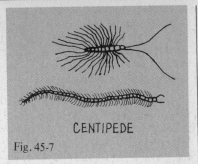
CENTIPEDE
Fig. 45-7

thrives indoors, where it feeds on soft-bodied insects and spiders.

How to control centipedes: If you insist on getting rid of these insects, you must find and destroy them. Use pyrethrin as flushing agent in aerosol, liquid or dust. Then spray with diazinon or malathion. Sweep centipedes up with a broom and dust pan.

Clothes moths and carpet beetles

Two species of clothes moths and four species of carpet beetles are serious pests, attacking fabrics in the home. Adults of both species of clothes moths (see Fig. 45-8) look very much alike. They are yellowish or buff, and have a wingspread of less than ½ inch. Full-grown larvae are white and have dark heads; they are about ½ inch long.

Adult black carpet beetles (see Fig. 45-9) have solid black bodies and brownish legs. They are about ¼ inch long. The larvae are yellowish, golden or dark brown; their bodies are tapered from head to posterior, where there is a tuft of long, brown hairs; they grow to be no more than ½ inch long.

CLOTHES MOTH
Fig. 45-8

CARPET BEETLE LARVA
Fig. 45-9

Adults of the other three species of carpet beetles have mottled colorings of white, brown, yellow or black. The larvae are long and oval; they have brownish or black bristles, and grow to be about $\frac{1}{8}$ inch long.

Habits and damage: The larvae of clothes moths and carpet beetles feed on wool, mohair, hair, bristles, fur, feathers and down. They attack clothing and a wide range of household furnishings, including blankets, rugs, carpets, drapes, pillows, hair mattresses, brushes and upholstery. Most infestations happen when these materials are in long-term storage.

How to control clothes moths and carpet beetles: To control these pests you must practice good housekeeping, apply protective treatments to susceptible articles, use surface sprays and store articles properly.

Clean your home often enough to prevent lint, dust and hair from accumulating. Give close attention to rugs and carpets; drapes and upholstered furniture; closets, especially those in which woolens and furs are kept; surfaces under and behind radiators; corners, cracks, baseboards, moldings, and other hard-to-reach surfaces. The vacuum cleaner is the best tool for most of this cleaning. After using it, dispose of the bag contents promptly; they may include eggs, larvae, or adult insects. In addition to cleaning rugs and carpets frequently, it is advisable to rotate them occasionally. Rotation is important because insects usually feed under heavy pieces of furniture where cleaning is difficult, rather than in the open where regular cleaning, light, and movement of people keep down infestations.

The best method of controlling fabric-feeding pests is to have the materials dry-cleaned and, if desired, "moth-proofed" by the cleaner. Dry cleaning kills all stages of clothes moths and carpet beetles. If you have woolen rugs or carpeting that needs protective treatments, get professional help. Clothes moths cannot live in cleaned wool, but carpet beetles can reinfest dry-cleaned articles so you must store them properly.

After thorough vacuuming, treat surfaces over which insects are likely to crawl with a spray that contains 3 to 5 percent of premium-grade malathion or ronnel, or $\frac{1}{2}$ percent of diazinon. You may buy these insecticides in ready-to-use pressurized containers that deliver a coarse spray, or you may buy a liquid insecticide and apply it with a household hand sprayer that also delivers a coarse spray. When the spray dries, it leaves a thin layer of insecticide which kills insects that crawl over it.

Spray surfaces along the edges of wall-to-wall carpeting, behind radiators, along baseboards and moldings, in corners, cracks, and other hard-to-clean places. When spraying closets, take clothing out and apply the spray to corners; to cracks in the floor, walls and ceiling; along baseboards; around shelves; and at the ends of clothes rods.

Aerosol containers deliver a fine spray which does not moisten surfaces as coarse sprays do, and so do not give lasting protection. Do not use aerosols for surface spraying.

You can protect stored woolens and other susceptible materials by these procedures:

• See that closets or containers used for storage are made as airtight as practicable. A closet should be tightly closed, and the cracks around the door sealed with tape or rope putty. Protection is lost if the door is opened frequently. Cedar chests are excellent storage containers, chiefly because of their tight construction, not because of their aroma.

• Place paradichlorobenzene crystals or naphthalene flakes or balls in the closets or containers before sealing them. As these chemicals evaporate, they produce a vapor which repels both clothes moths and carpet beetles. In a trunk-size container, use one pound of crystals, flakes or balls; in a closet, use one pound for each 100 cubic feet of space. Since the vapors are heavier than air, the chemicals should be placed in a shallow container on a shelf, or suspended from a clothes rod or hook in a thin cloth bag or perforated container. Airing for a short time removes the odor.

• Clean woolens can be protected from feeding damage by wrapping them in plastic bags into which some of the crystals, flakes or balls have been placed. Be sure the woolens are not infested.

• To protect furs from insect damage during the summer months, place them in commercial storage where they will receive professional care and can be insured.

Cockroaches

Five species of cockroaches (see Fig. 45-10 for one example) are known to infest homes in the United States. When fully grown, they range in length from nearly $\frac{1}{2}$ inch to almost 2 inches, and vary in color from yellowish or reddish brown to black.

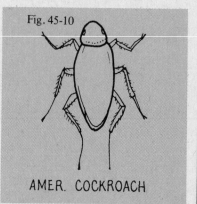
Fig. 45-10

AMER. COCKROACH

Habits and damage: Cockroaches seek shelter, moisture and food. They hide during the day in sheltered, dark places in the home, and come out at night to forage. Because they feed on garbage as well as human food, cockroaches may transmit human diseases, particularly some caused by food-poisoning organisms. The female cockroach lays her eggs in out-of-the-way places, in a leathery capsule which forms at the end of her body. Some females carry the capsule with them until the eggs hatch. Cockroaches contaminate and spoil human food.

How to control cockroaches: Good housekeeping and the use of insecticide when necessary are the only certain means of keeping your home free of cockroaches.

Baygon, chlorpyrifos, diazinon, malathion or ronnel will control all kinds of cockroaches. You can use a household surface spray or a dust. For severe infestation, use both. Spray first; then apply the dust after the spray has dried, forcing the dust into the cracks and openings difficult to reach with a spray.

Use an ordinary household spray gun, or use one of the surface sprays commonly sold in retail stores in pressurized cans. Apply enough spray to moisten surfaces thoroughly, but not enough to drip or run.

176

A space spray or aerosol mist containing pyrethrin may be used to penetrate into cracks, crevices, and other hard-to-reach places. This will rarely kill the roaches, but it will drive them into the open where you may kill them with a surface spray or dust. If you use a dust, apply it with an ordinary household dust gun.

For best results, apply insecticide to cracks and crevices where the roaches hide. For example:
- beneath the kitchen sink and drainboard;
- in cracks around or underneath cupboards and cabinets, and inside them, especially in upper corners;
- places where pipes or conduits pass along the wall or go through it;
- under, behind and beside refrigerators;
- behind window or door frames;
- behind loose baseboards or molding strips;
- on undersides of tables and chairs;
- on closet and bookcase shelves.

When treating cupboards and pantries, remove everything from the shelves and remove drawers so that food and utensils will not become contaminated by the insecticide. It is not necessary to treat the insides of drawers if you have thoroughly cleaned them. However, it is important to treat the sides, backs, and bottoms of drawers, and the insides of cabinets.

Crickets

Crickets (see Fig. 45-11) are usually not household pests. At times, however, two species—field crickets and house crickets—may enter homes. Occasionally, other species are found in basements.

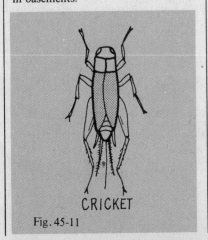

Fig. 45-11

Habits and damage: Field crickets breed outdoors, where they feed on all kinds of vegetation. They enter dwellings late in summer, when vegetation becomes scarce or after crops have been harvested. House crickets are most troublesome in dwellings located near city dumps or other areas that are being filled with refuse. Large numbers of crickets may develop in these places and swarm to houses at dusk during the period from July to September. In warm climates, house crickets may enter dwellings throughout the year. Crickets in the home may chew on and damage clothing and other fabrics, particularly if the articles are soiled.

How to control crickets: Close all openings to the house. Tighten screens, windows and doors. If the crickets persist in entering, use a household spray containing baygon, malathion or diazinon. Apply it around baseboards, in closets, and in cracks where the crickets may hide. Dusts containing these insecticides may be used on bare concrete floors of basements or out-of-the-way locations elsewhere in the house.

When large numbers of crickets develop outside the house, spray weeds with carbaryl before mid-August or September.

Fleas

Wherever dogs, cats or other furry pets are allowed inside the house, fleas (see Fig. 45-12) may become a problem. Fleas attack humans as well as animals. A house overrun by them is almost impossible to live in. The adult fleas feed on animal or human blood; they cannot breed or survive without it.

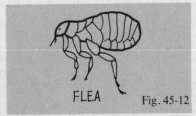

FLEA   Fig. 45-12

Habits and damage: The female flea lays her eggs on the pet. The eggs fall off and hatch in places where the pet spends most of its time. Indoors, these places may include a chair, sofa, rug, carpet, the pet's bed, or a part of the basement floor. Larval fleas that hatch from the eggs develop to maturity in cracks in the floor and other hiding places. A home may become heavily infested with developing larvae before they are noticed.

Adult fleas that result from the developing larvae can live several weeks without food.

Fleas inflict painful, itching bites, the discomfort of which may last from several days to a week or longer. More seriously, some species of fleas in some parts of the world can transmit to man the dreaded bubonic plague and other diseases.

How to control fleas: Fleas can be controlled in the home by a combination of good housekeeping and the use of insecticide. The best, most helpful step is to thoroughly clean infested rooms with a vacuum cleaner; don't forget carpets, rugs, upholstered furniture, and other items on which eggs or larvae may be deposited. Then apply insecticide.

Apply a surface spray containing methoxychlor, malathion, baygon, diazinon, pyrethrin or ronnel. Be sure to use a nonstaining product when spraying rugs, carpets and upholstered furniture. Treat baseboards, cracks in the floor, rugs, carpets, furniture, and places in the home where the pet habitually sleeps. You may need to repeat the treatment after a week.

The best way to prevent flea infestations in the house is to control fleas on the pets. Contact your veterinarian. He may recommend a dust containing 4 or 5 percent of malathion or 5 percent of methoxychlor, which is safe and effective when applied directly on dogs or cats. You will rub it into the fur so it reaches the skin. Protect the dog's eyes. Use flea collars if they do not result in neck irritation.

Head lice

Head lice are bloodsucking insects that are found on people's heads. Head lice usually inhabit only the hairy surface of the scalp, preferring the nape of the neck and the area behind the ears.

Habits and damage: These insect parasites are small—about $\frac{1}{8}$ inch long, or slightly larger than a pinhead. They vary in color from white to gray mottled with dark red or brown. They have hooklike claws and apposing thumbs at the end of each of their six legs, with which they grasp the shaft

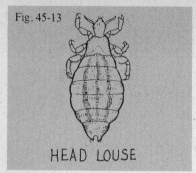

Fig. 45-13

HEAD LOUSE

of a hair (see Fig. 45-13).

Adult lice and their immature form (nymph) feed on human blood by piercing the skin with their mouth parts. Head lice do not feed for a long time, just often. Itching is the most common symptom of louse infestation. It is caused by this bloodsucking and the injection of saliva. Sometimes a secondary bacterial infection results from scratching. Unlike the body louse, the head louse is not known to transmit any of the louse-borne diseases.

Adult head lice are believed to have a life span of less than one month. A female will produce about three or four eggs per day during her lifetime, for a total of about 90. She attaches them firmly with a strong, cementlike substance on a shaft of hair close to the scalp. The eggs hatch in about a week and emerge as nymphs. They are immediately able to crawl, and become mature in about eight or nine days.

A person examining someone for head lice can usually see the crawling forms with the naked eye, but a hand magnifying glass and flashlight may be helpful. The only way to get rid of louse eggs is to use a very fine toothed comb. This method is irritating and even painful to elementary school aged children, by far the most likely to be infested. If an egg, or "nit," is attached over ¼ inch from the scalp, it has probably already hatched.

How to control head lice: Everybody, no matter how "nice and clean," is susceptible to infestation with head lice, although black children have many fewer head-louse infestations than white or Oriental children in the United States. All people have to do to become infested with lice is to come into close contact with someone who has them. Lice are most often transmitted by combs and

brushes, seldom by coats, caps, scarves or carpets. The length of a person's hair does not seem to be a factor in susceptibility or in spreading these parasites, except in that brushes are most often used by children with long hair.

Treat infested individuals and their personal articles. There are several shampoos to kill lice. Some can be bought over the counter at the local drugstore; others require a prescription. Treatment should be repeated in 10 days to kill newly hatched lice.

Always consult a physician or the local health department before applying louse shampoos. Any insecticide formulation that is not clearly labeled for use on the human body can endanger a person's health, or even life.

Washable clothing and bed linens that have been in contact with the infested person should be machine washed with hot water and detergent and dried at high heat for at least 20 minutes to destroy the lice. Dry cleaning will also kill lice and eggs. To disinfect combs and brushes, clean out hair and soak them for an hour in a quart of water with 1½ tablespoons of Lysol. You can also place them in hot water of 150° F for five to ten minutes. Boiling is not necessary. In using this method, be sure these articles are made of materials that are not damaged by heat.

Note. Body lice are much less common than head lice. They infest adults who cannot care for themselves well. Body louse eggs are laid on clothing. They are killed by bathing and by washing or dry-cleaning clothes.

Crab lice are controlled by using the same shampoos used for head lice.

Do not spray pesticides for louse control.

Houseflies

Houseflies are the most common flies that invade the home (see Fig. 45-14).

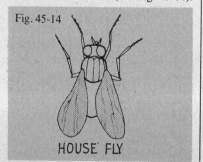

Fig. 45-14

HOUSE FLY

They are among the filthiest of insect pests.

Habits and damage: Houseflies breed in decaying organic matter and feed indiscriminately on pet manure, garbage and the food on our tables. They contaminate everything they touch, and spread many human diseases.

How to control houseflies: You may keep your home free of houseflies by practicing sanitation, using screens, and applying insecticides. If only a few flies are present, it is more effective to get rid of them by using a fly swatter rather than an insecticide.

Houseflies breed in places where garbage or manure accumulates. Clean up these places. See that your garbage cans are equipped with tight-fitting lids; dispose of garbage at least once a week—twice a week in summer. Promptly dispose of the droppings of pets. Do not allow food to stand where it will attract flies.

Keep houseflies out by placing screens tightly in your windows and doors. See that screened doors swing outward. Screens that have 14 meshes to the inch will keep out houseflies; if the screens have 16 meshes, they will also keep out many smaller insects. In a humid climate, use screens of copper, aluminum, bronze, plastic, or one of the rust-resisting alloys. In a dry climate, galvanized screens are satisfactory.

If you need an insecticide to control the flies in your home, apply a household space or aerosol spray containing malathion or pyrethrin. Be sure the container label says the spray is for flying insects. Follow directions.

Mice

At one time or another, almost every housekeeper finds mice (see Fig. 45-15) to be a source of annoyance and damage.

Fig. 45-15

HOUSE MOUSE

Habits and damage: These rodents usually migrate from outdoor areas into homes when the weather turns cold in the fall. They eat or contaminate human food; injure fabrics, wood and other materials; and transmit several human diseases.

How to control mice: The first and last steps in controlling mice are to seal any holes in the walls, floors and foundations of the house, and to see that food is not left in places where mice can get to it.

The quickest way to reduce a mouse problem, even a large one, in your home is with ordinary snap traps. Place the traps along walls and near openings, at right angles to the walls so the trigger mechanism will intercept the mouse's probable line of travel. One of the best baits to use in snap trays is peanut butter smeared over the trigger surface. Other good baits are cake, bacon, cheese and soft candies, particularly milk chocolate gumdrops. Use several traps. Some people may prefer to use traps that catch but do not kill the mice. They can then release the mice in the fields.

Where mouse infestations are chronic, use poison bait. Purchase materials labeled for this purpose. Follow the directions and observe all precautions on the container label.

Take care to avoid placing poison bait where it might contaminate food supplies. Never leave pesticides within reach of children, irresponsible persons, pets, or livestock. A qualified pest-control operator (exterminator) may be needed to get rid of mice. He has the experience and equipment needed to solve your mouse problem.

Mites

The kinds of mites (see Fig. 45-16) that may bite humans are rodent mites, bird mites, and chiggers. These pests seldom transmit human diseases, but their bites cause swelling, severe itching and sometimes fever. A chigger attached in a pore of the skin or at the base of a hair may become so en-

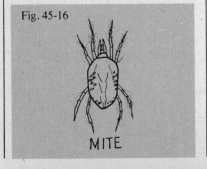
Fig. 45-16

MITE

veloped in swollen flesh that it appears to be burrowing into the skin.

Clover mites and certain grain mites sometimes infest homes, and they may become a nuisance, but they do not bite people.

Rodent and bird mites can infest and breed in a home where rats, mice or pet birds are present. Bird mites can also enter the home from wild birds that are nesting in a chimney or near a ventilator opening, or they may be carried in from a pigeon or poultry coop on your premises.

Chiggers breed outside—not in the house. They infest humans, causing a great deal of itching, but they cannot breed indoors.

Preventing or relieving bites: You may prevent mites such as chiggers from biting you by wearing socks and long pants, and by applying a repellant to your person and clothing. Use a repellant containing deet (diethyl metatoluamide), ethyl hexandeiol, dimethyl carbate or dimethyl phthalate; these are available at drug, hardware or sporting goods stores. Itching caused by mite bites may be relieved by applying an ointment containing benzocaine.

How to control mites: You can sometimes rid your home of mites that attack people by treating infested places with a household surface spray containing malathion. If you are troubled by rodent mites, first apply a spray to kill them; then rid your home of the rats or mice from which the mites come.

To eliminate the sources of bird mites, get rid of nests near openings in the house. Clean up bird coops and treat them with a surface spray containing malathion.

If food mites are a problem, first throw out the infested foods. Treat infested shelves with a household surface spray containing not more than 2 percent of malathion. Do not contaminate food or utensils with the insecticide. Cover shelves with clean paper or foil after the spray dries. Prevent future infestations by keeping all foods well covered, and by keeping shelves and cracks free of spilled food.

Use a vacuum cleaner to capture clover mites if they become numerous indoors.

Mosquitoes

Mosquitoes (see Fig. 45-17) disturb

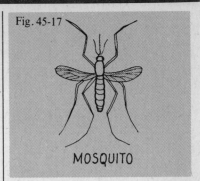
Fig. 45-17

MOSQUITO

our sleep by their humming, and inflict itching bites. Some species can infect us with diseases such as dengue fever and encephalitis.

Habits: In most parts of the United States, mosquitoes breed during the spring, summer and fall. In warm areas they may breed throughout the year. Female mosquitoes lay their eggs on water or in places that later become flooded.

How to control mosquitoes: The most effective way to control mosquitoes is to eliminate their breeding places from your premises. Follow these steps:
● Remove unneeded water containers.
● Place discarded automobile tires where water cannot get into them.
● Fill tree holes with concrete.
● See that cisterns, cesspools, septic tanks, fire barrels, rain barrels and tubs in which water is stored are tightly covered.
● Clean out rain gutters, and examine flat roofs after rains to see that no water remains on them.
● Look for mosquito larvae in the water in flower vases. Look for them also in water that may collect in saucers under potted plants. Replace stagnant water with fresh water.
● Examine fishbowls and aquariums for mosquito larvae. Some kinds of fish eat the larvae; other kinds do not.

Use insecticides when necessary. Use an aerosol spray designed to kill flying insects. Follow directions on the container label. Certain insecticides may be used also to kill mosquito larvae in breeding places on your premises. Contact your local extension office to obtain information on mosquito-control programs.

Pantry pests

Several kinds of insects can infest the dry-food products you keep in your pantry or kitchen cupboards. Most of them are beetles (see Fig. 45-18) or moth larvae. You can control pantry pests by using all of the following five measures:

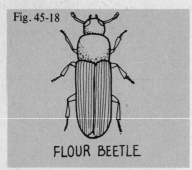
Fig. 45-18
FLOUR BEETLE

• Keep pantry shelves clean of spilled food. Discard infested products.
• Use insecticide if you are troubled by a persistent infestation of pantry pests. First empty the shelves and wash the cupboards. Then apply a household surface spray containing not more than 2 percent of malathion. Spray lightly; do not overapply. When the spray dries, cover the shelves with clean paper or foil before replacing packages of food in the cupboard.
• Inspect food packages. Almost all dry packaged foods are subject to infestation. Pantry pests also live in spices, especially red pepper, paprika and chili powder. Inspect all packages for breaks before buying.
• Sterilize doubtful products. If you think a dry food may be infested, sterilize it in the oven at about 140° F for half an hour. You may heat small packages as they are. The contents of large packages should be spread on cake pans or pie pans so that heat can penetrate easily.
• Store uninfested or heat-sterilized foods in clean metal or glass containers such as coffee cans or fruit jars. Be sure the covers fit tightly enough to prevent tiny insects from crawling in.

Powder-post beetles

There are several kinds of powder-post beetles (see Fig. 45-19). Among the more common is the old-house borer. These pests tunnel in soft wood (pine, spruce, fir). Some other species of powder-post beetles attack hardwoods, and still others attack bamboo products such as furniture, venetian blinds and baskets.

Detection: The presence of powder-post beetles in your home may be

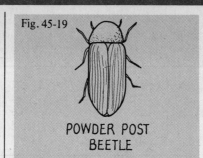
Fig. 45-19
POWDER POST BEETLE

detected by any of several signs. You may see surface holes in the wood; these may look like small shot holes or they may be as large as $\frac{3}{8}$ inch in diameter. There may be little piles of borings near the holes or, where overhead timbers are attacked, on the floor beneath the holes. You may actually see adult beetles, $\frac{1}{8}$ to 1 inch long, crawling on the wood. Clean up the wood dust, put down paper, and check daily to see if a pile of dust reappears.

How to control powder-post beetles: Consider whether the control problem is one you can handle yourself. If you have a heavy infestation or one that is behind paneled walls or in some other hard-to-reach place, it may require the services of an experienced pest-control operator who has the necessary equipment. For best results, get several estimates.

The chance of attack is lessened if the crawl space is well drained. If the soil cannot be kept dry, spreading a moisture barrier over it will prevent moisture vaporizing from the soil from condensing on the under parts of the house. Keeping the wood dry by this means will help protect against decay as well as insect damage. Consult your county extension service for further information.

Rats

Habits: Rats (see Fig. 45-20) destroy or pollute human food, transmit disease, and damage property. If cornered they are dangerous and will attack people or pets. They enter homes to find food and shelter.

Fig. 45-20
NORWAY RAT

How to control rats: There are four essential measures for getting rid of rats in the home.
1. Kill them. Poisoned bait is the best means. Purchase a suitable bait, labeled for this purpose. Follow directions on the label and observe the precautions to the letter. Poisons should never be left within the reach of children, irresponsible persons, pets or livestock.

Traps are also an effective means of killing rats in the home. Place traps as explained in the mice section above.
2. Keep them out. It may take time to see the results, but this is the ultimate answer to rat control. Close all holes in exterior walls. See that spaces around doors, windows and other necessary openings are no larger than $\frac{1}{4}$ inch. If rats are a serious problem in your neighborhood, install self-closing devices on frequently used doors to the outside.

To make your efforts effective, community action should be sought. Ask the assistance of your local board of health; it can send trained pest-control operators.
3. Starve them. Leave no food in open places; this includes food in unopened cardboard containers. Place garbage and refuse promptly in tightly covered metal containers.
4. Remove their shelter. Keep storage places orderly and clean. In the basement and storerooms, stack lumber, boxes, cartons, and other objects on racks at least one foot above the ground. If your house has double walls with spaces between ceilings and the floors below, make sure the spaces are tightly sealed. Rats make their homes in these spaces if they are accessible.

Scorpions

Scorpions (see Fig. 45-21) are usually found in the southwestern parts of the United States. Occasionally they enter homes. Their sting is painful, and the sting of one species may be fatal.

Habits: Scorpions feed mostly on insects and spiders. When they get into the home, they hide during the day in close quarters—in closets, attics, folded blankets, shoes and papers. At night they seek water. Usually they will not sting unless they are molested.

How to control scorpions: Use insecticide, such as a household surface

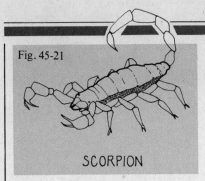

Fig. 45-21

SCORPION

spray containing diazinon. Apply the spray to baseboards, around window and door casings, and to the foundation of the house. Outside, use the spray also to treat the lower parts of tree trunks, stumps, piles of lumber and rock walls. A water-base spray is preferred for outdoor use; ready-to-use household sprays often contain oils that may burn vegetation.

Caution. If scorpions are in your neighborhood, do not have a children's sandbox, because the pests are attracted to them.

Silverfish and firebrats

Silverfish and firebrats are slender, wingless insects, ⅓ to ½ inch long (see Fig. 45-22). They are similar in appearance: Silverfish are shiny and silver or pearl gray; firebrats are mottled gray. The two pests cause the same kinds of damage.

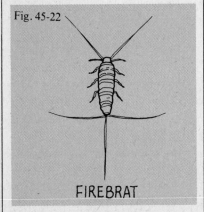

Fig. 45-22

FIREBRAT

Habits and damage: These insects are active at night, and usually hide during the day. Silverfish live and develop in damp, cool places—particularly in basements. Firebrats prefer warmer areas in the home, such as the attic in summer and near the furnace in winter.

Both insects crawl along pipelines and through openings in the walls or floors; they may be found in any part of the house. Silverfish and firebrats cause damage in homes by eating foods and other materials that have a high sugar or starch content. These include cereals, moist wheat flour, plus any paper on which there is glue or paste, the sizing in paper, starch in clothing and rayon fabrics, and starch sizing on book covers.

How to control silverfish and firebrats: Apply insecticide in the form of a surface spray or a dust. The results may not be immediate; but if the insecticide is properly and thoroughly applied, it will leave a residue that should be effective for a few weeks. If satisfactory control is not achieved in two or three weeks, make additional applications. (If you are troubled with firebrats but not with silverfish, you may need to apply insecticide only to warm parts of the house.)

Use a household spray containing diazinon, ronnel or malathion. Apply the spray to baseboards, door and window casings, closets and places where pipes go through walls, and in cardboard packing boxes. Some sprays have oil-solution bases; do not apply these near electric motors, gas pilot flames or other places where they may start fires.

Use a dust that you apply with a hand duster. Blow it into the cracks and on surfaces of the places recommended for sprays. Dusts may be applied safely to places where oil-solution sprays might start fires.

Reduce moisture in areas of silverfish infestations.

Spiders

Most species of spiders that occur in the United States are harmless to humans. They destroy many injurious household insects, and are therefore beneficial.

However, a dangerous species—one to watch out for—is the black widow. The female of this species is about ½ inch long and shiny black (see Fig. 45-23). The front and back parts of the body are globular; the legs are long and slender. It usually has a red or orange mark shaped like an hourglass on the underside. Occasionally this marking is incomplete or is absent.

Habits and damage: Black widow spiders are not aggressive, but they will bite instinctively when touched or threatened. The female inflicts a poisonous bite that can be fatal. The bite causes extreme pain, which usually

Fig. 45-23

BLACK WIDOW

extends to the abdominal muscles, where it localizes. A person bitten by this spider should call a doctor immediately.

Black widow spiders seldom appear in living quarters of homes, but often are found in basements, in basement window wells, beneath lawn benches or porches, and in garages, tool sheds, old lumber piles, trash piles, sand boxes, and outdoor toilets.

Another dangerous spider is the brown recluse, whose body is about ½ inch long when fully grown (see Fig. 45-24). It is found in the southern United States from western Georgia northwest to Missouri, Kansas and Texas. The bite of the brown recluse causes sores that are slow to heal. The victim may not be aware of the bite for several hours, or there may be intense pain at once. So if you feel intense pain continuing after being bitten by a small brown spider, call a doctor immediately. See the chapter "Poisoning" for giving emergency medical treatment.

How to control spiders: The following treatment to control black widow spiders may be used to control dangerous spiders in the home.
● Remove loose brick, wood, tile or trash from around the yard or base-

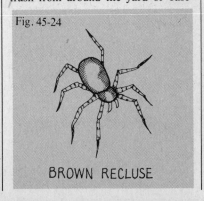

Fig. 45-24

BROWN RECLUSE

ment where the spiders may live or hide.

• Use a stick or broom to knock down webs, spiders and egg sacs. Crush them underfoot.

• Apply a pesticide to spider-infested areas. Use a household spray or dust containing diazinon.

• Do not spray spiders overhead. A spider hit by the spray may drop straight down onto you and still be capable of biting for some time.

Squirrels and chipmunks

Squirrels and chipmunks may enter the house, usually from the chimney or holes in the attic. It is best to close the openings by which they entered with a piece of sheet metal. Do this during the daytime when the animal or animals are outside finding food. You can also try to trap the animal. Bring it out of hiding by scattering mothballs around its resting places. Or set a special live animal trap baited with dry peanuts which captures but does not kill the animal. Once you have caught the animal, release it in the woods. Handling a live squirrel requires care, so you may want a pest-control operator to perform this service.

Termites

Termites cost homeowners many millions of dollars each year in repairs to structures and in control measures. There are two major kinds of termites—subterranean and nonsubterranean, or drywood, termites.

Subterranean termites, found in every state except Alaska and particularly prevalent in the southern half of this country and the Pacific Coast states, live in colonies in the ground, close to a source of wood. They often build tunnels called termite tubes upward between the soil, from which they obtain moisture, and the wood of the house, which serves as their food. These tubes are about ¼ inch in width and protect the termites in their travels between their food and their shelter. These termites can eat out the woodwork, leaving a shell of sound wood to conceal their activities, but damage seldom proceeds so far as to cause collapse of parts of a structure before discovery. Winged termites inside a house, most often in spring, are a sure sign of trouble. They have brown to black bodies and two pairs of long, whitish, translucent wings of

equal size. Soon after their entry into the building, they shed the wings. Discarded wings are often found beneath doors or windows (see the section on ants above).

Nonsubterranean, or drywood, termites are found primarily in Florida, southern California and the Gulf Coast states. They fly directly to the wood they attack and live in small colonies in cavities they make in the wood. They damage all kinds of wooden objects, including structural timbers, furniture, posts, poles and piles of lumber, but the damage is less serious than that caused by subterranean termites. You can recognize the presence of these termites by the broad pockets or chambers they have cut across the grain of comparatively dry wood. These cavities contain tiny, hard pellets of partially digested wood, and piles of these pellets below damaged wood are often the first signs of infestation. Drywood termite entrance holes are difficult to detect because they are sealed with a brownish-black, paper-thin secretion, which may contain pellets.

How to recognize termites: For subterranean termites, look for tunnels along masonry foundation and basement walls, around openings where pipes enter walls, and along surfaces of metal pipes. Also, examine all cracks in slabs and in masonry walls. Check all joints where wood meets with concrete or masonry, at walls, slabs, piers. Inspect all wood and wood structures near the ground. Pay attention to any that touch the ground, such as fences and carports. Examine crawl spaces. Check windows, door thresholds, porches and the underside of stairways. If you think wood has termite damage, probe with a sharp point such as an ice pick or a penknife. If the point penetrates the wood to a depth of ½ inch when you use ordinary hand pressure, it is a good indication of wood damage by termites.

How to control termites: If you live in a termite-infested area, you should have an inspection once a year. To control subterranean termites, it is best to call a pest-control operator. Since drywood termites do not have a ground connection, they can be killed by applying insecticide to galleries in the wood they are attacking. To reach the galleries, bore holes into the wood.

After the insecticide is injected, seal the holes.

Severe drywood termite infestations may require fumigation if the areas under attack are inaccessible. A major job such as that can only be done by a pest-control operator.

Caution. Chemicals that control termites are toxic to animal and plant life and therefore require extreme care. Do not contaminate surface water when using chemicals.

How to prevent termites: The best time to provide protection against termites is during the planning and construction of the building. The first requirement is to remove all woody debris like stumps and discarded boards from the soil at the building site before and after construction. Steps should also be taken to keep the soil under the house as dry as possible. Next, the foundation should be made impervious to subterranean termites so that they cannot crawl up through hidden cracks to the wood in the building above. Properly reinforced concrete makes the best foundation, but unit-construction walls or piers capped with concrete are also satisfactory. Pretreat the soil before construction with chlordane. No wood member of the structural part of the house should be in contact with the soil. Any wood used in secondary appendages such as wall extensions, decorative fences, and gates should be pressure-treated with a good preservative.

It is always safest to have a certified pest-control operator perform these chores since the chemicals are toxic. Get several estimates.

In regions where drywood termites are found, the following measures should be taken to prevent damage:
1. Inspect all lumber, particularly secondhand material. If infested, discard the piece.
2. Screen all doors, windows and other ventilation openings with metal wire having at least 20 meshes to the inch.
3. Use preservative treatment to prevent attack in construction timber and lumber.
4. Apply several coats of house paint. This will provide considerable protection to exterior woodwork in buildings. Fill all cracks, crevices and joints between exterior wood members with

a mastic caulking or plastic wood before painting.

5. Use the heartwood of foundation-grade redwood, which, particularly when painted, is more resistant to attack than most other native commercial species of wood.

Ticks

Several kinds of ticks may be found in your yard and in other open spaces. Only one kind—the brown dog tick—infests homes in the United States (see Fig. 45-25). This tick is a parasite of dogs only. It does not breed in the woods or in open country.

Fig. 45-25

BROWN DOG TICK

Habits and damage: If there are ticks in your home, they probably are brown dog ticks that entered on your dog. After feeding on the dog, brown dog ticks hide in places such as cracks and crevices, under carpets and rugs, in upholstered furniture, and behind baseboards. There the female lays her eggs; and each stage of each successive generation of ticks eventually finds the dog, feeds on his blood, and drops off to seek hiding places in the home and keep the cycle going. Brown dog ticks rarely bite humans; they do not carry human diseases. However, their presence in the home is annoying, and they can make your dog's life very uncomfortable.

How to control ticks: There are several methods you can use to rid your animal of ticks, including a tick collar, powder or bath. Check with your veterinarian if you decide to dip the animal in a bath. You may prefer that he dip the animal. If you decide to dip the animal yourself, follow these general guidelines: Protect the animal's eyes by putting a drop of mineral oil in each one. To do this, hold its head and open its eyes, one at a time, by spreading the skin above and below the lids apart with your fingers. Use an eyedropper to drop the oil into the open eye. When the dog

blinks, the oil will spread over the surface of the eye. The ears should also be protected by stuffing a wad of cotton which has been moistened with tick dip into each one. When the cotton is removed, ticks within the ear will have been exposed to the dip and can then easily be removed. Next pick up the dog and put it into the bath. If the dog is too little to stand in the bath, support it on one arm as you work the dip into its fur with the other hand. Don't let its head go under, but make sure you get the dip into the fur on its face and ears. If there are any ticks inside the ears, you will have to remove them one by one later. If the dog is too big or too aggressive to be lifted into the bath, you will have to stand it near a drain and pour the dip over it. Work the solution all the way into the coat, making sure it gets in between the toes and under the body. Let the dip dry onto the dog; do not rinse it off.

If you use the tick dip properly, any ticks left hanging on to a dog will die. You may, however, have to pull some ticks out of the dog's ears, or off an infested cat. The tick will come away cleanly if you dab it with a cotton swab dipped in alcohol. Grasp tick with a pair of tweezers or small wad of cotton and rock it back and forth as you pull. Do not pour alcohol into the ear canal. Try not to rupture the tick because the mouth part may become lodged in the skin and subsequently cause an infection.

Get rid of new broods of ticks that are developing in the home. Vacuum well first, then use a household insecticide containing baygon or diazinon. Spray or paint it on cracks in the floor, around baseboards and window casings, on places where the dog habitually sleeps and on other places

where ticks may be hiding. Repeat after two or three months.

Cats cannot be tick dipped. If a cat has ticks, they will usually be on hindquarters or under its body. Take the cat to your veterinarian.

Wasps

The term *wasp* applies to hornets, yellow jackets, mud daubers, and cicada killers. All are slender-waisted flying insects (see Fig. 45-26).

Habits and damage: All these wasps except mud daubers and cicada killers build paper nests in bushes, in trees, under eaves, or in the ground. Mud daubers build clay or mud nests. Cicada killers build tunnels in well-drained slopes of ground. Both rarely sting. Wasps are beneficial because they kill destructive insects. However, they can inflict serious and sometimes even fatal stings on allergic individuals. Wasps should be controlled when they nest in places where they can endanger human safety.

How to control wasps: Treat the nest with a pyrethrin aerosol to stun the wasps. Direct the insecticide as closely as possible into the nest opening. Then use diazinon as surface spray or dust, which leaves a deposit of insecticide to kill wasps that crawl over it.

If you use a dust, apply it with a hand duster or garden-type duster. The extension tube of a garden-type duster may be inserted into the nest opening; two or three strong puffs of dust will filter through the nest, and usually will kill the colony within 24 hours.

After treating an underground nest, throw a shovelful of moist earth over the entrance. This will prevent the dying wasps from reaching the surface. All treatments should be made at

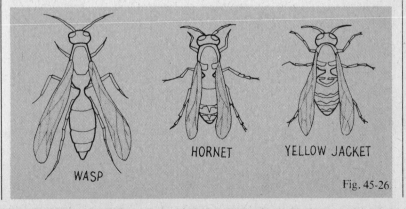

WASP   HORNET   YELLOW JACKET

Fig. 45-26

183

night, when there is less danger of being stung. If a person having a history of asthma, hay fever or other allergy is stung by a wasp, seek immediate medical help.

For local information on household pests, contact your county extension office, listed under county government in the telephone book.

Note. Pest-control operators should be registered or certified by the state government. Operators advertising membership in local, state, or the national pest-control association are reputable, and these organizations usually have committees which aid in resolving consumer complaints.

46
REMOVING STAINS AND MILDEW; CLEANING HOUSHOLD SURFACES

This chapter contains instructions for removing stains at home, for preventing and removing mildew, and for cleaning household surfaces.

REMOVING STAINS

Immediate steps

It is important to treat stains promptly with the correct methods. Many stains are relatively easy to remove if they are treated promptly but become permanently set if neglected. With the wrong treatment, some stains become more difficult or even impossible to remove. When a staining accident occurs, it is always safe to absorb excess liquid with a clean cloth, a white paper towel or tissue, a sponge, or absorbent cotton. Barely touch the drop of liquid with the tip of the absorbent material to avoid forcing the staining material further into the fabric. Do not apply any pressure to the stained area.

If the stain is not greasy, you may be able to remove some of the liquid that has soaked into the fabric by adding a little water to it. However, water may cause spotting on some fabrics. It is safe to use water if the care label says the article is washable. If the garment is not washable or there is no

care label, test the fabric first in an inconspicuous area. Place clean, dry, absorbent material under the stained area. Sprinkle a few drops of cool water on the stain and blot immediately with more clean, dry, absorbent material. Repeat until no more stain appears on the absorbent material. Use a new piece or section of the absorbent material above and below the stain each time water is added.

Oily stains should be sponged as soon as possible with dry-cleaning solvent (see page 185). If the stain is on a garment being worn, be careful not to let dry-cleaning solvent come into contact with the skin, because it may cause irritation. Use only a very small amount of solvent, and place absorbent material between the garment and the skin. Do not allow areas of clothing sponged with dry-cleaning solvent to touch the skin until all the solvent has evaporated. Dry-cleaning solvent is poisonous and may be flammable; follow precautions given on page 185, as well as any precautions on the label.

If the staining material has the consistency of paste, remove the excess with a dull knife or spoon, taking care not to force the stain further into the fabric.

Stain removal supplies

If you keep on hand the supplies listed in this section, you will be prepared to remove almost any stain. Most of these items are ordinary household supplies. Substitutes are suggested for a few materials that may be difficult to obtain. Follow carefully all precautions for the storage and use of hazardous chemicals.

You will need an ample supply of clean, absorbent materials, such as absorbent cotton, white paper towels, white facial tissues, and soft white cloths. Sponges are also useful, but test them with stain removers to make sure they will not be damaged.

Alcohol: Use rubbing alcohol or denatured alcohol (70-percent or 90-percent concentration). Do not use alcohol with added color or fragrances. Alcohol fades some dyes, so test the fabric for colorfastness before using alcohol on a stain. For use on acetate, dilute alcohol with two parts water to one part alcohol. *Caution:* Poisonous and flammable. Observe all precautions on the label.

Ammonia: Use household ammonia. Do not use ammonia with added color or fragrances. Ammonia changes the color of some dyes. To restore the color, rinse the color-changed area thoroughly with water and apply a few drops of white vinegar. Rinse well with water again. For use on wool and silk, dilute ammonia with an equal amount of water. *Caution:* Poisonous. Avoid inhaling ammonia fumes. Ammonia will cause burns or irritation if it comes in contact with the skin or eyes. Observe all precautions on the label.

Amyl acetate: Amyl acetate (banana oil) is sold in drugstores. Ask for chemically pure amyl acetate. If you cannot obtain amyl acetate, you may substitute fingernail-polish remover. Do not use oily-type nail-polish remover. *Caution:* Amyl acetate is poisonous and flammable. Do not breathe the vapors. Avoid contact with the skin. Amyl acetate is a strong solvent for plastics. Do not allow it to come in contact with plastics or furniture finishes.

Brushes: Brushes are used for a stain-removal procedure called tamping. The most suitable brush is the type used for applying shoe polish, usually sold in a package of two. Brushes used for stain removal should be new and should not be used for any other purpose. It is best to have two brushes so that one can be used for stain removers that contain water and the other for dry-cleaning solvent and amyl acetate. The brushes should have nylon bristles, because hair bristles become soft when wet with water. The bristles should be cut square, with all the bristles the same length. If the brushes have plastic handles, test the handles with stain-removal chemicals, especially amyl acetate, to make sure that chemicals will not damage the handles. This could cause additional stains. If the handle is damaged by amyl acetate or some other stain remover, use a smooth spoon on the stain rather than a brush (see page 187).

Chlorine bleach: Chlorine bleach is used to remove many kinds of stains. Check the label of the bleach to be sure that it contains chlorine. Chlorine bleach damages some fibers, dyes, and finishes, so read the care label as well as the label on the bleach container for any cautions. Test the fabric in an inconspicuous place before you use bleach on the stain. Do not use chlorine bleach on fabric with a fire-retardant finish unless the care label states that chlorine bleach is safe. The resin in some special finishes absorbs and retains chlorine, which weakens and yellows the fabric. Some fabrics do not show evidence of damage until they are ironed; then they may be severely weakened or discolored. (See page 191 for a method of removing chlorine from such fabrics.) Chlorine stains on silk, wool, or spandex fibers cannot be removed.

Do not use bleach in metal containers or with metal objects, because metal may speed up the action of the bleach enough to cause fiber damage. Also, metal in contact with bleach may tarnish and cause additional stains on fabrics. Avoid spilling or spattering bleach on garments and nearby surfaces. *Caution:* Poisonous. Chlorine bleach will cause burns or irritation if it comes in contact with the skin or eyes. Observe all precautions on the label.

Coconut oil: Coconut oil is sold in drugstores and health food stores. It is used in the dry spotter solution (see page 185), which is used to remove many kinds of stains. If you cannot obtain coconut oil, you may substitute mineral oil (sold in drugstores), which is almost as effective.

Color remover: Color remover is sold in drugstores, grocery stores, and variety stores, usually in the display of home dyes and tints. Color remover is safe for most fibers, but fades or removes many dyes. If color remover causes a distinct color change rather than fading, you may be able to restore the original color by rinsing the area immediately with water. Hang the article to dry. If color remover causes fading, the original color cannot be restored. Do not use or store color remover in metal containers or use it with metal objects. *Caution:* Poisonous. Avoid prolonged contact with skin. Observe all precautions on the label.

Detergent: Use liquid hand dishwashing detergent. Detergents for automatic dishwashers, heavy-duty household detergents, and laundry detergents may contain alkalies that could set some stains.

Dry-cleaning solvent: Dry-cleaning solvent is sold in drugstores, grocery stores, variety stores, hardware stores, and automobile service stations. It may contain any or all of the following ingredients: petroleum solvent; petroleum hydrocarbon; petroleum distillate; 1, 1, 1 trichloroethane; perchloroethylene; or Varsol.

Caution. Poisonous, may be flammable. Store dry-cleaning solvent in tightly capped unbreakable containers. Store it out of the reach of children and where it cannot be ignited by flames or sparks. Dry-cleaning solvent gives off poisonous fumes and can be poisonous on contact with the skin. When using dry-cleaning solvent, work outside or in a well-ventilated room, and arrange work so that fumes are blown away from you. Do not lean close to your work. Use only a small quantity at a time. Do not pour solvent into a bowl. Do not allow children or pets into the room. If you spill dry-cleaning solvent on your skin, wash it off immediately. If you spill it on your clothes, change immediately and hang garments outdoors until all solvent has evaporated. Neither flammable nor nonflammable solvent should be used in a room with an open flame or gas pilot light, or where there is a chance of electrical sparks from refrigerators, fans, vacuum cleaners, or static. Do not smoke. Although nonflammable solvents do not ignite in contact with a flame or spark, they decompose and produce extremely toxic vapors. These vapors are especially toxic to persons who have consumed even a small amount of alcohol. Never use dry-cleaning solvent in a washing machine. Do not put articles that are damp with solvent into a dryer. Observe all precautions on the label.

Dry spotter: To prepare dry spotter, mix one part coconut oil and eight parts dry-cleaning solvent. This solution is used to remove many kinds of stains. Dry spotter keeps well if the container is tightly capped to prevent evaporation of the dry-cleaning solvent. If you cannot obtain coconut oil, use mineral oil in the same amount as coconut oil. *Caution:* Dry-cleaning solvent is poisonous and may be flammable. Follow all precautions given above for dry-cleaning solvent.

Enzyme product: You may use either an enzyme presoak or an enzyme-containing laundry detergent. These products may be stored as purchased, but become inactive if stored after they have been made into a solution.

Glycerine: Glycerine is sold in drugstores. It is used to prepare "wet spotter," which is used to remove many kinds of stains. It is also used to remove ballpoint-ink stains.

Hydrogen peroxide: Use the 3-percent solution sold as a mild antiseptic. Do not use the stronger solution sold in cosmetic departments for bleaching hair. Hydrogen peroxide is safe for all fibers, but dyed fabrics should be tested for colorfastness. Store in a cool, dark place. Hydrogen peroxide loses strength when stored for extended periods of time. Bleach that contains sodium perborate, or "oxygen-type" bleach, may be substituted for hydrogen peroxide, although it is slower acting. Thorough rinsing is needed to remove this type of bleach from fabric. Do not use or store hydrogen peroxide or oxygen-type bleach in metal containers or use it with metal objects. Metal may speed up the action of the bleach enough to cause fiber damage. Also, metal in contact with hydrogen peroxide or bleach may tarnish and cause additional stains on fabrics.

Iodine: Use tincture of iodine, which can be purchased at a drugstore. It is used only for removal of stains in Group 9 (see page 190). *Caution:* Poisonous.

Sodium thiosulfate: Use pure sodium thiosulfate, or "fixer," sold in drugstores and photo supply stores. Do not use photo fixer solution that contains other chemicals in addition to sodium thiosulfate. Sodium thiosulfate solution is used to remove iodine and chlorine bleach stains. (Chlorine bleach stains cannot be removed from wool, silk, or spandex.) This solution keeps for several months if it is tightly capped.

Vinegar: Use white vinegar; colored vinegar can leave a stain. Vinegar is safe for all fibers but changes the color of some dyes. If a dye changes color after vinegar has been used, rinse the color-changed area thoroughly with water and add a few drops of ammonia. Then rinse with water again.

Wet spotter: Prepare wet spotter by mixing one part glycerine, one part liquid hand dishwashing detergent, and eight parts water. Shake well before each use. This mixture is used to remove many kinds of stains. Wet spotter may be conveniently stored in a plastic squeeze bottle with a small cap.

Miscellaneous supplies: You will need bowls for soaking stained articles, medicine droppers, and a stainless steel spoon.

TREATING STAINS

Read this section to learn the most effective techniques for using stain removers.

Testing stain remover

Before you use any stain remover, including water, test it to be sure that it will not harm the fabric or dye. Test each stain remover and each method of treatment on an unexposed portion of the article—a seam allowance, hem, inside of pocket, or tail of a shirt or blouse. Some stain removers or treatments damage certain fibers. They may also cause fading or bleeding of dyes, loss of luster, shrinkage, or stretching. They may remove non-permanent finishes, designs, or pigment prints. Loosely woven fabrics and fabrics woven from low-twist yarns are likely to suffer yarn slippage if brushed or rubbed while wet. Velvets with acetate pile should never be treated with a stain remover that contains water. Even the slightest rubbing can cause matting of acetate velvet pile that is wet with water. If the substance needed to remove a stain will damage the fabric, take the article to a dry cleaner as soon as possible. However, even a dry cleaner cannot correct damage caused by some stains. Liquids that contain a high percentage of alcohol bleed some dyes, making it impossible to restore the color. Some fingernail polishes and polish removers cause permanent damage to acetate fabrics.

Working surface

The working surface for stain removal should be a hard surface of a material that will not be affected by any of the chemicals used. A heavy glass pie pan, turned upside down, makes a good working surface. Other glass surfaces may also be used. The table or coun-

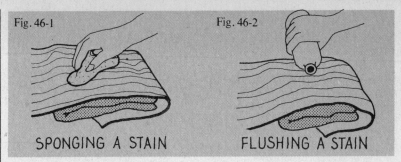

Fig. 46-1 · Fig. 46-2 · SPONGING A STAIN · FLUSHING A STAIN

tertop should be protected from spilled or dripping chemicals with aluminum foil. Chemicals used for removing stains can damage the finish of a table or countertop and then transfer a new stain to the fabric you are working on.

Sponging

When directions call for sponging, use the following procedure. Place the stained area, stained side down, over a pad of absorbent material (see Fig. 46-1). Dampen another piece of absorbent material with the stain remover you have been directed to use. Sponge the stain lightly, from the center toward the edge so that it is less likely to form rings. Keep the wet area around the stain as small as possible. Sponge the stain irregularly around the edges so there will be no definite line when the fabric dries. Change the sponging pad and the absorbent material under the stain as soon as you can see that any stain has been transferred to them. They should be changed frequently so that the released staining material will not be returned to the fabric.

Preventing rings: If a fabric tends to form rings when sponged with a stain remover, use special care in sponging the stain. Apply only enough stain remover to the sponging pad to barely dampen it. Touch the pad to the stain very lightly so that the fabric will absorb the stain remover slowly. Try not to let the wet area spread. Before you dry the article, place the sponged area between dry, absorbent material to remove excess moisture. Dry as rapidly as possible, but do not use heat on fabric treated with anything besides water.

Hardened stains: For hardened stains, such as old paint or tar, place an absorbent pad under the stain and a pad dampened with the recommended stain remover on top of the stain.

Allow the article to soak until the stain has softened. This may take half an hour to several hours. Keep the stain damp by adding more stain remover as needed. If the fabric is strong enough, you can use the edge of the bowl of a smooth spoon or a tamping brush to speed up release of the stain.

Flushing

Flushing the stain is necessary to remove released staining material as well as the stain-removal chemicals. When the directions call for flushing, place clean, absorbent material under the stain, then add the proper stain remover in small amounts with a medicine dropper or a container from which you can pour slowly (see Fig. 46-2). Do not add stain remover faster than the absorbent material can soak it up. Keep the treated area as small as possible. Change the absorbent material several times as you flush the stain. Flushing is one of the most important steps in stain removal. If a stain-removal chemical remains in the fabric, it may later damage the fabric or cause another stain. When directions call for flushing with water, and you are working on a washable article, you may substitute rinsing in a bowl of water. Dip the stained area repeatedly up and down in a bowl of warm water. Change the water at least twice.

Tamping

Tamping with a brush is highly effective in removing stains. Place the stained area directly on the working surface without any absorbent material under the stain. The best way to hold the brush is shown in Fig. 46-3. By holding the brush as shown, you will be able to control the amount of pressure applied. The tamping action is similar to driving a tack with a small hammer. Raise the brush two or

186

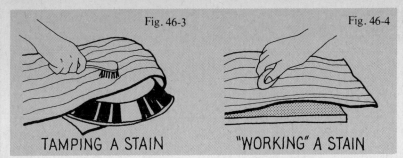

Fig. 46-3   Fig. 46-4

TAMPING A STAIN   "WORKING" A STAIN

three inches above the fabric and place it down squarely. Use a light action. Never apply so much pressure that the bristles bend; fabric damage is much more likely to occur if the edge of the brush strikes the fabric squarely. Striking with the edge is also less efficient in removing stains.

Use the least amount of tamping that will remove the stain. Too much tamping can chafe the yarn or cause yarn slippage. The amount of tamping a fabric can take without damage depends on the weave and yarn. A closely woven fabric of high-twist yarn will not be damaged as easily as a loosely woven fabric of yarn with a slight or moderate twist.

Using a spoon

The bowl of a smooth stainless steel teaspoon is an effective tool for loosening stains. Place the stain directly on the working surface without any absorbent material underneath. Add the stain remover. Hold the spoon as shown in Fig. 46-4. Move the spoon back and forth about 1/4 inch in each direction. Short strokes are the most effective. Do not press down with the spoon; this could damage the fabric. Do not use this procedure on delicate fabrics.

STAIN-REMOVAL GUIDE

Most stains in this section are classified into nine groups. Stains that do not fall into these groups are listed alphabetically. Use extra care in treating nonwashable fabrics. Keep the treated area as small as possible and do not wash the fabric. Nonwashable fabrics are more likely to be damaged by a tamping brush or spoon. It may not be necessary to go through all the steps to remove the stain. When all the stain is gone, or when you have finished all the steps, wash the article if it is washable. If the stained article is not washable, be sure that all

chemicals are thoroughly flushed out. Work carefully and patiently. Often the results depend as much on the way the job is done as on the remover used.

Group 1

Adhesive tape
Automobile wax
Calamine lotion
Crayon, wax or grease
*Eyebrow pencil
*Eyeliner
*Eye shadow
Face powder
*Felt-tip marker ink
*Floor wax
*Furniture polish
Furniture wax
Grease
Hair spray
Hand lotion
India ink
Insecticides
Lard
Lubricating oil
Makeup, liquid or pancake
Margarine
*Mascara
Nose drops
Ointment or salve
Paint, solvent-base or
   water-emulsion
Putty
Rouge
*Shoe dye, black
*Shoe polish, all colors
   except white
*Smoke
Soot
Tar
Typewriter-ribbon ink

For washable and nonwashable fabrics:

1. Sponge with dry-cleaning solvent (see page 185).
2. For delicate fabrics, apply dry spotter to stain and cover with a pad of absorbent material dampened with dry spotter. Let stand as long as any

stain is being removed. Change pad as it picks up stain. Keep stain and pad moist with dry spotter.

For stronger fabrics, apply dry spotter and tamp or use a spoon (see pages 186–187). Keep stain moist with dry spotter and blot occasionally with absorbent material. Continue as long as any stain is being removed.

3. Flush with dry-cleaning solvent (see page 186).
4. Repeat steps 2 and 3 until no more stain is removed.
5. Allow to dry completely.
6. Sponge with water.
7. For delicate fabrics, apply wet spotter and a few drops of ammonia. Cover with a pad of absorbent material dampened with wet spotter and let stand as long as any stain is being removed. Change pad as it picks up stain. Keep stain and pad moist with wet spotter and ammonia. For stronger fabrics, apply wet spotter and a few drops of ammonia, then tamp or use a spoon. Keep stain moist with wet spotter and ammonia and blot occasionally with absorbent material. Continue as long as any stain is being removed.
8. Flush with water.
9. Repeat steps 7 and 8 until no more stain is removed.
10. Chlorine bleach may remove the final traces of stains above marked by an asterisk (*). Chlorine bleach should not be used on certain fabrics (see pages 184–185). Test colors to be sure they will not be changed. Use a solution of one teaspoon bleach to one tablespoon water. Apply with a dropper. Do not allow this solution to remain on the fabric more than two minutes. When the stain is removed, or after two minutes, flush with water onto clean, absorbent material. Apply one teaspoon vinegar and again flush with water. Be sure that all bleach is removed.

Group 2

*Cake frosting
*Catsup
*Cheese
*Cheese sauce
*Chili sauce
*Chocolate
Cocoa
Cream, dairy
Egg yolk
Gravy
Ice cream

187

Mayonnaise
Milk
Pudding
Salad dressing
Sauces
Soups containing
vegetables
*Steak sauce

For washable fabrics:
1. Sponge with dry-cleaning solvent (see page 186).
2. For delicate fabrics, apply dry spotter to stain and cover with a pad of absorbent material dampened with dry spotter. Let stand as long as any stain is being removed. Change pad as it picks up stain. Keep stain and pad moist with dry spotter. For stronger fabrics, apply dry spotter and tamp or use a spoon (see pages 186–187). Keep stain moist with dry spotter and blot occasionally with absorbent material. Continue as long as any stain is being removed.
3. Flush with dry-cleaning solvent (see page 186).
4. Repeat steps 2 and 3 until no more stain is removed.
5. Allow to dry completely.
6. Sponge with water.
7. For delicate fabrics, apply a few drops of liquid hand dishwashing detergent and a few drops of ammonia. Cover with a pad of absorbent material dampened with water and let stand as long as any stain is being removed. Change pad as it picks up stain. Keep stain and pad moist with detergent and ammonia.
For stronger fabrics, apply a few drops of liquid hand dishwashing detergent and a few drops of ammonia, then tamp or use a spoon. Keep stain moist with detergent and ammonia and blot occasionally with absorbent material.
8. Flush with water. It is important to remove all ammonia.
9. Soak in a solution of one quart warm water and one tablespoon enzyme product for 30 minutes. Rinse with water.
10. Bleaching may remove the final traces of stains marked by *. For chocolate stains, proceed to step 11. For other stains marked by *, use chlorine bleach as directed on page 187 for Group 1, step 10.
11. For chocolate stains, bleach with hydrogen peroxide. Wet the stain with hydrogen peroxide and add a drop or

two of ammonia. Add more hydrogen peroxide and a drop of ammonia as needed to keep stain moist. Do not bleach longer than 15 minutes. Rinse with water.

For nonwashable fabrics:
1. Follow steps 1 to 8 for washable fabrics.
2. Moisten the stain with a solution of ½ teaspoon enzyme product and ½ cup warm water. Cover with a clean pad that has been dipped in the warm enzyme solution and squeezed nearly dry. Let stand 30 minutes. Add more warm enzyme solution if needed to keep the area warm and moist, but do not let the wet area spread.
3. Flush with water.
4. Bleaching may remove the final traces of stains marked by *. For chocolate stains, proceed to step 5. For other stains marked by *, use chlorine bleach as directed on page 187, step 10.
5. For chocolate stains, use hydrogen peroxide as directed for washable fabrics, step 11.

Group 3

Aftershave lotion
Bath oil
Blood
Body discharge
Egg white
Eye drops
Fish glue
Fish slime
Hide glue
Mouthwash
Mucus
Sherbet
Soups containing meat
Starch
Vomit

For washable fabrics:
1. Soak in a solution of one quart warm water, ½ teaspoon liquid hand dishwashing detergent, and one tablespoon ammonia for 15 minutes.
2. If the fabric is strong enough, tamp or use a spoon (see pages 186–187). Blot occasionally with absorbent material. Continue as long as any stain is being removed.
3. Soak another 15 minutes in the solution used in step 1.
4. Rinse with water. It is important to remove all ammonia.
5. Soak in a solution of one quart warm water and one tablespoon enzyme product for 30 minutes.
6. Wash.

7. For all stains except blood, repeat step 5, then wash again.
8. For a bloodstain that is not completely removed, wet the stain with hydrogen peroxide and add a drop of ammonia. Do not bleach longer than 15 minutes. Rinse with water.

For nonwashable fabrics:
1. Sponge with water (see page 186).
2. For delicate fabrics, apply wet spotter and a few drops of ammonia. Cover with a pad of absorbent material dampened with wet spotter and let stand as long as any stain is being removed. Change pad as it picks up stain. Keep stain and pad moist with wet spotter and ammonia.
For stronger fabrics, apply wet spotter and a few drops of ammonia, then tamp or use a spoon (see pages 186–187). Keep stain moist with wet spotter and ammonia and blot occasionally with absorbent material. Continue as long as any stain is being removed.
3. Flush with water (see page 186). It is important to remove all ammonia.
4. Moisten the stain with a solution of ½ teaspoon enzyme product and ½ cup warm water. Cover with a clean pad that has been dipped in the warm enzyme solution and squeezed nearly dry. Let stand 30 minutes. Add more warm enzyme solution if needed to keep stain warm and moist, but do not let the wet area spread.
5. Flush with water.
6. If any stain is left, except a bloodstain, repeat steps 2 to 5, then dry.
7. For a bloodstain that is not completely removed, wet the stain with hydrogen peroxide and add a drop of ammonia. Do not bleach longer than 15 minutes. Flush thoroughly with water.

Group 4

Airplane glue
Carbon paper
*Carbon typewriter
ribbon
Contact cement
Corn remover
Cuticle oil
Cuticle remover
Fingernail hardener
Fingernail polish
Household cement
Lacquer
*Mimeograph correction
fluid
*Mimeograph ink

Mucilage
Plastic
Plastic glue
Solder, liquid
Varnish

For washable and nonwashable fabrics:

1. Sponge with dry-cleaning solvent (see page 186).
2. For delicate fabrics, apply dry spotter to stain and cover with a pad of absorbent material dampened with dry spotter. Let stand as long as any stain is being removed. Change pad as it picks up stain. Keep stain and pad moist with dry spotter.

For stronger fabrics, apply dry spotter and tamp or use a spoon (see pages 186–187). Keep stain moist with dry spotter and blot occasionally with absorbent material. Continue as long as any stain is being removed.
3. Flush with dry-cleaning solvent (see page 186).
4. Repeat steps 2 and 3 until no more stain is removed. Allow to dry.
5. Apply amyl acetate to stain and cover with a pad of absorbent material dampened with amyl acetate. Keep moist for 15 minutes, blotting occasionally with absorbent material. Use a spoon to help loosen the stain. When not working on the stain, keep it covered with an inverted bowl to minimize evaporation.
6. Flush with dry-cleaning solvent.
7. Bleaching may remove the final traces of stains marked by *. Use chlorine bleach as directed on page 187, step 10.

Group 5

Beer
*Caramelized sugar
Casein glue
*Coffee
*Cordials
Corn syrup
Cough syrup
Fruit
*Fruit juices
*Fruit preserves
Home permanent
*Jam
*Jelly
Maple syrup
*Mixed drinks
Molasses
*Mud
Shaving cream
*Soft drinks
*Suntan lotion

*Tea
*Tobacco
Toothpaste
*Vegetables
*Vinegar, colored
*Whisky
*Wine

For washable fabrics:

1. Soak in a solution of one quart warm water, ½ teaspoon liquid hand dishwashing detergent, and one tablespoon vinegar for 15 minutes.
2. Rinse with water.
3. Sponge with alcohol (see page 186).
4. Wash.
5. Soak in a solution of one quart warm water and one tablespoon enzyme product for 30 minutes.
6. Wash.
7. Bleaching may remove the final traces of stains marked by *. Use chlorine bleach as directed on page 187, step 10.
8. Wash.

For nonwashable fabrics:

1. Sponge with water (see page 186).
2. For delicate fabrics, apply wet spotter and a few drops of vinegar. Cover with a pad of absorbent material dampened with wet spotter and let stand as long as any stain is being removed. Change pad as it picks up stain. Keep stain and pad moist with wet spotter and vinegar.

For stronger fabrics, apply wet spotter and a few drops of vinegar, then tamp or use a spoon (see pages 186–187). Keep stain moist with wet spotter and vinegar. Blot occasionally with clean absorbent material. Continue as long as any stain is being removed. Flush with water (see page 186).
3. Flush with water (see page 186).
4. Apply alcohol to stain and cover with a pad of absorbent material dampened with alcohol. Let stand as long as any stain is being removed. Change pad as it picks up stain. Keep stain and pad moist with alcohol.
5. If any stain is left, moisten the stain with a solution of ½ teaspoon enzyme product and ½ cup warm water. Cover with a pad that has been dipped in the warm enzyme solution and squeezed nearly dry. Let stand 30 minutes. Add more warm enzyme solution if needed to keep stain warm and moist, but do not let the wet area spread.
6. Flush with water.
7. Bleaching may remove the final

traces of stains marked by * Use chlorine bleach as directed on page 187, step 10.

Group 6

Antiperspirant
*Candy (for chocolate candy, see Group 2)
Deodorant
*Fabric dye, red
*Food coloring, red
*Hair dye, red
*Ink, red
*Mercurochrome
*Merthiolate
*Metaphen
*Perspiration
Picric acid
*Stamp pad ink, red
*Urine
*Watercolor paint, red

For washable fabrics:

1. Soak in a solution of one quart warm water, ½ teaspoon liquid hand dishwashing detergent and one tablespoon ammonia for 30 minutes.
2. Rinse with water.
3. Soak in a solution of one quart warm water and one tablespoon vinegar for 1 hour.
4. Rinse with water. Dry.
5. For delicate fabrics, apply alcohol and cover with a pad dampened with alcohol. Let stand as long as any stain is being removed. Change pad as it picks up stain. Keep stain and pad moist with alcohol.

For stronger fabrics, apply alcohol and tamp or use a spoon (see pages 186–187). Keep stain moist with alcohol and blot occasionally with clean, absorbent material. Continue as long as any stain is being removed.
6. Rinse with water.
7. Bleaching may remove the final traces of stains marked by *. Use chlorine bleach as directed on page 187, step 10.

For nonwashable fabrics:

1. Sponge with water (see page 186).
2. Apply wet spotter and a few drops of ammonia. Let stand as long as any stain is being removed. Press stain every five minutes with clean, absorbent material. Keep moist with wet spotter and ammonia.
3. Flush with water (see page 186).
4. Apply wet spotter and a few drops of vinegar. Let stand as long as any stain is being removed. Press stain every five minutes with clean, absorbent material. Keep moist with wet spotter

189

and vinegar.

5. Flush with water.

6. Apply alcohol to stain and cover with a pad of absorbent material dampened with alcohol. Let stand as long as any stain is being removed. Change pad as it picks up stain. Press pad hard onto the stain each time you check it. Keep stain and pad moist with alcohol.

7. Flush with water.

8. Bleaching may remove the final traces of stains marked by *. Use chlorine bleach as directed on page 187, step 10.

Group 7

Bluing
Fabric dye, all colors except red and yellow
Food coloring, all colors except red and yellow
Gentian violet
Hair dye, black or brown
Ink, black, blue, green, or violet
Shoe dye, brown
Stamp pad ink, all colors except red and yellow
Watercolor paint, all colors except red and yellow

For washable fabrics:

1. Soak in a solution of one quart warm water, ½ teaspoon liquid hand dishwashing detergent, and one tablespoon vinegar for 30 minutes. Agitate occasionally.

2. Rinse with water. Dry.

3. Apply alcohol to stain and cover with a pad of absorbent material dampened with alcohol. Let stand as long as any stain is being removed. Change pad as it picks up stain. Press pad hard onto the stain each time you check it. Keep stain and pad moist with alcohol.

4. Flush with alcohol (see page 186). Allow to dry.

5. Soak in a solution of one quart warm water, ½ teaspoon liquid hand dishwashing detergent, and one tablespoon ammonia for 30 minutes.

6. Rinse with water.

7. If any stain is left, use chlorine bleach as directed on page 187, step 10.

For nonwashable fabrics:

1. Sponge with water (see page 186).

2. Apply wet spotter and a few drops of vinegar. Let stand 30 minutes or more. Blot at least every 5 minutes with clean, absorbent material. Add

wet spotter and vinegar as needed to keep stain moist.

3. Flush with water (see page 186). Dry.

4. Apply alcohol to stain and cover with a pad of absorbent material dampened with alcohol. Let stand as long as any stain is being removed. Change pad as it picks up stain. Press pad hard onto the stain each time you check it.

5. Flush with alcohol. Allow to dry.

6. Sponge with water.

7. Apply wet spotter and a few drops of ammonia. Let stand at least 30 minutes. Blot with clean, absorbent material every five minutes. Add wet spotter and ammonia as needed to keep stain moist.

8. Flush with water. Dry.

9. If any stain is left, use chlorine bleach as directed on page 187, step 10.

Group 8

Asphalt
Butter
Castor oil
Chewing gum
Coconut oil
Cod liver oil
Corn oil
Linseed oil
Olive oil
Peanut oil
Rubber cement
Safflower oil
Vegetable oil

For washable and nonwashable fabrics:

1. Place clean, absorbent material under the stain. Apply dry-cleaning solvent and cover stain with a pad of absorbent material dampened with dry-cleaning solvent. Change the absorbent material as it picks up stain. Keep stain and pad moist with solvent.

2. Apply dry spotter. Cover stain with a pad dampened with dry spotter. If the fabric is strong enough, remove pad every five minutes and tamp or use a spoon. Continue the alternate soaking and tamping or working with the spoon until all stain has been removed.

3. Flush with dry-cleaning solvent. Allow to dry.

Group 9

Argyrol
Iodine

Penicillin
Photo developer fluid
Silver nitrate

For washable and nonwashable fabrics:

1. For Argyrol stain only, mix one tablespoon enzyme product with one quart warm water. Wet stain with this solution and allow to soak for 30 minutes. Flush or rinse with water (see page 186) and proceed to step 2.

For other stains, sponge with water (see page 186) and proceed to step 2.

2. For all stains except iodine, add just enough tincture of iodine to cover the stain.

3. Add one teaspoon of sodium thiosulfate crystals to ½ cup warm water and stir until completely dissolved. Wet the stain with this solution. Add a few drops of ammonia.

4. Flush with water.

5. If any stain is left, repeat steps 2 through 4.

Acids

1. Sponge with water and ammonia (see page 186).

2. Flush with water (see page 186).

3. Add more water and ammonia and flush with water again.

Note. Strong acids may cause permanent damage.

Alkalies

1. Sponge with water (see page 186).

2. Flush with water (see page 186).

3. Add more vinegar and flush with water again.

Note. Strong alkalies may cause permanent damage.

Ballpoint-pen ink

1. Apply lukewarm glycerine. If fabric is strong enough, tamp or use a spoon. Blot frequently by pressing hard on the stain with absorbent material. It is important to remove loosened stain immediately. Keep stain moist with glycerine. Continue as long as any stain is being removed.

2. Flush with water (see page 186).

3. Apply wet spotter.

4. For fabrics that will not be damaged, tamp gently with a brush (see pages 186–187).

For delicate fabrics, use a spoon very gently (see page 187).

5. Add several drops of ammonia and continue to tamp or use a spoon.

6. Flush with water.

7. Repeat steps 3 to 6 until no more stain is removed.

8. Flush with water.

9. If any stain is left, use chlorine bleach as directed on page 187, step 10.

Black walnut

1. Sponge with water (see page 186).

2. For delicate fabrics, apply wet spotter and a few drops of vinegar. Cover with a pad of absorbent material dampened with wet spotter and vinegar. Let stand five minutes, then flush with water (see page 186). Repeat alternate soaking and flushing until no more stain is removed.

For stronger fabrics, apply wet spotter and a few drops of vinegar, then tamp or use a spoon (see pages 186–187). Keep stain moist with wet spotter and vinegar. Blot occasionally with clean, absorbent material. Continue as long as any stain is being removed.

3. If any stain is left, use chlorine bleach as directed on page 187, step 10.

Candle wax

1. Place stain between blotting papers or folded paper towels. Iron at low temperature. Replace papers and iron again. Continue changing papers and ironing until no more wax melts.

2. Sponge with dry-cleaning solvent (see page 186) until all wax has been removed.

3. If any stain is left, use chlorine bleach as directed on page 187, step 10.

4. If any stain is left, apply wet spotter and a few drops of ammonia. If the fabric is strong enough, tamp or use a spoon (see pages 186–187). Otherwise, let stand.

5. Flush with water (see page 186).

6. Repeat steps 4 and 5 until no more stain is removed.

Chlorine

1. Mix ¼ teaspoon color remover with ½ cup cool water. Sponge stain with this solution (see page 186).

2. Flush with water (see page 186).

Epoxy cement

This stain cannot be removed.

Grass

1. Sponge with dry-cleaning solvent (see page 186) as long as any stain is being removed.

2. Allow to dry.

3. Apply amyl acetate and rub stain gently with a pad of absorbent material dampened with amyl acetate.

4. Flush with dry-cleaning solvent (see page 186). Allow to dry.

5. Sponge with water. If fabric is strong enough, tamp or use a spoon (see pages 186–187).

6. Add a small amount of wet spotter and several drops of vinegar. Continue tamping or using the spoon as long as any stain is being removed.

7. Flush with water. Allow to dry.

8. Sponge with alcohol and rub gently with a pad dampened with alcohol.

Lipstick

1. Apply dry-cleaning solvent and dry spotter and blot immediately with absorbent material.

2. Repeat step 1 until no more stain is removed. If stain begins to spread, flush immediately with dry-cleaning solvent (see page 186). Then continue to repeat step 1.

3. Let all dry-cleaning solvent evaporate.

4. Sponge with water (see page 186).

5. Apply wet spotter and a few drops of ammonia. If the fabric is strong enough, tamp or use a spoon (see pages 186–187). Blot frequently with absorbent material.

6. Flush with water.

7. Apply wet spotter and a few drops of vinegar. If fabric is strong enough, tamp or use a spoon. Blot frequently with absorbent material.

8. Flush with water. Allow to dry.

9. Sponge with alcohol. Allow to dry.

10. If any stain is left, use chlorine bleach as directed on page 187, step 10.

Metal

Take to a dry cleaner.

Mustard

1. Place stain on a smooth surface and brush or carefully scrape off excess mustard.

2. Flush with dry-cleaning solvent (see page 186).

3. If the fabric is strong enough, tamp or use a spoon (see pages 186–187).

4. Flush with dry-cleaning solvent. Allow to dry.

5. Sponge with water (see page 186).

6. Apply wet spotter and vinegar. If the fabric is strong enough, tamp or use a spoon.

7. Flush with water.

8. Repeat steps 6 and 7 until no more stain is removed.

9. If any stain is left, wet the stain with hydrogen peroxide and add a drop of ammonia. Do not bleach longer than 15 minutes.

10. Flush with water.

Pencil

1. Erase excess stain with a soft eraser. Be careful not to distort the weave.

2. Flush with dry-cleaning solvent (see page 186).

3. Apply dry spotter and rub gently with a pad of absorbent material dampened with dry spotter.

4. Cover stain with a pad dampened with dry spotter. Let stand 30 minutes.

5. Flush with dry-cleaning solvent. Allow to dry.

6. Sponge with water (see page 186).

7. Apply wet spotter and a few drops of ammonia. If fabric is strong enough, tamp or use a spoon (see pages 186–187).

8. Flush with water.

9. Allow to dry.

10. If any stain is left, repeat step 6 or step 8 until no more stain is removed.

Perfume

For washable fabrics:

1. Sponge with water (see page 186).

2. Apply wet spotter.

3. If the fabric is strong enough, tamp or use a spoon (see pages 186–187).

4. Flush with water (see page 186).

5. Apply alcohol and cover with a pad of absorbent material dampened with alcohol. Let stand as long as any stain is being removed. Change pad as it picks up stain. Keep stain and pad moist with alcohol.

6. Flush with water.

For nonwashable fabrics:

1. Sponge with water (see page 186).

2. Flush with water (see page 186).

3. Apply alcohol and cover with a pad of absorbent material dampened with alcohol. Let stand as long as any stain is being removed. Change pad as it picks up stain. Keep stain and pad moist with alcohol.

4. Flush with water.

Rust

Take to a dry cleaner.

Scorch

Note: Scorched fabrics may be weakened. Stain-removal treatment may further damage the fabric.

1. Wet the stain with hydrogen peroxide and add a drop of ammonia. Let stand for at least several minutes. Full bleaching action may take up to an hour. Keep area moist with hydrogen peroxide and ammonia.
2. Flush with water (see page 186).

Shellac

1. Sponge with dry-cleaning solvent (see page 186).
2. Apply dry spotter. If the fabric is strong enough, tamp or use a spoon (see pages 186–187).
3. Flush with dry-cleaning solvent (see page 186).
4. Apply alcohol. If the fabric is strong enough, tamp or use a spoon.
5. Flush with alcohol.

White shoe polish

1. Sponge with dry-cleaning solvent (see page 186).
2. Apply dry spotter. If the fabric is strong enough, tamp or use a spoon (see pages 186–187).
3. Flush with dry-cleaning solvent (see page 186).
4. Repeat steps 1 to 3 until no more stain is removed.
5. Sponge with amyl acetate. If the fabric is strong enough, tamp or use a spoon.
6. Flush with dry-cleaning solvent. Allow to dry.
7. Sponge with water.
8. Add a few drops of vinegar. If the fabric is strong enough, tamp or use a spoon.
9. Flush with water.
10. Repeat steps 7 to 9 until no more stain is removed.

Unknown stains

1. Sponge with dry-cleaning solvent (see page 186).
2. Apply dry spotter. If the fabric is strong enough, tamp or use a spoon (see pages 186–187).
3. Flush with dry-cleaning solvent (see page 186).
4. Repeat steps 1 to 3 until no more stain is removed.
5. Apply amyl acetate. If the fabric is strong enough, tamp or use a spoon.
6. Flush with dry-cleaning solvent. Allow to dry.

7. Sponge with water. Add wet spotter and a few drops of vinegar. If the fabric is strong enough, tamp or use a spoon.
8. Apply wet spotter and a few drops of ammonia. If the fabric is strong enough, tamp or use a spoon.
9. Allow to dry.
10. Sponge with alcohol and pat with a pad of absorbent material dampened with alcohol.
11. Allow to dry.
12. If any stain is left, use chlorine bleach as directed on page 187, step 10.

SPECIAL CASES

Removing stains from suede and leather

It is safest not to attempt any major stain removal from suede and leather garments. These articles are impregnated with oils and finishes that dry-cleaning solvent usually disturbs, producing a light-colored area. The most that should be done is to dust or very lightly sponge the surface with a cloth barely dampened with solvent.

Most dyes on suedes, especially the darker colors, are easily bled by stain removers containing water. Before trying any removal method, test the colorfastness of the article by very lightly sponging an unexposed seam allowance with a damp cloth. If no color is transferred to the damp cloth, you may very lightly sponge small stained areas with a cloth that is barely damp with water only. Do not use detergent or any other stain-removal agents.

When a suede or leather article becomes damp with water, whether from rain or stain removal, it must be dried in air at normal room temperature. Do not apply heat in any way.

Removing stains from vinyl

Some vinyl articles are resistant to dry-cleaning solvents, but many are likely to be damaged by solvents. Dry-cleaning solvent can remove the plasticizers used to soften vinyl, causing stiffening and greatly reduced garment life. If removal of an oil or grease stain is attempted, the procedure should consist of very lightly sponging the surface of the vinyl with a cloth barely dampened with dry-cleaning solvent. Do not make more than a few strokes of the sponging

cloth. Repeated rubbing will remove the plasticizer and may change the appearance of the vinyl surface.

Stain-removal procedures using water and liquid hand dishwashing detergent with vinegar or ammonia are usually safe on vinyl. Test a hidden seam allowance before trying to remove the stain. A blotting action is the safest method for treating stains on vinyl. Do not use a rubbing or tamping action, because this may change the surface appearance.

TEXTILE FIBER CLASSES AND CARE LABELING

Under the Textile Fiber Products Identification Act of 1960, all textile products must have a label or tag giving the percentage of each fiber. The following table shows the classes of textile fibers that are used on labels of fiber content.

Protein-based: azlon.

Mineral-based: glass, metallic.

True synthetics: acrylic, modacrylic, anidex, aramid, novoloid, nylon, nytril, olefin, PBI, polyester, rubber and lastrile, saran, spandex, vinal, vinyon, Teflon.

Natural fibers
Cellulosic (plant): cotton, jute, linen.

Minor fibers include: abaca, banana, cattail, cisalpha, hemp, henequen, kapok, pina, ramie or grass linen, sisal.

Protein (animal): silk, wool.

Minor fibers include: alpaca, angora (rabbit), camel hair, cashmere, fur fibers (pelt removed), horsehair, llama, mohair, vicuña.

Mineral: asbestos.

Man-made fibers
Cellulose-based: acetate and triacetate, and rayon.

Before treating a stain on a garment, read the information on the care label. Garments produced since 1972 are required by law to have a permanent label giving instructions for proper care. Labels for washable items carry information on washing method, water temperature, drying method, drying temperature, and whether bleach can be used. Items that are washable are assumed to be dry cleanable unless the label says "Do not dry-clean." Labels may indicate that dry cleaning only is recommended. Items that cannot be washed or dry-cleaned may be labeled "Wipe with damp cloth only" unless they cannot be maintained by any method.

Stores that sell piece or yard goods are required by law to include an appropriate care label with each piece of fabric sold (except remnants). If you sew, be sure you get these labels, then attach them permanently.

MILDEW

Mildew is a thin, often whitish growth produced on many kinds of surfaces by molds. Molds are simple plants belonging to the group known as fungi. They commonly develop in muggy summer weather, especially in houses that are closed. In homes they develop most often on cotton, linen, rayon, silk, wool, leather, wood, and paper. Many man-made fibers are resistant to mildew.

As the molds grow, they cause considerable damage. They often leave a musty odor. They discolor fabrics and sometimes eat into them so severely that the fabrics rot and fall to pieces. They also discolor leather and paper.

Keep closets, dresser drawers, basements—any place where mildew is likely to grow—as clean as possible. Soil on articles can supply sufficient food for mildew to start growing when moisture and temperature are right. Greasy films, such as those that form on kitchen walls, also contain many nutrients for mildew organisms.

In addition, get rid of dampness. Control dampness in a basement and in crawl spaces; dry the air with air conditioners and dehumidifiers; or get rid of dampness by heating the house for a short time and then opening doors and windows to let the moisture-laden air out. You may use moisture-absorbing chemicals such as silica gel, activated alumina, and calcium chloride. Good ventilation can also remove excess moisture.

Get rid of musty odors, which indicate mold growth. Usually musty odors disappear if the area is well heated and dried. In cellars with dirt floors, sprinkle chlorinated lime (chloride of lime or bleaching powder) over the floor. Let it stay until all mustiness disappears, then sweep it up. On cement floors and on tiled walls and floors in bathrooms, get rid of mustiness by scrubbing with a dilute solution of sodium hypochlorite or other chlorine bleach available in grocery stores. Use ½ to one cup of liquid household bleach to a gallon of water. Rinse with clear water and wipe as dry as possible. Keep windows open until walls and floors are thoroughly dry. *Caution:* Work quickly and carefully on plastic and asphalt tile to avoid spotting the surface. Aerosol sprays for cleaning and sanitizing bathroom walls are also available.

Keep clothing and household fabrics dry to avoid mildew. It is a good idea to wash or dry-clean fabrics before storing, as soiled articles are more likely to mildew than clean ones. From time to time on warm, dry days, sun and air articles stored in closets. It is worthwhile to inspect occasionally cotton, rayon, leather, and woolen clothing put away in garment bags. Unless such materials are stored with a mildew inhibitor, they may mildew. Certain volatile chemicals protect fabrics during storage. Paradichlorobenzene effectively controls mildew when used in packages, trunks or garment bags kept as nearly airtight as possible. Scatter paradichlorobenzene crystals through the folds of garments to be packed in boxes, or hang bags of crystals at the top of garment bags so the vapors settle on the materials being protected. Use about one pound of the crystals for 100 cubic feet of air space. Paradichlorobenzene is also available in spray cans. Because paradichlorobenzene damages some plastics, you should remove plastic buttons and ornaments from garments and use wooden or metal clothes hangers instead of plastic ones.

Paraformaldehyde is another volatile chemical that has mildew-inhibiting properties. It is sold in powder form at drugstores. Use 3.15 ounces actual paraformaldehyde per 500 cubic feet in a combination formulation of 90 percent paraformaldehyde and 10 percent paradichlorobenzene. Use 2.35 ounces actual paraformaldehyde per 350 cubic feet in a combination formulation of 50 percent paraformaldehyde and 50 percent paradichlorobenzene. Place bags of the chemical where the vapors can circulate and reach all surfaces of the stored articles. Avoid inhaling paraformaldehyde fumes—they are poisonous.

To protect leather against mildew, treat with low-pressure aerosol formulations that carry specific directions. Before treating the article, test the spray on a small inconspicuous area to see whether it will change the color of the leather. A good wax dressing will also help to protect leather goods. During warm, humid weather, protect stored shoes, jackets, luggage and other leather articles with paradichlorobenzene or paraformaldehyde. After treating, allow articles to dry and then wrap the articles in packages and seal them. Do not spray near a flame.

In damp summer weather, keep papers and books as dry as possible to help control mold growth. You can use a chemical dehumidifier, such as silica gel or calcium chloride, in a closed space.

Removing mildew

From clothing and household fabrics: Remove mildew spots as soon as they are discovered. Brush off any surface growth outdoors to prevent scattering the mildew spores in the house. Sun and air fabrics thoroughly. If any mildew spots remain, treat washable articles yourself and dry-clean nonwashable articles. Wash mildew-stained articles with soap or detergent and water. Rinse well and dry in the sun. If any stain remains, moisten the area with a mixture of lemon juice and salt. Spread in the sun to bleach. Rinse thoroughly. Or use a bleach, but test colored fabrics first for colorfastness.

To use peroxide bleach, mix one to two tablespoons of sodium perborate (or a powdered bleach containing sodium perborate or potassium monopersulfate) with one pint of water. Use hot water if safe for the fabric; otherwise use lukewarm water. Sponge stain or soak stained area in the solution. Or sprinkle the dry powder directly on the dampened stain. Let solution or powder remain on the stain 30 minutes or longer, then rinse thoroughly. If mildew stains have been on the fabric for some time, it may be necessary to soak in the bleach solution overnight. If safe for the fabric, the use of sodium perborate solution at or near the boiling point may remove stubborn stains.

To use chlorine bleach, mix two tablespoons of liquid chlorine bleach with one quart of warm water. Sponge stain or soak stained area in the solu-

193

tion. Allow bleach to remain on fabric from 5 to 15 minutes, then rinse thoroughly. Never use a chlorine bleach on silk, wool or spandex fabrics. Some fabrics with wash-and-wear or other special finishes may be damaged by chlorine bleaches. Articles with such finishes should have a warning on the label or hang tag cautioning against the use of chlorine bleach.

From upholstered articles, mattresses, rugs: First remove loose mold from outer coverings by brushing with a broom. Do this outdoors if possible to prevent scattering mildew spores in the house. Run a vacuum cleaner attachment over the surface of the article to draw out more of the mold. Do everything possible to dry the article, such as using an electric heater and a fan to carry away moist air. Sun and air the article to stop mold growth. If mildew remains, sponge lightly with thick suds of soap or detergent, and wipe with a clean, damp cloth. Or you can remove mildew by wiping it with a cloth dipped in dilute alcohol (one cup denatured or rubbing alcohol to one cup water) and then wrung out. Dry the article thoroughly. Sponge mildewed rugs and carpets with thick suds or a rug shampoo. Then remove the suds by wiping with a cloth dampened in clear water. Dry in the sun if possible. Use a low-pressure spray containing a fungicide to get rid of mildew. Vapors of paradichlorobenzene or paraformaldehyde used in closed areas will stop mold growth. If molds have grown into the inner part of an article, send it to a reliable disinfecting and fumigating service.

From leather goods: To remove mildew, wipe with a cloth that has been dipped in dilute alcohol (one cup denatured or rubbing alcohol to one cup water) and then wrung out. Dry in a current of air. If mildew remains, wash with thick suds of a mild soap or detergent, saddle soap or a soap containing a germicide or fungicide. Then wipe with a damp cloth and dry in an airy place. Polish leather shoes and luggage with a good wax dressing. A good way to stop mold growth in leather goods is to place the articles in a container along with crystals of commercially prepared paradichlorobenzene-paraformaldehyde. Close the container tightly and allow the chemicals to vaporize. The vapors are effec-

tive in killing molds that have grown, but they give no lasting protection against future contamination. As the vapors leak out, the chemicals must be replaced. Before using the leather goods, air them thoroughly.

From wood: Use heat and improved ventilation to get mildewed wood as dry as possible. Wood that is badly infected may need to be replaced, preferably with wood that has been treated or that is naturally decay resistant. Clean mildewed wood surfaces by scrubbing them with a mild alkali such as washing soda or trisodium phosphate (four to six tablespoons to a gallon of water), or with disinfectants such as a quaternary disinfectant or pentachlorophenol. Rinse well with clear water and allow the wood to dry thoroughly. Then apply a mildew-resistant paint. If the mold has grown into the wood under paint or varnish, it may be necessary to scrub the wood first with an abrasive cleaner. Then wash with a solution containing four to six tablespoons of trisodium phosphate and one cup of household chlorine bleach to a gallon of water. Finally, rinse the wood well with clear water. Dry thoroughly and apply a wood preservative before repainting.

From paper and books: Remove any dry, loose mold from paper with a clean, soft cloth. If mildewed paper is damp, dry it first in an airy place if possible. To dry wallpaper, heat the room for several hours or even days to dry the plaster as well as the paper. Plaster should be dried slowly to prevent it from cracking. If mildewed paper is washable, wipe it with a cloth wrung out of thick soapsuds, then of clear water. Take care not to wet the paper more than necessary. Do not rub it. Finally pat with a soft, dry cloth. If stains remain, bleach with a solution of a household bleach, then sponge with a cloth moistened with clear water and then wrung out. For small stains a commercial ink eradicator may be useful. Spread pages of books out fanwise to air. If the books are very damp, sprinkle cornstarch or talcum powder between the leaves to take up the moisture. Leave starch or powder on for several hours, then brush off. Use a mildew inhibitor such as paradichlorobenzene to stop mold growth.

CLEANING HOUSEHOLD SURFACES

Walls: Dust with a vacuum brush or a soft cloth pinned over a mop. Wash from the floors up—the only way to prevent streaking. You can wash vinyl or paint (except lacquer or shellac) that has been on the wall at least three weeks if it does not come off on the cloth when you test cleaning solution in an obscure area.

Windows: Wash windows from left to right on inside, top to bottom on outside. Then if there are streaks, you will know which side they are on. Do not wash windows with the sun right on them—it dries them too fast and leaves streaks.

Wood floors: Brush-vacuum light soil. Once a week go over the floor with a barely damp mop, then dry. For medium soil or rusty water marks, sand gently with fine steel wool dipped in paste wax. Remove heavy soil with a soft cloth wrung in turpentine or mineral spirits (flammable). Then wax. Apply paste wax by hand with a soft cloth. Rub in the direction of the grain or inlay. Let dry as long as possible so the paste moisturizes the wood. Buff by machine weighing at least 60 pounds, but preferably 100. With paste wax and a floor that gets average wear, wax two or three times a year, three to six times for high-traffic areas. New floors are thirstier. Wax them two or three times in the first six months. Paste wax never needs stripping. Liquid waxes take up surface soil plus some old wax. They are faster and easier to apply, but need waxing more often (once a month) and stripping (about twice a year). Whatever wax you choose, use very thin, even coats, making sure that each coat is completely dry before the next is applied. The more coats you apply, the less often you have to wax.

Wood furniture: Be sure people never put a drink directly on a piece of wood furniture. Use coasters. A remedy for water and heat stains is to apply a paste of cigarette ashes and olive oil to the stain. Let stand, rub gently with the grain with a damp cloth. Dry. Rewax. To lift wax, dirt and other stains, wipe with benzene.

Ceramic tile: Clean with ammonia solution. Use vinegar on hard-water spots, kerosene on soap scum. To ease cleaning, seal cement grout twice a year with a naphthalsilicone brick sealer.

Mirrors and glass: To make mirrors and glass sparkle, use a spray and wipe it off with newspaper. Newspaper is lintless and more absorbent than cloth. Glass scratches, so dust only with a damp cloth to keep the soil from leaving its mark.

Rugs and upholstery: Vacuum thoroughly at least once a week, high traffic areas more often. Most experts discourage do-it-yourself cleaning except for stain emergencies. In most cases, use a professional service.

Acrylic plastic: Never dust a dry surface. Spray on a weak solution of mild dishwashing liquid and wipe with a cotton cloth. To wash, flood the surface with the same solution, using a sponge; rinse; blot dry. Remove grease with naphtha. Never use strong solvents or window cleaner.

EMERGENCY STAIN REMOVAL

For emergency stain removal when you do not have the previously mentioned supplies on hand or the time to go through the required steps, use the chart below for removing common stains from washable fabrics. When a method suggests using a detergent paste, make it by mixing detergent granules with water. There are also specialty products available, such as prewash soil and stain removers, for treating stains. Check instructions on package for the stains which can be removed and how to use the product correctly. Some stains may be impossible to take out. For nonwashables, tell the cleaners the fiber content of the fabric and the kind of stain.

Treatment for various types of stains

The following instructions come from The Soap and Detergent Foundation.

Blood: Soak in an enzyme presoak product. Launder as usual.

Candle wax, crayon: Use a dull knife to remove surface wax. Place stain between paper towels and press with warm iron. Place stain face down on paper towels and sponge back of any stain remaining with dry-cleaning solvent. Allow to dry, then launder.

Chewing gum: Put ice on gum to harden it. Take gum off fabric with a dull knife. Place fabric face down on paper towels and sponge with a dry-cleaning solvent. Launder.

Coffee or tea: Soak in enzyme presoak product or oxygen bleach. Use hottest water safe for the fabric. Then wash. If stain remains, use chlorine bleach if safe for the fabric.

Cosmetics: Dampen stain. Rub with bar soap or detergent (liquid or paste). Then rinse and wash.

Deodorants, antiperspirants: Rub liquid detergent on light stain and wash in hottest water safe for the fabric. For heavy stains, place garment face down on paper towels and sponge back of stain with dry-cleaning solvent, rinse. Rub with liquid detergent and rinse. Launder in hottest water safe for fabric.

Fabric softener: Dampen stain and rub with bar soap. Rinse and repeat if necessary. Then wash.

Grass: Soak in an enzyme presoak product. Then wash. If still stained, use chlorine bleach if safe for fabric and launder.

Greasy stains (car grease or oil, butter, margarine, lard, salad dressings, cooking oils): Place stain face down on paper towels. Put dry-cleaning solvent on back side of stain. Brush from center of stain to outer edges with a clean white cloth. Dampen stain with water and rub with bar soap or liquid detergent. Rinse and launder.

Ink, ballpoint: Place stain face down on paper towels. Sponge back of stain with dry-cleaning solvent. If some ink still remains, rub with bar soap. Rinse and wash.

Lipstick: Place stain face down on paper towels. Sponge back of stain with dry-cleaning solvent. Move fabric to clean area of towel frequently to take out more of the color. Dampen stain with water and rub with bar soap or detergent (liquid or paste). Rinse and wash.

Mildew: Wash with detergent and chlorine bleach, if safe for the fabric. If not, then wash in hottest water safe for fabric.

Milk, cream, ice cream: Soak in warm water with an enzyme presoak product. Wash as usual.

Nail polish: Place stain face down on paper towels. Sponge back of stain with nail-polish remover (acetone), moving the stain to a clean part of the paper towel frequently. Continue sponging until the stain disappears. Then launder. *Do not use nail polish remover on acetate or Arnel fabrics.* Send to dry cleaner.

Paint, water-base: Rinse fabrics in warm water while stains are still wet. Then launder.

Paint, oil-base, and varnish: Use the solvent that the label on the can tells you to use as a thinner. If can is not available, use turpentine. Rinse and rub with bar soap or detergent (liquid or paste). Rinse and wash.

Perspiration: Dampen stain and rub with bar soap. Soak in an enzyme presoak product. Launder in hot water and chlorine bleach if safe for fabric. If color of fabric has changed, use ammonia for fresh stains and vinegar for old. Rinse and launder in hottest water safe for color.

Rust: A few spots can be removed with a rust-stain remover. Rinse and wash. If a full load of white items shows rust, use a fabric color remover. Launder. Most often you will have to take it to a dry cleaner.

Scorch: Soak in an enzyme presoak product or oxygen bleach. Then launder. If stain remains, use chlorine bleach if safe for fabric and launder again using hottest water safe for fabric.

Urine, vomit, mucus: Soak in an enzyme presoak product. Launder using a chlorine bleach, if safe for the fabric, or an oxygen bleach.

Wine, soft drinks: Soak in an enzyme presoak product or oxygen bleach using hottest water safe for fabric. Launder. If stain remains, launder again using chlorine bleach if safe for the fabric.

Yellowing of white nylon, permanent press: Soak in an enzyme presoak product. Launder in hot water, a generous amount of detergent and chlorine bleach, if safe for fabric. Or use an oxygen bleach.

Note. When using any stain removal material, read and follow instructions carefully. Some products may be flammable or toxic. Follow all safety suggestions. Work where there is plenty of fresh air.

47

IN THE GARDEN

PEST MANAGEMENT

When pesticides are applied to the land, every precaution should be taken to avoid contaminating streams, lakes or ponds in order to protect fish and wildlife. Do not apply pesticides, particularly insecticides, to fish-bearing water unless the label specifically recommends such uses, and then apply only at the specified rates. Avoid drift of pesticides. Do not spray or dust in the garden if the day is windy.

Pesticide is a general term covering all chemical control materials as a group. In addition, chemicals are classified according to their primary use: insecticide—to kill insects; fungicide—to prevent or cure plant diseases caused by fungi; bacteriocide—to prevent or cure bacterial diseases of plants; herbicide—to prevent or kill weeds; nematicide—to kill nematodes, tiny microscopic round worms that live mostly in the soil; rodenticide—to control rodents. The Environmental Protection Agency (EPA) requires that the intended use of a pesticide be printed on its label or covered by a Pesticide Enforcement Policy Statement (PEPS) issued by EPA.

Pesticides can be purchased in dry or liquid form, and are usually applied as dusts, sprays or granules. They are formulated to contain a percentage of the active chemical ingredient. This percentage is shown on the label. Dusts and sprays are practical for small applications. Dusts are applied in the form they come in, while sprays must be diluted with water before applying. Make an even, thorough application, forcing the material into the foliage so that it coats all sides of the leaves, stems, and fruits.

Pesticides used improperly may injure man, animals and plants. Follow all label directions, and read the cautions for handling. Do not use the same sprayer for herbicides and insecticides and fungicides, as minute traces of weed killers can kill garden plants.

Timely application is critical for reasonable insect control. Diseases can rarely be cured; they must be prevented. You can get your garden into good shape by treating the soil with soil amendments and nutrients, and by removing any plant that has been severely damaged by pests or is rotten, wilted or moldy. Once you have a healthy garden, keep it that way by raking up any debris, and by digging in fresh mulches each year. Good gardening helps control pests.

Protecting the lawn

Many insects and insectlike pests damage lawn and other turf. They cause the grass to turn brown and die, or they build unsightly mounds that may smother the grass. Some pests infest the soil and attack the plant roots; some feed on the plant leaves and stems; and some suck juice from the plants. All these pests can be controlled with insecticides.

Control with insecticides: Insecticides are sold under various trade names by garden supply houses, and hardware, seed and drug stores. Granules are ready-made formulations that are used dry. Apply them with a lawn fertilizer spreader. Wettable powders and emulsifiable concentrates are used in sprays. Mix the purchased product with water, and apply the spray with a garden-type compressed-air sprayer or a knapsack sprayer. The quantity of water needed depends on the type of sprayer you have. If a wettable powder is used, frequent agitation of the mixture is necessary. A quart-jar attachment for a garden hose will provide good distribution of an insecticide on a lawn. Use an attachment that delivers a coarse spray and a large volume of water. A quart jar of insecticide mixture will cover about 500 square feet of lawn. Baits are usually purchased ready-mixed, but a bait for controlling slugs and snails may be prepared as described below.

Apply insecticides at any time except when the ground is frozen. Spring or fall is best for grubs.

To get rid of underground lawn pests, apply an insecticide and, immediately afterward, sprinkle the lawn thoroughly. Be patient; it may take a month or more before the insecticide becomes fully effective. However, one application may control the pests for several years.

To control aboveground lawn pests, apply an insecticide to the grass. Sprinkle lightly with water to wash the insecticide down around the crowns of the plants. Do not water again for a few days; then sprinkle the grass thoroughly to wash off the insecticide. One application may control pests for several weeks. Repeat the application if they reappear.

The chart on page 197 gives insecticide recommendations for most lawn pests. Recommendations for others are given below.

Millipedes. To control millipedes, use an emulsifiable concentrate of one of the following insecticides: one-half pint of 4-pounds-per-gallon diazinon or 5 fluid ounces of 5-pounds-per-gallon malathion. Apply the insecticide to millipedes crawling about the yard and to places where they congregate.

Slugs and snails. Use a ready-mixed bait, or a bait made by mixing 1 ounce of metaldehyde with 2 pounds of wheat bran or cornmeal and adding water to moisten. Apply in the late afternoon.

Billbugs. Apply 6 pounds of 2-percent diazinon granules or 4 ounces of 50-percent diazinon emulsifiable concentrate.

Fruit fly. Apply 4 ounces of 50-percent diazinon emulsifiable concentrate.

Protecting fruits and vegetables from pests

You should be able to prevent most pest problems. Timing is the key to success once you have determined what measures to apply. See the chart below for proper timing. (The U.S. Department of Agriculture also has a Home and Garden Bulletin, No. 211, entitled "Control of Insects on Deciduous Fruits and Tree Nuts in the Home Orchard—Without Insecticides," that is available from the Superintendent of Documents, U.S. Government Printing Office, Washington, D.C. 20402.) The "what to do" is a basic guide only. Follow local recommendations on rates, restrictions, and alternatives. Never use a chemical on a plant unless the label says you can. Follow all label instructions and precautions.

Other garden pests: Noninsect pests and diseases can cause considerable damage. Different parts of the country may have unique problems.

Rodents. Rodents may burrow

196

LAWN PESTS AND INSECTICIDES TO USE IN CONTROLLING THEM

Insecticide	Grubs and Ants	Sod Webworms, Wireworms, Cicada-killer Wasps, and Wild Bees	Chinch Bugs and False Chinch Bugs	Armyworms, Cutworms and Mole Crickets	Earwigs, Fiery Skippers and Lucerne Moths	Chiggers, Fleas, and Ticks	Leafhoppers, Leaf Bugs, and Mites
	See Note 1	See Note 2	See Note 3	See Note 4	See Note 5		See Note 6
GRANULES							
Carbaryl	X	X	X				
Diazinon		X	X	X	X		
Ethion			X				
SPRAYS (WETTABLE POWDERS)							
Carbaryl		X	X	X	X	X	X
Diazinon	X	X	X	X	X	X	X
Ethion			X				
EMULSIFIABLE CONCENTRATES							
Diazinon	X	X	X	X	X	X	X
Ethion			X				
Malathion						X	X

Note 1: If only a few ant nests are present, treat them individually. Wash the insecticide into the nests or drench the mounds with it. Special treatment is required to control fire and harvester ants; consult your state agricultural experiment station for latest recommendations.

Note 2: To control sod webworms, apply the insecticide in late afternoon or evening and delay watering until the following morning. To control wireworms, the cicada-killer wasp and wild bees, apply diazinon. To eliminate a nest of the wasp, pour or spray the insecticide into the nest after dark and seal the entrance with dirt.

Note 3: A preventive spray program to control chinch bugs in the South requires treatment about every 6 weeks.

Note 4: To control cutworms, apply the insecticide in late afternoon.

Note 5: A ready-mixed bait is also effective against earwigs. Follow directions on the container. Apply bait in the evening. To control the fiery skipper and lucerne moth, apply diazinon.

Note 6: To control leafhoppers, apply carbaryl or malathion. To control leaf bugs and mites, apply malathion. To control the eriophyid mite, apply diazinon.

PEST- CONTROL PROGRAM

Crop	Critical time(s)	Pest and what to do
Fruits	As a general rule, critical times for preventing the most likely fruit pests are from the start of growth in spring through fruit set.	
Apples and pears	Early spring, when buds have ¼-inch green tip	Apple scab—Spray with fungicide, every 7 days through bloom
	Early spring, when buds have pink tips	Overwintering insects on tree—Spray with dormant oil spray
	Late spring at petal fall	Codling moth, leaf roller, plum curculio, apple scab—Spray with insecticide and fungicide
	Normal or wet summer	Apple maggot fly (railroad worms)—Spray every 10-14 days with insecticide
Brambles raspberries, blackberries, gooseberries, currants, etc.	Spring, when leaf buds are ⅛ inch long	Anthracnose, spur and cane blight—Spray with fungicide
	Spring, just before blossoms open	Sawfly, borers, anthracnose, spur and cane blight—Spray with fruit combination spray containing fungicide and insecticide. Repeat in 3 days and then in 10 days
Grapes	Spring, when new shoots are 6-8 inches long	Black rot—Spray with fungicide
	Spring, just before blossoms open and after petal fall	Black rot, leafhoppers, rose chafer, moths—Spray with fungicide and insecticide
	Spring, just after blossoms fall	Powdery mildew and above insects—Spray with fungicide and insecticide

(continued on next page)

197

PEST- CONTROL PROGRAM (continued)

Crop	Critical time(s)	Pest and what to do
Stone Fruits cherries, peaches, plums, apricots, etc.	Dormant, before growth starts in spring	Peach leaf curl, black knot—Spray with fungicide
	Petal fall	Brown rot, leaf roller moth, curculio—Spray with fungicide and insecticide
	7-10 days after petal fall	Brown rot, leaf spot, curculio, fruitworm—Spray with fungicide and insecticide
Strawberries	Early spring, right after uncovering or just before buds appear	Leaf spot, leaf scorch, aphids, plant bugs, leaf roller—Spray with fungicide and insecticide
	While in blossom, every 10 days until 3 days before first picking	Leaf spot, leaf scorch, berry rot, berry mold—Spray with fungicide
Vegetables	Most vegetables can be put into one of two categories for critical time(s): (1) as seedlings, and (2) at blossom and fruit set. Use seeds treated with a fungicide to assure good seed growth.	
Beans	Blossom through fruit set	Leafhoppers, aphids, lygus bugs, beetles—Spray with insecticide
Beets and Chard	Before planting	Cutworms—Spray ground with insecticide
Cabbage and related plants, such as broccoli, brussels sprouts, cauliflower, collards, kale	As seedlings and mature plants	Aphid, looper, webworm, diamondback, cabbage worm, harlequin bug—Spray with insecticide
Carrots	As seedlings	Aster leafhopper—Spray with insecticide
Celery	As seedlings	Aster leafhopper, blight—Spray with insecticide and fungicide
Cucumber and related vine crops, such as squash, pumpkins	As seedlings	Striped cucumber beetle—Spray with insecticide
Melons	At vining out and/or at blossoming	Striped cucumber beetle, pickle-worm, squash vine borer—Spray with insecticide
Lettuce	As seedlings	Aster leafhopper—Spray with insecticide
Okra	During fruiting	Corn earworm—Spray with insecticide
Peas	At blossom and fruit set	Cowpea curculio, pea weevil—Spray with insecticide
Peppers	At blossom and fruit set	Pepper weevil, aphid, European corn borer—Spray with insecticide
Potatoes	Before planting	Grubs, wireworms—Spray ground with insecticide
	Seedlings to blossom	Beetles, aphids, leafhoppers, blight—Spray with insecticide and fungicide
Radish	Before planting	Root maggots—Spray ground with insecticide
Sweetcorn	At silking, and every 5 days for 2 more sprays	Earworms—Spray with insecticide
Tomatoes	At blossom, and possibly at weekly intervals thereafter	Leaf spot, blight, flea beetles, hornworms, leaf miners—Spray with fungicide and insecticide
Turnip and Mustard	First true leaves	Aphid—Spray with insecticide

198

and feed on roots and tubers, or they may eat plant tops and fruit. Control is limited to traps or chemicals. Chemical baits are available for mice in fruit orchards.

Rabbits. Rabbits can be repelled by sprinkling dried blood meal on the ground throughout the garden. It must be reapplied every few days, or after a heavy dew or rain. Buried fencing around small gardens can be effective. Some people have kept rabbits out by placing green wine bottles filled with water halfway into the ground. The rabbits are frightened off when they see their reflection.

Deer. Deer can be repelled with dried blood meal as above, moth balls scattered around, creosote rags in various spots, dogs, noisemakers, fencing.

Birds. Birds can be kept off fruit trees with special-purpose nets, scarecrows, or noisemakers.

PRUNING SHADE TREES

By pruning as soon as the need becomes apparent, you can easily correct defects that would require major tree surgery if left untended. The basic tools for pruning are hand clippers to cut twigs, small branches and vines; a pruning shears to shear foliage; and pruning saws to remove limbs.

Improper pruning can induce disease or decay. Pruning cuts should be made flush to the trunk or connecting branch because branch stubs permit invasion by decay-producing organisms. Cuts will heal by forming calluses. Remove injured or diseased branches before they die.

Broad-leaf trees

Although small branches and twigs are commonly pruned just above an outside bud or at a fork, they may be clipped or sheared without much regard for the position of dormant buds. New growth normally develops on small branches and twigs a short distance below pruning cuts.

Pruning to a fork or bud that is toward the outside of the tree's crown tends to induce growth that broadens the crown. However, the amount of light the tree receives, the direction of the light, and the nature of the tree also affect the direction of new growth. Some trees do not broaden regardless of the way they are pruned.

When removing large branches, be careful not to tear loose the bark be-

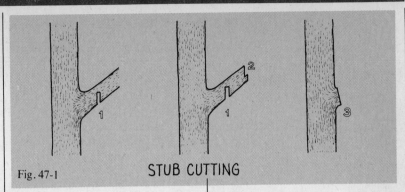

Fig. 47-1   STUB CUTTING

low the cut. Stub cutting will prevent this.

Stub cutting: To prevent stripping the bark, stub-cut all branches that are too large to be supported by hand. Stub cutting requires three saw cuts (see Fig. 47-1). Make the first cut on the lower side of the limb, one to two feet farther out on the limb than the final cut will be made. Saw upward about halfway through the limb, or until the wood pinches the saw blade. Make the second cut a few inches farther out on the limb. Cut downward from the top until the limb is severed. Finally, saw off the stub. Leave no bark or wood—or only a very narrow ledge—at the top of the cut. A narrow ledge may be left on the base. Make this cut as smooth as you can; smooth it with a chisel, if necessary. Short stubs that are not removed usually die. These dead stubs are points through which fungi can enter the tree.

V-crotches: To avoid leaving a stub when pruning out one member of a V-crotch, make the final cut to the point where the two members join solidly (see Fig. 47-2). On large limbs or trunks, this point of solid juncture usually is lower than it appears to be.

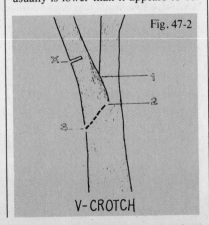

Fig. 47-2

V-CROTCH

To find this point, first make a cut from the outside of the branch to the apparent point of juncture. Then, using a chisel, carefully chip away the wood at the crotch until you reach the actual point where the wood joins. When you have found the point of juncture, shape the cut so it slopes downward from the point. Make the angle of the slope no larger than is necessary to permit normal healing—an angle of 30 to 45 degrees is about right. A sharper angle leaves too large a wound. A shallower angle commonly retards healing, presents more opportunity for water to soak into the wood, and encourages growth of decay fungi.

Needle-leaf evergreens

Arborvitae and other needle-leaf evergreens of its class can be shaped by overall shearing. Evergreens of the pine-tree class do not respond as well to shearing; they usually are shaped by pruning individual parts. To thicken the crown of trees that don't tolerate shearing, pinch back the young "candle" growth while it is still soft. This encourages the development of numerous small branches. Shorten small branches in spring by cutting at a fork; remove only the growth of the previous season. Dormant buds will then soon begin to grow and form new branches. If drastic pruning is required on pines or similar trees, remove some whole limbs. Do not prune branches to leafless stubs; these seldom develop new foliage.

If the leader is broken or cut from pines, spruces or other trees of that class, the tree often fails to develop a new central stem. Height growth is retarded. This results in the tree having a low, broad shape that is not typical of the species. Sometimes you can help the tree develop a new leader and

199

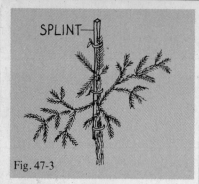

SPLINT

Fig. 47-3

avoid this unusual shape.

First, select a pliable branch in the uppermost whorl of growth. Bend this branch upward. Hold it in a vertical position by tying it to a splint that is attached to the tree's main trunk (see Fig. 47-3). After a year or two the vertical branch begins to grow as a leader; new branches grow from it in a whorl typical of these trees. When this branch formation is apparent, the stake or pole can be removed from the tree.

Note. Big trees can be dangerous to prune. Large limbs are very heavy. If a severed limb gets out of hand, it may cause extensive property damage or may maim or kill workers or bystanders. A misstep while climbing in a tall tree, momentary loss of balance, or misplaced confidence in the strength of a branch can cause the pruner to fall to his death. For greatest safety, engage professional arborists or tree surgeons to do work that requires removal of large limbs or climbing in tall trees. Select tree workers who are insured against personal injury and property damage.

REPAIRING INJURIES OF SHADE TREES

Prompt treatment of injured trees can keep them from becoming unsightly or dangerous, and may even keep them from death. Wounds should be treated by removing dead and torn bark tissues and by shaping the wound into a vertical oval. This will help the tree heal quickly.

Commercial tree dressings such as orange shellac or those with an asphalt base can be painted over the treated wound. They can protect the tree until the wounds heal. No dressing, however, will always prevent decay.

Small cuts of less than one inch in diameter on deciduous trees usually heal quickly if they are smooth. Large cuts—over one inch in diameter—should be treated to prevent entrance of decay or disease while the wound is healing. For best results, treat the wound with asphalt varnish containing an antiseptic. The antiseptic prevents spread of harmful organisms that may contaminate the treating material. Asphalt varnish containing antiseptic is available at some garden-supply stores. If you cannot get a dressing containing antiseptic, use ordinary asphalt varnish. But before applying plain asphalt varnish, swab the wound with alcohol or coat it with shellac. Apply the dressing as soon as the wound is dry. Most wounds can be painted as soon as they happen. If the wound is wet or bleeding, however, asphalt varnish will not adhere; let the wound dry before applying the dressing. Keep an unbroken film of dressing over pruning wounds. One coat of paint will last two or three years—long enough for small wounds to heal completely. Larger wounds may need to be recoated with the dressing several times before they heal. Inspect the wounds periodically and apply additional dressing if the coating is cracked or peeling.

Needle-leaf evergreens usually seal small wounds with natural gums and resins. If a resin coating forms over the wound, the wound need not be painted. If no resin forms, treat the wound as described previously for deciduous trees with asphalt dressing.

Lightning damage

Usually you cannot tell how badly a tree is damaged by lightning until about a year after it has been struck. Trees that seemed to be badly damaged may live, while others apparently only mildly injured may die. However, exposed wood on lightning-damaged trees should be painted. Remove all shattered parts and dangerous hanging limbs.

Split trunks and crotches

These can often be ended by restoring the damaged part to its original position and securing it permanently.

Split trunk: First, smooth edges of the damaged parts. Disinfect the wound with denatured alcohol or shellac. Then draw the parts together with bolts inserted into holes drilled straight through the separated parts. Finally, cover the crack with antiseptic paint. Splits caused by freezing sometimes cannot be held with bolts. These splits often heal without treatment but open again in the winter when they freeze.

Split crotches: These can be drawn together by bolting. However, they usually require additional support from lag-threaded screw rods or from cables with toggle bolts. Installation of lag rods or cables with toggle bolts requires skill. If tree repair calls for complicated bracing, cabling or cavity filling, consider hiring a competent arborist to do the work. The tension on cables should hold them firmly without slack during the dormant season. They should be installed from one-half to two-thirds of the distance from the damaged crotch to the upper end of the damaged members, whenever possible. Short cables installed near the crotch often fail because of the severe strains imposed upon them.

Uprooted trees

Cover the exposed roots immediately to keep them from drying until you can make arrangements to restore the tree to position. Use wet burlap, hay, clay mud, plastic sheets or any other convenient material. Just before you return the tree to its original position, cut away shattered roots and dress the wounds with antiseptic asphalt paint. If you cannot put the tree back by hand, try block and tackle, winch, drag line, jacks or even a bulldozer. Protect bark with padding where pressure is applied.

If the tree has been blown over while in foliage, spraying the leaves with an antiwilting preparation may help the tree recover. If the root system has been partly destroyed, it may be advisable to prune off part of the crown. Water the tree during droughts until new roots have formed. Fertilize if necessary. After the tree has been restored to its original position, install guy wires to hold it in place until the root system regenerates. Place at least three guy wires high enough for good support. A crotch is a good place to anchor the wires. Use a short length of rubber hose around each wire to protect bark from injury. Loop the hose-covered wire around the trunk and twist the end of the wire back around the main

200

part of the wire. Fasten the wires securely to sturdy stakes or other solidly anchored objects. Remove wires after one or two years.

Protect weakened trees from bark- and wood-boring insects by applying an insecticide. Use any garden-type insecticide whose container label recommends its use against these insects. Spray the trunks of small trees and the major branches, limbs and trunks of larger trees.

Beware of power lines: When surveying or repairing tree damage after a windstorm or ice storm, beware of power lines. Before approaching a damaged tree, inspect the area carefully to be sure that the storm has not also knocked down power lines. If electric wires pass through or near damaged trees, be sure before touching the tree that damaged parts are not resting against the wires. If wires are down or if branches are lying on the wires, notify your electric company immediately. Do not try to correct the trouble yourself; the electric company has emergency crews to remove dangerous branches and to repair downed wires.

USING GARDEN EQUIPMENT SAFELY

Using lawn mowers

The U.S. Consumer Product Safety Commission estimates that more than 50,000 adults and children are treated each year in hospital emergency rooms for injuries associated with power lawn mowers. Everyone who owns a lawn mower should know how to use it and maintain it.

Causes of accidents: Four types of accidents involved in using or being near power lawn mowers cause the majority of injuries.

Contact with rotating blades. This accident is often caused when the victim clears the discharge chute of grass clippings, especially when the grass is wet; when the victim performs other maintenance tasks while the engine is running; or when the machine hits an obstacle such as a rock and the victim's foot slips under the housing.

Propelled objects. Stones, glass, and wire can be hurled at great speeds 50 feet or more, causing injuries ranging from severe bruising to total blindness, or death.

Overturning. This occurs primarily with riding mowers which are used on steep slopes or embankments. The victims usually sustain injuries during the fall and may be struck by the blades.

Mower running over the victim. This often occurs when a riding mower or garden tractor is being driven in reverse; the victims are usually young children who are not visible to the operator of the mower. Another frequent accident is the pulling of the mower backward over a foot.

Purchase of machine: Reel lawn mowers are safer than rotary lawn mowers because their blades move more slowly, but most consumers prefer rotary mowers because they are more effective.

There should be a rear guard to prevent your hands or feet from coming into contact with the rotating blade. The discharge opening should be aimed downward. The handles should have upstops which prevent them from rising up when the machine hits an obstacle. The engine exhaust should not be directed at the grass-catching bag because sparks from a backfiring engine could ignite the bag. The grass-catching bag should be located or guarded so that it cannot come into contact with the muffler when it is in use. Safety instructions should be provided with the mower, and there should be warning labels on the machine itself.

Use of machine: Read the owner's manual and pay attention to its recommendations before using the mower. Follow these tips:
● Never allow young children to operate power lawn mowers, and keep them away from the area when you are mowing.
● Wear sturdy, rough-soled work shoes and close-fitting slacks and shirts. Never operate the mower in bare feet, sandals or sneakers.
● Rake away wires, cans, rocks and twigs before you start mowing.
● Never mow a wet lawn because you could slip and be hit by the rotating blade. The wet grass could clog the blades and tempt you to try to clear the machine without first turning it off.
● Always turn off the mower and wait at least one-half minute for the moving parts to stop before you leave it. Always turn off the machine and

disconnect the spark plug wire or the electric plug when you need to unclog or adjust the mower; a slight rotation of the blade could start the engine.
● Mow across the slope when using a hand (walk-behind) mower. With a riding mower, however, drive up and down the slope for stability.
● When using an electric mower, be very careful not to run over the cord or entangle it in the blades. Start mowing the grass nearest to the electrical outlet and gradually move out.
● Push—do not pull—a hand mower.
● Never remove the safety shield or any other safety devices on a lawn mower.
● Never refuel a mower while it is running or while the engine is hot. Never refuel a mower indoors because vapors may be ignited. Start the mower outdoors, not in a garage or basement where carbon monoxide gas can collect. Do not smoke around the mower or gasoline storage can because the gasoline fumes can easily ignite. Keep children away from machines and gasoline.

Maintenance: Replace all loose or broken parts, especially blades. Keep gasoline in a well-ventilated area, away from your living quarters, and in tightly capped safety cans. Get expert servicing regularly; it can save you injury and money.

Using garden tractors

Many adults and children are injured each year by garden tractors. Everyone who owns a garden tractor should know how to use it properly and maintain it.

Causes of accidents: Three types of accidents involved in using or being near garden tractors cause the majority of injuries.

Overturning. This can occur when driving over uneven terrain, steep slopes or embankments. The rider can come into contact with the tractor when it overturns or sustain injuries during the fall. Garden tractors may also overturn if they are used to pull heavier vehicles out of mud or from a ditch. The front end of the garden tractor can rise and turn over on the victim.

Garden tractor running over the victim. This can occur when a garden tractor is in reverse and the operator does not see someone, often a young child, behind him.

201

Ignition of flammable liquids. The use of gasoline around a garden tractor can be hazardous if the gasoline spills and is ignited by a spark or heat source. Do not smoke around the tractor or gasoline storage area.

Purchase: Look for garden tractors that have safety guards for all moving parts to reduce the hazard of touching belts, chains, pulleys and gears. Buy a garden tractor that has throttle, gears and brakes which are accessible and can be operated smoothly and with minimum effort. Be sure that safety instructions are provided with the garden tractor, and there should be warning labels on the machine itself.

Use: Wear only sturdy, rough-soled work shoes and close-fitting slacks and shirts to avoid getting clothes entangled in the moving parts. Clear the area before you go over it with the garden tractor. Always turn off the machine and disconnect the spark plug wire when you need to adjust the machine. Start the garden tractor outdoors, not in a garage where carbon monoxide gas can collect. Keep children away from the machines and the gasoline.

Maintenance: Replace or tighten all loose or broken parts, especially blades. Keep gasoline in a well-ventilated area, away from your living quarters, and in tightly capped safety cans. Get expert servicing regularly; it may prevent serious injuries.

48

EXTERIOR REPAIRS

Owning a home has long been an American dream. Many buyers, preoccupied with their most significant lifetime investment, forget that even homes in the best condition over the years require a lot of maintenance and repair. And as costs of materials and labor increase, more homeowners are serving as their own handymen for both emergencies and general repair work.

Examine your house once a year. Its parts and materials wear out with use and time. But if you make repairs on a continuing basis, you can avoid the kind of hidden damage or decay that can become a serious problem.

DOORS AND WINDOWS

Glass doors and windows

The U.S. Consumer Product Safety Commission estimates that more than 183,000 persons each year require hospital emergency room treatment for injuries from glass door and window accidents. The following are some common patterns:

● walking or running into, or falling against, a sliding glass door, usually because the victim is unaware that the door is closed;

● pushing on the glass portion to open or close storm doors, losing one's balance and falling against the glass in these doors, or opening or closing the doors against a person in the flow of traffic;

● slipping and falling, usually because of wet, slippery floors, against glass bathtub and shower enclosures;

● walking or running into, or pushing on, fixed glass panels, typically because the victim is unaware of their presence or mistakes them for doors;

● falling against a window, knocking or striking the glass when opening or closing a window, or coming into contact with unmounted glass or storm windows in storage, or broken glass in windows.

Ordinary glass breaks easily into large, daggerlike pieces that can cut and pierce the body. Safety glass can prevent many serious injuries, since it usually is more impact resistant and does not break into large, jagged pieces. Many states have passed laws requiring use of safety glass in sliding glass doors, storm doors, entrance doors, fixed glass panels and in bath and shower doors and enclosures in new homes, apartments, and public and commercial buildings. You should also use safety glass when replacing broken glass in existing homes and buildings.

The U.S. Consumer Product Safety Commission offers the following suggestions for safely installing and using glass doors and windows.

Selecting glass doors: Install safety glazing in sliding glass doors, fixed glass panels, storm doors, entrance doors and bathtub and shower enclosures of new homes. Also, consider replacing ordinary glass with safety glass in these locations in older homes.

There are four types of safety glass:

1. *Tempered glass.* This type of glass is heated and then cooled in a special way that makes it many times stronger than ordinary glass. When broken, it crumbles into small pieces that minimize the chances of serious injury. It is the least expensive of the four types and the most commonly used in the home, although it cannot be cut but must be bought in the exact size you need.

2. *Laminated glass.* This clear glass is made by heating layers of ordinary glass with a resilient plastic material between to bond them together. It is resistant to breakage; and if it does break, the pieces generally stick to the plastic and do not scatter.

3. *Wire glass.* This glass contains a wire mesh completely embedded in the body of the glass during manufacture. When it breaks, the larger pieces are usually held together by the wire. Since the wire is normally visible, this glass may not be desirable for sliding doors.

4. *Rigid plastic.* This glazing material is made from one or more layers of plastic heated together and sometimes contains reinforcement material to make it stronger.

To help you make your selection, all safety glass carries a permanent label at one of the corners that identifies the manufacturer and the type of material. Before buying a storm door, check to see that it is free of sharp edges and corners, especially along the bottom edge and corners. Make sure that the door is hung properly to resist shocks from slamming and minor collisions.

Using glass doors: Watch where you are going and do not rush when you are using a door containing glass. Place a piece of furniture or a tall planter in front of fixed panels to prevent collisions. Place decals or colored tape on glass doors and panels to show that glass is present. Attach them at both adults' and children's eye levels. Install safety bars at door-handle level on sliding glass doors that slide inside a fixed glass panel. They not only show that the door is closed but also can prevent contact with the glass. Install protective screens or grilles over the glass in storm doors. Push on the handle—not the glass—to open a glass door. Keep the area in front of a glass door clear of loose rugs, toys, and other small articles that might cause a person to trip or fall.

Using and storing windows: Do not knock or hang on windows or storm windows. Remember, they are fragile. Do not store unmounted glass or storm windows unprotected, or in areas easily accessible to children. Do not push on glass while opening a window. Take care not to paint your window shut. If your window does stick, try to free it with a tool rather than push it with your hands.

Place obstacles such as a piece of furniture in front of picture windows or similar panes to protect children from walking into them.

Replacing a window pane: Reglazing is not difficult. Here are the basic procedures. Work from the outside of the frame. The best protection when removing the broken glass is to wear gloves and goggles and to work with a pair of pliers. Use a knife, chisel or putty knife to work out old putty. Do not remove putty in a single strip; break it into small pieces to prevent splitting the wood frame. Then, using a screwdriver or pliers, remove glazier's points, the small metal triangles driven into the frame beneath the putty to hold the pane in place. Place a thin ribbon of putty in the frame. Install new pane firmly against the putty. Replacement glass should be cut to size—in fact, a little smaller than the space it is to fill. Put pane in place and install new glazier's points on each side to hold it in place (see Fig. 48-1).

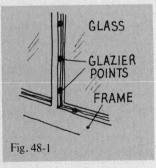

Fig. 48-1

Points should be placed near the corners first, and then every four to six inches along the glass. Lay them flat on the pane; press into wood frame with chisel point carefully to prevent breaking the glass. Fill the groove with putty or glazing compound. Press it firmly against the glass with putty knife or fingers. Smooth the surface with the putty knife. The putty should form a smooth seal around the window (see Fig. 48-2).

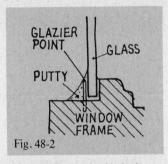

Fig. 48-2

Screened doors and windows

Repairing screens: Use shears to trim the hole in the screen to make smooth edges. Cut a rectangular patch an inch larger than the hole. Remove the three outside wires on all four sides of the patch. Bend the ends of the wires. An easy way is to bend them over a block or the edge of a ruler. Put the patch over the hole from the outside. Hold it tight against the screen so that the small, bent wire ends go through the screen. From inside, bend down the ends of the wires toward the center of the hole. You may need someone outside to press against the patch while you do this. Or you can apply several coats of shellac to the front of the patch and edges of the screen.

You can mend small holes by stitching back and forth with a fine wire or a nylon thread. Use a matching color.

Replacing screens in wood frames: Replace a screen when it is damaged and cannot be patched, when it is weakened from rust or when it is torn from the frame. Aluminum, galvanized steel or plastic screens are recommended, since they will not stain, rust or need painting. Match other screening when practical.

Examine the frame. Is the screen built into the frame (see Fig. 48-3), or is it attached to the edge of the frame with a molding trim piece (see Fig. 48-4)?

For screens attached to the frame with a piece of molding trim.
1. Measure the length and width of the screened opening. Cut screening six inches longer and three inches

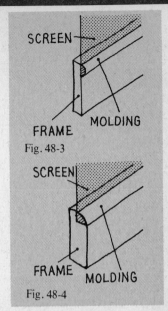

Fig. 48-3

Fig. 48-4

wider than the opening.
2. Remove door or window. Place on a flat surface such as a table. Remove the molding that holds the screen in place. Remove the old screen.
3. Examine the joints of the frame to see if they are sturdy and firm. If joints are weak, reinforce them by placing L-type or T-type braces over each joint.
4. Carefully place new screen over the frame. Make sure the screen is aligned with the frame. The top of the screen should be one inch above the top of the opening. Staple or tack every two inches across the top of the screen (see Fig. 48-5).

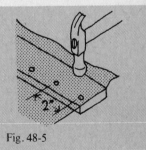

Fig. 48-5

5. To pull screen tight lengthwise on the frame, place a board against the bottom of the frame. Nail screening to the board. Slip the frame to the edge of the table so that the board nailed to the screen can be bent downward. This tightens the screen for nailing (see Fig. 48-6).
6. Nail across the bottom every two inches. Nail sides and center rail. Cut away the excess screen. Replace mold-

203

Fig. 48-6

ing. Attach molding with finishing nails.

If the screen is built into the frame.

1. Follow steps 1 through 5 above. At step 6, nail the screen to the outer side of the frame (the outdoor side; see Fig. 48-7).

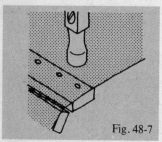

Fig. 48-7

2. Measure the screened opening. Add one inch to this measurement and mark this length on a molding strip. Saw off the required length of molding.

3. Mark off a distance of ½ inch at each end of the molding strip. Using a saw, cut this portion off at a 45-degree angle to have mitered corners (see Fig. 48-8). Using a hammer and finishing nails, nail the molding over the screen along the inner edge of the frame surface (see Fig. 48-9).

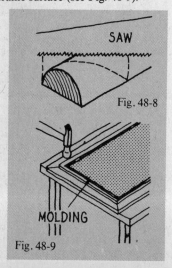

SAW

Fig. 48-8

MOLDING

Fig. 48-9

4. Repeat these steps for the opposite end and sides of the frame and also the center rail if you are repairing a screened door.

5. Cut away the excess screen and paint the new molding with two coats of paint.

Replacing screens in metal frames:

1. Use the procedures described in steps 1 and 2 for wood frames (page 203). The screen usually will be held in place by a strip of neoprene, a type of synthetic rubber, forced into a groove of the frame (see Fig. 48-10).

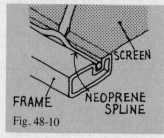

SCREEN

FRAME

NEOPRENE SPLINE

Fig. 48-10

Using a screwdriver, carefully remove the neoprene strip, or spline, and remove the old screen.

2. Proceed as described in steps 4 and 5 for wood frames (see above). Now with the screen taut and in place over the frame, fasten screen to the frame by replacing the neoprene spline in the grooves, using a screwdriver.

3. Remove the braces and cut away the excess screen.

Replacing screen-door hinges: Examine the old door hinges to see what type you need. The hinge may be either a loose-pin type that allows removal of the pin, or a fixed-pin type that does not. The hinges also may be the full surface-mounted type with the hinge fully exposed when the door is closed (see Fig. 48-11), or the half-surface-mounted type in which the hinge is only partially exposed when the door is closed (see Fig. 48-12).

To remove the door from the frame. For loose-pin hinges, remove the pin from both the top and bottom hinges by tapping the pin upward with a hammer and screwdriver. Lay the door flat on the floor. Remove the hinge leaves attached to the door. Then remove the hinge leaves from the doorjamb.

For fixed-pin hinges, remove the door by first removing the screws that attach the hinge leaves to the door frame. Lay the door down flat. Unscrew the hinges from the doorjamb.

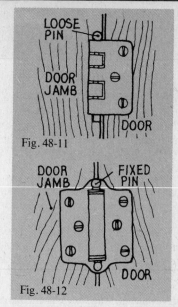

LOOSE PIN

DOOR JAMB

DOOR

Fig. 48-11

DOOR JAMB

FIXED PIN

DOOR

Fig. 48-12

To rehang the door in the frame. For loose-pin and fixed-pin hinges, place the new hinges on the door in the same location as the old hinges. For a tighter fit, use slightly longer screws than the old ones. Lift the door and place it in the door openings. Using small wood strips or other scrap material, shim the door until it is in the proper position. Now attach the hinge to the door frame. Fill enlarged screw holes with a wood filler, let dry, and make new holes.

Storm doors and windows

To repair storm doors and windows, you may need to replace cracked and loose putty in wood sashes or replace cracked or broken glass in either wood or metal window and door frames. It is a good idea to use safety glass in storm doors, whether or not local building codes require it.

Replacing putty: Using a chisel, remove the cracked and loose putty from the frame. Apply a coat of linseed oil to the exposed wood frame. Using a putty knife, reseal the glass with a bead of putty or plastic glazing (see Fig. 48-13). Press the putty firmly

PUTTY KNIFE

Fig. 48-13

in place to assure a tight seal. Allow approximately a week for the putty to dry, then paint it to match the existing trim. Follow the directions on the paint container.

Replacing glass in wood frames:
1. (a) Measure the opening to be glazed. Subtract $\frac{1}{16}$ to $\frac{1}{8}$ inch from each of the two dimensions to allow for irregularities in the frame. The glass may be ordered cut to size or it can be cut using a glass cutter. (b) If the glass is cut on the job, first lay the sheet of glass flat on a table. Mark the measurements on the glass with the glass cutter. Place a thin coat of turpentine on the glass cut line. Take care not to cut your hands on glass edges. Using a square as a guide, draw the cutter carefully and firmly along the cut line only once. Additional strokes of the cutter can break the glass. Move the cut line to the edge of the table. Tap the cut line lightly for a clean break.
2. Using the chisel, remove the damaged glass, old putty, and old glazier's points from the frame. Apply a coat of linseed oil to the frame. Using the putty knife, spread a thin layer of putty on all sides of the frame in which the glass is to rest. This "back-puttying" of the glass will assure a tight joint and also cushion the glass.
3. Place the new glass in the opening and press it firmly against the bed of putty. Now place the glazier's points flat against the glass about every 8 inches and drive the points into the frame with a nail set and hammer. Make sure that at least $\frac{1}{8}$ inch of the glazier's point is left projecting along the glass to hold the glass in place.
4. Apply putty along the four edges of the glass and the outer edges of the frame or molding. Press the putty down firmly at an angle from the glass to the edge of the frame to provide a tight seal. Allow the putty to dry for at least a week, then paint it to match the existing trim.

Replacing glass in metal frames:
This repair will depend upon the type of metal frame (sash) and the manner in which the glass is held in place. The most common types of frames used in residential construction will consist of one of the following: (A) frames in which the glass rests against a raised portion of the frame and is held in place by a snap-in glazing bead or

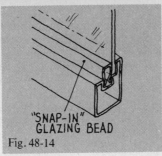
Fig. 48-14

strip that fits into a groove (see Fig. 48-14). Mastic or some form of rubber seal may be used to seal the glass. (B) frames in which the glass is sandwiched between the two halves of the frame or sash and held together by rivets or screws. Some form of rubber seal, attached to each inside half of the frame, should be used to make the glass joint airtight (see Fig. 48-15).

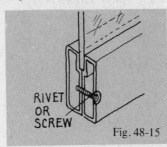
Fig. 48-15

If the frame is similar to type (A), first use step 1 (a) and step 1 (b) for wood frames (page 204). Then proceed as follows: Remove the glazing beads from the frame or sash with the tip of a screwdriver, and then carefully remove the damaged glass. If mastic has been used to seal the glass, remove the old mastic from both the frame and the glazing beads. Then clean both free of all grime, using a cloth soaked with a solvent. With the putty knife, spread a layer of mastic on the frame where the glass is to rest. Place the new glass in the opening and press it firmly against the mastic. Now apply a heavy layer of mastic along the edge of the glass, $\frac{1}{8}$ inch thick and a width equal to the raised portion of the glazing bead. Carefully replace the glazing bead. Examine the edge of the bead to assure that the mastic is tight between the glass and the bead. Remove any excess mastic along the edge of the bead. Then use the cloth and solvent to finish cleaning.

If the frame is similar to type (B) above, and is held together with

screws, first use steps 1 (a) and (b) for wood frames (see above). Next remove the screws holding the two frame halves together. Then separate the frame halves and carefully remove the damaged glass. Place the new glass in the frame on the rubber seal. Screw the two frame halves back together.

Caulking and filling cracks around windows and doors

Caulking should be applied wherever two different materials or parts of the house meet.

Caulking cracks and holes (nonmasonry): Check the following places for cracks and holes that need caulking: between window and door frames and the main frame of the house; gaps in siding and at the corners of the house; joints formed by siding and masonry; the underside of eaves where wall and eave meet; the joints where steps and porches meet the house; the surfaces of wood siding, trim, fascias, outside water faucets, or other special breaks in the outside house surface.

Before applying new caulking or putty, remove the old and wipe the area clean with a cloth soaked with a solvent such as cleaning fluid. Caulking compound is available in several types: (1) Oil- or resin-base caulk; readily available and will bond to most surfaces—wood, masonry and metal; not very durable but lowest in first cost for this type of application. (2) Latex-, butyl- or polyvinyl-base caulk; all readily available and will bond to most surfaces; more durable, but more expensive than oil- or resin-base caulk. (3) Elastomeric caulks; most durable and most expensive; includes silicones, polysulfides and polyurethanes; the instructions on the labels should be followed carefully. (4) Filler; includes oakum, caulking cotton, sponge rubber, and glass-fiber types; used to fill extra-wide cracks or as a backup for elastomeric caulks. *Caution:* Lead-base caulk is not recommended because it is toxic. Many states prohibit its use.

Caulking compound comes in rope form which you unwind and force into cracks with your fingers; in bulk caulking for large openings or cracks for which you use a putty knife or small trowel; or in a disposable cartridge that fits into a caulking gun.

205

Note. To use cartridges of caulking, make sure the bead of caulk overlaps both sides for a tight seal. Fill extra-wide cracks like those at the sills (where the house meets the foundation) with oakum or glass-fiber insulation strips. In places where you can't quite fill the gaps, finish the job with caulk.

To seal around glass in windows and doors, use putty and apply with a putty knife. Lay a small roll of putty, ⅛ inch to ¼ inch thick, around the sash or frame so that it fills the groove in which the glass rests. Make sure that the putty is fully applied to both the glass and the sash or frame. Press the putty firmly with the knife to assure a good seal. Trim away excess as you work. For holes in wood surfaces, use putty and apply with a putty knife.

Filling masonry cracks: Using a chisel, chip out loose mortar from all joints to be filled. Mix a batch of mortar according to the directions on the package. Wet masonry thoroughly before you begin and keep it wet as you work. Apply mortar with a small pointing trowel. Press mortar firmly into joint, making sure the joint is full. Take off any excess mortar with the edge of the trowel. Now finish the joint to match the existing joints. You can make the V shape with the tip of the pointing trowel. Hold the trowel at a 45-degree angle to the joint, push the tip into the joint and then firmly move the trowel along the joint. You will need a special masonry tool called a jointer to make a concave joint. The concave joint is formed by placing the jointer over the mortar joint lengthwise and pressing the mortar firmly into the joint to form the concave shape. Fill and finish a joint equal to 8 to 10 brick lengths before you start another. Keep the newly filled joints damp for two or three days by frequently wetting with a fine spray from a water hose or by covering with wet burlap.

Problem doors

For noise: You can usually stop a door from squeaking by putting a few drops of oil at the top of each hinge. Move the door back and forth to work the oil into the hinge. If the squeaking continues, raise the pin and add more oil.

To stop a rattle in the knob, loosen the set screw on the knob. Remove the knob. Put a small piece of putty or modeling clay in the knob. Put the knob back on. Push it on as far as possible. Tighten the screw.

For sticking or dragging doors: Tighten screws in the hinges. If screws are not holding, replace them, one at a time, with longer screws. Or insert matchsticks in the hole and put the old screws back in. Look for a shiny spot on the door where it sticks. Open and close the door slowly to find the spot. Sand down the shiny spot. Do not sand too much, or the door will not fit as tightly as it should. If the door or frame is badly out of shape, you may have to remove the door and plane down the part that drags. *Note:* Sand edges of the door before painting to prevent a paint buildup, which can cause the door to stick.

Locks: If the lock is tight, will not turn or is noisy or squeaky, you may need to lubricate it with graphite, which can be bought at a hardware store. Apply graphite to key, not to lock tumblers. Move the key in and out of the hole several times. If the door still sticks, the mechanism may need to be replaced.

ROOFS

To prevent unnecessary repairs, have a qualified roofer inspect your roof every two years. If you make your own repairs, use a roof ladder with secure ridge hooks, and be careful in walking on an unprotected roof.

Flat roofs

Locate leaks as closely as possible from inside the house. Place and secure the ladder, then examine the condition of the roof from the outside.

Loose felt edges: Using a brush, clean out any dirt that may have blown under the loose felt. Then using broad-head roofing nails, nail loose felt in place. Start nailing away from the felt edge and work toward the edge, to prevent making a blister in the felt. Place the nails about 1 inch apart. After the felt is nailed in place, cover the patched area with asphalt cement. Make sure the cement extends 1 to 1½ inches beyond the repair area.

Blisters in the felt: Using a knife, cut the blister. Then put asphalt cement into the area, similar to filling a crack. Continue using the repair procedures for cracks (see steps 2 and 3 below).

Cracks in the roofing: (1) Clean out crack and area around crack. (2) Using a brush or putty knife, place a thin layer of asphalt cement over crack. The cement should completely cover the cleaned area around the crack. (3) Cut a piece of roofing felt a little larger than crack. Place it over cement and press it firmly in place. Nail edges on felt piece, spacing nails 1 to 1½ inches apart. Spread another layer of cement over the felt piece. Make sure cement extends 1 to 1½ inches beyond all edges of felt piece.

Deteriorated or damaged: This condition is harder to repair. Never build up or cover the old or damaged roofing with a series of felt layers. This may change the drainage pattern of the roof and create more problems. Remove damaged roofing. Cut out damaged felt in a rectangle. Clean the surfaces in and around the cut-out area. Cut pieces of felt to neatly fit cut-out area. The number of new felt strips should equal the number of layers of felt removed. Cut the top patch 2 to 3 inches larger so that it will overlap the cut-out area on all sides. Spread a thin layer of asphalt cement over the cut-out area. Then take the first felt strip, place it into the cut-out area, and press it firmly in place. Now spread a thin layer of cement over that strip. Then place and firmly press down a second felt strip. Continue placing strips this way until the cut-out area is level with the original roofing. After the cut-out area has been built up to its original level, spread a thin layer of cement over the cut-out area. Spread the cement so that it extends 3 to 4 inches beyond all edges of the area. Place the oversized felt strip over the cement and press it firmly in place. Using broad-head roofing nails, nail a strip along all four edges. Then cover the strip with cement, making sure that the cement extends 1 to 1½ inches beyond all edges of the strip.

Shingle roofs

Wood shingles: If the roof leaks, find the location of the leak as nearly as possible from the inside. Place and secure ladder. Examine the condition from the outside. If the shingle is loose, nail it down. If the shingle is cracked, it is better to repair the crack rather than to replace the shingle. Repair the crack according to directions below, whether crack is small or wide.

If the crack is small (¼ inch or less), pull out loose splinters so that only the large, solid pieces remain. Check the roofing material under the shingles to determine where the nails should go. Sometimes shingles are nailed to wood slats spaced 4 or 5 inches apart. Sometimes they are nailed to wood sheathing. After the loose splinters are removed, butt the solid pieces tightly together and nail the split shingle together with galvanized roofing nails. Do not drive heads of the nails into the shingle and damage its surface. Cover crack fully with asphalt roofing cement. Apply a dab of cement over nailheads.

If the crack is wide, add a sheet-metal patch. To do this, drive a square piece of sheet metal up under the cracked shingle. Make sure that the top of the sheet metal goes beyond the upper edge of the crack. Now complete the job as described above for the small crack.

If shingles are damaged beyond repair, replace them. This can be trickier than repairing a cracked shingle. Remove the damaged shingle. Using a screwdriver or chisel, cut the damaged shingle into smaller pieces that can be removed by pulling with your fingers. Using a hacksaw blade, cut the nails off flush with the wood slats or sheathing. Since shingles overlap, you may have to pry up the shingle above enough to get at all the nails. Take care not to crack the good shingle. Measure the empty space and cut a replacement shingle to fit the space. Using a block of wood and hammer, drive replacement shingle into place. Nail new shingle in place with galvanized roofing nails. Apply a dab of asphalt cement to cover the nailheads.

Asphalt shingles: Work on asphalt shingles on a warm day because these shingles are brittle and crack easily in other types of weather. Locate damaged area and examine the condition. If the shingle does not need replacing, simply raise the damaged or torn shingle and apply an ample amount of asphalt cement to the underside. Now press shingle firmly into place and nail it down with broad-head, galvanized roofing nails. Remember to apply asphalt cement to the nailheads.

If the shingle needs replacing, select a strip the same size as the piece to be replaced. Most asphalt roofing comes in shingle strips, although some roofing is in single, separate shingles. Raise the shingles above the damaged one. Pull the nails from the damaged shingles with a claw hammer. If the nails cannot be reached with a hammer, cut them off with a hacksaw blade. Remove the damaged shingle. Slip the new shingle into place. Nail the new shingle in place with broad-head, galvanized roofing nails. Place two nails to each tab; this means six nails to each full shingle strip. The shingle should be blind nailed—that is, the nails should be covered by the upper shingles when they are lowered into place. Apply a dab of asphalt cement over the nailheads and lower the upper shingles into place.

Flashing and caulking joints at the roof

Around the chimney:

Loose mortar joints. Examine masonry joints to see if the water leaks are due to crumbling or loose mortar in the joints (see Fig. 48-16). If

Fig. 48-16

so, repair the cracks, using procedures described for caulking and filling cracks around windows and doors on pages 205–206.

Faulty flashing joints. If the leak is due to loose mortar where the flashing enters the brickwork, the repair is simple. First, clean any dirt out of joint. Then, using putty knife, spread a heavy layer of asphalt cement over the joint. Make sure that the cement extends ½ inch above the joint (onto the brick) and ½ inch below the joint (onto the flashing).

Faulty flashing. The flashing has two parts: the lower part, or base flashing, and the upper part, or counter flashing. The base flashing will be built into the shingles (or other roofing material) along the sides of

the chimney, and turned up against the chimney brickwork (see Fig. 48-17). Repairing this base flashing can be complicated; it is best to call a professional roofer for this.

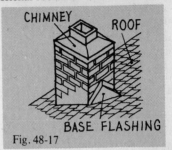
Fig. 48-17

Lower side of chimney: You can repair the counter flashing (see Fig. 48-18). To repair counter flashing on the lower side of the chimney, it is best to cover the existing counter flashing with a new strip rather than attempt to remove the old strip. (The old flashing will be embedded into the mortar joint at a depth of at least 3 inches.) Follow these steps:

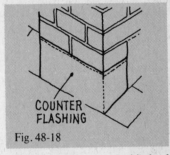
Fig. 48-18

1. Using a hammer and chisel, chip out the mortar from the joint to a depth of at least one inch, along the full width of the chimney and around the corner a distance of four inches.
2. Measure width of the chimney. Using metal-cutting shears, cut a rectangular strip of flashing. (Flashing comes in copper, galvanized steel or aluminum 16-ounce sheets.) Cut strip 10 inches wide and make the length equal to the width of the chimney, plus eight inches to allow for end folds that will wrap around the corners of the chimney.
3. Fold the strip 4 inches from each end, to make the end folds. This shape now forms an apron that will fit around the end of the chimney (see Fig. 48-19). Cut a portion of the end folds off at an angle similar to the slope of the roof, along the sides of the chimney (see Fig. 48-20). The angle that is cut should match the existing

207

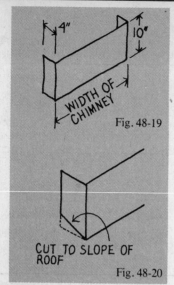

WIDTH OF CHIMNEY
4" 10"
Fig. 48-19

CUT TO SLOPE OF ROOF
Fig. 48-20

counter-flashing apron that is being covered.

4. Using the shears again, cut the top of the apron at the corners of the end folds, a distance of 1 inch (see Fig. 48-21). Now fold the top edge of the apron at the 1-inch depth to form the flashing portion that is to be inserted into the joint (see Fig. 48-22). Try it to see that it fits properly.

5. Clean any loose dirt from the old flashing. Using the putty knife, spread a layer of aluminized caulking compound on the back side of the new flashing apron, including the end folds and the flashing edge that fits into the joints.

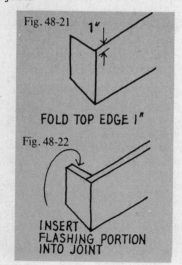

Fig. 48-21
1"

FOLD TOP EDGE 1"

Fig. 48-22

INSERT FLASHING PORTION INTO JOINT

6. Place the new flashing apron over the old flashing and press into place. Using a chisel, run the flat side of the tip along the inside of the joint and seal the flashing in the joint in place. Make sure that the new flashing apron is held tight or braced tight against the old flashing long enough for the caulk to set.

7. Fill the joint with mortar. After the mortar has set, spread a layer of asphalt cement along the joint. Apply a layer of asphalt cement to vertical edges of the apron.

Sides of chimney: If the faulty flashing is located at the sides of the chimney, this condition will require "stepping" the flashing (see Fig. 48-23). Make the repair according to

"STEPPED" FLASHING
Fig. 48-23

steps 1 through 7 above, except for the following variations.

In step 1, remove the mortar from both horizontal and vertical joints in which the old flashing is embedded. In steps 2 and 3, cut the strip to a length to allow for 4-inch end folds, and cut the strip out in the step fashion similar to the existing flashing. In step 3, do not cut off the bottom of the end folds. In step 4, make sure that both the vertical and horizontal edges of the apron are cut and folded to fit into the joints.

Cracks around chimney flue: Clean the joint of all loose caulk and other debris. Using the butyl-type caulking compound (gun form or rope form), seal the joint between the flue and the chimney mortar cap, and any cracks in the surface of the mortar cap (see Fig. 48-24). Also seal the joint between the cap and the top course of bricks.

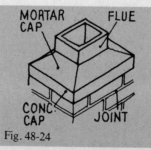

MORTAR CAP   FLUE

CONC CAP   JOINT
Fig. 48-24

Vertical walls that penetrate the roof. Walls that penetrate the roof are usually built of wood and are covered with siding. The following procedures apply to walls covered with siding and a roof surfaced with shingles.

Faulty or defective joints. The joint where the wall siding and roofing meet will be sealed with flashing but will not normally be caulked. Examine the joint. If the flashing appears to be in good condition, the water leaks may be due to seepage through the joint, independent of the flashing. If this is the case, using caulking compound in gun or rope form, seal the joint along its full length (see Fig. 48-25).

FLASHING JOINT
Fig. 48-25

Faulty or defective flashing: The intersections of walls and roofs are flashed much as chimneys are, except the counter flashing is omitted since the base flashing is turned up under the siding or other wall covering. If the flashing is faulty, both the siding and shingles must be removed along the joint. Follow these steps:

1. First, using a hammer and chisel, remove the siding to expose the standing edge of the flashing. If the roof is flat at this point, only one or two boards of siding will require removal. If the roof forms a slope along the wall, several boards must be removed.

2. Next, remove each overlapping strip of shingles along the wall to fully expose the flashing. Clean the area of all debris.

3. Cut a piece of flashing 15 inches wide and the length required to cover the defective flashing. Fold the piece to make one side 6 inches wide and the other 9 inches wide.

4. Place the 6-inch side of the new piece of flashing over the roof portion of the existing flashing and nail it into place with roofing nails. Cover the nailheads with asphalt roofing cement. Also, seal the ends of the new flashing with asphalt cement.

5. Place the remaining portion of the new flashing up against the wall portion of the existing flashing and nail it into place. Apply asphalt cement. Replace roofing shingles and wall siding boards.

Plumbing vents: Plumbing vents are flashed with a specially made device consisting of a circular collar soldered to a flat sheet. If the leaks occur at the joint between the collar and the flat surface, seal the metal with aluminized caulking compound. If the leaks occur between the flat metal surface and the roofing, make certain that the surface is properly nailed in place and then apply a heavy coat of asphalt roofing cement where the two join (see Fig. 48-26).

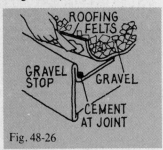
Fig. 48-26

Gravel stops on flat roofs: Gravel stops are placed at the edge of the roof and may consist of a one-piece or two-piece preformed device (see Fig. 48-27). The roofing felts overlap the flat

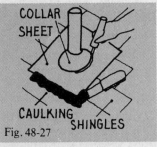
Fig. 48-27

portion of the gravel stop to provide the water seal. If the roofing felts have loosened and lifted at the edge, make the repair by sealing the felts back in place with asphalt roofing cement applied to the underside of the felts. Then apply a coat of cement at the joint between the exposed top layer of felt and the standing portion of the gravel stop. If greater damage has occurred at the joint or if the gravel stop is defective, call a professional roofer.

Changes in pitch of the roof: Where a roof changes pitch, such as at valleys or adjoining porches, the flash-

ing will normally be built in when roofing or shingles are put on. Such repair can be complicated. You may need to call a professional roofer for these repairs.

Metal gutters and downspouts

Cleaning and adjusting: To avoid gutter and downspout problems, inspect and clean your gutters and downspouts at least twice yearly. Use a sturdy extension ladder to reach them (see page 122). Remove all leaves and other debris from the gutters and check for loose joints. Clogged gutters cause water to back up under shingles and in time produce leaks. Check the gutter outlet opening where the water flows into the downspout. The outlet should have either a leaf guard or a leaf strainer. Clean debris from the leaf guard or strainer and replace in position (see Fig. 48-28). Check all gutter hangers for tightness.

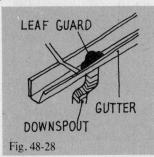
Fig. 48-28

If the hanger is a strap type (straps, if added, must be of the same type of metal as your existing gutters) and is loose, renail it with a galvanized nail or tighten it with a galvanized screw. Broken or damaged straps should be replaced (see Fig. 48-29). If the hanger is a sleeve-and-spike type and is loose, renail it with a galvanized or aluminum spike (see Fig. 48-30). Pour water into each gutter, using a hose or pail of water. As the water flows, check each gutter for proper pitch for water drainage and for leaks. Check each downspout for water flow and leaks. Should water stoppage occur in the downspout, clean the downspout at the gutter outlet with a plumber's snake or a piece of flexible metal cable. If the water does not drain completely from the gutter, the gutter hangers should be adjusted to give proper slope to the gutter. If the hanger is a strap type, lift the edge of the shingle or other roofing material to

expose the strap. Remove the end of the strap from the roof. Then unscrew or unsnap the attached end of the strap from the gutter. Raise the strap to a higher position on the roof and renail it to the roof with galvanized nails. Make certain that the new nail is located at least 3/4 inch from the old nail hole to avoid weakening the new hole. Cover the nailheads with a dab of asphalt cement. Raise the gutter into position and fasten the other end of the strap to the gutter.

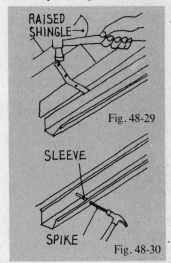
Fig. 48-29
Fig. 48-30

A different procedure is required if the hanger is a sleeve-and-spike type. If so, you must free the gutter by cutting the spike with a hacksaw blade. Place the sleeve at least 3/4 inch from the old location, raise the gutter, and refasten it to the roof board by nailing a new galvanized spike through the sleeve and into the board.

Repairing small leaks: Once you locate the leak, use a wire brush to clean the area of loose metal and rust. Then wipe clean with a cloth. Using a putty knife or flat piece of scrap wood, apply roofing cement over the leak area and spread it with the knife. If the crack or hole is greater than 1/4 inch, use the technique described in the following two steps:

1. Cut a small piece of canvas 1/2 inch to 3/4 inch larger than the hole.

2. Apply a thin layer of roofing cement over the leak area. Place the canvas patch over the cement and press it firmly. Now apply a second heavy coat of cement, fully covering the patch.

Clean the putty knife with solvent or a similar cleaning fluid.

Splash blocks and drywells

You will need splash blocks or drywells if your home has one of the following problems: water discharged from the downspout to the ground does not flow away from the wall of the building; water standing near the building damages the foundation or causes damp basement walls; water is standing in crawl spaces.

Use of splash blocks: If you are going to use splash blocks, you will need one for each downspout. Place the splash block on the ground directly under each downspout (see Fig. 48-31). Instead of splashing on the

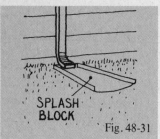

SPLASH BLOCK
Fig. 48-31

ground, the water falls on the splash block and is directed away from the house. For best results, make sure the splash block extends at least three feet from the house and that the grade slopes about six inches in ten feet. Check the position of the splash blocks each time you inspect and clean the gutters and downspouts because they tend to settle into the ground over a period of time. If they have settled, rebuild the ground back to its original surface and replace the splash block.

Use of drywells: Like splash blocks, drywells collect water from the downspouts. Unlike splash blocks, however, drywells spread the water over a larger ground area, and at a greater distance from the wall of the house. Use a drywell when you are reasonably sure that the soil will absorb the water. Also, downspouts are connected to a drywell only when public underground storm water systems are not available. You can build a drywell according to the following directions.

Place a 55-gallon drum flat on the ground, either end up. Using a hammer and steel punch, make a hole in the end near the edge. Insert a keyhole saw with plumber's saw blade in the hole and cut out and remove the

end. Save this end piece. Remove the other end of the drum the same way. Punch a series of holes approximately six to seven inches apart around the surface of the drum. Cut a circular opening in the drum large enough to receive a drainage pipe (tile or vitrified clay). The opening should be approximately six inches from one end of the drum. Dig a hole in the ground large and deep enough to bury the drum. Place the drum upright in the hole. Dig a trench from the downspout to the drum opening. Fill the drum with rocks, gravel and cinder blocks. Put one of the ends that was cut out of the drum back in place. Fill the drum hole and the trench with the excavated earth, bringing the ground back to its original surface and level. Seal the connection of downspout and underground drainage pipe with cement mortar (see Fig. 48-32).

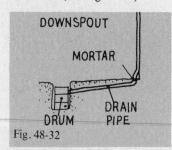

DOWNSPOUT
MORTAR
DRUM
DRAIN PIPE
Fig. 48-32

WALL SIDING AND SHINGLES

A variety of problems can arise with siding and shingles: boards or shingles may warp or split; holes may develop from loose knots; boards or shingles may rot or become damaged.

Fixing warped boards or wood shingles

Use screws rather than nails to straighten the warped board. First drill guide holes for the screws into the thicker portion of the board. Then drill the larger holes to countersink the screws. Pull the warped board into line by tightening the screw into the sheathing. Cover the head of the screw with putty.

Fixing split boards or wood shingles

Cut a piece of building paper to slip underneath the split board or shingle. Make it wide enough to fit between the nails in place. Butt the two halves of the split shingle tightly together.

Then nail both halves into place with galvanized nails. Countersink the nailheads and cover them with putty.

Replacing damaged wood shingles

Using a chisel and hammer, splinter the shingle into small, slender pieces. Carefully remove the splintered pieces so as not to damage the remaining shingles. Pull the exposed nails with a claw hammer. Examine the building paper underneath and patch any tears or cuts with asphalt cement. Slip the new shingle into position. Nail shingle in place with galvanized shingle nails.

Repairing wood siding

Instead of replacing the entire siding board, it is easier to cut out the damaged portion. Using a framing square, mark the board for cut lines. Pry up the bottom edge of the board and insert wedges underneath. Using a hand saw, cut out the damaged portion of the siding. Make the cut carefully. Do not damage siding boards above or below. Splinter the damaged portion into smaller pieces with a hammer and chisel. Then, using a pry-bar or chisel, remove pieces. Remove remaining nails with claw hammer. Examine the building paper underneath. Patch any tears or cuts with asphalt cement. Use asphalt cement sparingly, as too much will prevent the exterior from breathing. Measure the damaged board opening, mark the saw cut lines and cut the replacement board to fit the opening. Slip the new board into position and drive it into place with a hammer. Hammer against a small wood block to avoid damaging the board. Nail the board into place with galvanized siding nails, using the existing nailing pattern.

Replacing asbestos shingles

Remove the damaged shingle simply by shattering it with a hammer. If the shingle is not brittle enough to shatter, splinter it into pieces. Remove the shingle pieces and the exposed nails. Drill nail holes in the new shingle at its lower edge. Position the holes like the old nail holes. Continue the repair, following the steps for repairing wood shingles. With the saw, cut out the damaged portion of the siding. Make the cut carefully. Do not damage siding boards above or below. Splinter the damaged portion into smaller pieces, using the hammer and

210

chisel. Then, with the pry-bar or chisel, remove the pieces. Remove remaining nails with the claw hammer.

EXTERIOR PAINTING

Take time to do a good job when you paint. Use quality paint. Prepare the surface properly and apply the paint correctly. Improper application can be as damaging as a poorly prepared surface.

Selecting paint

Determine the type of paint to use according to the type of surface you are painting and any special requirements, such as resistance to mildew. See the Appendix for a paint guide.

Preparing the surface

In general, a surface that is to be painted should be firm, smooth and clean. Remove all dirt, especially under the eaves and overhangs. With oil-base paint, the surface must also be dry. Before you paint, correct any conditions such as blistering, cracking or peeling of old paint. Otherwise, you may run into the same trouble again. Old paint may be removed by sanding, scraping or burning, or with chemical paint remover. Scraping is the simplest but hardest method. Sanding is the most effective on smooth surfaces. Chemical paint remover can be expensive for large areas. Only experienced persons should attempt burning.

Application

Exterior paint should be applied when the weather is clear and dry and the temperature is between 50° and 90° F. Never paint when the temperature is below 40° F. Do not paint when it is windy or dusty, or when insects may get caught in the paint. Do not try to remove insects from wet paint; brush them off after the paint dries. Avoid painting surfaces while they are exposed to direct sunlight.

Paint failures

Following are some of the more common paint failures. Many can be avoided simply by following the directions on the paint can label. In fact, some of the newer paints are guaranteed against specific failures if applied according to directions. Before repainting, ascertain the probable cause of the old paint's trouble.

Blistering and peeling: Excessive moisture in the wood behind the paint will cause blistering. Outside water may be coming in, inside water may be working out, or cold weather may be causing condensation. Blisters appear first; cracking and peeling follow.

Prevention. Correct any possible sources of moisture before you paint. Repair leaks in roofs and sidewalls. Ventilate a damp basement or crawl space. Get rid of moisture originating in the house by means of vents and fans. Repair leaky plumbing.

Correction. Correct the cause of the moisture before you repaint. Remove all loose paint. Apply a water-repellent preservative to joints that show damage from rain or dew; allow it to dry two days, or as directed on the label. Prime bare surfaces and repaint. Consider using blister-resistant paint.

Cross-grain cracking: Cross-grain cracking may be caused by too frequent repainting. The thick paint coating built up by many paintings becomes too hard to stand the constant expansion and contraction of the wood and eventually cracks.

Prevention. Repaint only when necessary.

Correction. Remove all of the paint, down to the bare wood. Prime the bare wood properly and repaint.

Mildew: Mildew may occur where continuous warm and damp conditions prevail.

Prevention. Use mildew-resistant paint or add a mildew-resistant compound to paint.

Correction. To remove mildew, wash the surface one or more times with a solution of ⅔ cup of trisodium phosphate (like Soilax), ⅓ cup of detergent, 1 quart of household bleach and enough water to make one gallon. *Caution:* Wear rubber gloves when applying mildew-resistant paint or when using the trisodium phosphate solution.

Intercoat peeling: Peeling usually is caused by lack of adhesion between the top and under coats. The primer and top coat were incompatible, the surface was too smooth or glossy, or oil or grease was not removed.

Prevention. Use primer and top coats of the same brand. Remove gloss with a strong detergent, steel wool or sandpaper. Remove oil or grease with mineral spirits.

Correction. Remove all loose paint, sand the edges, prime the bare surfaces and repaint.

Excessive chalking: Chalking may occur where poor quality paint was used, the paint was improperly applied, or the paint was thinned excessively.

Prevention. Use a paint formulated not to chalk.

Correction. Remove the chalk by brushing the surface or washing it with mineral spirits. Apply two coats of good-quality paint. Allow three days' drying time between coats.

For more information on exterior painting, write to the Superintendent of Documents, U.S. Government Printing Office, Washington, D.C. 20402, for a copy of "Exterior Painting," Home and Garden Bulletin No. 155, Department of Agriculture.

SWIMMING POOLS

Accident statistics show that home swimming pools can be dangerous, but constructing, using and maintaining your pool properly can go a long way toward making this popular recreation safe. Here are suggestions from the U.S. Consumer Product Safety Commission.

Construction

1. Use nonslip materials on the deck surrounding your pool and on the diving boards and ladders. Be aware, however, that the use of these materials may cause water to collect on the deck; and if the deck is not regularly cleaned, algae may begin to grow.
2. Do not build sudden drops into the bottom surface of your pool. Indicate safe diving areas with a different color on the pool bottom. Paint numbers on the edge of the pool showing the water depth at various points.
3. Make all water pipes flush with the walls or bottom of the pool.
4. Have the electrical system installed by licensed electricians and in accordance with recognized standards for safety.
5. Install sufficient lighting so that people can see at night. If the pool is to be used at night, there should be underwater lighting.
6. Ladders should be equipped with handrails on both sides. The diameter of the handrail should be small enough for a child's firm grip. There should be at least one ladder at each

end of the pool.

7. The steps of the ladder should be at least three inches deep and made of a nonslippery material.

8. There should be a fence around all four sides of the pool area to keep children out when there is no supervising adult. Do not provide direct access to the pool area from a house door or patio door. Toddlers, in particular, could wander out and fall into the pool.

9. Any barrier should be at least four feet high and difficult to climb. The gates should be self-closing and secured with a lock.

Note. Check local ordinances for safe pool construction requirements.

Opening your pool

Olin Corporation, maker of pool chemicals, offers this outline for maintaining your swimming pool. Steps listed below are applicable to most pools, but in-ground concrete types may have special needs that you should be aware of before following the outline. Consult your pool builder for this information.

If your pool was wintered empty:

1. Sweep down the coping, walls and bottom, and remove debris.

2. Close all drain plugs and flush all piping. Drain.

3. Remove surface stains and grease.

4. Make pool repairs, if necessary.

5. Reconnect chemical treatment equipment, if any.

6. Refill the pool.

7. Backwash the filter thoroughly; check filter air valve; put filter and pump in operation.

8. Remount diving boards and ladders.

9. Test the pH (defined below). Adjust it to between 7.2 and 7.6.

10. Use a chlorine test kit to determine the chlorine residual and add the appropriate amount of chlorine. One ounce of dry chlorine per 1,000 gallons of water will satisfy the initial demand. If, after testing, the chlorine level is below 1.0 ppm (parts per million), repeat the chlorine dosage until this level is reached. If the available chlorine level tests out above 3.0 ppm, allow the pool to stand unused until the chlorine residual drops to between 1.0 and 3.0 ppm.

If your pool was wintered full:

1. Remove the pool cover and ice buffers.

2. Close all drain valves on filter and heater. Flush all piping and drain to sewer. Next, follow steps 3, 8, 9 and 10 as given above. Be sure to wait five days before you take your first plunge.

Caring for the pool

To keep the pool in good condition, Olin Corporation suggests these steps:

Water care: Every pool needs regular water care. Dirt, rain, sun and heavy use all affect its chemical make-up and lower the supply of free chlorine in the water. The lower the supply of free chlorine, the less the water's ability to fight and destroy bacteria and algae.

There are two steps to maintain clean, inviting water. First, get your pool water pH into the 7.2 to 7.6 range and keep it there; and second, add chlorine on a regular basis. Swimming pool water is either acid or alkaline, depending on a number of factors, including water source, pool use, and weather. The measure of whether water is acid or alkaline, and how acid or alkaline, is called the pH level, which is measured on a scale from 0 to 14. A pH of 0 is very acid; 14 is very alkaline; 7 is neutral. The most beneficial pH level is slightly alkaline: 7.2 to 7.6. Chlorine sanitizing power is most efficient at this level. Use a pH test kit to measure pH level. Your pool supply dealer will recommend one. Follow instructions that come with the kit. If pH proves to be low—below 7.2—you must raise it. Low pH can cause corrosion of metal fixtures and strip copper piping. Add a pH adjuster such as HTH brand PH-Plus, and follow label directions. If the pH is high—above 7.6—you must lower it or risk cloudy water and scale on fixtures. Use a pH adjuster such as HTH brand PH-Minus.

To determine how much chlorine your pool needs, check with your pool builder to learn how many gallons your pool holds. A 5,000-gallon pool, for example, requires 3–4 ounces of dry chlorine every day. Most common pool problems that originate with the water can be cured by specific extra doses of chlorine. You can use a regular chlorine product or other products marketed just for these purposes. Follow label directions carefully and add only the specified doses.

Miscellaneous maintenance tips: The U.S. Consumer Product Safety Commission adds the following tips. Keep the fence in good repair. Do not put anything outside the fence which will enable a child to climb over it.

Check the electrical equipment regularly for compliance with local codes.

Inspect diving boards often during the swimming season to insure that the slip-resistant surfaces are in good repair.

Using the pool

Also from the U.S. Product Safety Commission comes the following advice for safely using a swimming pool.

1. Always have competent adult supervision while children use the pool. Many children drown when swimming alone. Inadequate fences contribute to this problem because children can get into a pool without the owner's knowledge.

2. Never swim alone, even if you are an adult.

3. Do not use diving boards in pools which are not deep enough for them. The frequently recommended depth of 8½ feet is not necessarily deep enough. A safe depth depends upon the kind of diving and the skill of the diver. In addition to striking the bottom of the pool, people are injured when they hit protruding water pipes, ladders, or other objects in the pool.

4. When diving, go straight off the end of the board, not the side.

5. Standards for water depth under slides have not been established, but never put a slide in the shallow end of a pool because a person entering the water head-first can hit the bottom and be seriously injured. The safest way to come down a slide is on your seat with legs in front.

6. Place a safety float line where the bottom slope begins to deepen (approximately at the four-foot level).

7. Keep essential rescue devices and first-aid equipment ready at the pool: a floatable shepherd's crook at least 10 feet long, personal flotation devices, a ring buoy with attached ³⁄₁₆-inch line of length. (A pond should also be equipped with rescue devices and first-aid equipment in a weatherproof container.)

8. Do not swim after drinking, eating heavily, or taking drugs.

9. Keep all electrical appliances, such as radios, away from the pool because of the potential shock hazard

which they present.

10. Do not show off by swimming long distances underwater.

11. Never run or push others into the pool.

12. Learn to swim well.

13. Post in a conspicuous place a list of emergency telephone numbers for the doctor, ambulance, police, fire and rescue units, and instructions for water rescue and artificial respiration.

Winterizing the pool

As autumn sets in, close your pool properly. No matter if your pool is to be wintered full or empty, preparing it for winter (winterizing) will make opening procedures easier next spring. Follow this checklist from the Olin Corporation:

1. Backwash the filter thoroughly.

2. If you have an in-ground pool, check with your pool builder or manufacturer to learn whether to drain the water. Above-ground pools in areas subject to frost must be winterized full.

3. If the pool is to remain full, again consult with your pool builder or pool-cover manufacturer to learn whether to drain the water to a level one foot below normal. Some recommend it.

4. Chlorinate at a rate of 3 ounces of dry chlorine per 500 gallons. Chlorinating a covered wintered pool prevents algae from gaining too strong a foothold during the time the pool is not used.

5. To prevent scuffing to pool walls or liners, or damage from ice, add air-filled plastic buffer logs, secured properly, to at least two sides of the pool.

6. Drain water from filter, pump and piping exposed to freezing temperatures. In most cases this can be done by opening drains and plugs in low places on equipment and piping.

7. Remove debris from strainer and skimmer.

8. Remove diving boards and ladders. Store diving boards flat to prevent warping.

9. Disconnect, clean and store chemical treatment equipment.

10. Store water treatment chemicals in a cool, dry place in original containers with lids firmly clamped or capped tightly.

11. Clean general pool area.

12. Cover pool.

13. Turn off main electrical switches and remove fuses that control power to pool and accessories.

14. Remove all light bulbs and glass elements from pool fixtures.

15. Secure pool fence and storage shed. Store keys where you will find them easily.

If you have a porous pool cover or do not use one, a specific extra dose of 1 ounce dry chlorine per 1,000 gallons should be added weekly to minimize algae growth.

For the free booklet "Easy Spin Guide to Pool Water Care," write to Olin, Dept. MR, 120 Long Ridge Road, Stamford, Connecticut 06904.

ON THE ROAD

213

49

AUTOMOBILES

This chapter is designed to help keep your car on the road and out of the repair shop. It explains the key systems of your car, the regular service required, and the cures for some common malfunctions. It also explains what to do for such automobile emergencies as driving in snow, changing a flat tire, coping with brake failure, and what first-aid supplies to keep in your car.

REGULAR CARE AND PREVENTIVE SERVICE SIGNALS

Skipping routine care or skimping on maintenance is directly to blame for many car breakdowns and emergencies, and can permanently cripple your automobile. So can missing or ignoring early signs of faulty operation. To help you avoid such mistakes, the working systems of your car are outlined below, together with the usual maintenance procedures and the more common signals for preventive service. For the exact procedures to follow for your car, consult your owner's manual. Your car may not be exactly like the one in Fig. 49-1, but the parts should look basically the same.

Carburetor: The carburetor, which delivers a mixture of fuel and air to the engine cylinders, requires periodic checking. Idle speed and automatic choke adjustments should be made, if necessary, at each tune-up, and are particularly important in the spring and fall because of seasonal changes in gasoline formulas.

Service signals. Hard starting, hesitation when you press the accelerator, stalling at stoplights, idling too fast or too slow, sluggishness at road speeds, a tendency to "run on" after you turn off the ignition, poor gasoline mileage.

Carburetor air cleaner: If your carburetor has a dry air cleaner, the filter element should be replaced periodically. Between replacements, check occasionally to see that the filter has no holes or other damage, and tap it gently to dislodge dirt. Never wash it or try to clean it with air under pressure. If the carburetor has a wet (oil-bath) filter, it should be cleaned and the oil changed as the automobile manufacturer recommends.

Service signals. Hard starting, poor mileage, loss of power.

Emission-control devices: Modifications of ignition and carburetion cut down air pollution from exhaust gases, while other devices decrease fumes from the gas tank, carburetor, and crankcase. The manufacturer's recommendations for maintenance and adjustment should be followed precisely;

otherwise, operating problems may develop.

Service signals. Hard starting, stalling, hesitation, "running on" after the ignition is turned off, poor gasoline mileage.

Engine valves: The intake valves admit the fuel-air mixture from the carburetor into the engine cylinders; the exhaust valves permit the escape of waste gases after the gasoline burns. Mechanical lifters to open and close the valves should be adjusted at every tune-up or as the manufacturer recommends. Hydraulic valve lifters do not normally require adjustment.

Service signals. Loss of power, ragged or uneven engine performance, a light clattering noise, hard starting—especially when the engine is cold.

Electrical charging system: When you start your car, the source of electric current is the battery. After the car is running, the source is the alternator or generator, and a voltage regulator protects the battery from overcharge. Check the battery water level often and add water, preferably distilled water, as needed. Battery cable connections should be kept clean and tight.

Service signals. Sluggish starting, dim lights when the engine is not running, the battery frequently needs water.

Ignition system: Electricity from the battery, alternator, or generator flows to the coil, where it is stepped up to higher voltage. From the coil, the current travels to the distributor, which channels it to the spark plugs in the engine cylinders. At each plug, the current ignites the fuel-air mixture. Periodically, the ignition system should be checked and the spark plugs and distributor points changed as needed.

Some recently built cars are equipped with an electronic ignition system that creates a hotter spark, reduces or eliminates point wear, lengthens spark plug life, provides more precise ignition control, and in general requires less frequent maintenance.

Service signals. Hard starting, uneven acceleration, loss of power at high speed, rough idle, a partial or complete "miss" in one or more cylinders causing rough performance and a severe loss of power.

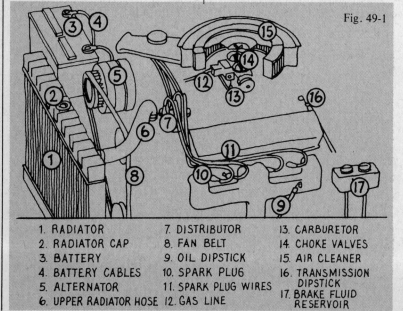

Fig. 49-1

1. RADIATOR	7. DISTRIBUTOR	13. CARBURETOR
2. RADIATOR CAP	8. FAN BELT	14. CHOKE VALVES
3. BATTERY	9. OIL DIPSTICK	15. AIR CLEANER
4. BATTERY CABLES	10. SPARK PLUG	16. TRANSMISSION DIPSTICK
5. ALTERNATOR	11. SPARK PLUG WIRES	17. BRAKE FLUID RESERVOIR
6. UPPER RADIATOR HOSE	12. GAS LINE	

Timing system: For efficient engine operation, the spark plug must fire in each cylinder at precisely the right moment. This firing is regulated by the distributor, which can be adjusted to advance or retard the timing of the spark.

Service signals. Hard starting, pinging, or a rough feel during driving if the timing is too "fast"; hard starting, sluggish performance, excessive gasoline consumption, or overheating if the timing is too "slow."

Gasoline: Gasoline with too low an octane rating for your engine will burn unevenly, or explode, inside the cylinders instead of smoothly producing power. The usual symptom is a light clattering or pinging during acceleration or when the engine is pulling hard. Continued use of the wrong gasoline could result in serious damage. Gasoline with an unnecessarily high rating, however, costs more and wastes energy. If your car accelerates without ping on the gas you use now, try a tankful of the next lower octane. After the car has warmed up, accelerate hard from a full stop. If the engine pings, go back to the higher octane. If it does not, repeat the test with gas with a still lower rating.

Engine oil, oil filter, and lubrication: Have the oil level checked at least every other time you fill up with gasoline. If the level is at or below the "add" mark on the dipstick, put in oil of the type specified for your car. Do not use additives unless called for by the manufacturer. Have the oil changed at recommended intervals.

Generally, the filter is changed every other time the oil is changed; but if you live in a dusty climate or do a lot of stop-and-start driving, your mechanic may suggest a filter change with every oil change.

For lubrication, follow the manufacturer's recommendations.

Service signals. If the oil warning light shows red while the engine is running at or above idle speed, turn the engine off immediately. Oil is not reaching all the engine parts, and continued operation will result in major engine damage.

Transmission fluid: Check the fluid level at intervals in either a manual or an automatic transmission, and replace the fluid at recommended mileages with the type specified for your car model. Learn the correct checking procedures. For example, if you have an automatic transmission, the engine must be running and, usually, the shift should be in the "park" position.

Service signals. Whine during driving, uneven growling noises, jerky acceleration.

Clutch: In a car with manual transmission, depressing the pedal disengages the clutch, slows the transmission gear rotation, and permits you to shift gears. Clutch linkage should be checked and adjusted at regular intervals.

Service signals. A tendency for the gears to clash when you shift, clutch slippage under start-up or hard acceleration, clutch "chatter" at start-up.

Brakes: All late-model U.S.-built automobiles using conventional drum-and-shoe brakes have assemblies that adjust automatically for wear unless mechanical troubles develop. Disc brakes, also, need no adjustment. All brakes, however, should be inspected as recommended by the manufacturer, and the brake linings or disc pads should be replaced as needed. Occasionally, brake fluid must be replenished.

Service signals. A spongy feel when you press the brake pedal, longer pedal movement, scraping noises, the car pulling to one side when slowing or stopping. Uneven, "grabby" brakes are especially dangerous on slippery surfaces.

Tire pressure: Correct tire pressure is necessary for safe driving, good tire mileage, and responsive steering. Check at least monthly that your tires and the spare are at the recommended pressure. Buy a good tire gauge and learn to use it; air towers at service stations are frequently incorrect. Occasionally inspect the tire treads. Wear on the edges indicates too little pressure; too much pressure causes excessive wear in the center. When the car is on a lift for an oil change, have the tires inspected for cuts, bruises or tread separations. This precaution could prevent a blowout.

Service signals. Pulling to right or left, uneven braking, excessive squealing on corners.

Tire balance: Tires should be kept in balance for comfortable and safe driving and for long tread life. For the best results, have the tires spin-balanced on the car whenever vibration becomes objectionable. Follow the recommended tire rotation for your automobile make and model and the type of tire.

Service signals. Vibration, usually felt through the steering wheel for the front tires or through the seat for the rear tires.

Front suspension: Front-wheel suspensions should be properly aligned at all times for safe handling and economical tire wear. Potholes and other rough road conditions may gradually throw wheels out of alignment.

Service signals. Abnormal or uneven tire wear, or the car pulling hard to the right or left even when the pressure and balance are correct.

Lights: Headlamps must be set to provide maximum road illumination and minimum glare for oncoming motorists. Check periodically to be sure all lights are in working order.

Air engine-cooling system: Air-cooled cars have a powerful fan, driven by a belt from the engine, that forces a large volume of air over the hot engine. The fan belt should be regularly checked for correct tension and freedom from wear. If the fan belt should break while you are driving, stop the engine immediately to prevent it from overheating.

Air conditioner: Just before the operating season, have the drive belt checked for correct tension, and examine the liquid in the sight glass for bubbles that could mean the system needs more refrigerant. During the winter, most conditioners will benefit from a 5-minute workout every two or three weeks as long as the temperature is above 40 degrees Fahrenheit. Check with your mechanic to see if this is good advice for your particular car.

Service signals. A drop in cooling power, unusual noises from the fan or rapid cycling of the compressor. You can hear the compressor click off and on or detect the added load on the engine.

Liquid engine-cooling system: All the car engines currently manufactured in the United States are cooled by a liquid-circulating system assisted by a fan. The system includes a liquid coolant (water plus antifreeze), hoses, a water pump, a thermostat and a radiator.

Ask the service attendant to check the coolant level in the system every other time you fill up with gasoline. Whenever you take the car in for routine maintenance, have the mechanic check the hoses for soundness and the belt that drives the fan for correct tension. Have the belt replaced if it is frayed. Each spring and fall, have the concentration of the antifreeze-water mixture tested; if too little of the antifreeze is present, you are inviting either a freezeup or a boilover.

Service signals. The temperature gauge often reads high, or you must add liquid frequently to the system.

Batteries: When you turn your ignition key to the "start" position, the electrical circuit involving the starter is closed and the plates of the battery begin to react chemically with the electrolyte and the electrical energy begins to flow through the coils and armature of the starter, causing the armature to turn. The starter gear spins the engine until it starts.

Service signals. Power loss such as dim lights or marked slowdown in starter operation. The problem may be: a short in the electrical system, causing excessive drain on the battery; trouble in the alternator, causing a drop-off in the charging rate; a slipping alternator belt; insufficient driving to keep the battery adequately charged, in which case you may need to have your service station or garage recharge the battery occasionally; or lights or accessories operating too often when the engine is off and the alternator is not operating.

Getting the best service

During the warranty period, have the car serviced exactly as recommended. For repairs under warranty, you must take the car to an authorized dealer.

When repair or service is necessary after the warranty period, be sure to take the following steps: Inquire if the shop offers a warranty on service and replacement parts and how long it is effective; tell the service manager or mechanic all the car's symptoms and problems; find out exactly what work is to be done, if possible obtain a written estimate, and insist that the shop obtain your approval before doing any additional work. When you pick up the car after repairs, check each item on the list or estimate. Do not accept the car unless everything is complete and satisfactory. Road-test the car be-

fore you drive home, and return it to the garage immediately if it is not performing well.

"Where to Find a Certified Mechanic" is a list of shops nationwide whose employees have passed special tests on automotive repairs. To order, send a check for $1.75 to Employers Directory, National Institute for Automotive Service Excellence, Suite 515, 1825 K Street, N.W., Washington, D.C. 20006.

FIRST-AID SUPPLIES FOR THE CAR

You need not be a mechanic to fix many of the little problems that can disable a car along the road. Often all you need is a simple tool or some tape or wire. The following is a list of some of the things you should carry in your glove compartment and trunk, and some other suggested useful items.

Necessary items

Glove compartment: The name, address, and phone number of someone to call in an emergency; a good flashlight; spare fuses for the electrical system; an ice scraper for winter driving; a pocketknife with clippers and corkscrew; and a road atlas.

Trunk: Spare tire with air in it; fire extinguisher; first-aid kit; jack and lug wrench for changing tires; flares or reflective day/night devices; jumper cables; pillow and blanket; rope or chain for emergency tow; shovel and sack of sand in wintertime.

Useful items

An empty can to carry gasoline in case you run out of gas, or water in case your engine boils over and you lose your coolant. *Note:* Never carry gasoline in this can in your trunk; it is extremely dangerous.

Also carry a box, tucked into the corner of the trunk, containing: tape to repair broken or frayed wires and to stop small leaks in a hose until you can get to a service facility; pliers for tightening clamps or small nuts that may work loose and for twisting wires; screwdrivers of several sizes, including a Phillips type; adjustable wrench to tighten nuts and bolts that may have worked loose; wire to hold a muffler or tailpipe in place if one of the hangers breaks or falls off; rags which can be used to dry up your dis-

tributor or wet wires if your motor is drowned out in a heavy rain or from driving through high water; sandpaper to clean dirty battery terminals when the car will not start; can of engine oil.

Other useful items include a tire pump for when a tire develops a slow leak and you would rather drive to a service station to have the tire changed than do it yourself, and a plastic sheet to use in changing a tire in the rain or if you have to get under the car to check something.

CAR EMERGENCIES: MALFUNCTIONING OF THE VEHICLE

At some time most drivers encounter an emergency situation involving a malfunction of their vehicle which, if not handled promptly and correctly, can result in an accident, injury or death. The following are the most common emergency situations and how they can be handled.

Stopping on the highway

An emergency may require that you stop along the highway. This is dangerous, so if you must stop, observe the following precautions:

● If the highway has paved shoulders, signal your intention to pull off the highway, pull off at near traffic speed, then slow down. If the shoulder is unpaved, signal a right turn and slow down to a safe speed before pulling off the paved roadway.

● In dusk, darkness or bad weather, leave your low-beam headlights on and turn on your interior lights and your four-way flashers.

● If you have to stop in a risky location such as over the crest of a hill or on a curve, get everyone out of the car and well away from traffic.

● Place a flare or other warning device just behind the car, about 10 feet, and another at least 300 feet farther back. (Check to be sure you have flares before starting to drive.) Never place flares near spilled gasoline.

● If you need help, raise the hood and tie a white cloth to the antenna or left door handle.

● If a telephone booth is nearby, call AAA or a similar organization if you are a member, or call the state police. *Note.* The hazard (emergency) lights on most cars will not operate when the brakes are applied, so once you are off the road, or if stranded on the road, shut off the engine, put the car in "park," apply the parking brake and take your foot off the brake pedal.

Throttle sticking

What can you do when the throttle sticks? If it occurs on the open highway and you have a lot of distance between you and other traffic, you can first lightly tap the accelerator (which controls the throttle) a few times to see if it will spring back to its normal position. If this fails, try to pull the pedal up with the tip of your shoe, or have a front-seat passenger reach down and do it. Do not reach down yourself because you must keep your attention on the road.

If you must slow down or stop rapidly, turn your ignition to "off" and apply the brakes. But be sure you turn the key to "off," not "lock." On most cars you cannot turn the steering wheel when the key is in the "lock" position. Also, remember that if you have power steering and power brakes, turning off the ignition will require increased physical effort to steer and brake the car as the car slows down. Do not pump brakes and you may retain some power.

As the car slows down, guide it off the roadway, if possible.

After you stop the car, look for the source of trouble. The accelerator pedal may be binding on the floor mat or the rug in your car. You can easily free the pedal by moving the rug or mat. If this is not the case, and if you know something about engines, look in your engine compartment and check the accelerator linkage. Some of the parts may be stuck and binding, and a little oil (from the dipstick used to check your oil) may solve the problem.

If you cannot locate and remedy the problem (it may be caused by a broken or missing accelerator return spring or by a broken motor mount), do not drive the car—get help.

If you think you have corrected the problem, make certain before driving the car. Apply the emergency, or parking, brake firmly, put the gear selector in "park" or "neutral," and start the car. Exercise the accelerator pedal a few times to make sure it returns to its normal position after you remove your foot from the pedal. Then put the car in gear and try rev-ving the engine a few times before releasing the parking brake and proceeding on your way. *Note.* By "off" is meant any key position that will turn off the engine but not lock the steering. Ignition systems on vehicles vary. Make sure you know which position will cut the engine without locking the steering.

Brake failure

If the brake failure light comes on, slow down, pull off the road, and do not proceed until you have the problem corrected or until you determine that you can drive safely to the nearest service facility. Because of the split braking system, the chances are that you will have some braking power left, but you may have to apply more force to the brake pedal and will need a greater distance to stop. If half of the braking system remains, proceed cautiously to the nearest service station or garage.

If you have a complete brake failure, there are several things you can try, but you must act rapidly:

● First, get off the highway onto the shoulder or other clear area, if possible.

● Try pumping your brakes rapidly to bring up your brake pressure.

● If pumping does not work, put the gear selector in a lower range to give some braking power from the engine, and apply the emergency or parking brake with increased force. On vehicles with no manual parking or emergency brake release lever, use a modulated pressure on the pedal, as necessary, to prevent total locking of brakes.

● If none of the above works and you are in danger of crashing into someone or something, or of going down an embankment, there is one more thing you can try—but only as a last resort. Turn the ignition off and move the gear selector to low. This may damage your transmission, but it may help you stop.

● If your brakes fail on a hill or mountain grade and the above remedies do not work, look for something to sideswipe—a snowbank, a guardrail, dirt mounds on the side of the road, or anything that will slow you down.

Loss of steering

Loss of steering can occur suddenly and without warning. Something in the steering mechanism or its related components may break, fall off, or jam, leaving the driver with no control of the car's direction. (Partial loss in power-assist steering can occur if a drive belt breaks; steering control is not lost, but it requires additional effort.)

In this situation, there is little you can do except to apply the brakes to come to a stop as quickly as possible. While applying the brakes, warn other motorists and pedestrians by turning on your emergency flashers, blinking your headlights, blowing your horn, and using hand signals.

When your car finally comes to a halt, try to move it off the road. Assistance from passing motorists or pedestrians may be sufficient to turn the wheels by hand enough to permit pushing the vehicle off the road. Before attempting this, position your emergency warning devices—flares or highway triangular warning signs—to alert other motorists.

Leave the car where it is until you get the steering repaired or until you get a wrecker to move the car to a repair facility. Lift the hood of the car and attach a white cloth to your radio antenna or door handle to indicate to other motorists or police that you need assistance.

Note. Steering problems are often preceded by such symptoms as extreme tightness in the steering, which indicates something is binding or obstructing the mechanism, or extreme looseness. If your car develops such symptoms, have the problem diagnosed and remedied at once.

Loss of power-assisted braking and steering

To a driver accustomed to power steering or power brakes, a malfunction in the system providing the power may lead him to think his brakes or steering have failed. If your car is equipped with these power features, and if you suddenly find that steering is more difficult or the brakes will not respond when you touch the brake pedal, you can probably still steer and brake, although it will take considerably more effort. Proceed with caution until your vehicle is repaired.

Fires

Under the hood or under the dash: Fires are generally caused by a fault in the electrical system or by leakage in the fuel system, which may cause raw gas to leak onto a hot engine. When such a fire develops, pull off the road just as soon as it is safe to do so. Turn off the ignition and get out of the vehicle in a safe manner (see note below).

Every vehicle should have a fire extinguisher for such emergencies. If you do not have an extinguisher, fires in the engine compartment can sometimes be put out by throwing dirt on them. You can also try smothering the fire with a heavy cloth. Be careful when raising the hood to get at such a fire—use a rag to cover your hand when releasing the hood latch so that you do not get burned. Also, turn your head aside as the hood is released to prevent facial burns from flashing flames.

Note. Consider the severity of the fire and the risk involved before trying to put it out. If the fire is a major one or is a fuel-fed fire, stand clear of the vehicle and wait for the fire department.

If you do not have a fire extinguisher and there is a passenger in your car, have him flag down a passing vehicle, especially a truck, which may have a fire extinguisher.

If the fire occurs while you are driving in a city or town, ask a passerby to summon the fire department.

Finally, do not attempt to drive the car until the cause of the blaze has been determined and the problem corrected, including any damage caused by the fire itself.

In the rear of the car: Fires in the rear of the car are potentially the most hazardous since most cars have their gas tanks there. The biggest danger here is explosion of the gas tank.

If you notice smoke or flames coming from the rear of your car, immediately pull off the road to a safe spot. Get all passengers out of the car and remain at a great distance from it. Warn motorists and passersby of the danger, and have someone call the nearest fire department.

Loss of lights

A complete loss of lights in conjunction with total power loss is usually caused by the burnout of a fuse, a fused wire, or by loosened battery cables. If your lights go out, pull off the road and take care of the problem be-

fore proceeding. Know where the fuse panel is in your car (check your owner's manual). Also, carry spare fuses of the type used in your car's electrical system. Find your fuse panel and identify the fuse for your lights. The panel should be marked to identify the fuse for the various systems. Replace the blown fuse with a good one. If the new fuse does not solve the problem, or if the new fuse blows, your problem is more serious and requires repair by a competent automotive electrical systems repairman.

If you do not have a spare fuse, never wrap a piece of tinfoil around the old fuse. This defeats the prime purpose of the fuse and may result in an electrical system fire.

Loss of just one light such as a taillight or one of the headlights is probably the result of a bulb burnout, and you will still have enough visibility to drive carefully to the nearest service facility to have the problem corrected.

If only the headlamps go out, the problem may be in a circuit breaker which has opened. These are heat-actuated to open and close, so they may come on and go off intermittently, giving you some light to help you to safety.

Overheated engine

Engine overheating can be caused by a number of things—a leak in the radiator or hoses permitting loss of coolant, a faulty water pump, a bad thermostat, or a broken fan belt. There may be nothing seriously wrong. Some engines (particularly when they are supporting air conditioners) have a tendency to get hot when being overworked on hot days, as, for example, when moving slowly in stop-and-go traffic.

Become familiar with the regular position of the needle on your temperature gauge when your car has reached normal operating temperatures. Knowing this, if you notice the needle moving abnormally close to the hot position, it is time to do something. On some cars a light goes on when the engine is hot.

If you notice steam or liquid coming from the front of your car, this is a definite indication that it is overheating.

If your car has a tendency to heat up when moving slowly in dense traffic in hot weather, there are several

things you can do:

● If possible, pull off the road, turn off the engine, and let it cool down before proceeding.

● If you cannot pull off the road and if the engine has not reached the critical overheat point, as shown by needle movement on the gauge, turn off the air conditioner if you have it on. In stop-and-go traffic, shift into neutral while stopped. Both these actions reduce the strain (load) on the engine and may bring the temperature down. During long waits in traffic, a slight increase in the engine's idling speed (press the accelerator lightly) can also help reduce overheating through the action of the fan on the coolant in the radiator.

● If none of the above works, turn on your heater (in addition to the other actions mentioned) and roll the windows down. This helps to reduce the engine's temperature, even in cars not equipped with air conditioners, by increasing the radiator capacity.

● If the temperature rise is not normal for your car, pull off the road. Look for the source of trouble and let the engine cool. Do not remove the radiator cap. If the radiator cap is removed before the engine has cooled, steam or liquid may spew out and cause severe burns. After the engine cools, drive slowly to a service station to identify the cause of overheating unless you have lost radiator coolant by boilover. For lost coolant, add enough water to drive to a service station for repairs and new coolant.

Remedial action for overheated engines: Never pour cold water into an overheated engine or you may crack the engine block. Wait for the engine to cool and then remove the radiator cap and check the coolant level. If your car is equipped with a surge, or radiator overflow, tank, check the coolant level at that point. Surge tanks contain markings that indicate when coolant is low, normal or hot; they are designed to take the overflow liquid from the radiator when the radiator gets hot, rather than have the coolant lost. When the radiator cools, the overflow should return to the radiator.

Look for leaks or breaks in the radiator, surge tank or hoses, including heater and radiator hoses.

Correct the problem if possible.

Friction tape or adhesive tape can sometimes be used to temporarily stop or slow a leak in a hose until you can get to a service facility to have it replaced. If the hose is split or ruptured near the end, sometimes you can remove the hose end (using a screwdriver or pair of pliers, depending on the type of clamp used), cut off the damaged section with a knife and replace the hose.

Note. This often works for the smaller-diameter (¼ or one inch) hoses that are flexible and a little longer than they have to be. It may not be possible with shorter hoses, or hoses of larger diameter that are preshaped during manufacture.

If water is available, replace the lost fluid. Then if engine temperature drops to normal range after taking the remedial action indicated, drive to the nearest service facility and have proper repairs done. Never drive a car with the engine overheated or with insufficient coolant. If no water is available to replace lost coolant, if the car returns to an overheated condition, or a hose is ruptured too badly, arrange for roadside repairs to correct your problem.

Caution. If you are able to make temporary repairs so that you can drive to the nearest service facility, do not move the car until the engine has cooled down. When you get to the service facility, warn the attendant that the engine has been overheating so that he can take precautions to make sure he is not burned or scalded.

Loss of oil pressure

A sudden loss of oil pressure, if not promptly corrected, can result in extensive damage to your car's engine as well as a highway breakdown. Most cars have an oil pressure light on the instrument panel. This light comes on as soon as you turn on the ignition. Shortly after the engine starts, this light should go out. If the light does not go out when the engine is running or if it comes on while you are driving, you have trouble. You may not have enough oil or the oil pump may not be getting oil through the engine.

If the oil light comes on and stays lit, the first thing to do after pulling off the road is to turn off the ignition and check your oil. If the oil level is at or below the "add" mark on the dip-

stick, add oil before driving the car any farther. A spare can of oil should be carried in your trunk for just such an emergency. If this was the problem, the oil light should go out when you restart the car.

Normally, it is advisable not to operate the engine with the oil light on so as to protect the engine, but if there are no abnormal engine noises and if your check shows you have enough oil and the light is still on, in an emergency you may drive cautiously a few miles to the nearest service facility, but no farther. Get a good mechanic to check the car because something else is wrong.

Alternator/generator failure

Most newer cars have an alternator. Older cars have a generator. Both serve the same purpose. They make the electric current that keeps your car's battery charged and operate the lights and anything else in the car that needs electricity.

If the alternator/generator light comes on and stays lit, something may be wrong with the electrical system in your car. First, check the alternator/generator belt because if this belt is loose or broken, your car may also be about to overheat. Have a service facility correct the problem as soon as you can.

If this happens out on the highway, you can often run the car on the electrical current from your battery alone. But you can do this only for a short distance until the battery power is exhausted. If you must run your car for a short distance to get to a service facility, turn off all electrical accessories such as the air conditioner and radio, but do not turn off the ignition.

If this happens at night, the extra drain on the battery from the lights will shorten the distance you can drive, but you should be able to drive several miles to a service facility.

Windshield wiper failure

Windshield wipers may fail when you need them most—when it is raining or snowing. To lower the odds of your wipers failing, periodically check them or have a service facility do it for you. Make sure you have good blades and that they are properly adjusted to conform to your windshield.

If you have the disappearing-type wipers, periodically check the opening

to the front of your windshield. Do this more often in the fall and winter. Remove leaves, twigs, snow or ice from the wiper recesses and from around the wiper motor shaft and wiper arms. These obstructions can place a strain on your wiper motor and result in wiper failure.

If you have a failure on the highway such as a loose wiper, get off the highway and see if you can correct the problem. Again, some obstruction may be hampering wiper movement, or it may be possible to push the wiper arm on the spindle more firmly. Before you pull off the road, make certain it is safe to do so. Open the window and stick your head out to see, if necessary.

If you find that you cannot fix the wipers, wait until the rain or snowstorm has let up, then proceed with caution to the nearest service facility. If it is impractical to wait, you will have to get help.

Dropped driveshaft

One of the most dangerous problems to occur on the highway is a dropped driveshaft. In vehicles with front-mounted engines, the driveshaft is the long tubular device underneath your car. It is connected on one end to the transmission and on the other to the differential in the rear of the car. Its purpose is to transfer power from the transmission to the rear wheels, which propel the car. The driveshaft connections at the front and back are called universal joints. If one of these fails, on some vehicles the driveshaft may drop to the roadway.

Failure of the rear universal joint is not as serious, from a safety standpoint, as failure of the one in front. If the universal joint in the rear fails, the rear end of the driveshaft may drop to the roadway. Power will be lost, and the car cannot be driven until the driveshaft is repaired.

If the front universal joint fails, a serious accident can result, and the faster the car is moving, the greater the danger. In this case, the front of the driveshaft may drop and dig into the pavement. The forward motion of the car can then lift up the rear end of the car and flip the car over. Your first and most important precaution is to slow down before pulling off the road.

To reduce the chance of this happening to your car, have your service facility examine and lubricate your car's universal joints periodically and check for possible looseness in the joint assemblies or in the bearings. Universal joints will be obviously noisy before they fail completely. Generally, this is accompanied by a severe vibration throughout the vehicle at all speeds.

Further, if you ever hear a dragging noise under your car, slow down and pull off the road, and look for the problem. It may be your muffler or tailpipe dragging, and you may be able to temporarily raise it and hold it in place with a piece of wire. But if it is the driveshaft, the car will not move and you will have to get assistance.

Hood popup

Failure of hood latches (both primary and secondary) or improper closure of the hood and subsequent failure of the secondary latch can result in the hood popping open while you are driving, blocking your view of the road.

This problem is not as prevalent today as it was prior to 1969. A federal safety standard, which became effective in January 1969, requires a front-opening hood that in any open position partially or completely obstructs a driver's forward view through the windshield to be provided with a second latch position on the hood-latch system or with a second hood-latch system. Despite this, hood-latch failure can occur, and you should know what to do if your hood suddenly pops open while driving.

The first thing to remember is: Do not panic and do not panic-stop. Ease the car to the right or left, depending on the lane of traffic you are in and the room you have on either side, as seen with your limited vision from the left window.

You may have to stick your head out the window to look. Also, glance in your rear-view mirror to see how much room you have between you and the vehicle behind you. Remove your foot from the accelerator and apply your brakes slowly. Then turn on your emergency flashers and give a hand signal to indicate that you are going to stop. After you have signaled drivers to the rear, pull off the road and try to remedy your problem.

If you cannot get the car off the highway (for example, if you are driving on a bridge), do not leave your car. After traffic has cleared behind you, proceed with caution to the nearest point at which you can leave the highway.

Caution. A frequent cause of this problem is the failure of a service station attendant to close the hood properly after checking the oil, radiator or battery. Learn to recognize the sound made by your hood when it is closed firmly. If you fail to hear the customary "thunk" when an attendant closes your hood, check the hood yourself before proceeding.

Submersion of your car

An emergency of this nature is more critical than any other. The following tips may help you survive:

● Cars with their windows and doors closed will float for a few minutes. Do not try to open a door to get out because the water pressure will hold it shut. Windows can be rolled down easily, so open the window or windows and use the opening as an escape route.

● If you have power windows, open them immediately before they short out. If they do short out and will not open, your only recourse is to try to break them out with a heavy, hard object. The tempered glass used in modern cars is difficult to break.

● If you cannot open or break a window and must open a door, remember—cars with engines in the front will sink nose first. This action will push some air to the rear of the car near the roof, helping to equalize the pressure and making it easier to open a door.

Note. None of these measures will help you if you are tossed about and knocked out because you have not worn your safety belt. Always wear your safety belt.

Loss of lug nuts on the wheels

If you notice a wobble in a wheel or hear a rattling noise coming from a wheel, especially at low speeds, the problem may be loose lug nuts or a lug nut that has come off the wheel stud and is rattling inside the hubcap or wheel cover. This problem is often caused by nuts not tightened when a tire is replaced, or by faulty lug bolt threads.

Take care of such a problem immediately before you lose a wheel. Pull off the road; display warning devices; remove the hubcaps or wheel covers; and check all the lug nuts. Tighten any nuts that may be loose. If all the lug nuts are tight, the sound could be caused by a faulty or burned-out bearing. Caution should be taken in driving to the nearest service facility for repairs.

If you have already lost more than one nut from a wheel, borrow one nut from another wheel so that you can tighten the wheels adequately. Then, at your first opportunity, replace all the missing lug nuts.

If two or more of the wheel studs are too badly stripped to permit re-tightening of the nuts, leave the car beside the road and get help. Have all faulty lug nuts or lugs replaced.

Exhaust system failures

There is nothing you can do about a blown muffler or broken tailpipe when you are out on the highway, but get the problem taken care of as soon as you can. Sometimes a hanger holding your muffler or tailpipe in position can break due to rust and corrosion. The muffler or tailpipe may separate and drag along the pavement. You may be able to hear the dragging noise. You will also hear the loud engine noise caused by a blown muffler or one that has separated and is dragging. When this happens, pull off the road and examine your tailpipe and muffler. Often a temporary fix can be made. First wait for the exhaust system to cool down; you can be severely burned if you grasp a muffler or tailpipe while it is hot. Then try pushing the muffler/tailpipe into place or raising it and holding it in place with a piece of wire or a coat hanger. Until the exhaust system is repaired, drive with a side window at least partially open to avoid carbon monoxide accumulation in the passenger compartment.

Battery emergencies

Sooner or later most drivers are confronted by a dead battery. When the battery lacks the necessary power to start a car, most motorists will try to start their cars by using booster cables to borrow starting power from the battery of another car. Improper jump-starting or carelessness with a battery can be hazardous and can cause damage to the vehicle's electrical system. One of the possible hazards—though not common—is battery explosion, which can cause damage to the eyes or skin.

Explosions: Batteries can explode unless simple precautions are taken. One type of explosion is caused by an excessive charging rate, which releases hydrogen gas. When there is insufficient ventilation near the battery, a spark or flame can ignite this gas. To prevent this type of explosion:

1. If you attempt to charge your own battery using a battery charger purchased from an automotive specialty shop, follow the instructions provided with the charger—especially those dealing with battery voltage, connections to the battery, and when the charger should be disconnected. Disconnect the charger when connecting or disconnecting the battery.

2. Provide adequate ventilation near the battery.

3. Keep sparks and flame away from batteries.

Another type of explosion can occur if two batteries are connected, as for jump-starting, with the terminal polarities reversed, or if batteries of widely different voltages are connected together. To prevent this type of explosion, always follow the instructions in the owner's manual for the particular make/model/year car that is to be started in this fashion. If the owner's manual is not available, follow the rules for jump-starting provided below.

The prime danger from battery explosions is particles flying into the eyes and battery acid getting into the eyes or on the body. Some general precautions:

• Wear eye shields when working with batteries.

• Battery acid causes severe burns. If you get battery acid on your skin, flush thoroughly with water. If you get acid in your eyes, immediately flush your eyes with water and get prompt medical attention. Continue flushing the eyes for at least 15 minutes, or until medical attention is obtained.

• Keep batteries and acid out of the reach of children.

• If you add acid to a dry-charge battery, be careful not to let the acid get on your body or on anything else. To dispose of excess acid, neutralize with baking soda and rinse the empty container with water.

Jump-starting: If you must jump-start your car, it is important to understand that you are carrying out a procedure which can be dangerous to you and harmful to your automobile unless you are careful and do it right.

Most automobile owner's manuals include instructions for jump-starting the vehicle, but not all owner's manuals agree. This is because some makes/models have special equipment, or are provided with special battery hookups which require a special jump-start procedure.

The first rule for proper jump-starting is to follow the directions given in the owner's manual for that particular make/model/year—that is, for the vehicle with the rundown battery. Do not borrow a manual from a friendly motorist unless his manual is for the same make, model and year as the one you are trying to start.

In very cold weather, check the battery to see if the electrolyte is frozen. Do not use jumper cables if the electrolyte is frozen—you may damage the battery beyond repair.

Before attaching booster cables, make sure that both the booster battery and the rundown battery have the same voltage—6 volts or 12 volts. Generally, the battery voltage can be determined by the number of vent openings on the battery—6-volt batteries have 3 vent openings; 12-volt batteries have 6. Some of the modern 12-volt batteries have no vent openings. If in doubt about your battery voltage, consult your owner's manual. If you do not have it and cannot wait to borrow or refer to one, but you are sure both batteries have the same voltage, the following steps should be used *only* as an emergency procedure to jump-start your car:

1. Position the cars so that the booster cables will reach both batteries, but do not allow the vehicles to touch. If the vehicles touch, they will be "grounded," one with the other. If certain differences exist in the wiring of the two vehicles, jump-starting them while they are touching could be hazardous.

2. Place the gearshift or gear selector of each car in "park" for cars with automatic transmissions or in "neutral" for cars with manual transmis-

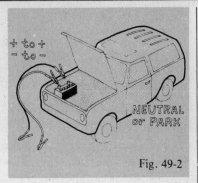

Fig. 49-2

sions (see Fig. 49-2).

3. Apply the parking brakes, shut off all accessories in both cars, and turn the ignition key to the "off" position.

4. Keep sparks and flame away from batteries. Do not smoke.

5. Some owners have been injured while jump-starting their vehicles from a careless electrical contact with rings or metal watchbands. It is wise to remove these when working with a battery. For reasons noted previously, use protective glasses. If glasses are not available, do not lean directly over the battery (even with glasses this is a wise precaution).

6. Make sure both cars have the same battery voltage—usually 12 volts. If both batteries are not of the same voltage, do not jump-start.

7. Before jump-starting, be sure that vent caps are tight and level on both batteries. If water is available, you might also place a damp cloth over the vent caps on each battery. After using the cloth, be careful not to touch your eyes. After the jump-starting procedure is over, discard the cloth and wash your hands immediately to avoid possible eye injury due to the inadvertent rubbing of your eyes or face with a cloth that has been exposed to battery acid. Even if you used your handkerchief, do *not* put it back into your pocket—discard it.

You are now ready to connect cables.

8. Look at your booster cables and the vehicles' batteries so that you can properly identify the cables and connection points. If cables are twisted, separate them to avoid mistakes. Some booster cables are color-coded or marked with a "+", "P" or "Pos" for positive connections; and "−", "N" or "Neg" for negative connections. Battery terminals are similarly identified.

9. Make sure the cars are not touching. Then connect one end of the positive booster cable (usually red) to the positive terminal of one car, and the other end to the positive terminal of the other car.

10. Connect the negative booster cable (usually black) to the negative battery terminal of the car with the good battery. You now have one final connection to make—the other end of the negative cable to a negative, or ground, connection at some point on the vehicle with the rundown battery.

There are two points at which this final connection can be made, as described below. With each procedure there is some element of risk. Even knowledgeable people disagree on which procedure is better when both simplicity and safety are considered.

11. Most motorists, and even service personnel, connect the other end of the negative booster cable to the negative battery terminal of the car with the discharged battery. This is done thousands of times without incident, yet there is some possibility that in making this connection a spark will result which could ignite battery gases. This possibility is considerably reduced, however, if damp cloths are placed over the battery vent caps, or if the battery has flame-arrestor vent caps, or the battery is of the maintenance-free type without vent caps.

12. The preferred method is to connect the final end of the negative booster cable, away from the battery, to some point on the car frame, engine block, or some other good metallic ground (except the carburetor) on the vehicle with the discharged battery. *Note:* If you do not know enough about your automobile to make this connection, do not attempt it yourself. Get some knowledgeable person to help you. There have been instances when motorists have injured themselves attempting to make this final connection to the engine cooling fan or carburetor.

You are now ready to attempt to start the car.

13. Make a final check to be sure that all cables are clear of fan blades, belts, and other moving parts on both cars, and everyone is standing away from the vehicles. Then start the car with the good battery. Wait a few minutes, and then try to start the car with the discharged battery.

14. If the car with the discharged battery will not start after cranking for thirty seconds, stop the jump-starting procedure and seek professional help.

15. After the car starts, or if it does not start, remove the negative booster cable first, starting with the last connection made to the car with the discharged battery. Then remove the positive cable by first disconnecting the end connected to the discharged battery. In removing cables, be careful of moving engine parts.

If you cannot start your car with the aid of jumper cables and a booster battery, think twice before you take emergency measures. If your car has a standard (stick-shift) transmission, you can push it or have it towed without danger of damage. If you have an automatic transmission, however, you cannot push your car to start it; and if you have it towed, be sure the tow truck has a crane. Your drive wheels must be lifted entirely off the ground; otherwise your car may suffer serious damage. Your other alternatives are to replace the battery or have it recharged.

General tips on battery care:

● Periodically check the water level in your battery. Do this at least once a week in hot summer weather, at least once a month in cold weather. Do not use a match or other source of flame for light when making this check, and do not smoke. Do not fill the battery above the level of the indicator.

● Have your battery tested at least once a year, and recharged or replaced as necessary. A good time to do this is in the fall before cold weather sets in.

● Keep your battery terminals clean and cable connections tight.

● Have the alternator belt checked for tightness by a serviceman at intervals recommended by your car manufacturer, or whenever you take your car in for a tuneup. If the belt stretches and begins to slip, the alternator will not produce a normal amount of electrical current for recharging the battery, and the battery will gradually lose power.

● Clean corrosion from cable clamps with a wire brush and water. After cleaning, coat the clamps with petroleum grease, silicone grease or vaseline to prevent or slow corrosion. If the cable clamp is too badly damaged

from corrosion, replace it. A corroded clamp means a poor connection, and a poor connection means a loss of power. Also, keep clamps tight or you will experience a power loss or a complete power failure.

● A film of moisture, grease and dirt on your battery case and around battery terminals can cause a slow leakage of electricity, even while the car is idle. Remove loose dirt with a slow stream of water, being careful to prevent it from entering the battery vent holes. Use a stiff brush to remove corrosion. A cloth dipped in a solution of baking soda (two ounces of soda to one quart of water) will help neutralize acid which may have accumulated on the case and connections. Clean vent caps periodically. Remove corrosion and rust from battery tray and hold-down clamps with a stiff brush and a solution of baking soda and water. Rinse with clean water, dry and then coat with acid-proof paint. Do not paint the terminals. Avoid getting baking soda solution into battery cells.

● Keep your engine tuned, because otherwise you may be literally working your battery to death. Have a complete tune-up in the spring and late fall—more often if the car is hard to start, tends to stall or is used heavily.

Tires, flats and blowouts

Inspect tires regularly: Look for excessive or abnormal tread wear, fabric breaks, cuts or other damage. Removing nails, small stones or bits of glass embedded in the tread will help prevent flats or blowouts.

Bald tires have been found to be up to 44 times more likely to have flats than new tires. The risk of skidding is doubled with bald tires.

The impact of a tire hitting a curb or chuck hole can cause irreparable damage. Driving even a short distance on a seriously underinflated or flat tire will result in damage inside the tire which cannot be repaired.

Excessive heat is a tire's worst enemy. Heat results from the flexing of the tire body. Flexing increases rapidly as speed increases. It is aggravated by underinflation or overloading. Running a tire at sustained high speeds under such conditions may raise temperatures above the critical level of about 250° F, reduce its

222

strength and tread life, and increase the risk of sudden tire failure.

You can increase tire life by avoiding these practices: driving at excessive speeds; making fast turns on curves and around corners; driving over curbs, chuck holes or other obstructions; using jackrabbit starts and panic stops; driving at excessive speeds on rough washboard roads; riding on the edge of pavement.

Repair flats permanently: If a tire loses all or most of its air pressure, particularly at high speeds, it must be removed from the wheel for complete internal inspection to be sure it is not damaged. Tires that run even short distances while flat are usually damaged beyond repair. Punctures, nail holes or cuts up to $\frac{1}{4}$ inch, confined to the tread, may be repaired permanently by using industry-approved methods. Applied from inside the tire, a plug-and-patch combination, chemical and hot vulcanized patches and head-type plugs can seal the inner liner and fill the injury. Never try to repair tires with tread punctures larger than $\frac{1}{4}$ inch or any sidewall puncture. Never repair tires worn below $\frac{1}{6}$ inch tread depth. The best bet in an emergency is a good spare tire properly inflated. Never use a tube in a tubeless tire as a substitute for a permanent repair.

If you have to change a flat tire, first check your owner's manual. It should show you exactly what to do on *your* car. Generally, there are nine basic steps:
1. Park on level and solid ground. If you have an automatic transmission, put the car in "park." If not, put it in gear. Always put your emergency brake on. You should also block the wheel on the opposite corner of the car to keep it from rolling. A piece of wood or large stone will do.
2. Take the wheel cover off. Usually you can use a screwdriver or the tapered end of the lug wrench to pop it off.
3. Take the lug wrench and loosen each lug nut one turn.
4. Next get out the spare tire. Then place the jack on solid ground near the flat. Following owner's manual instructions, jack up the car until the tire is at least two or three inches off the ground.
5. Remove the lug nuts. Put them in the wheel so you won't lose them.

Then pull off the flat tire.
6. Put the spare tire on and tighten each lug nut snugly, being careful not to jar the car off the jack. Jack the car down until the tire is just touching the ground. Then finish tightening the nuts.
7. Tighten the lug nuts as tight as you can. Don't tighten them in circle sequence. That could cause the wheel to come loose as you drive. Tighten one, then the one opposite it, and so on. Finish lowering the car.
8. Don't put the wheel cover back on. Put it in your trunk. Every time you see the wheel without it, you'll be reminded to get that flat fixed.
9. Put your jack, tools and flat tire back in the trunk.

You are ready to travel again. Get that flat fixed right away. Driving without a spare tire is asking for trouble.

Blowouts and flats while driving: A blowout will be sudden. You will feel it in the wheel and you may hear it. You may also feel a part of the car dip. Control of the car may be difficult. A flat tire will also be felt in the handling of the car and steering may become unnatural, but this is more gradual than in a blowout.

If you have a flat or a blowout on the highway, get a firm grip on the wheel and apply your brakes gently to slow down. Do not slam on the brakes, because that may throw your car out of control. Pull off the road to a safe spot where you have enough room to park and get out of the car without danger to yourself or without causing a traffic hazard for other motorists.

If you cannot pull off the road where you are, drive to a spot where you can pull off and change the tire safely. Do this even if you have to drive on a flat or blown-out tire, but drive slowly and put on your emergency flashers. Do not try to change a tire on uneven or hilly ground. It is better to risk ruining a tire or wheel by driving on a flat than to risk having a jack slip when you are changing a tire on uneven ground and possibly being crushed.

WINTER DRIVING

Winter driving is hazardous, and requires skill from you and top efficiency from your vehicle. Since not all winter driving problems can be avoid-

ed, the best rule is to plan and be prepared.

Maintaining the car in winter

Battery: Keep battery and terminals clean. Keep the battery fully charged. Recharge or replace the battery when necessary. Have your voltage regulator checked. Make sure the battery will be up to the extra power required for cold-weather starts.

Ignition system: Check condition of ignition wires and distributor cap. A cracked cap or faulty wires can result in engine drownout when it snows or when wet slush is thrown onto your car and into the engine compartment. A tune-up before cold weather sets in should reveal any ignition problems.

Heating and cooling system: Have the antifreeze in your radiator checked. If there is a leak in your radiator or hoses are deteriorating, have them repaired or replaced before adding antifreeze. Test your heater and defroster to make sure they are functioning. Also check your intake vents and remove any debris or other matter that can cause blockage.

Exhaust system: Leakage from an exhaust system into a vehicle interior is always dangerous. It is even more dangerous in the winter when many drivers keep all windows shut. Have the entire exhaust system checked and components replaced as necessary.

Windshield wipers and washers: Check functioning of wipers and condition of blades. Replace blades that streak the windshield. Keep the windshield washer reservoir filled with a washer antifreeze solution.

Tires: Mount your winter snow tires and keep them properly inflated to give you good traction. Air pressure should be checked at least once every two weeks. When tires reach $\frac{2}{32}$ inch in tread depth, replace them.

Chains: If you prefer to use chains, inspect them to make sure they are serviceable. Check the condition of the cross chains and replace broken links or those that are almost worn through.

Cold-weather equipment

Do not wait until the last minute to load your trunk with the items needed to combat snow and ice. Put the following items into your trunk or glove compartment.

Glove compartment: Flashlight, ice scraper, brush to remove snow, matches, extra fuses, rag to clean lights and windshield. If you cannot store all this in your glove compartment, put some items under the seat.

Trunk: Chains and extra chain links to repair those that may break while driving, spare container of washer fluid, pair of work gloves, small shovel, small bag of sand or road salt for traction, blanket and extra heavy clothing if you expect to be doing long-distance driving in remote areas and in case you become stranded in a snowstorm, and booster cables to enable you to get your car started in the event of battery failure.

Snow and ice removal

Visibility is always critical, but in cold, wintry weather many motorists take unwarranted chances by clearing just a portion of the windshield and rear window that have been iced over, or by brushing off snow only from the windshield and rear window. Laziness invites disaster.

Snow removal: If your vehicle is covered with snow, it is essential that all snow be removed from hood, trunk, glass surfaces, roof and lights before driving.

Removal of ice from glass surfaces: There are a number of types of windshield de-icing fluids that can be sprayed on glass to melt ice. These generally have an alcohol base which, while it melts the ice, tends to cool the glass. Subsequently, the moisture in the air may suddenly freeze over the glass surface again, obscuring driver vision. Before using a de-icing fluid, start the car and turn on the defroster to warm the windshield and keep it free of ice. If ice continues to form, pull off the road and clear your windshield and rear window. Ice scrapers should be used with care. When edges become burred or chipped, the scraper should be replaced. Using a damaged scraper or trying to dig out encrusted ice with the point of the scraper can result in scratches to the glass and may even cause the glass to break because its strength has been weakened.

Recessed wipers: If you have windshield wipers that disappear into a recess below the windshield when not in use, be especially careful to keep such recesses free of obstructions during snowy weather. They must be cleared of snow and ice before wiper use. In cold weather, even if there has not been snow, it is a good idea to check wiper blades before driving to make sure they operate properly.

Special techniques for safe driving on ice and snow

The best safety rule for driving on snow or ice is DON'T. Roads are obviously slippery. Stay off the roads until they are clear unless you absolutely have to drive.

Glare: Snow produces a glare which can impair vision. The sun shining on the snow makes the problem worse. Keep a pair of sunglasses or yellow lenses in your car and use them.

Fog: When driving under cold-weather conditions, on slippery roads, follow cars at a safe distance with enough room to stop. With moisture on the ground in the form of snow, you are apt to run into fog, and the combination of poor visibility and slippery conditions requires more alertness, attention to maintaining a safe following distance, and driving with lights on low beam to improve your own vision and the chances of your being seen by other drivers.

Braking: Know how and when to brake. When possible, use the braking power of the engine by downshifting to a lower gear rather than the brakes. When you must brake, do not jam on the brakes—tap and release them in a pumping motion. Do not brake in the middle of a curve. If your vehicle goes into skid, take your foot off the brake.

Skid: Do not panic and oversteer or jam on the brakes. Ease up on the accelerator and steer in the direction the rear of the vehicle is skidding. When you are able to regain steering control, you may be able to resume braking by pumping the brakes lightly.

To avoid skids and to avoid swerve on braking, test traction on different road surfaces and in bad weather by occasional light braking. Also, keep tires properly inflated—front-tire pressure must be equal. Do not tailgate. Slow down on slippery roads, and when braking, pump to avoid locking wheels.

Traction: To retain traction and avoid skids, start out slowly if parked on a slippery surface. If your wheels start spinning, let up on the accelerator until traction returns. Before going up a hill, increase speed, within reason, to build up momentum to help you climb. Before going down a hill, especially a steep one, slow down by shifting into a lower gear. Do not use your brakes when going down a slippery hill. When approaching a hill, observe how other vehicles are reacting to the conditions. Stay well behind the vehicle in front so that you can go around it if it becomes stuck. If other cars begin to slide or spin out, or if you have to back down the hill, wait until you have enough room to maneuver.

Use your judgment. From observing what other vehicles are doing, you may conclude that the hill is too slippery and dangerous. Pull over to the side as far as you can without the risk of getting stuck, and wait for a salt or a sand truck.

Stuck in a rut: The action you take depends on how badly you are stuck. Whatever you do, avoid spinning your wheels—that will only aggravate the problem. A tire spinning at a speed above 40 mph may disintegrate with explosive force sufficient to cause severe personal injury and/or vehicle damage. If the snow is deep, shovel it from in front and back of the wheels. Also shovel out as much snow from under the car as you can. If you have salt or sand, spread some in front and in back of your driving wheels, or use traction mats if you have them. Do not let anyone stand directly behind the rear wheels. While a little pushing assistance from a friendly passerby will often add that extra momentum needed to get going, warn him not to stand directly behind the car where he may be injured by rocks or objects thrown rearward by the spinning wheels. If possible, try to keep the front wheels pointed straight ahead until the car is moving. If your wheels keep spinning and the vehicle does not move, stop and let the tires cool. Tires heated from spinning will just dig you into a deeper rut. If nothing works, try to rock the vehicle out of the rut by alternately shifting from "reverse" to "drive" for cars with automatic transmissions. (Check your owner's manual to make sure this procedure can be followed with your car.)

Tire care: Check tire inflation every two weeks and before long trips. Use your own air-pressure gauge, as service station gauges may be inaccurate. Do this before starting out, since pressures can increase up to six pounds or more when tires are warmed up from driving. Checking air pressure is particularly important when the temperature has dropped substantially since the inflation pressure drops as the temperature drops. When tires reach $\frac{2}{32}$-inch tread depth, replace them. This can be determined by inserting the top edge of a penny into the tread groove. The top of Lincoln's head is $\frac{2}{32}$ inch from the coin edge. If the top of the head shows, the tires should be replaced.

Additional hints and precautions:
• Keep your tires inflated properly.
• Make sure all passengers use safety belts, including shoulder belts.
• On slick roads, stay well behind cars in front.
• If your wheels begin to spin, let up on the accelerator. Often this will permit traction to return.
• Always keep your gas tank at least half full, and periodically add some "dry gas" to the tank.
• If your parking brake freezes, try rocking the car (see page 224). Under such conditions it may be wise, when parking the car, to avoid setting the parking brake, relying on the "park" gear position (or "reverse" in cars with manual transmissions) to keep the car from moving.
• If your door locks freeze, try warming the key with a match or lighter before inserting it into the lock.
• Cars equipped with catalytic converters should never be idled for extended periods to warm up, as this may cause the converter to overheat.

Adjusting to other bad road conditions

Rain: Water on the pavement reduces traction, and as the water accumulates on the road surface, tires begin to hydroplane, or surfboard, as speed increases, particularly over 40 mph. This can lead to loss of traction and steering control. If you encounter deep puddles or high water along the highway, drive through them slowly. If you can see that the road is flooded, do not cross it.

If your car stalls out, try to coast to the side of the road and wait for the engine to dry out. If you know the parts of your electrical system, the drying-out process can be quickened by taking a dry rag and wiping the plug, wires and coil, and by drying the inside of the distributor cap.

If your car stalls in the middle of a puddle or if you are in the vicinity of a stream that is overflowing onto the highway, be alert to the possibility of a flash flood. For your own safety you may have to leave the car where it is and seek shelter until the water recedes. Each year many people drown trying to drive across flooded areas.

After moving through water, your brakes may have lost their stopping power. Apply your brakes lightly while driving to dry out the linings and other components.

DRIVING EMERGENCIES

In the car

Unruly children: Accidents have occurred because the driver turns around to try to discipline unruly children. If you must discipline young children in your car, do not let go of the wheel and turn around. Pull off the road and switch off the engine first.

Insects: Accidents have happened when drivers lost control of their cars while trying to get rid of flies, bees, or other insects in the car. Do not get frantic and try to kill an insect while driving. Pull off the road in a safe spot, turn off the engine, and then get rid of the insect by opening windows and letting it fly out. Accept the possibility of a bee sting until you can pull off the road safely; it's a lot better than risking a more serious accident or injury.

If an insect or dirt gets into one of your eyes, close that one eye and pull off the road before you attempt to clear foreign matter from your eye.

If you get foreign matter in both eyes, force yourself to keep your eyes open despite the discomfort. Pull off the road safely and then clear your eyes.

Animals loose in the front seat can also interfere with attention, visibility, steering and braking. Keep them in the back seat and under control.

Clothing and upholstery fires: Clothing and upholstery fires are usu-

ally smokers' problems. Ashes or lighted particles may drop on your clothing or on the upholstery from your cigarette, pipe, or cigar. Do not try to put out the fire while moving. Do not stop in traffic and get out of your car to brush off burning ashes. Put up with any pain or damage involved. Retain control of the car and pull off or to the side of the road before attempting to cure the problem.

Fire in the ashtray: If you have paper in your ashtray, putting a cigarette, cigar, pipe or match in your ashtray can cause a fire. If you have a fire, close the ashtray to diminish the flames or even smother the fire. Then pull safely off the road and make sure the fire is out.

In traffic

A car is coming toward you: You can usually try to escape by steering toward the right. Chances are best that you will survive if you can avoid a head-on collision. Swerve to the right even if you have to hit something or another car going in the same direction. When you swerve, honk your horn. If you can see you are going to collide with another car, brake hard.

If you cannot drive to the right, try dodging to the left. The driver coming toward you may return to his proper lane when he sees you trying to dodge him.

Someone is tailgating your car: Slow down so that the tailgater can pass you.

DRIVING SAFETY

Consider your health

Never drive when you are emotionally upset or tired. When driving long distances, rest every two hours to stay alert at the wheel with coffee (or other caffeinated drinks) and fresh air. Never take medication before you drive that might make you drowsy. Alcoholic beverages are a factor in about half of all fatal motor vehicle crashes, so avoid mixing driving and drinking. Even as few as one or two drinks can impair your judgment (see chart, page 29). Keep your eyes in good shape with regular checkups, and always wear glasses when driving if you need them. If you are a diabetic, check with your doctor if it is safe for you to drive. An older person should also

225

AUTOMOBILES/BICYCLES

check with his doctor regarding his driving ability; his reflexes and co-ordination may not be sufficiently sharp.

Never drive with someone under the influence of alcohol or drugs; you may be endangering your own life.

Use safety belts

Safety belts can be effective in protecting you and your family from injury. The National Safety Council estimates that safety belts save more than 3,000 lives annually. Many traffic collisions occur within 25 miles of the driver's home, frequently at neighborhood intersections where people feel secure—sometimes so secure that they are not using their seat belts.

Adult safety belts: For an adult, the most effective safety belt is the combination lap-shoulder harness. In the event of a crash, the safety belt will prevent you from being thrown against the windshield, against other parts of the automobile interior, or out of the vehicle.

Safety belts for children: Automobile accidents are one of the major causes of death among children, claiming more lives than drowning, poisoning and childhood diseases. Children should not wear adult-type safety belts until they are four or five years old, or until they weigh at least 50 pounds. Instead, they should use one of the more than 20 different models of restraints for children that meet crash-testing standards and are sold by retail, discount and juvenile

product stores, catalog outlets and car dealerships. Remember to buckle an infant or toddler for every trip. Even a sudden stop can injure a child who is not big enough to brace himself.

Restraints fall into five groups (see Fig. 49-3).

Infant. The baby rides backwards in a semireclining position. This device is suitable for infants up to 20 pounds.

Birth to 40 pounds. Restraints of this type are suitable for infants when placed in a backward-riding position. For the toddler and older child up to 40 pounds; these tilt up and face forward.

Harness in a seat. The chair-type restraint must have a 5-point harness, one that comes across the lap, over both shoulders and through the crotch. This is suitable for children who are able to sit up unaided and who weigh at least 15 pounds. They can be used until the child reaches 4 years or weighs 40 pounds.

Harness alone. This is a 5-point harness which is secured by a strap around the seat back and is bolted to the floor or to the rear-window shelf. It will fit a child who can sit up unaided and weighs 15 to 50 pounds.

Shield-type. Children weighing over 20 pounds can use a restraint featuring a C-shaped shield which is secured by the standard safety belt. Some infant restraints have their own individually designed shields which snap on when the restraint is faced forward for use by an older child.

When purchasing a car restraint, be sure to consider the size of both your child and your car. Some restraints in the backward position may not fit in the rear seat of compact cars.

If car restraints are to give protection, they must be used properly. This means that the restraint must always be securely fastened by the adult; tether straps, if provided, should be tightly fastened; and all other manufacturer's instructions should be followed.

If the restraint is in the rear seat, anchor the top tether strap to a bolt in a metal portion of the rear window shelf. If the restraint is in the front seat, anchor it to a rear-seat safety belt. In station wagons and vans, anchor the top strap to the cargo compartment floor at a 45° or greater angle. A restraint with a tether could be hazardous if the strap is not used.

The back seat of the car is safest, unless the driver must supervise the child closely. The center of the seat is preferred.

Never fail to buckle up your infant or preschooler even on short trips around town. Most accidents happen within 25 miles of home at speeds under 30 mph.

Tiny infants may require additional padding to prevent their flopping from side to side while traveling in a car restraint.

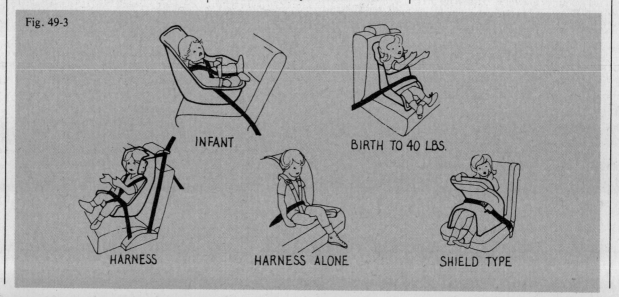

Fig. 49-3

INFANT · BIRTH TO 40 LBS. · HARNESS · HARNESS ALONE · SHIELD TYPE

ON THE ROAD

SETTING OFF ON A TRIP BY CAR

Take your car to a service station for a tune-up. Have the serviceperson check tires (including the spare) when they are cold—when you have driven less than a mile at moderate speed. Have the oil, gas, coolant, battery, brakes, lights and windshield washer also checked.

Wear your safety belt at all times, and wear the shoulder harness also if the car includes one. Drive only two hours at one time before you take a rest. When you leave the car, lock it and always take your keys with you.

Travelers with a history of motion sickness or sea sickness can attempt to avoid symptoms by taking, before departure, anti-motion-sickness pills or antihistamine pills. These pills may make you drowsy, so never drive immediately after taking them.

50

BICYCLES

Bicycling provides healthful fun and inexpensive transportation, but accident statistics reveal many potential dangers. To prevent bicycle accidents, select a bicycle carefully and maintain it properly. Also, develop safe riding habits.

SELECTION OF A BICYCLE

Use the following guidelines for buying a bicycle.

Size

If you are buying a bicycle for a child, choose one to fit his size as he is today, not one he will "grow into" later. He may lose control or be unable to brake quickly enough if his feet barely reach the pedals.

To test for correct size for a boy, have him straddle the horizontal top bar on a boy's bicycle. He should have a one-inch clearance with both feet flat on the ground.

To size a girl's bike, have her sit on the seat at its lowest position, with the bike upright. With one leg extended nearly straight on a pedal at its lowest position, she should be able to reach the ground with the ball of her other foot.

Adults should be able to straddle the bicycle with both feet flat on the ground and with no less than one inch of clearance between the frame's top bar and the rider's crotch.

Type of bicycle

Choose one suited to the rider's abilities and the kind of riding he expects to do. Children under 11 ordinarily do not have enough experience and co-ordination to shift gears, use hand brakes, and maintain balance on a complex bicycle.

Middleweight bicycle: A middleweight bicycle offers stability for everyday riding. Usually it is single-speed, with balloon tires, fenders, and coaster brakes (see Fig. 50-1).

Fig. 50-1

MIDDLEWEIGHT

Lightweight bicycle, or racer: A lightweight bicycle responds well in distance riding. Typical lightweights come with 3, 5 or 10 gear speeds and hub or derailleur gear-shift mechanism (see Fig. 50-2).

Fig. 50-2

LIGHTWEIGHT

High-rise bicycle: A high-rise bicycle is mainly for fun since it maneuvers easily, but is hard to pedal for long distances. A long "banana" seat and vertical backrest could invite the rider to perform hazardous "wheelies" that could flip the bike and rider over backward (see Fig. 50-3).

Fig. 50-3
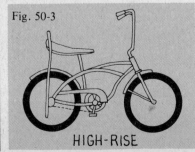
HIGH-RISE

Parts of a bicycle (see Fig. 50-4)

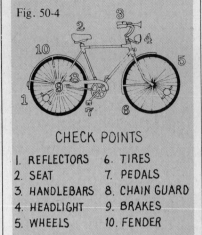
Fig. 50-4

CHECK POINTS

1. REFLECTORS   6. TIRES
2. SEAT   7. PEDALS
3. HANDLEBARS   8. CHAIN GUARD
4. HEADLIGHT   9. BRAKES
5. WHEELS   10. FENDER

Reflectors: It is more hazardous to ride a bicycle at night than in the daytime, but reflectors and reflectorized tape visible at night from any angle help make a bicycle more recognizable.

Full reflectorization means:

Front reflector—colorless
Rear reflector—red
Pedal reflectors—colorless or amber
Spoke reflectors—amber in front, red on rear wheel
Tape along the metal body of the bicycle

The top of the rear reflector should be set at least three inches below the seat. Both the rear and front reflectors must be mounted straight so they reflect directly toward the eyes of a driver of an approaching car. The center of each reflector mounted on the wheel should be within $3\frac{1}{2}$ inches of the inside of the rim. Reflectorized tire sidewalls can be used instead of spoke-mounted reflectors.

Other good ideas include using a headlight and a taillight, sewing reflectorized tape on your clothes, or strapping front-back flashlights on legs and arms so you and your bike are clearly visible to motorists.

Sharp points: Avoid bicycles with sharp points, rough edges or protruding bolts. On older bicycles, cover these areas with heavy waterproof tape or file them down. There should be no protrusion between the bicycle seat and handlebar stem that extends more than $3\frac{1}{2}$ inches to the rear of the handlebar stem.

227

Frame: Improperly welded joints or a fracture caused by improper handling in the manufacturing or shipping can result in a weak frame. Even a hairline crack can cause metal to break under a sudden jolt.

Seat: The seat must be firmly attached to the seat post tube so that it will not move or break under normal riding conditions. Its height should be comfortable for reaching pedals and ground. Replace a damaged saddle. Avoid equipment or materials which rise more than five inches above the rear of the seat. These can interfere with a quick and safe dismount.

Handlebars: Handlebars must be symmetrically positioned. Also, they should be tight and adjusted to a comfortable height. The handlebar ends should be not more than 16 inches above the seat surface when the seat is in its lowest position and the handlebar ends are in their highest position. Replace missing handlebar grips.

Tires: Tires have two important functions that contribute to the rider's safety. The first is cushioning the rider against potholes or rough places in the road. The second is braking. Tires with good tread enable the rider to stop more quickly in an emergency. Always inflate tires to the recommended pressure. Replace worn tires.

Wheels: Be sure wheels are firmly attached. If wheels wobble, have the bicycle "trued" or otherwise adjusted promptly, so that there is at least $1/16$-inch clearance between the tire and fork or any part of the bicycle frame.

Pedals: To prevent foot slippage, choose rubber-treaded pedals, or metal pedals with firmly attached toeclips.

Brakes: They should stop the bicycle quickly, without sticking. Always road-test a bike before you buy. There is no other way to be sure the brakes are going to give you quick, smooth stops. If you are buying a bike with handbrakes, be sure the levers can be moved easily. If the bicycle has extensions on the handbrakes, they should give a full braking effect before the hand levers touch the handlebars.

Bicycles capable of speeds of 15 miles per hour or greater (many of these have handbrakes) must be able to stop in 15 feet from 15 miles per hour. Those bicycles capable only of slower speeds (many of these have foot brakes) must be able to stop in 15 feet from 10 miles per hour. Small bicycles with seat height less than 22 inches and not equipped with brakes must be labeled with the words "No brakes" and cannot have a free-wheeling coasting feature.

Fenders: Check for sharp or rough edges on fenders.

Chainguard: All single-speed bikes need a chainguard to prevent clothes and shoelaces from catching between the chain and sprocket. Be sure your bike has one, unless the pedals can be rotated backward to release quickly any clothing that might get caught. Leg bands or clips are an added protection for keeping clothing out of pedals or wheels.

Bell or horn: Secure a bell or horn to the front of the bicycle. Be sure it is in good working order and can be heard from 100 feet away.

Clearance: There should be at least $3\frac{1}{2}$ inches of clearance between the pedal and the front fender or tire. This is important to prevent the toe of a shoe from getting caught between the frame and the front wheel. The pedals must not touch the ground when the bike is tilted at least 25 degrees. Otherwise, a pedal could catch the ground on a turn and cause a spill.

MAINTENANCE OF A BICYCLE

Regular maintenance is essential to keep a bike in safe riding condition. You can learn to do basic repairs. Take your bike to an experienced repairman for complicated jobs such as brake, spoke and gear adjustments.

To maintain your bicycle properly:
- Spin the wheels to check for smooth, straight rotation. Wobbly wheels need to be "trued," or aligned, and spokes may require adjustment or replacement.
- Replace all missing, damaged, or worn parts—for example, chainguards, chain links, spokes, screws and bolts, handlebar grips, seats and brake pads and cables on handbrakes.
- Tighten and/or adjust loose parts.
- Keep your bicycle indoors when not in use. Moisture may cause rust and ruin the bicycle's controls.

SAFE RIDING HABITS

Before setting out, be sure your new bicycle is fully assembled. Assembling a new bike should be done by an experienced person using the proper tools and following the instructions in the manual that should be included in the bike package.
- Riders are at the mercy of every car, bump and sewer grate, so be alert and cautious at all times.
- Warn children against riding double, and against hazardous games and stunts.
- For increased visibility in the dark, apply reflective trim to clothing, or strap front-back flashlights on legs and arms.
- Avoid loose clothing or long coats that can easily catch in pedals, wheels or cover reflectors. Leg clips or bands keep pant legs from tangling in the chain.
- Always ride near the curb in the direction of traffic, single file. Children should not ride in traffic until they can understand and obey traffic rules, such as "stop," "caution" and "yield."
- When possible, avoid congested intersections and heavy or high-speed traffic. At busy intersections or hazardous left-turn corners, walk—do not ride—your bicycle across the street.
- Don't ride in rain or snow unless you must. When wet, handbrakes are especially unreliable and may require a long distance to stop. Also, wet tires tend to skid. Going through deep puddles at high speed can cause loss of control.
- Sewer grates, potholes, rocks and other surface conditions can easily throw the most skillful rider. Ride slowly enough to avoid unexpected obstacles such as car doors suddenly opening, cars backing out of driveways or parking lots, or children running in front of the bicycle.
- Tires are safer if properly inflated as recommended by the manufacturer. Underinflated tires give poor protection. Overinflated tires do not grip the road effectively when you apply the brakes. Tires with worn treads should be replaced.
- Know traffic laws and signals. Most laws and regulations that govern automobile traffic apply to bicyclists. Show the same courtesy to motorists and to other bicyclists as you want shown to you.
- Adult riders should set a good example for children and protect themselves by also obeying all traffic rules.

228

- Neither adults nor children should ever carry packages in their hands; they should use a basket attached to the bicycle.

Bicycle repair kit

A repair kit kept in a bicycle basket will come in handy in case of a breakdown on the road. Include a pump, a patch kit or new tube, and a set of tire irons for fixing a flat tire.

51

MOTORCYCLES

As the popularity of motorcycles increases, so do the accident and death rates. One of the main reasons, of course, is that motorcycles provide less protection in a crash than automobiles.

CAUSES OF MOTORCYCLE ACCIDENTS

Many of the causes of motorcycle accidents are the same as those of automobile accidents. But many others are attributable to the driver's lack of training, or failure to appreciate the operating characteristics and limitations of the motorcycle, which require special precautions and more emphasis on defensive driving. A motorcyclist, for example, has to be more careful at intersections, where most motorcycle-automobile collisions occur. He must remain visible at all times. He has to be more alert than drivers of other vehicles. For example, he has to anticipate that drivers backing their cars out of driveways may not see him. He has to be more cautious when riding in bad weather or on slippery surfaces, or when he encounters obstacles on the road. He must also wear a helmet, eye protection and clothing covering the entire body to reduce the severity of any possible accidents.

BUYING THE RIGHT MOTORCYCLE

Select a motorcycle for fit and functional requirements.

Fit

Do not buy a motorcycle that is too big or too heavy. A motorcyclist should be able to stand with both feet flat on the ground when astride the vehicle. (This is not always possible for small people.) It's important while waiting for a light or when stopped in heavy traffic to be able to balance the motorcycle.

If you carry passengers, make sure the motorcycle you select has a passenger seat as well as footrests (footpegs).

Check the location of the controls. Make sure you can reach and operate them easily.

Functional requirements

Buy the power you need, but only as much as you can handle. Large motorcycles are heavy. From time to time you will have to push your motorcycle or pick it up when it has fallen. Be sure you have the strength to do this. Try the motorcycle in the showroom before buying. Remember that smaller bikes (e.g., a 100-cc machine) may not have the cruising speed required on high-speed roads.

Do not buy a trail bike for highway use, or a highway bike if most of your cycling will be off the road. Some motorcycles are built especially for trail use, having special tires for traction, special suspension systems, and less powerful brakes than street cycles. Other motorcycles have special characteristics for highway use, including tires designed to grip pavement and more powerful braking systems. If you have dual requirements, combination cycles are available that make a compromise between the pure trail motorcycle and the type especially designed for highway use.

AFTER YOU BUY, BUT BEFORE YOU DRIVE

Read your owner's manual thoroughly. Become familiar with it and with your motorcycle. Keep in mind that there is no substitute for good instruction from an experienced cyclist.

Buy the proper helmet, clothing and equipment (see below).

Practice before going out on the highway. Find a safe area and a competent instructor. Practice until use of proper controls becomes automatic, until you become thoroughly accustomed to requirements for balance, making turns, stopping, and other routine maneuvers.

A motorcyclist using the streets and highways has to abide by the same traffic rules as other motorists. Before you take your cycle on a public street or highway, become familiar with these rules as well as special regulations for motorcycles.

Riding with a passenger requires skill. Don't ride with a passenger until you have had plenty of solo riding time.

PROTECTIVE CLOTHING AND EQUIPMENT

The parts of a motorcyclist's body most often injured in an accident are the head, arms, and legs. Internal injuries and multiple injuries are also common, but the most serious injuries are those to the head. Protective clothing and equipment serve a threefold purpose for the motorcyclist: They protect him from the elements, they offer some protection in the event of a spill or accident, and, when colorful or made of reflective material, they make the cyclist visible to other drivers.

Jackets and trousers

These should be of strong material such as heavy denim or leather. Jackets should have long sleeves. While clothing should be comfortable to operate the motorcycle in, it should also provide some measure of protection from abrasion in the event of a spill. Trousers should not be baggy or flared at the bottom, to prevent entanglement with the chain, kick-starter, footpegs, or other protrusions on the side of the motorcycle.

Gloves

Durable gloves are recommended. They should be nonslip so that the cyclist can keep a firm grip on the controls. Leather gloves are excellent, as are special-fabric gloves with leather grip strips on the fingers. The gloves should have gauntlet-type sleeves to keep air out of the cyclist's sleeves.

Footwear

Proper footwear affords protection for the feet, ankles, and lower parts of the legs. Leather boots are best. Durable shoes that cover the ankles are a good second choice. Sandals, sneakers and similar footwear should not be used because they provide little protection from abrasion or a crushing impact during a crash.

MOTORCYCLES/TRAVEL AND CAMPER TRAILERS

Eye protection

Good vision is critical. Most motorcycles do not have windshields, so the cyclist must protect his eyes from bugs, dirt and other airborne matter. Even the wind can cause the eyes to tear and thereby blur vision. Eye protection can consist of goggles, glasses with plastic or safety lenses, or a helmet equipped with a face shield. Goggles, glasses and face shields should be scratch free, shatter proof and well ventilated to prevent fog buildup on the lenses. Only clear lenses should be used at night since tinted lenses reduce vision. Eye protection is recommended even if the cycle has a windshield.

Helmet

This is the most important piece of protective equipment. Statistics confirm that approved safety helmets save lives and reduce the extent of injuries in the event of accidents. Many good helmets are available. Look for the symbol DOT on the outer surface of the helmet, indicating that it conforms to federal safety standards. Any passenger you carry should also wear a helmet. Use of an approved safety helmet at all times is required by law in most states.

Note. Part of the clothing used for daytime cycling should be orange or some other eye-catching color. Some cyclists wear light-weight orange or red vests over their jackets. Reflective tape on clothing, helmet and motorcycle helps make the cyclist visible at night. A high percentage of car-cycle collisions occur because the driver of the automobile fails to see the cyclist in time to avoid the crash.

DRIVING TIPS

Avoid offensive driving

Practices of some cyclists offensive to other motorists include weaving in and out of stalled traffic and riding on the shoulders to get ahead. They create a bad image of all motorcyclists and can cause accidents. Follow these rules:
- Treat motorists with courtesy and respect.
- Avoid tailgating.
- Do not drive aggressively.
- Avoid driving between lanes of slow-moving or stopped traffic.
- Avoid excessive lane weaving in traffic.

- Know and obey traffic laws, including ordinances in your community.

Drive defensively

Be alert and slow down at intersections, especially where shrubbery, parked vehicles or buildings limit vision. Watch for automobiles that may unexpectedly turn left in front of you or pull out from a side street or driveway. In general, drive as if others do not see you.

Make your motorcycle and its riders as visible as possible. Use your headlight day and night. Automobile drivers have blind spots to the left and right rear of the vehicles where they cannot see the motorcyclist or his signal, but they will usually be able to pick up a reflection from the headlight of the motorcycle.

Maintain a safe speed consistent with driving conditions and your capabilities. Do not tailgate, and do not let other drivers tailgate you. Following too closely behind another vehicle may make it difficult for you to stop if the driver brakes suddenly. In addition, you will not be able to check road hazards and traffic conditions ahead of you. If another motorist is following you too closely, wave him off with a hand signal or tap your brake pedal. If he continues to follow too closely, let him pass.

Pass only when it is safe to do so. Avoid passing or riding on the shoulder. Pull over to the left third of the lane before passing, and make sure you are at a safe following distance. Check your rearview mirrors before changing lanes. Use your turn signals, and also make a head check. Avoid crowding the other vehicle as you pass.

Use your brakes wisely. Brake very cautiously on slick surfaces and in turns. If necessary, you can use both brakes in a turn if you avoid locking the wheels. Remember, too, that as with an automobile, driving through water can adversely affect your brakes. After clearing water, check for following traffic and, when safe to do so, test your brakes by applying light pressure.

Watch the road surface and traffic well ahead to anticipate problems and road hazards. Gravel or other substances on the road make it slippery and require caution. Avoid sudden braking on such surfaces and avoid

sudden, sharp turns. When driving in the rain, motorcyclists find they get better traction by driving in the tracks of vehicles in front, but again, don't follow too closely. On slick roads, avoid riding on painted lines and metal surfaces such as manhole covers. If caught in a sudden shower while riding, pull off the highway under some shelter such as an overpass and wait for the rain to stop. If you must drive in the rain, remember that roads are most slippery during the first few minutes of rainfall because of oil on the roadway.

Because an automobile has better stability, road conditions that are minor irritations for the motorist can represent major hazards for the two-wheeled motorcycle. Hazards include potholes, oil slicks, puddles, debris or other objects on the road, ruts and railroad tracks. A motorcyclist should slow down before reaching an obstacle and make sure it is safe to swerve to avoid it. Railroad tracks crossing the highway at an angle are particularly hazardous. To prevent loss of traction and control, the cyclist should cross such tracks at an angle of between 35 and 90 degrees. Dogs can be a problem, too. Do not become distracted and do not kick out at a dog. As you approach a dog, gear down; when you reach the dog, accelerate.

EMERGENCY SITUATIONS

Read your owner's manual, know your motorcycle and keep it in good condition. Carry the manual and recommended tools and spare parts on your motorcycle. Adhere closely to the maintenance schedule contained in your manual. Before each day's riding, check lights, turn signals, tires, brakes, fuel and oil levels, mirrors and control cables. Replace broken, worn or frayed control cables at once. Lubricate and adjust your chain as prescribed in your owner's manual.

These precautions will cut down on emergencies. But if you do have an emergency, know how to react.

Throttle stuck
or clutch cable broken

Use your emergency cut-off switch or turn your ignition key off. If this does not work, stall the engine by using the choke or apply both brakes.

Blowouts

When this happens, do not use your

230

ON THE ROAD

brakes. Ease off the throttle and slow down gradually. When your speed is low enough, ease off the road slowly. Keep a firm grip on the handlebars throughout. Consider installing devices such as rim-locks that will retain the tire on the rim after a blowout.

Emergency braking

To get the most braking from a motorcycle, both brakes must be used together. If you feel either wheel slipping, or your cycle starts to lean over, or you start to slide sideways, slowly let up on your brakes. To prevent all-out skids, your wheels must keep moving.

To brake on a curve, slow down before reaching the curve. If you go into a curve too fast, you may be able to slow down by intermittent light braking or a combination of intermittent light and heavier braking. Hard braking, however, should be avoided.

52
TRAVEL AND CAMPER TRAILERS

Each year millions of Americans embark on camping trips in recreational vehicles, either their own or rented. There are many types of recreational vehicles. This chapter deals with highway safety in driving and handling camper and travel trailers. A camper trailer is a small trailer which, when in use, is expanded through pop-up or foldout features and which may have canvas (tent-type) or light metal enclosures and roofs, or a combination of the two (see Fig. 52-1). A travel trailer is generally a larger trailer than the camper. It is practically ready for use either attached to or detached from the towing vehicle. Its basic configuration generally does not change through pop-up or foldout features (see Fig. 52-2).

MATCH YOUR EQUIPMENT

Before buying or renting a trailer, be sure it does not make demands that your vehicle cannot meet. Pay special attention to the type of hitch required, as well as possible needs for an oversize radiator, transmission cooler, stronger springs and shock absorbers, and larger tires. Base your purchase or rental of the trailer on the requirements and capabilities of the towing vehicle, and make any modifications necessary for safety. Check the labels attached to the trailer and the towing vehicle to determine vehicle load limits. Know how to load and weigh your trailer, and how to distribute the load properly. In addition to overall loaded weight of the trailer, you must concern yourself with the weight on the hitch and the weight on each axle. Never overload either the towing vehicle or the trailer.

SAFETY TIPS AND PROCEDURES
Predeparture checks

Check out the trailer and towing vehicle completely. Inspect tires for treadwear and proper inflation. Examine the condition of the hitch and associated safety devices. Check condition of brakes on both vehicles. Check radiator coolant and level of transmission fluid. Check tightness of the lugs on the wheels, particularly when vehicles are new, or when starting on a trip. Repeat this check periodically during your trip.

Equip your towing vehicle with large mirrors for the front fenders so that you can see well behind your trailer on both sides. If the towing vehicle is a station wagon or a van and the trailer is a low-slung camper type, visibility to the rear through the vehicle's inside rearview mirror is also helpful. Never load the vehicle so that you block the rear windows.

Make sure the shocks and springs on both vehicles are in good shape.

Check for leaks in propane gas bottles, heating equipment, and associated tubing, and be sure they are functioning properly. Before final departure, make sure valves on gas bottles are turned off.

Load tools, emergency equipment and foul-weather gear in a readily accessible location in the towing vehicle.

Load your trailer so that it is properly balanced front and rear and side to side, and the suspension system and tires on the towing and towed vehicles are not overloaded. Once you have established a good loading plan, make a list of things you normally take along on a trip and a loading diagram of where they are placed on the trailer. Never leave articles loose in the trailer or in the back of a station wagon. Secure all doors, drawers, and anything movable in the trailer.

After you load the trailer and hitch it to the towing vehicle, but before you drive off on your trip, observe the attitudes of the towing and towed vehicles. Is the back end of the towing vehicle resting low to the ground with the front end up in the air? Is the rear end of the towing vehicle too high? Is one end of the trailer much lower than the other? Is the trailer sagging to one side? Look under both vehicles and check the effect of the sag on the springs. If the sag is too great or the springs appear ready to bow in the opposite direction of their normal curvature, you have overloaded.

If you are satisfied that both vehicles are loaded properly, make a last check of the hitch and safety mechanism, including safety chains. Check the condition of the wire connections between the electrical systems of the two vehicles. The wires should have enough slack to allow for turns but not be so long that they drag on the road and short out or break. (Reduce any extra length by taping the excess wire to a portion of the trailer tongue.)

Finally, before driving off, have someone stand in back of the vehicle while you test the running lights, brake lights, and turn signals. Check the functioning of the brakes themselves.

Driving down the highway

While moving, do not let anyone stay in the towed vehicle. Observe speed limits. In some states the speed limit

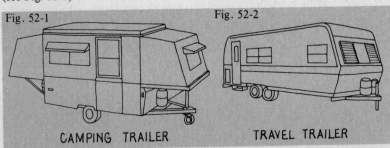

Fig. 52-1   CAMPING TRAILER

Fig. 52-2   TRAVEL TRAILER

for passenger vehicles towing a trailer is lower than the limit for the passenger vehicle by itself. Check routes and restrictions on bridges and tunnels beforehand. If you have bottled gas on your vehicle, you may not be able to drive through some tunnels.

Maintain at least twice the normal following distance between your vehicle and the one in front. Since you are pulling a trailer, you may need a lot more room to stop, and it's easier to go out of control. Drive defensively and try to anticipate requirements for stopping so that you will be able to slow down and avoid panic braking, which could cause your trailer to jackknife.

When passing, remember you cannot accelerate as fast as you normally would because of the load you are pulling. Make sure you have enough room to pass. After passing, allow plenty of room for your trailer before changing lanes again. Check your mirrors before making any lane changes.

When traveling over bumpy roads or when crossing railroad tracks and ditches, slow down. Driving over these obstacles too rapidly can cause the bottom of your towing vehicle and the trailer hitch to scrape.

If you are near a large truck, bus or tractor-trailer, the wind from such vehicles can cause your trailer to fishtail. Get a firm grip on the steering wheel, and keep tension on the hitch ball. If the trailer can be braked separately by hand, use short, quick actions to slow the trailer sufficiently to eliminate sway.

Backing up a vehicle and a trailer is very tricky. Before embarking on a trip, practice such maneuvers until you know how. You will need a much greater turning radius, and the front vehicle will move further to the right or left than if that vehicle alone were being backed up. So, when backing up, watch the rear, of course, but also watch the right front and side and left front and side of the towing vehicle to make sure you don't hit anything. Steer by holding the bottom of the steering wheel. If you must back up a trailer, make sure you use the mirrors on both sides of the vehicle, and have another individual walk to the rear of the trailer on the driver's side—but well away from the vehicle—to guide you.

A heavy load will limit your power going up hills and give you greater momentum going down. You will find that to get up some hills, you will have to use second gear; it is also a good idea to use second gear to slow your descent because depending solely on brakes could overheat them and cause them to fail.

TIRES AND WHEELS

Maintenance

Periodic inspection and maintenance of trailer tires and wheels are essential to trailer safety. All tires on the trailer should be of the same type, size and construction. Always carry a spare tire, and on long trips consider carrying two. Some sizes of tires used on trailers may be very difficult to locate in remote areas, especially at night. Keep your tires properly inflated. Check tire pressures cold, before starting on your trip. Periodically check your tires for treadwear, cracks, blisters and signs of tread separation, and replace worn or defective tires. It may help to buy your own tire gauge since some service station gauges may not be able to measure high pressures, and your own gauge will probably be more accurate than most service station gauges.

Signs of tire trouble: If you have a blowout or tread separation on your camper trailer or develop a blister on a tire, you may be able to detect the problem by a change in how the steering wheel handles; a noticeable drag, particularly on the side of the trailer where the tire failed; or bouncing of the trailer, which can be felt in the towing vehicle. Slow down, but do not panic-brake. A sudden application of the brakes with the loss of one of these tires will cause jackknifing and possibly rollover. Instead, slow down by applying the trailer brakes first, if possible. Find a flat spot off the road. This is important not only because the vehicle should be stable for jacking, but because the trailer body may rest so close to the ground (due to small wheels and tires) that jacking is difficult on an uneven surface.

Jacking up the camper trailer to change a wheel: Follow the jacking recommendations of your camper trailer manufacturer. If it gives none, follow this advice.

The best way to change a wheel on

a camper trailer is to raise the vehicle by using a scissors-type jack or a piston-type jack (screw-type or hydraulic). The jack and a lug wrench should be stored in a readily accessible location in the towing vehicle, along with some wooden blocks to chock the wheel on the opposite side of the trailer (the one that is not to be changed and which will remain on the ground), as well as the rear wheels of the towing vehicle. Because of the size of the wheels on some camper trailers, you may not have enough space to place the jack under the axle to raise the wheel unless you have installed skids, as described later. If you cannot place the jack under the axle, you may be able to place it under some sturdy part of the frame near the wheel.

Another method of jacking the trailer—but one which requires that it be disconnected from the towing vehicle—is to use the jacking assembly built into the tongue of the camper trailer and the extendible jacks at the rear of the camper. Attach the dolly wheel to the jacking assembly at the tongue of the trailer. Next extend the jack to raise the tongue to permit unhitching the trailer from the towing vehicle. Retract the jack to lower the tongue to its lowest position, which will also raise the rear of the trailer. Extend the folding jacks at the rear of the trailer to their fullest position, and then jack up the front of the trailer once more. This will raise the entire trailer, including the wheels. And it takes a great deal of time.

Regardless of how you raise your camper to change a tire, loosen the lug nuts on the wheel *before* jacking, and chock the wheels on the opposite side, as well as the rear wheels on the towing vehicle. Never let any part of your body get under the trailer. The lug wrench from your towing vehicle may not fit the lugs of the trailer wheels, so you may have to buy a special wrench. In addition, some campers may be so designed that there is insufficient space between the wheel and the overhung camper body to permit use of a conventional automobile lug wrench; in such cases you may have to use a socket wrench.

Storing your camper trailer for the winter: Raise the vehicle and use jack stands or heavy wooden blocks to support it. The jack stands or blocks should be placed under the frame at

232

the rear of the trailer, while the front is supported by the jack at the tongue (jack extended). It is also a good idea to remove the dolly wheel from the front jack and let the jack rest on a flat board to prevent the wheel from burying itself in the ground over the winter. Reduce air pressure in the tires. Storing your camper in this fashion will take the weight off the suspension system and the tires, and avoid tire problems that could occur the next camping season. Many camper trailer owners remove their wheels and tires and store them in a cool, dry place for the winter.

Changing tires on a travel trailer: Again, check your owner's manual and follow its instructions for jacking procedures and jack placement. Be careful to pull onto a relatively level surface to change a tire. If the ground slopes, in addition to the danger of the trailer slipping off the jack there is the danger of trailer tipover. With some two-axle trailers, you can change a tire without using a jack by pulling the trailer up on a ramp until the wheel that is to be changed moves freely. Many travel trailer owners construct such inclined ramps from heavy lumber stock such as 2 by 4's placed on edge and nailed together with both ends sawed to form an incline on both sides. As with camper trailers, winter storage should involve raising the vehicle and supporting it on heavy blocks.

A tire problem—blowout, tread separation, large blister—will produce the same telltale signs of trailer trouble as described for the camper trailer (see page 232) and requires the same precautionary measures.

Miscellaneous tips: The problem of having enough room to jack up a camper trailer can be alleviated somewhat by installing safety skids. These devices are U-shaped and are generally attached to the springs and over the bottom of the axle. The prime purpose of such skids, whose use is optional, is to prevent the axle housing from digging into the pavement or getting hung up on a rut or raised portion of the road in the event of blowout or loss of a wheel. The camper will travel on the skids like a sled until the vehicle is stopped.

When driving through hilly country, keep a container of water in the towing vehicle in the event the radiator overheats.

Because of long storage in the open under adverse weather conditions, the studs on trailer wheels can get corroded, making the removal of wheels difficult. Do not try to ease this situation by applying oil or grease to the wheel studs, as this may cause you to lose a wheel later while driving down the highway.

Make sure your trailer is properly grounded before using outside or auxiliary power supplies. If you ever remove the hitch from your towing vehicle, make sure all installation holes are sealed to prevent entry of exhaust fumes into the trunk.

BRAKES, SAFETY CHAINS, AND BREAKAWAY SWITCHES

General guidelines

In many states, a separate braking system is required for trailers of over 1,000 pounds loaded weight. Safety chains and a breakaway switch to activate the trailer brakes in the event of failure of the hitching mechanism may also be required to prevent separation of the trailer from the towing vehicle. Safety chains should have some slack to permit sharp turns by the trailer, but should not drag on the roadway. They should cross under the trailer tongue to prevent the tongue from dropping to the highway in case of failure of the hitching mechanism. Breakaway switches are part of the breaking system. They are located on the tongue of the trailer and activate the trailer brakes if the towing vehicle and the trailer become accidentally separated.

There are several different types of braking systems. The most common currently in use are electric brakes and the surge type, with the electric type being the more popular.

Maintenance of your braking system: To understand the braking system on your trailer, read the owner's manual thoroughly and get your dealer or a competent serviceman to explain things you're not sure about.

Have your trailer braking system inspected at least once a year and adjusted or serviced as necessary. Do not neglect the components that are attached to the towing vehicle. The inspection should cover all electrical wiring and connection, hydraulic lines and fittings, adjustment of the brake controller as necessary, and the condi- tion of brake shoes, drums, wheel cylinders, and magnets.

Warning signs of brake trouble:

Brakes lock or grab. Could be caused by controller not working properly, grease or brake fluid on linings, or loose or broken items inside the wheels.

Weak brakes. Could be caused by bad electrical connections, defective magnets, short circuits, improper controller adjustment, improper brake adjustment, greasy linings, excessive trailer loading, or wrong gauge of wire used in the system.

Intermittent, or surging, brakes. Could be caused by drums that are out of round, poor grounding in the electrical system, broken magnet wires, or loose or defective wheel bearings.

Dragging brakes. Could be due to incorrect brake adjustment, improper controller adjustment or defective controller, brake assembly corrosion, defective brake shoe springs or, with surge brakes, a problem with the master cylinder on the tongue of the trailer.

Noisy brakes. Could be caused by loose parts, worn-out or contaminated brake linings or improperly adjusted, damaged or worn bearings.

No brakes. Could be caused by broken wires, loose connections, poor grounding in the electrical system, bad connector plugs, short circuits, poor brake adjustment or defective controller or magnet.

53

MOTORHOME AND PICKUP CAMPERS

With more and more leisure time and more money to spend on recreational activities, Americans today are taking to the open road in motorhomes and pickup campers. To be safe, owners of recreational vehicles should know the capacity of the suspension systems on their vehicles, how to weigh the vehicle properly, how much weight can be carried in or on the vehicle, how it should be loaded and distributed, and how to perform safety checks on the vehicle.

A motorhome is a self-powered unit that contains complete living facilities, including cooking, sleeping, bath, and toilet. There are two main varieties: a chopped van, or mini-motorhome, in which the motorhome is built directly onto the frame of a van that has been chopped off behind the cab or onto the frame of a pickup truck without a load bed (see Fig. 53-1), and the conventional model, which is larger and offers more space and more luxurious accommodations, and is usually built on a truck chassis (see Fig. 53-2). A pickup camper, or slide-in camper, is a self-contained unit with living facilities which is designed to fit (slide in) the bed of a pickup truck (see Fig. 53-3). When the camper unit is not needed, it can be removed and the pickup truck can be used for other purposes. A van conversion is a conventional van which has been altered by adding living facilities to the cargo area (see Fig. 53-4). Extra windows and additional headroom may be provided through roof alterations.

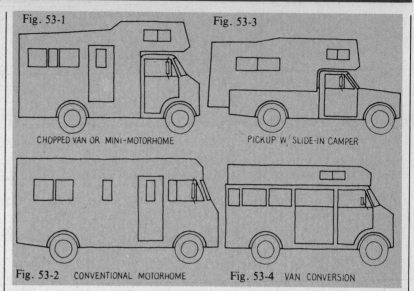

Fig. 53-1
Fig. 53-3
CHOPPED VAN OR MINI-MOTORHOME
PICKUP W/ SLIDE-IN CAMPER
Fig. 53-2   CONVENTIONAL MOTORHOME
Fig. 53-4   VAN CONVERSION

BASIC RULES
FOR SAFE OPERATION

Read the owner's manual

Read the owner's manual provided with your motorhome. Also, check the labels attached to the vehicle to determine weights and load limits. Know how to load your vehicle so that you do not damage its suspension system.

Match your equipment

If you are contemplating purchasing a pickup truck and slide-in camper, make sure the pickup is adequate for the camper you will be using. Select the model pickup that fits your needs based on the size, weight, and configuration of the camper unit.

Inspect and maintain

Follow a rigid schedule of inspection and maintenance to insure that your recreational vehicle is safe. Pay particular attention to brakes, tires, suspension system components, exhaust system, electrical systems and the bottled gas system. Follow all maintenance and safety suggestions regarding LP gas systems.

Drive cautiously

Many motorhomes are big, high and wide. The added height and configuration of a slide-in camper make it more susceptible to tipover in a sudden turn. With both motorhomes and pickup campers, you have a great deal of weight that must be controlled. Take special precautions on the highway, especially when making turns, changing lanes, passing and controlling speed on downgrades.

MAINTENANCE

Do not let vehicle breakdowns or accidents spoil a vacation trip. Practice preventive maintenance, and perform scheduled maintenance services in accordance with recommendations in your owner's manual. At least once a year, have your entire vehicle—engine, brakes, exhaust system, steering system, suspension system and wheel bearings—inspected and serviced by a competent service establishment.

When traveling, each morning before leaving a campground, check your brakes, lighting system and tires. Maintain proper air pressure as recommended in your owner's manual. Carry your own tire gauge, since it will probably be more accurate than those found at service stations. Check all fluid levels in your vehicle, battery, radiator coolant, engine oil, power steering and brake fluid, and transmission fluid. Check tightness of the wheel lugs daily.

Once a year make a complete inspection of your electrical system, including wiring in the motorhome or slide-in camper. Be especially attentive to any wires that run under bunks or in any areas where they may be subject to abrasion.

FIRE AND EXPLOSIONS

LP gas system

The possibility of a fire or explosion is ever present in vehicles having an LP gas system. Be alert to any possible signs of gas leaks, and avoid mistakes that can cause fires and explosions. For example, do not cook while traveling. Turn off the pilot lights on appliances and always shut off the main gas valve. Before pulling up to the gas pumps at a service station, pause and make sure the main gas valve is turned off. Pilot lights can cause explosions at service station pumps.

Be alert to signs of gas leaks while using gas appliances. These can often be detected by an odor of onions or garlic. Never use a match to detect leaks; instead, paint heavy soapy water or a special solution available from your dealer over joints where leaks are suspected. While searching for a leak, do not smoke and do not turn electrical switches on or off.

Electrical system

Inspect accessible wiring periodically for signs of abrasion. Check especially wiring located in areas where it may be abraded by the movement of bunks and other fold-up equipment.

Follow commonsense rules of electrical safety. For example, do not overload circuits. Use extension cords of the three-wire type for proper ground connections. See that your vehicle is properly grounded when using external power sources, and make sure the wire in the extension cord

234

used for such hookups is of the proper gauge—especially if you have an air conditioner.

Install a battery-operated smoke detector. Keep a fire extinguisher handy. Two are better in a pickup camper: one for the trunk cab and one for the camper. In a motorhome, keep one toward the front and one toward the rear of the vehicle.

Tire fires

Tire fires are not rare in motorhomes equipped with dual tires and wheels. Such fires are almost impossible to notice when they first start and extremely difficult to extinguish. They are caused by running on a flat tire. With dual tires, it is difficult to see or feel a flat since the other tire-wheel combination will support it. To avoid this problem, inspect your tires and check tire pressure regularly.

EXHAUST SYSTEM

Every vehicle requires a periodic inspection of all exhaust system components; with slide-in campers, maintaining proper system condition is critical. Deaths have resulted from carbon monoxide poisoning when camper occupants were resting inside their slide-in units with the vehicle engine running. Owners who build their own camper units for installation on their pickups should make sure the vehicle tailpipe is long enough to deliver the exhaust well out from under both the truck body and the overhanging camper unit, or out to the side.

In addition, owners of vehicles equipped with accessories such as air conditioners and heaters that require the vehicle engine to be running should, as a precaution, provide for the operation of these accessories by a different power source.

As an additional precaution, rear doors or windows should be kept shut when driving, to prevent pulling exhaust gases into the camper.

MISCELLANEOUS SAFETY TIPS

● Driving a motorhome is much like driving a bus. The vehicle is big, high and wide. Make sure the mirrors on both sides are properly adjusted so that you can see traffic behind you.
● Avoid backing up a motorhome unless you absolutely must. If you must, have a person stand well to the rear of the vehicle on the driver's side.
● When driving a pickup with a slide-in camper, avoid sudden maneuvers and take curves and turns slowly. The added height and configuration of the camper make it more susceptible to tipover in a sudden turning movement.
● With both motorhomes and pickup campers, make frequent use of mirrors on both sides of the vehicle when changing lanes. Allow a great deal of room before cutting back into a lane in front of other traffic. When reaching the crest of a hill, downshift so that gear ratios may be used to control speed on the downgrade, thereby conserving brakes.
● Before departing on a trip, check your routes. Some tunnels prohibit motorhomes or campers with an LP gas system. Know the height of your motorhome or pickup with slide-in camper. You need this information to be able to determine whether you can go through tunnels, over bridges, and under overpasses. When pulling into a gas station with an overhanging canopy, remember the height of your vehicle.
● When traveling, make sure all doors are closed and that cabinets, drawers, and loose objects are secure.
● Instruct your family on what to do in case of fire, and hold fire drills periodically. Keep a fire extinguisher (preferably two) handy. Some states require a fire extinguisher in recreational vehicles. A foam-mist extinguisher is best.
● You will need a hydraulic jack and a lug wrench in case you have a flat tire or blowout. Carry a tool box containing the following items: electrical tape; friction tape; hand tools such as screwdrivers, pliers, wrenches, pocket knife; extra quart or two of engine oil and a can of hydraulic brake fluid; assorted wooden blocks; triangular highway warning devices or flares; flashlight or flashlights; some wire; tire gauge; small paintbrush to help detect gas leaks; spare fuses; and windshield washer fluid.
● Keep a first-aid kit handy and keep it well stocked with plastic strips, adhesive tape, absorbent cotton, gauze bandage, nonadherent pads, ammonia inhalants, first-aid cream, anti-motion-sickness tablets, aspirin, antiseptic wipes, scissors, tweezers, sterile pocketknife or blades.

54
CAMPING OUTDOORS

This chapter is designed to help you have a safe, pleasant hiking or camping trip. Remember, in case of fire or other emergency, notify the nearest forest office.

KEEP YOUR FIRE SAFE

Select a site on level ground sheltered from high wind, and away from heavy brush, logs, tree trunks, overhanging branches and other combustible materials. Clear the ground down to mineral soil in a circle 10 feet across. Keep your fire small and never leave it unattended. When you break camp, put your fire dead out by drowning it with water, stirring the coals, and then drowning it again.

In some regions, and at certain times of the year, open fires may be prohibited. It is a good idea to check before going into the forest.

If you are camping overnight, build your campfire several yards away from your tent, and be sure the fire is downwind from the tent. Always extinguish campfires and other flame sources before you go to sleep. Never build a fire in a tent. Each year many people are burned and some die in tent fires started by candles, fuel-fired cooking and heating stoves, lanterns such as kerosene lamps, or sparks from a campfire.

Take care if you smoke. Do not smoke while riding or hiking. Use a flat rock as your ashtray or dig down to mineral soil with your heel. Crush out your smoke before you move on.

TRAVEL SAFELY IN THE WOODS

No one expects to get lost in the woods, but it can happen—even to an experienced woodsman and camper. Do not let it happen to you. Never overtax yourself. Plan your travel route. Try to get official maps of the area from the Forest Service or the U.S. Geological Survey. Inquire locally before traveling into back country. Check your clothing and equipment. Be prepared for bad weather, particularly at high altitudes. Wear sturdy shoes or boots. Always carry essential

235

equipment, including matches in a waterproof container, maps, a compass, and a knife. Take food and shelter to meet your needs, but do not overload your pack.

Tell someone where you are going and when you expect to return. Allow plenty of time to reach your campsite; extra time means less temptation to take risks.

Hiking tips

Be observant. Watch the trail and remember your route. Note landmarks, streams, mountains and the lay of the land. Keep track of time and weather. Be alert for loose rocks, ledges and other hazards.

Travel alone only if you are an experienced woodsman. If you are in a group on the trail, keep together; do not let anyone lag behind. Make camp before dark. Traveling in darkness or during a storm may lead to tragedy.

If you get lost

Try to be calm. Sit down and take it easy. A cool head and courage make things appear not too bad after all.

Think. How did you get here? Try to remember mountains, trails, streams, and other points of reference. Can you see any landmarks? Is your situation an emergency or just an inconvenience? What are the dangers of staying put? Of pushing on?

Decide whether to stay put or to push on.

Stay put: Stay put if you are injured or near exhaustion, if the terrain is rugged, if nightfall or bad weather is imminent, if shelter is available, or if you know someone will be looking for you soon.

If you stay, find or make the best shelter possible. Build a signal fire; this will attract the attention of forest fire lookouts and someone will be sent to investigate. If you are still on a trail, do not go far from it without leaving a marker such as a peeled stick pointer or pile of stones to show searchers which way you went.

Push on: Push on if you are still strong enough, if it is still daylight and the weather is good, and there is a reasonable chance for you to get your bearings.

If you push on, go slowly and carefully. Try to find a high point with a good view. Get the lay of the land and plan your route—you may even find your way back to the trail.

If you stay lost, follow a drainage downstream; in most areas this will bring you to a trail, road or transmission line, which you can follow until you reach help. In rugged canyon country, it may be better to follow a ridge uphill until you reach natural shelter among trees or rocks; then build a signal fire and stay put.

SURVIVAL TIPS

Shelter

Always take a tent or tarp, a sleeping bag, a ground pad and ground cloth for overnight sleeping trips. Exposure to the elements is more dangerous than hunger and thirst. You can live more than a week without food and three days without water, but only a few hours in severe weather. Be careful in selecting a tent. Tests have shown that children's cotton tents will ignite and burn completely within a few minutes, and over 80 percent of all tents are cotton. Other tests have shown that the paraffin treatment used to make some tents waterproof actually increases their flammability. Some manufacturers have begun to produce flame-retardant tents, and you should purchase flame-retardant tents whenever possible. Even if you buy a flame-retardant tent, do not take chances with fire. "Flame-retardant" does not mean "flame-proof." Never put gasoline, LP gas, or kerosene in or near a tent. Store flammable liquids in tightly capped safety cans and keep them away from children.

Try to seek shelter in daylight. Get out of the wind. Move from exposed ridges or open flats. Go to the lee (sheltered-from-the-wind) side of a mountain, behind trees, rocks or other natural barriers.

Find natural shelter in rock formations, caves, dense evergreen forests, or behind large logs. In winter, be sure that snow from overhead branches will not fall into your fire.

If you cannot find a natural shelter, build a lean-to with poles and evergreen thatch. If you are unable to do this, make a windbreak of evergreen boughs stuck into the ground or snow.

Do not camp on low ground such as a gulch or ravine bottom; a sudden storm could wash you out (see pages 259–260).

Never seek shelter under a tree because if a thunderstorm comes up, lightning may be drawn to it.

Fire

Conserve your matches. Carry a candle as a fire starter. Be sure you have dry deadwood. If the forest is wet, find dry wood by splitting dead timber that is well off the ground. For tinder, make shavings of dry center wood. Build your fire out of the wind if possible. Start with small twigs or dry duff. Lay twigs so air can circulate. Add larger twigs and branches as fire grows. Clear the area directly around fire of grass that may cause the fire to spread.

Water

Take along canteens filled with water. If you are in dry country and run out of water, look for springs in hollows on the side of a mountain. Some types of trees and plants show the presence of water: willow, cottonwood, sycamore, box elder, alder, birch, and eastern hemlock.

Food

Always bring sufficient food. Dehydrated foods are practical. Also take along utensils, including a cup, plate, pot, silverware and matches.

Many wild fruits and nuts are edible if you run out of food. Look for those favored by birds and animals.

Be sure you can distinguish nonpoisonous foods from poisonous foods. Do not eat mushrooms, holly berries, unknown roots and greens and poisonous plants.

Clothing

Dress properly for hiking and camping. Protect yourself from strong sun by taking along a hat, and protect yourself from inclement weather by taking weatherproof gear. Also pack extra socks for warmth. It is safest to wear long pants to avoid insects and dangerous brush, and to wear boots for good traction in slippery terrain and protection against snakes.

IN CASE OF INJURY

Injury in the woods can be the beginning of a real emergency. Stop immediately. Treat the injury if you can. Make the injured party comfortable, and send or signal for help. If rescue is delayed, make an emergency shelter. Do not move until help arrives—unless there is more danger in remaining where you are. Use extreme care in moving injured persons.

Always take along a first-aid kit. If you do not purchase a prepackaged kit, include the following items: insect repellent, gauze bandage, plastic strip bandages, absorbent cotton, adhesive tape, aspirin, scissors, tweezers, antiseptic wipes, ammonia inhalants, sterile pocketknife or blades. If a hiker suffers from severe allergies, be sure he takes along an insect sting kit, which is available only with a prescription.

Emergency first aid

In case of injury, the following problems should be attended to first.

Restore breathing: If the victim has stopped breathing, use mouth-to-mouth artificial respiration. Tip the head back with neck raised and extend jaw. Clear air passages, pinch nostrils, blow in until chest rises, release. Repeat 12 times per minute for adults, 20 for children. Use shallow puffs for children. Continue until normal breathing resumes (see pages 17–18 for more detailed treatment).

Stop severe bleeding: Use direct pressure over wound with clean cloth, using fingers or heel of hand. Bandage when bleeding stops. Use tourniquet only as a last resort and do not leave the tourniquet on too long (see pages 19–20 for more detailed treatment).

For internal bleeding, treat as for shock (see below and page 21).

Treat for shock: Make victim lie down. Loosen collar and belt. Never give an unconscious person food or drink; this also applies if you suspect internal injuries (see page 21 for more detailed treatment).

SOS SIGNALS

If alone or unable to send for help, signal by whatever means are available. The universal call for help is three signals in rapid succession repeated at regular intervals: three shots, three flashes of light, three blasts on a whistle, three puffs of smoke. A signal fire will help guide rescuers, but be careful not to let it turn into a wildfire. It may be easiest to carry a police whistle in your pocket or pack.

AT SEA

55
BOATS

While boating is certainly one of the most delightful of pastimes, it is also one that requires common sense and responsible behavior. On top of that, you should have a basic knowledge of how to operate a boat and what equipment to bring along. You can't buy a boat, hoist a sail or start a motor, and take off. Boats can run aground, they can capsize, they can be swamped by a wave, they can be dismasted, the rudder can break or fall overboard, the engine can explode, and so on. None of these things need happen, but you have to know what you are doing, and know how to cope with these and other emergencies. The sea is very unforgiving to boaters who act foolishly. So take a course, read a boating guide, talk to skilled boaters, and learn as much as you can before you get underway. You'll enjoy it more and you'll be safe.

EQUIPMENT

The United States Coast Guard Auxiliary of the Department of Transportation recommends the equipment described below for safe boating. The Coast Guard Auxiliary offers a courtesy marine examination of your boat's safety-related equipment, covering all federal and state requirements plus additional standards recommended by the Auxiliary. Legal requirements are based upon the length and construction of the vessel. Bowsprits, outboard motor brackets and similar attachments are *not* considered in determining the length of the vessel. *Note*: Legal requirements are based on the Federal Boat Safety Act of 1971, which applies to all noncommercial boats, however they are propelled and whatever length they are.

The Auxiliary also gives public education classes for safe boating, including Principles of Sailing, Basic Boating, Skipper's Outboard Special, and Introduction to Sailing. For information, contact the director of the Auxiliary branch nearest you. Other sources of information and education include the U.S. Power Squadrons,

various state organizations and the American Red Cross.

Personal flotation devices

Personal flotation devices (PFDs) must be Coast Guard approved, in serviceable condition, readily accessible, and of a suitable size. They are designed to perform as described in calm water and when the wearer is not using any other flotation material.

Type I: most effective in rough waters; easiest to don in an emergency; reversible and comes in two sizes—Adult (90 lbs. plus) and Child (less than 90 lbs).
Type II: more comfortable to wear; sizes—Adult (90 lbs. plus), Medium Child (50 lbs. to 90 lbs.), Small Child (30 lbs. to 50 lbs.), Infant (30 lbs. or less); preferred where there is a probability of a quick rescue.
Type III: the most selection in sizes; preferred where there is a probability of quick rescue.
Type IV: Not recommended for nonswimmers and children.

All recreational boats 16 feet or over in length, except canoes and kayaks, must have one Type I, II or III wearable PFD of a suitable size for each person on board, and one Type IV PFD throwable in each boat.

All recreational boats less than 16 feet in length (and canoes and kayaks of any size) must have one Type I, II, III or IV PFD of a suitable size for each person on board.

Many kinds of PFDs are available. The conversion table (Fig. 55-1) gives equivalent "type" information for existing devices that may not be marked as Type I, II, III or IV. It is best, however, to choose Coast Guard approved PFDs that have the type listed on the device.

Backfire flame control

Efficient means of backfire flame control are required for each carburetor on every inboard engine installed after April 25, 1940. Acceptable means of backfire control are:
• a Coast Guard-approved backfire flame arrestor secured to the air intake of each carburetor; or
• an engine and fuel intake system which provides equivalent protection and is labeled to indicate Coast Guard acceptance; or
• any attachment firmly secured to the carburetor or arrangement of the air intake by means of which flames caused by backfire will be dispersed to the atmosphere in such a way as not to endanger the vessel, persons on board or adjacent area.

Fire extinguishers

Fire extinguishers are classified according to type and size (see Fig. 55-2). There are four types: (1) carbon dioxide (CO_2), (2) dry chemical, (3) foam, (4) halon. A letter will designate the type. A number represents the size of the fire the extinguisher will put out and the amount of agent it holds. Extinguishers approved by

PFD CONVERSION TABLE

Number on label	Devices marked	are equivalent to
160.002	Life preserver	Performance Type I personal flotation device
160.003	Life preserver	Performance Type I personal flotation device
160.004	Life preserver	Performance Type I personal flotation device
160.005	Life preserver	Performance Type I personal flotation device
160.009	Ring life buoy	Performance Type IV personal flotation device
160.047	Buoyant vest	Performance Type II personal flotation device
160.048	Buoyant cushion	Performance Type IV personal flotation device
160.049	Buoyant cushion	Performance Type IV personal flotation device
160.050	Ring life buoy	Performance Type IV personal flotation device
160.052	Buoyant vest	Performance Type II personal flotation device
160.055	Life preserver	Performance Type I personal flotation device
160.060	Buoyant vest	Performance Type II personal flotation device
160.064	Special-purpose water-safety buoyant devices	A device intended to be worn may be equivalent to Type II or Type III. A device that is equivalent to Type III is marked "Type III Device—may not turn unconscious wearer." A device intended to be grasped is equivalent to Type IV.

Fig. 55-1

AMOUNT OF EXTINGUISHING AGENT REQUIRED

Classification (type-size)	Foam (minimum gallons)	Carbon Dioxide (minimum pounds)	Dry Chemical (minimum pounds)	Halon (minimum pounds)
B–I	1¼	4	2	2½
B–II	2½	15	10	None

Note: Carbon tetrachloride extinguishers and others of the toxic vaporizing-liquid type such as chlorobromomethane are no longer approved and are not accepted as required fire extinguishers.

Fig. 55-2

MINIMUM NUMBER OF HAND PORTABLE FIRE EXTINGUISHERS REQUIRED

Length of vessel	No fixed system in machinery space	Fixed fire extinguishing system in machinery space
Less than 16′	1 B–I	None
16′ to less than 26′	1 B–I	None
26′ to less than 40′	2 B–I or 1 B–II	1 B–I
40′ to 65′	3 B–I or 1 B–II and 1 B–I	2 B–I or 1 B–II

Fig. 55-3

the Coast Guard for motorboats are hand portable and of either B-I or B-II classification.

The number of approved extinguishers required depends upon the length and construction of the motorboat. When the engine compartment of the motorboat is equipped with a fixed, or built-in, extinguishing system, you will need one less hand portable B-I extinguisher. Equivalent sizes and extinguishing agents are shown in Fig. 55-3.

On outboard motorboats less than 26 feet long, constructed so that entrapment of flammable vapors cannot occur, you do not have to carry fire extinguishers, but it is a good precaution to do so.

On motorboats which do not meet the above exception, you are required by federal law to have fire extinguishers on board that are charged, in good working order and regularly inspected.

Bell, whistle or horn

The requirement to carry a bell depends upon the length of the boat. All bells must emit a clear, bell-like tone when struck. The type of whistle or horn required differs with the length of the boat. All horns or whistles must be capable of producing a blast of two seconds or more in duration. The requirements for bell, whistle or horn are shown in Fig. 55-4.

Lights

Vessels less than 150 feet in length under inland rules are required to show one all-around (32-point) white light forward. This light is visible to a boat approaching from any direction, and is displayed in the fore part of the vessel. Power boats under 26 feet may utilize their 32-point white stern lights, provided other navigational lights are not displayed.

Rowing boats, whether under oars or sail, must have on hand a lantern showing a white light, which must be exhibited whenever there is a danger of collision.

Navigation lights: All motorboats are required to display navigation lights prescribed for their length when operated between sunset and sunrise. The international configuration may be displayed on the high seas and by motorboats on inland waters (see Fig. 55-5).

Length	Bell	Whistle or Horn
☐ < 16′	none required	none required
☐ 16′ to < 26′	none required	mouth, hand or power operated, audible at least ½ mile
☐ 26′ to < 40′	required	hand or power operated, audible at least 1 mile
☐ 40′ to ≤ 65′	required	power operated, audible at least 1 mile

Note: While it is not required that all lengths of boats carry the bell, whistle or horn, Rules of the Road require ALL vessels to give proper signals if a signaling situation develops.

Fig. 55-4

Place lights high enough so that people or parts of the boat will not obstruct the light. "10 pts. 1 mi." means that the light can be seen by another vessel through an arc of 10 points for a distance of 1 mile (see Fig. 55-6).

Ventilation

Every engine and fuel tank compartment which was constructed or decked over after April 25, 1940, and before August 1, 1979, must have at least two ventilator ducts fitted with cowls or their equivalent, to efficiently ventilate the bilges of every engine and fuel compartment containing fuel with a flash point of less than 110° F. (Gasoline has a flash point lower than 110°—diesel fuel has a flash point above 110°.) One cowl must face forward as an intake, ducted to at least halfway to the bilge or at least below the level of the carburetor air intake. The other cowl must face backward as an exhaust, ducted to the lower portion of the bilge.

Boats with construction dates of August 1, 1979, or after are required to have (1) powered ventilation system on all inboard (33 CFR 183.610 Subpart K), (2) natural ventilation system for fuel tank compartment (33 CFR 183.620 Subpart K).

Exceptions include: (1) open boat—a boat so constructed that it will not permit the entrapment of explosive fumes, (2) diesel-powered vessels, (3) boats constructed or decked over prior to April 25, 1940.

Distress flares

Distress flares are not a federal requirement; however, it is a good safety idea to have *visual distress signals* on board. There are many types to choose from. Use distress signals to alert another person or vessel that someone is in trouble, and as a locator to guide assistance to him. Not all devices are effective for both day and night, or for all weather and visibility

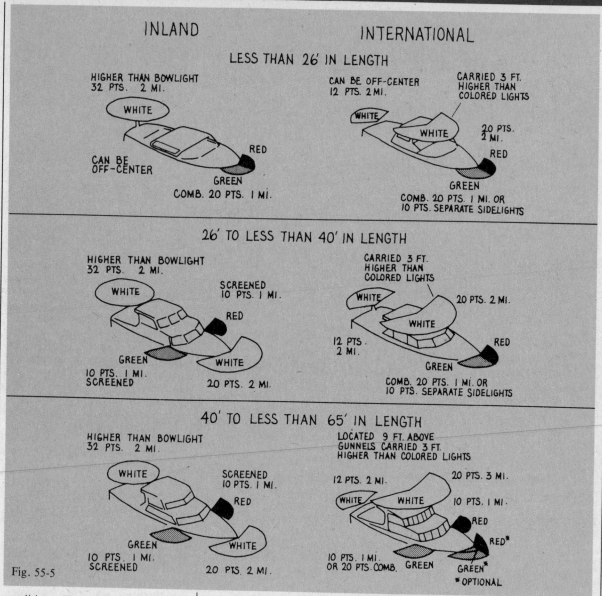

INLAND   INTERNATIONAL

LESS THAN 26' IN LENGTH

HIGHER THAN BOWLIGHT
32 PTS. 2 MI.

WHITE

CAN BE
OFF-CENTER

RED

GREEN
COMB. 20 PTS. I MI.

CAN BE OFF-CENTER
12 PTS. 2 MI.

CARRIED 3 FT.
HIGHER THAN
COLORED LIGHTS

WHITE

WHITE

20 PTS.
2 MI.

RED

GREEN
COMB. 20 PTS. I MI. OR
10 PTS. SEPARATE SIDELIGHTS

26' TO LESS THAN 40' IN LENGTH

HIGHER THAN BOWLIGHT
32 PTS. 2 MI.

WHITE

SCREENED
10 PTS. I MI.

RED

GREEN
10 PTS. I MI.
SCREENED

WHITE
20 PTS. 2 MI.

CARRIED 3 FT.
HIGHER THAN
COLORED LIGHTS

WHITE

WHITE

20 PTS. 2 MI.

12 PTS.
2 MI.

RED

GREEN
COMB. 20 PTS. I MI. OR
10 PTS. SEPARATE SIDELIGHTS

40' TO LESS THAN 65' IN LENGTH

HIGHER THAN BOWLIGHT
32 PTS. 2 MI.

WHITE

SCREENED
10 PTS. I MI.

RED

GREEN
10 PTS. I MI.
SCREENED

WHITE
20 PTS. 2 MI.

LOCATED 9 FT. ABOVE
GUNNELS CARRIED 3 FT.
HIGHER THAN COLORED LIGHTS

12 PTS. 2 MI.

WHITE

WHITE

20 PTS. 3 MI.

10 PTS. I MI.

RED

RED*

GREEN
10 PTS. I MI.
OR 20 PTS. COMB.

GREEN*
* OPTIONAL

Fig. 55-5

conditions. Keep these facts in mind when considering which device or devices to purchase. A visual distress signal of any kind works only if someone is around to see it. Conserve your signals until you are reasonably sure of being detected. Wait until you see or hear a vessel or aircraft before you ignite a flare or use any one-time device (see Fig. 55-7).

If you see a distress signal, notify the nearest Coast Guard office or state authorities. Assist the vessel if you can do so without endangering your own life.

Note. The Federal Boat Safety Act of 1971 contains a "Good Samaritan"

section whereby "any person . . . who gratuitously and in good faith renders assistance at the scene of a vessel collision, accident, or other casualty without objection of any person assisted, *shall not be held liable for any civil damages* as a result of the rendering of assistance or for any act or omission in providing or arranging salvage, assistance where the assisting person acts as an ordinary, reasonably prudent man would have acted under the same or similar circumstances."

Day:

Orange smoke, either hand held or floating, makes an excellent signal. Use it on clear days with winds under

10 knots. Higher winds tend to disperse it, making it hard to distinguish. Most devices last up to two minutes. Use the signal only when another boat is visible or an aircraft can be heard. A combination hand-held device—smoke on one end and a flare on the other—is available to the boater. If you select this device, carry at least three.

Flags should be bright orange, with a black ball and square superimposed. This signal is especially eye-catching in bright sunlight. Wave it from a paddle or display it from a mast.

Night:

Red meteors or stars are good sig-

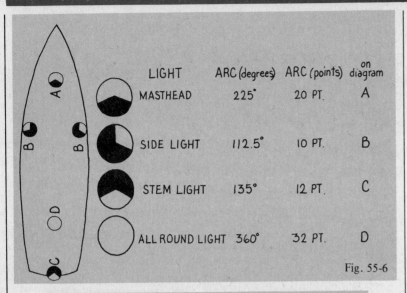

LIGHT	ARC (degrees)	ARC (points)	on diagram
MASTHEAD	225°	20 PT.	A
SIDE LIGHT	112.5°	10 PT.	B
STEM LIGHT	135°	12 PT.	C
ALL ROUND LIGHT	360°	32 PT.	D

Fig. 55-6

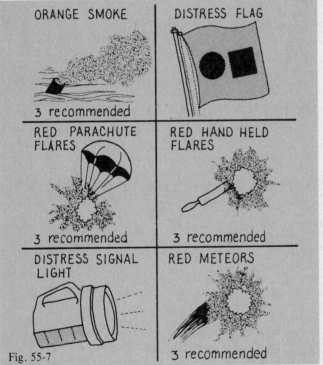

ORANGE SMOKE — 3 recommended

DISTRESS FLAG

RED PARACHUTE FLARES — 3 recommended

RED HAND HELD FLARES — 3 recommended

DISTRESS SIGNAL LIGHT

RED METEORS — 3 recommended

Fig. 55-7

ly seen. It does drift with the wind. In winds above 15 knots, it will rapidly move downwind from the distressed craft. Use a red parachute flare when another boat or an aircraft is in sight or you hear engines. If you select this device, carry at least three of them.

Red hand-held marine flares are widely used as distress signals on boats. They are most effective at night or in conditions of restricted visibility such as fog or haze. Always be careful when using a flare. Hold it firmly at arm's length at about a 45-degree angle to the body, pointed downwind to prevent burns from molten residue. If you select this device, carry at least three. Be extremely careful if you have gasoline or oil sloshing around in the bilges. By the authority of the Commandant of the Coast Guard, any vessel that has an accumulation of fuel in the bilges or a compartment other than a fuel tank is considered to be operating in an "unsafe condition," and is subject to termination of the vessel until the unsafe condition has been corrected. Never ignite or use a flare close to a gasoline container. Do not use highway-type flares, since they usually will not fire when wet, and are not bright enough to be seen from any distance.

Other methods: There are several other methods for indicating distress. The flashing of a mirror, a flag or national ensign flown upside down, a gun fired at intervals of one minute, the continuous sounding of a horn or whistle, the slow and continuous raising and lowering of arms stretched to each side, signals transmitted by emergency position—indicating radio beams (EPIRB), "May Day" broadcast on channel 16 VHF (FM) (156.8 MHz) or channel 9 CB, an open flame in a bucket. *Note:* If the Coast Guard or another rescue organization responds to your call, you may be asked many questions that seem unnecessary. Every question is important, since each item of information increases your chances of rescue. If you are in immediate danger, help will be dispatched while the information is being taken.

Basic tools and spare parts

A few basic hand tools and spare parts are a must for every boat. The following list will give you some idea of what to have, but many more tools

nals and have been recognized as distress signals for many years. Because of their rapid descent, they are affected less by high winds. Their short duration demands that you fire them only when you see another vessel's lights or hear an aircraft. If you select this device, always carry three or more.

A distress signal lantern or automatic distress signal light is a good signaling device when used to flash the internationally recognized distress signal, SOS (three short flashes, three long, and three short). Flashed slowly (four to six times each minute), it is an unmistakable signal to most boaters. You can check this device at any time for serviceability. *Note:* A flashlight may not be powerful enough to be visible at distances greater than one mile.

Day or night:

A red parachute flare is a good distress signal, and is widely recognized. Its altitude and slow descent, coupled with a brilliant intensity, make it easi-

and parts, especially tools of a special nature for your engine, should be carried aboard.

Test lamp: The test lamp is handy and easy to make (see Fig. 55-8). Simply purchase a socket to fit the bulbs used on your boat and attach two lengths of wire about six feet long. Strip one inch of the ends for test prods. Make sure the bulb is the same voltage as the electrical system—for example, 6 volts or 12 volts. Attach the end of one wire to the positive terminal of a battery and attach the other wire to a grounded current. If the bulb lights up, the system is operating.

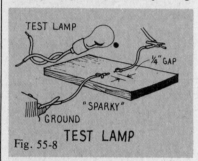

Fig. 55-8 TEST LAMP

Sparky: Staple two pieces of wire to a piece of wood and leave a ¼-inch gap between the ends. Alligator clips at each of the other ends are fastened to (1) spark plug wire and (2) engine block (ground) according to the diagram above. Use this device for a quick spark test (see below).

Hand tools: Insulated adjustable tools are best for the average small job. Some of them are: an adjustable end wrench, slip joint pliers, pipe wrench, vise grip, screwdrivers in various sizes, box end wrench set, hammer plug wrench, hammer, strong knife.

Spare parts: Basic spare parts include points for distributor, condenser, coil, spark plugs, fuel pump, fuel filter for diesel engines.

Other essentials: Keep a compass or battery-powered radio direction finder on board in case you get lost at sea. It is also helpful to have an inflatable dinghy and paddle on hand.

EMERGENCY REPAIRS AFLOAT

As a boat owner or operator, you may be in a serious situation if your engine fails, or some other emergency develops at sea and you are unsure of what to do or how to make repairs. The information and illustrations here, from the Coast Guard pamphlet "Emergency Repairs Afloat," will acquaint you with basic principles, although they may have to be adapted to the equipment on your own craft. Most manufacturers provide specific troubleshooting manuals and repair charts for their products. Keep these manuals on board.

Troubleshooting

Never make more than one adjustment at a time when troubleshooting. Proceed slowly and cautiously. Nearly all causes of engine trouble are simple and curable. Before working on any electrical parts or doing anything that may cause a spark, *get rid of any gas fumes.* If the smell of gasoline persists, find the source and repair it before going on.

Starting motor will not operate:

1. *Discharged or low battery.* Check the battery with a hydrometer or voltmeter. If you don't have one of these, touch both terminals carefully with a piece of metal, such as the handles of a pair of pliers. A fat spark indicates a live battery.

2. *Loose or corroded terminals.* Disconnect the terminals, then check the battery terminal posts and cable ends. Clean terminal posts and cable ends until they shine; reconnect and tighten to insure good contact.

3. *Corroded, acid-eaten cables.* Battery acid may corrode the cables. Check both cables for good conduction.

4. *Defective ignition switch.* If your instruments (fuel and temperature gauges and ammeter) operate when you turn the key in the ignition, the switch is probably all right. If the gauges do not work, check the terminals on the back of the switch for tightness; then check the other end of each wire for a good connection.

5. *Defective starter switch.* Examine the connections to the switch, the solenoid, and the starter. If the connections are good, connect the small and the large terminals on top of the solenoid, using a screwdriver with an insulated handle. If the starter motor turns, the switch must be replaced, but the engine can be started using the screwdriver as described above (see Fig. 55-9).

Starting motor operates but will not engage: Loosen the starting mo-

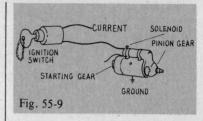

Fig. 55-9

tor from the engine by removing the attaching bolt. Check the small pinion gear (the so-called bendix) to see if it is stuck on the shaft. If it is stuck, free it up with a hammer and oil it with a few drops of oil from the engine dipstick.

Starting motor operates but engine will not start:

1. *Engine primary electrical circuit (small wires).* Look for corroded, dirty, damaged or loose connections in the ignition primary circuits. This includes the wires from the junction box to the ignition switch, as well as the wires to the coil and to the distributor.

2. *Engine secondary electrical circuit (large wires to plugs).* Look for broken or damaged wires to spark plugs and from the coil to the distributor cap. There may be moisture on the wires or on the spark plugs that will cause the spark to be grounded.

3. *Ignition.* Check the distributor points to see if they are opening and closing as the engine is cranked. Stop the cranking with the points in their maximum open position. The opening should be about .020 inches. *Note:* A matchbook cover may be used in an emergency to measure this point gap.

Inspect the distributor cap to see if the contact button is in place and is free to move. This contact is to carry current from the coil to the spark plug wires and must make contact with the rotor. *Don't forget to replace the rotor after you have inspected the distributor* (see Fig. 55-10).

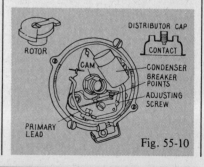

Fig. 55-10

4. *Quick spark test.* Using a pair of insulated pliers, hold a spark plug wire ¼ inch from the engine while cranking the engine over with the ignition switch on. *Caution:* Don't hold the wire with bare hands while cranking the engine. It may give you a strong shock. You may place the wire on the engine block or use a sparky (see page 242). If spark occurs, then trouble may be with the plugs or the fuel system. If no spark occurs, then remove the secondary wire from the distributor cap to the coil (see Fig. 55-11). Repeat the ¼-inch test, and if spark occurs the trouble lies between the center terminal on the distributor cap and the spark plugs. This would include the distributor cap, the rotor contact, and the spark plugs and wires.

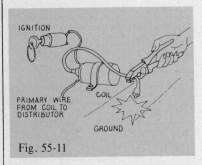

Fig. 55-11

If no spark occurred in the above check, the trouble is in the primary circuit.

5. *Overheated engine.* An overheated engine might not start until you allow it to cool.

Starting motor operates, spark is good but engine will not start:

1. *Out of fuel?* Always check fuel before leaving port. A good rule to follow is never to cruise farther than one-third of your fuel supply. Save two-thirds for the return trip.

2. *Is fuel reaching the fuel pump?* See if the fuel filter or sediment bowl is filled with fuel. If it is not, and if the tank is full, then the shut-off cock may have vibrated closed or a fuel line may be clogged. Disconnect the inset side of the pump and blow through the line. Look for dents in the fuel line, and air leaks in the fuel pump gaskets or in the fuel line connections. Make sure the gasoline tank vent is open (see Fig. 55-12).

3. *Is fuel reaching the carburetor?* Remove the sediment bowl from the fuel pump and see if the screen in

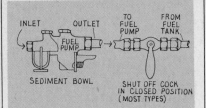

Fig. 55-12

the pump body is clean. Then disconnect the outlet line from the fuel pump to the carburetor and see if fuel flows out when the engine is cranked. Make sure ignition is off when making this test. Pulling out the coil wire will insure that the ignition is dead.

4. *Is fuel reaching the cylinders?* Remove a spark plug and see if it is moist. If there is no fuel on the plug, the idling jet may be clogged. Refer to the engine manual and determine which hole is the idling jet. Never touch the main jet. It never goes into operation at engine cranking speeds.

5. *Is the choke closing properly?* This is especially important on dual carburetors because if the linkage permits one choke to remain open, both chokes will be out of service.

6. *Is the engine flooded?* If the spark plugs are wet, this indicates flooding caused by using the choke too long. The correct way to dry out the cylinders is to open the throttle wide. Put the choke in the open position (nonchoking), and with the ignition on, crank the engine several times. This draws nothing but air through the carburetor. *Note:* Always replace the flame arrestor before cranking the engine.

Warning. Before attempting any electrical repairs as outlined, make sure bilges and engine compartment are free of explosive vapors. And before making any checks in which fuel may be spilled, turn off all electrical equipment, have a container ready to catch any spilled fuel, and have someone stand by with a fire extinguisher.

Diesel engines: The diesel engine is relatively trouble free. There are only two basic considerations when checking for trouble: Is the engine getting air, and is the engine getting fuel?

1. *Air.* Some diesel engines are equipped with automatic air dampers

that close off the air supply in case of overheating or loss of oil pressure. Check the air inlet cleaner and screen and see that the passage to the intake manifold is clear.

2. *Fuel.* Fuel problems will usually fall into the following categories:

● A shutoff valve in the fuel line may have vibrated closed.

● Out of fuel.

● Water in the fuel. Locate the fuel filter and open the drain cock in the bottom. Watch for water. If there is water in the filter, drain it all out and prime the fuel system with the prime pump or by cranking the engine.

● Clogged or dirty filter. Change the filter element.

● Air leaks in the fuel system. Check all connections in the fuel lines from the tank to the fuel pump, and tighten. Check gaskets on the fuel filter and strainer housing or cap. Disconnect the fuel return line and allow fuel to flow until no air shows in the fuel.

● Fuel not reaching engine. Some diesel engines have electrical stop switches or solenoids in the fuel system which cut off the fuel when you shut down the engine. You may find such a switch in the fuel line near the engine fuel pump. A short circuit may have closed the solenoid. Disconnect the wires of the solenoid and try to start the engine.

● Air in fuel lines. When fuel tanks are changed, some air can enter the lines and cause the engine to stop running. Use the prime pump to restore fuel pressure and try to restart.

Electrical problems. Know your engine and all the various systems installed on it. Most electrical problems will be in the starting system. (See "Starting motor will not operate," page 242.) Other electrical problems are centered on fuel cutoffs, as mentioned before, and overspeed trip devices and emergency alarm systems. The overspeed trip, a device which automatically triggers air and fuel shutoffs when the engine speed is excessive, is often overlooked when troubleshooting. If you have an overspeed trip on your vessel, have a mechanic point it out to you and show you how to reset it.

Emergency repairs

Most emergency repairs can be made with what you have on board.

Broken fan belt: Fan belts are

243

made to last, but it's a good idea to carry a spare. In an emergency, a replacement can be made from a piece of line or rope. Simply tie the line around the pulleys, securing the ends with a square knot. Tighten the movable pulley and you're underway again.

Broken pipe or hose: Bandage the break with rags or a piece of canvas and tie it with line or your belt.

Lost rudder: Make an emergency steering device by using buckets, deck covers or anything you can tie to a line and drag behind your boat. By shifting the line from side to side (as shown in Fig. 55-13), you can control

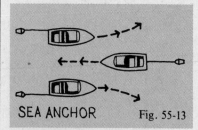

SEA ANCHOR   Fig. 55-13

your direction fairly well. This makeshift rig is called a sea anchor, and works well if used properly.

Engine oil leak: Simply catch oil in a pan or bucket and pour it back into the engine.

Complete electrical failure: To get the engine running, disconnect all electrical equipment from the battery except the large cables from the battery to the starter. Connect a length of wire from the battery post (positive or large post) to the coil where the thin wire from the ignition switch is connected and start the engine by grounding the small terminal on the starter solenoid (see the diagrams on pages 242–243) with a screwdriver. To stop the engine, disconnect the coil wire. In most cases you will not be able to proceed at high speed while nursing a sick engine, but the important thing is getting into a port where permanent repairs can be made.

Staying afloat

If you find a large quantity of water in the bilges, your first thought may be that the boat is sinking. *Don't abandon your boat right away.* Put on your personal flotation device and have signaling devices ready. Then look around for the reason for all the water in the boat.

Most boats have openings in the hull that are necessary to the operation of the craft. Some of these openings are: engine-cooling water suction; head suction and discharge; galley drain; bait-box pump supply; propeller shaft, with packing; boat plug. Any of these items could be leaking. Check them all and any other hull fittings. The engine-cooling water line may be broken. While the engine is running, it may be pumping the boat full of water. While checking the hull fitting, look for damage to the hull. If you find damage, you may be able to save the boat and yourself by stuffing blankets or a pillow into a damaged area. Wedge them down with a deck cover or paddle. Tear off a railing if necessary to make repairs. Get underway if possible and head for the nearest land or other boats.

If you must abandon, keep everyone together and calm. Use a length of rope to connect all survivors together facing each other. This position will give the most buoyancy and will help keep the group warm and in good spirits until help arrives. Stay with the boat. Most boats will not sink completely; instead they will reach equilibrium with the decks awash and the bow or stern on the surface, or may roll over with the underwater body on the surface. The best procedure is usually to stay with the boat until help arrives. Not only will you have something to hang on to, but you will be more easily spotted by searchers.

SURVIVAL IN THE WATER

Man overboard

One of the most serious emergencies that can happen in boating is for a person to fall overboard. The following instructions come from the National Safety Council's pamphlet "Suddenly in Command."

Get to the driver's seat and shut off the motor. Locate the person in the water quickly, restart the motor and approach slowly from downwind—that is, with the wind in your face—so you don't drift into the victim after the motor stops. Get to where you can throw a flotation cushion, and stop the motor. Get the cushion as close to the victim as possible. If you miss, throw another one, or a flotation jacket. Don't waste time trying to pick up the bad throw. Toss the victim a line.

A ski tow rope often is handy. Tie one end to the boat, coil the rope and heave it. Get it as close as you can. When the victim has grasped the line, pull him slowly toward the boat. Never bring a person alongside or try to get him aboard with the motor running; it may slip into gear and the spinning prop is extremely dangerous.

Try to get a PFD on him, or at least loop the line under his arms and fasten it to the boat so he can rest. If you are not strong enough to get the victim into the boat without his help, the best thing to do is to sit tight and signal for help. Before you signal, anchor the boat to prevent drift, if the water is not too deep for the available anchor line. Be sure the line is attached to the boat. Then lower the anchor over the side—do not toss it.

Hypothermia and cold-water survival

The source of the following information is the U.S. Coast Guard pamphlet "Hypothermia and Cold Water Survival."

Hypothermia is a subnormal temperature within the body core. When a person is immersed in cold water, the skin and nearby tissues cool very fast. However, it may take 10 to 15 minutes before the temperature of the heart and brain starts to drop. When the core temperature reaches 90° F, the victim may become unconscious. When it drops to 85° F, his heart usually fails, causing death. However, a person in cold water may drown because he loses the use of his arms and legs and his consciousness becomes clouded (see Fig. 55-14).

Survival in cold water depends on many factors. The temperature of the water is only one; others include body size, fat and activity in the water. Large people cool more slowly than small people, and fat people more slowly than thin. Swimming or treading water will increase a person's susceptibility to hypothermia and will cause him to cool about 35% faster than if he remains still. The so-called drown-proofing technique, which requies putting the head into the water and removing it every 10 seconds to breathe, will cause a person to cool even more—about 82% faster than if he floats still with the head out of the water.

An average person, wearing light

244

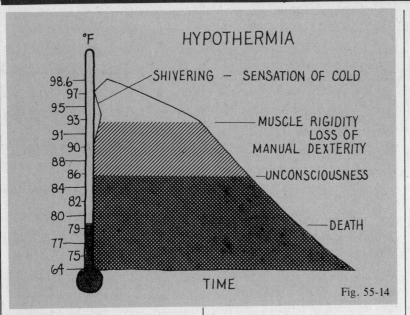

HYPOTHERMIA

°F
98.6
97
95
93
91
90
88
86
84
82
80
79
77
75
64

SHIVERING — SENSATION OF COLD

MUSCLE RIGIDITY
LOSS OF
MANUAL DEXTERITY

UNCONSCIOUSNESS

DEATH

TIME

Fig. 55-14

clothing and a PFD, may survive 2½ to 3 hours in 50° F water by remaining still. This survival time can be increased considerably by getting as far out of the water as possible and covering the head. Getting into or onto a boat or anything else that floats can be a real lifesaver.

The following table compares predicted survival times for an average person in 50° F water under various circumstances.

Situation	Predicted Survival Time (in hours)
No flotation	
Drown-proofing	1.5
Treading water	2.0
With flotation	
Swimming	2.0
Holding still	2.7
HELP	4.0
Huddle	4.0

If you fall into cold water, remember that water conducts heat many times faster than air. Therefore, get in or on the boat to get as far out of the water as possible. Most boats will float even when capsized or swamped. Wearing a PFD is a must. It will keep you afloat even if you are unconscious. Remaining still and if possible assuming the fetal position (called heat-escape-lessening posture, or HELP—see Fig. 55-15) will increase

your survival time. About 50% of the heat is lost from the head, so it is important to keep the head out of the water. Other areas of high heat loss are the neck, the sides and the groin.

HEAT-ESCAPE-LESSENING POSTURE

Fig. 55-15

If there are several people in the water, huddling close, side to side in a circle, will also help preserve body heat.

Whether to try to swim for shore is a difficult decision. It depends on many things. Some good swimmers have been able to swim almost a mile in 50° F water before being overcome by hypothermia. Others have not been able to swim 100 yards. Furthermore, distances on the water are deceptive. It is probably better to stay with the boat. Even a capsized boat is easier for rescuers to spot than a person in the water. Do not swim unless there is absolutely no chance of rescue and you are absolutely certain you can make it. If you do swim, use a PFD or some other flotation aid.

First aid for hypothermia victims: Incorrect treatment of hypothermia victims may induce a condition known as after-drop. This is caused by improper rewarming, which allows cold, stagnant blood from the extremities to return to the core of the body. When this happens, the core temperature may drop below the level which will sustain life. For this reason, hypothermia victims must be handled gently and should not be allowed to walk.

Move the victim to shelter and warmth as rapidly as possible. Gently remove all wet clothing. The feeble amount of heat energy the victim has left must not be expended on warming and drying wet clothing.

Apply heat to the core of the body (head, neck, sides and groin). Place the victim on a hard, flat surface to allow for cardiopulmonary resuscitation, should the need arise.

Wrap warm, moist towels or other textiles around victim's head, neck, sides and groin. As the packs cool, rewarm them by adding warm water (about 105° F). Check the temperature of the water with the elbow; it should be warm but not burn. You can also use hot-water bottles and heated blankets. An effective measure is for one or two of the rescuers to remove their own clothing and use their bodies to warm the victim's naked body. A sleeping bag or blanket should be used to conserve the body heat.

If the victim appears dead, heart massage and mouth-to-mouth resuscitation should be administered. Never put an unconscious victim in a bathtub. In cases of mild hypothermia, dry clothing and shelter may be all that are needed before the victim appears normal. However, all hypothermia victims should see a doctor.

Never give a hypothermia victim anything to drink, especially not alcohol. Do not rub frozen body areas, especially not with snow. Do not wrap a hypothermic in a blanket without another source of heat, unless it is to protect him against further heat loss before treatment.

Prevention of hypothermia: The best way to avoid hypothermia is to keep from winding up in the water. Do not stand or move around in a small boat. Do not overload your boat or distribute the load unevenly. Do not decelerate suddenly, allowing the stern wake to overtake and swamp the

245

boat by washing over the transom.

SAFE-BOATING TIPS

Following is a summary of important boating tips.

1. Have a working knowledge of your boat. Many community high schools, colleges, and other educational institutions have courses on topics that could help the weekend sailor. Always keep your boat and engine in good repair.

2. Know the various distress signals (See pages 240-241).

3. Gasoline vapors are explosive. Close all doors, hatches, and ports while fueling. Extinguish galley fires and pilot lights. Do not smoke. Keep the filling nozzle in contact with the tank to prevent sparks. Fuel portable tanks out of the boat. Do not use gasoline stoves, heaters or lights on board.

4. Do not operate electronic gear such as radios while fueling.

5. Know your fuel tank capacity.

6. After fueling, ventilate all compartments and check the machinery and fuel tank spaces for fumes before starting the motor. Keep fuel lines tight and bilges clean.

7. Always have children and non-swimmers wear personal flotation devices. Make sure everyone on board knows how to put them on. Have a sufficient number of personal flotation devices on board (see page 238).

8. Keep an alert lookout.

9. Do not operate in the vicinity of a diver's flag.

10. Watch your wake.

11. Know and obey the "rules of the road."

12. If you capsize, remember to stay with the boat if it continues to float.

13. Good housekeeping is important. Cleanliness diminishes the possibility of fire and tripping hazards.

14. Have an anchor and sufficient line to assure a good hold in a blow. Anchor by the bow of the boat, not the stern.

15. Carry a secondary means of propulsion on small boats—a second small engine or even oars or paddles.

16. Make sure your boat is equipped with a bailer. It's a good idea to carry a hand bailer or scoop even when equipped with an electric bilge pump. If there is any question about safety equipment, call your local Coast Guard, Coast Guard Auxiliary U.S.

246

FLOAT PLAN

1. Person reporting

   Name _____ Tele. no. _____

2. Description of boat. Type _____ Color _____

   Trim _____ Registration no. _____

   Length _____ Name _____ Make _____

   Other info. _____

3. Persons aboard

Name	Age	Address & tele. no.
_____	_____	_____
_____	_____	_____
_____	_____	_____

4. Engine type _____ H.P. _____

   No. of engines _____ Fuel capacity _____

5. Survival equipment (check as appropriate):

   PFD's _____ Flares _____ Mirror _____

   Smoke signals _____ Flashlight _____ Food _____

   Paddles _____ Water _____ Others _____

6. Radio: Yes/No Type _____ Freqs. _____

7. Trip expectations: Leave at _____ (time)

   From _____ Going to _____

   Expect to return by _____ (time) and in

   no event later than _____

8. Any other pertinent info. _____

9. Automobile license _____ Type _____

   Trailer license _____ Color and make of

   auto _____

   Where parked _____

10. If not returned by _____ (time), call the

    Coast Guard or _____ (local authority)

    Telephone numbers _____

    _____

    _____

Power Squadrons, Red Cross or various state authorities for current information.

17. Carry a compass if you normally operate on large bodies of water.

18. Learn the weather warning signals.

19. Water ski only when you are well clear of all other persons. There should always be at least two people in the tow boat: one to watch the skier and another to operate the boat.

20. Be careful of your footing. Falls are one of the chief causes of accidents. Stay seated in small boats.

21. Always instruct one other person on board in handling your boat in case you become disabled or fall overboard.

22. Before departing on any boat trip, leave a float plan, including the approximate time of arrival or return, with someone ashore (see example).

23. Properly maintain, stow and teach your passengers to use the safe-ty equipment carried on board your vessel.

24. Carry sufficient tools for minor repairs.

25. Instruct passengers where your emergency equipment is located and how to use it in case of an emergency.

26. Know how to load a boat properly. Distribute the load evenly; keep the load low; don't stand up in a small boat; don't overload. If the water is rough, the number of persons carried should be reduced. The weather and water conditions should be taken into account, too.

The number of persons you can safely carry in good weather can be determined by multiplying the overall length of the boat by its maximum width and then dividing by 15.

Boating first-aid kit

Plastic strip bandages (¾" x 3")
Sunburn lotion
Adhesive tape (½" x 2½ yards)
Absorbent cotton (½ oz.).
Gauze roller bandage (2" wide x 5 yards)
Nonadherent gauze pads (2" x 3")
Aromatic spirits of ammonia
Anti-motion-sickness tablets
Antiseptic wipes
Scissors
Tweezers
Elastic bandage (3" wide)
Thermometers, oral and rectal
Lomotil
Aspirin, for children and adults (or Tylenol)
Salt tablets
Hot-water bottle
Oval eye pads

Note. For seasickness, have the patient lie down and keep him or her warm by covering with a blanket. To combat dizziness and/or vomiting, give an anti-motion-sickness tablet such as Dramamine or Antivent.

YOUR PET

56
FIRST AID

Just like people, animals have accidents that require first aid. Some problems are minor and can easily be treated at home, but the more serious ones need professional attention. The American Society for the Prevention of Cruelty to Animals has compiled the following information to help you be prepared in the event of a pet emergency. They also have provided a list of problems which do not constitute an immediate danger, but which should be brought to a veterinarian's attention. In addition, there are instructions for taking a pet's temperature and giving it a pill or liquid medication; feeding a young or older animal in poor condition that is refusing regular food; and immunizing your pet. Tips on traveling with a pet come from the U.S. Department of Health, Education, and Welfare or from the pamphlet "Traveling with your Pet," which is available for $1.25 from the ASPCA, 441 E. 92nd Street, New York, NY 10028.

EMERGENCIES

To help you locate the correct procedures quickly, a wide variety of situations have been arranged alphabetically. Major emergencies, in which an animal's life is in immediate danger, are covered in the first section. These include uncontrollable bleeding, extremely difficult breathing, convulsions, unconsciousness, shock, and poisoning. Other serious conditions are listed afterward in charts with the symptoms to look for, the recommended treatment, and what one should do to avoid further complications.

These recommendations are not designed to take the place of treatment by a veterinarian, but only to help you administer emergency care to an animal that has sustained a serious injury. Any emergency situation requires that you get the animal to a veterinarian immediately. Attempting to treat serious injuries at home can result in grave complications, and even the death of your pet.

Once you have read the chapter and have a clear idea of what to do and how to do it, remember that the most important contribution you can make is to stay calm. Animals are very sensitive to the behavior of the people around them. An animal in great pain will only become more agitated if you do not keep your own anxiety in check.

For any serious injury, it will be useful to know how to restrain the animal in order to keep it from further injuring itself. In the case of a dog, this means fashioning an emergency muzzle, and, if necessary, keeping the animal on a lead or in an enclosed area. In the case of a cat, wrapping the animal in a heavy towel or blanket will serve the same purpose. Restraint is also important to protect a person from the bites or puncture wounds which an injured, frightened animal may inflict. You should always be prepared for the possibility of an animal lashing out in pain and confusion when hurt.

To fashion an emergency muzzle, cut a long piece of gauze bandage and make a loop in the middle (see Fig. 56-1). Slip the loop around the dog's muzzle with the ends on top. Pull tightly. Bring the ends of the bandage down below the chin, cross, tie firmly and bring the ends up behind the ears. Tie a bow over the top of the neck, just below the base of the skull. Make

certain that the muzzle is removed from animal when restraint is no longer needed. If the animal starts to vomit, remove the emergency muzzle immediately or your animal may choke to death.

In all emergencies, first make sure the animal is breathing. Then stop all bleeding. Keep the animal warm and quiet.

Breathing

Check the animal's mouth and throat for any obstructions. Wipe away any blood or mucus.

Treatment: Use artificial resuscitation.
1. Place the animal on its right side, making sure its tongue is extended.
2. Press down with your hands on the animal's ribs, just behind the shoulder blades. Press down for about two seconds, then release for three seconds (see Fig. 56-2).
3. Keep repeating the pressing and releasing with a smooth and steady rhythm. Do this until the animal starts to breathe on its own.

Bleeding

A cut artery will cause bright red blood to spurt from a wound, while a cut vein will cause a steady flow of dark or bluish blood. Heavy bleeding from either a vein or an artery is very serious and must be stopped immediately to save your pet's life.

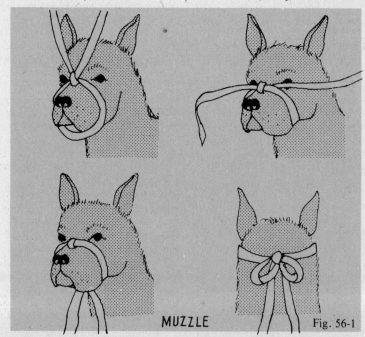

MUZZLE   Fig. 56-1

248

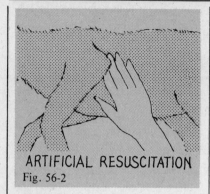

ARTIFICIAL RESUSCITATION
Fig. 56-2

Treatment: Apply a pressure bandage.
1. Apply a steady pressure directly over the wound with a sterile gauze pad or compress.
2. Do not remove the compress to see if the bleeding has stopped. If blood comes through the compress, apply more layers of gauze or cloth.
3. Keep compress firmly in place for 15 minutes. Then release.
4. Reapply if necessary.
5. Call a veterinarian immediately.

Note. Tourniquets are never recommended. The incorrect use of a tourniquet can seriously endanger your animal. Use only a pressure bandage to control heavy bleeding.

Shock

Shock is caused by loss of blood, severe injuries, fright, or exposure. Symptoms are unconsciousness, semiconsciousness, loss of body heat (cold to the touch), shallow breathing, bluish gray gums, dilation of pupils.

Treatment:
1. Keep the animal warm. Cover with a cloth, coat, blanket—anything that is available. It is important to retain body heat.
2. Keep the animal quiet. Prevent undue movement.
3. Call your veterinarian immediately.

Broken bones

If you suspect that your pet has broken a bone, administer only the following treatment.

Treatment:
1. Apply restraint.
2. Keep the animal quiet.
3. Do not attempt to splint the limb. The animal will probably hold the limb up to avoid as much pain as possible. Attempting to splint a fractured

limb can cause extensive damage to the animal and will probably produce more pain than is necessary.
4. Put an injured cat in a box or wrap closely. Never splint a cat's broken bone.
5. Let only a veterinarian apply a splint.

Convulsions

Following serious injury, an animal may go into convulsions. Convulsions are characterized by one or more of the following symptoms: uncontrollable running, "swimming" on the floor, foaming at the mouth, glassy eyes, shivering, staggering, dizziness.

Treatment:
1. Move furniture and other objects away from the animal.
2. Do not attempt to touch or restrain the animal.
3. Call your veterinarian immediately.

Poisoning

Keep all poisons safely out of the reach of your pets. Should you suspect your animal has ingested a poison, look for one or more of the following symptoms: intense abdominal pain (stomach area extremely sensitive to touch), vomiting, diarrhea, trembling and shivering, staggering and dizziness, difficulty breathing, weakness, depression, loss of appetite, extreme excitement. Symptoms vary according to the type of poison.

Do not attempt to treat poisoning if more than half an hour has passed. Induce vomiting in all cases, except where alkali, acid, or petroleum distillates are suspected. If you know which poison was consumed, call your veterinarian or local poison-control center for the prescribed antidote. The most common poisons are paints, disinfectants, insecticides and some pesticides.

Treatment: Induce vomiting, except as noted below.
1. Force a handful of salt down the animal's throat. Repeat if necessary.
2. If this does not work, give equal parts of 3% medical hydrogen peroxide and water.

Once the animal has vomited, administer one of the following antidotes:
• two parts heavily burned and crumbled toast, one part strong tea, one part milk of magnesia;

• two to three tablespoons of activated charcoal in a cup of warm water;
• as much milk and raw egg white as the animal will take.

Do not induce vomiting if one or more of the following substances have been ingested:
1. Alkali substances such as lye, drain cleaners or potash. Give the animal vinegar or lemon juice to counteract the poison.
2. Battery acid, sulphuric acid, or nitric acid. Give the animal milk, Pepto Bismol, or milk of magnesia to neutralize the poison.

The most reliable way of administering fluids is by the lip-pouch method. Insert an eye dropper or a small syringe (plastic, not glass) filled with the liquid medicine into the small pouch of the lower lip, located just forward of the corner of the mouth, and squeeze contents into mouth a little at a time (see Fig. 56-3). The medi-

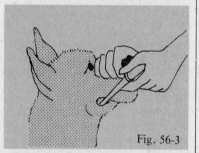

Fig. 56-3

cine will trickle through the animal's teeth and down its throat. Repeat this procedure until the entire dosage is given. Don't attempt to open the animal's mouth.

If the poison has come into contact with the skin, flush with plenty of water.

In any type of poisoning, be sure to consult your veterinarian. Bring a sample of the poison (in the original container, if possible) with you when you take your pet to the veterinarian.

SYMPTOMS TO KEEP IN CHECK FOR DOGS AND CATS

All of the following conditions or symptoms should be brought to a veterinarian's attention, but none of them constitutes an emergency.

External parasites

Fleas: Fleas infest both dogs and cats. They are very small and very fast. Generally you will be able to see the fleas by examining the animal's

249

skin. If you don't actually see fleas on an animal, you may still find evidence of them by looking for dark, gritty particles like pepper, down in their host's fur. Heavy flea infestations feel like beach sand if you run your hands along the fur. Fleas can spread tapeworms from one animal to another.

Check with your veterinarian regarding treatment. He may recommend a flea collar, powder, spray or bath. You must also get rid of the fleas from the areas the dog occupies or your pet will become reinfested. Ask your veterinarian what sprays to use.

Ticks: Ticks generally prefer dogs, but may occasionally be found on a cat. They are much bigger than fleas, and they move very slowly toward the animal's head. When they feed, they are stationary, burying their mouth parts in an animal's skin and sucking its blood until they swell up and fall off. Female ticks swell to a greater proportion than male ticks because the females are carrying eggs—as many as 6,000, depending on the species. Female ticks look like undersized grapes, and male ticks look like hanging scabs; both burrow under the fur and attach to the skin.

There are several methods you can use to rid your animal of ticks, including a tick collar, powder or bath. You may prefer that your veterinarian dip the animal. But if you decide to do it yourself, follow these general guidelines: Protect the animal's eyes by putting a drop of mineral oil in each one. To do this, hold its head and open its eyes, one at a time, by spreading the skin above and below the lids apart with your fingers. Use an eyedropper to drop the oil into the open eye. When the dog blinks, the oil will spread over the surface of the eye. The ears should also be protected by stuffing a wad of cotton which has been moistened with tick dip into each one. When cotton is removed, ticks within the ear will have been exposed to the dip and can then easily be removed. Next pick up the dog and put it into the bath. If the dog is too little to stand in the bath, support it on one arm as you work the dip into its fur with the other hand. Don't let its head go under, but make sure you get the dip into the fur on its face and ears. If the dog is too big or too aggressive to be lifted into the bath, you will have

to stand it near a drain and pour the dip over it. Work the solution all the way into the coat, making sure it gets in between the toes and under the body. Let the dip dry onto the dog; do not rinse it off. Be sure the dip is properly diluted prior to use.

If you use the tick dip properly, any ticks left hanging onto a dog will die. You may, however, have to pull some out of the dog's ears, or off an infested cat. The tick will come away cleanly if you dip a cotton swab in alcohol and apply it to the tick. Grasp tick with a pair of tweezers or small wad of cotton and rock it back and forth as you pull. Do not pour alcohol into ear canal. Try not to rupture the tick because the mouth part may become lodged in the skin and subsequently cause an infection.

Get rid of new broods of ticks that are developing in the house. Vacuum well first, then use a household insecticide; check with your veterinarian on which ones are best to use. He will probably suggest one containing baygon or diazinon. Spray or paint it on cracks in the floor, around baseboards and window casings, on places where the dog habitually sleeps and on other places where ticks may be hiding. Repeat after two or three months.

Cats cannot be tick dipped. If a cat has ticks, they will usually be on hind quarters or underside. Take the cat to your veterinarian.

Ear mites: Ear mites infest both cats and dogs, but are more common in cats. You will not see the mites themselves unless you are looking through a magnifying glass, but you will see a lot of dark brown sandy stuff inside the ear. Ear mites are spread by direct contact.

To treat ear mites, fill an eyedropper with mineral oil and squeeze the oil into the animal's ears. The oil will coat and loosen all the brown sandy matter in the ear canal and float it out so that you can remove it with Q-tips. Do not clean deeper than you can see. When the ears are clean, treat them with mite medicine according to the directions on the container. Get the medicine all the way in by massaging the base of the ear for a few seconds. If the animal objects to your attentions, you may have to get somebody else to hold it.

Mange: Mange is caused by a microscopic parasite that burrows down

under an animal's skin. There are different kinds of mange. Cats and dogs can get sarcoptic mange, which appears as red, itchy areas on the body. The skin may look thickened. In its first stages, mange may give a dog's ears a moth-eaten look. Mange is spread by direct contact or by transfer from materials such as towels, cages, brushes or collars that have been in contact with mangy animals. For treatment, take animal to a veterinarian.

Maggots: Maggots appear on an animal if flies lay their eggs in an open wound and the eggs hatch. Weakened animals are more susceptible to infestation. A wound full of maggots looks terrible, but actually those maggots help keep the wound clean by eating the rotten flesh. If the wound is going to be treated, the veterinarian will get rid of the maggots. Maggots can spread infection to their hosts.

Ringworm: Ringworm is not a worm. It is a fungus, related to athlete's foot. You usually see it on cats, but dogs and people can get it too. It is very contagious by direct contact. Ringworm may not be visible except under ultraviolet light. When it is visible, it looks like little circular spots with flaky areas toward the outside edge of the infected area. An animal's face or legs are affected, where the fur is shortest. The areas may be red or scaly.

For treatment, take animal to a veterinarian.

Internal parasites

Roundworms: Roundworms look like live strands of spaghetti. You may see them in the vomitus or excrement of an infested animal, or even crawling out of the anus of a seriously worm-infected puppy or kitten. Most of the time you won't see them at all. You'll see a skinny animal with a dull coat, a potbelly and chronic or intermittent diarrhea.

Roundworms can kill young animals. They are transmitted by direct contact with the old excrement of infected animals, or through the mother's bloodstream before her litter is born.

Tapeworms: You won't see adult tapeworms. What you will see is really a segment of the mature worm that contains a packet of eggs. The worm segment, which looks like a large grain of rice, crawls on the fur around its host's anus or over a pile of excrement. Both dogs and cats can get tapeworms.

Animals may get tapeworms from fleas or by ingesting carriers.

Hookworm: Hookworms potentially are one of the most dangerous of all internal worms. Young puppies and occasionally kittens are most susceptible to these parasites. Infestation occurs by ingestion, penetration of the skin or during the prenatal stage (prior to birth). Clinical signs are diarrhea (often bloody), vomiting, shock and anemia.

Coccidiosis and giardia: Coccidiosis and giardia are internal parasites that cause severe problems for their hosts. Symptoms include diarrhea (mucous discharge), bloody stool, dehydration and extreme weakness.

Note. As soon as you detect any sign of internal infection, bring the animal to a veterinarian. He will perform microscopic analysis of a stool sample in order to determine the specific parasitic infestation.

Feline disorders

Feline urinary syndrome, usually affecting males, is a disease in which the urinary passage becomes blocked by sandy, gritty material. This can be seen when a cat is straining to urinate, is in and out of the litter box frequently or is dribbling urine. It is often confused with constipation. The cat that has this abnormality is suffering and requires immediate treatment. The best thing you can do for the cat is bring it to a veterinarian promptly.

TAKING A PET'S TEMPERATURE

To take an animal's temperature, put some vaseline on the end of a rectal thermometer and slide it gently into the animal's anus. It should go two-thirds of the way in. Hold on to the end of the thermometer so it doesn't disappear into the animal or fall out. Leave it in at least half a minute.

Normal temperature for dogs and cats is 101°–102°F.

GIVING MEDICATION

Giving a pill

Open the animal's mouth by lifting its upper jaw and tilting its head back. This will usually cause it to drop its lower jaw. If it doesn't, pull the lower jaw down with your other hand. Roll the upper lip over the teeth before you open the mouth so that if the animal tries to bite, it will press its teeth into its lip instead of your fingers. Drop the pill as far back as you can—right down the throat if possible. Close the jaws and softly massage the throat.

If the pill comes out, put it in again. You may have to push the pill farther back with one finger before it will go down.

If the animal is unusually difficult to medicate, try rolling the pill up in a little ball of canned food and giving it as a treat.

Giving liquid medication

Tilt the animal's head back and squeeze the liquid slowly into the corner of its mouth with an eyedropper or syringe. Make sure the animal has time to swallow.

Another method used to administer liquids to dogs is to insert a plastic dropper into the small pocket at the corner of the dog's cheek and squeeze. The contents will trickle into the mouth.

FEEDING TIP FOR ANIMALS REFUSING REGULAR FOOD

The following formula contains all the essentials for a basic diet for both cats and dogs. It can be fed with a plastic eyedropper if the pet will not eat on its own.

Pour a little warm water into a blender (or a bowl, for beating by hand). Add four junior-size pet tabs (vitamins). Blend well. Add one teaspoonful of honey. Add three-quarters of a cup of protein powder. Add half a cup of evaporated milk. Add one-quarter cup of soya oil. Add one-quarter cup of cottage cheese. Mix ingredients. Add an egg yolk. Mix well.

To this basic mixture—as the animal grows older or stronger—add baby food (such as chicken or beef), canned dog food or cat food, blending it well.

Make the changeover to a regular diet slowly to avoid any upsets.

IMMUNIZATION FOR YOUR PET

You may hear the term "permanent vaccine," seeming to imply lifelong immunity, but in fact *no* vaccine is known to immunize for life. Distemper vaccinations, therefore, are not permanent, nor are they 100 percent effective in stimulating immunity in all animals. In order to assure optimal immunity, however, it is strongly recommended that a vaccination schedule be set up for your pet early in its life and followed rigorously. The table below will help you determine when to vaccinate your pet.

Dogs should receive a rabies vaccination at 6 months of age, and then every one or three years, depending on the type of vaccine used.

Canine distemper symptoms

Infectious and contagious, distemper is caused by a specific virus and affects other animals besides dogs, such as skunks, raccoons, wolves and coyotes. It is a separate virus from feline distemper and is not contagious to cats.

Initial symptoms range from a mild cough or sneeze, accompanied by nasal or eye discharge, to severe vomiting and diarrhea with depression and loss of appetite. During the usual course of the disease, many animals develop paralysis, muscular twitching or violent convulsions as a result of damage to the brain. Take your animal to a veterinarian if he develops any of these symptoms.

Canine distemper can be prevented by an annual vaccination.

Feline distemper symptoms

Feline distemper, also called feline panleucopemia and feline enteritis, is a viral disease which attacks the intestinal tract of cats. Most common in young cats, it is highly infectious among cats.

The signs are high fever, vomiting and diarrhea.

Feline distemper can be prevented by vaccination. The feline distemper virus does not affect dogs.

IMMUNIZATION SCHEDULE			
Age at first shot	2–3 months	4–5 months	6 months or over
Revaccination date	4 months	4 weeks	1 year

FURTHER PET EMERGENCIES

Condition	Treatment	Do Not
Abrasions	Muzzle if necessary. Wash with soap and water. Use 3% medical hydrogen peroxide diluted with equal parts of water, or other mild antiseptic, such as mouthwash.	
Anal Gland Problems Signs: Scooting along floor, chasing tail, licking or biting anal area	See veterinarian.	
Automobile Accident Signs: Shock, bleeding, internal injuries, broken bones, convulsions	Muzzle only if necessary to move animal. Treat each symptom individually. Keep animal warm and quiet.	Do not feed or water. Do not leave muzzle on animal.
Burns Signs: Hair loss, swollen or red skin, blistering		
Small	Apply ice or cold water.	Do not use greasy or oily medications.
Large	Call veterinarian immediately. Keep animal warm and quiet.	
Chemical burns	Call veterinarian immediately. Flush area repeatedly with cold water.	
Car Sickness	Call veterinarian for proper medication. Keep sufficient air in car by leaving windows partially open.	Do not feed for at least four hours before leaving home.
Choking Signs: Coughing, inability to breathe, pawing at mouth, foaming, salivating, vomiting, shaking	Look in mouth and throat for obstructions or foreign objects. Keep animal from moving around. If you are unable to dislodge object with your fingers, hold the animal upside down and shake, patting sharply between the shoulders and the neck. Call veterinarian.	
Constipation	Milk of magnesia, 1 teaspoon per 10 lbs. of body weight. If constipation persists, consult veterinarian.	If foreign object may have been swallowed, do not give milk of magnesia. Do not give any other laxatives.
Cuts	Remove any foreign objects (such as glass). Wash with soap and warm water. Stop bleeding, if necessary, using a pressure bandage. Cover with sterile gauze soaked in an antiseptic, such as mouthwash.	
Diarrhea	Give kaopectate—1 tablespoon per 10 lbs. of body weight. Feed only small quantities of chopped meat and boiled rice. Call veterinarian if diarrhea persists.	Do not feed milk or kibbled biscuits while animal has diarrhea.
Drowning Signs: Much splashing and sinking.	Try to get water from throat and lungs by lifting animal up by hind legs. Keep animal warm and quiet.	
Ear Problems Signs: Shaking head, scratching ears excessively	Clean ears with Q-tips moistened with baby oil or mineral oil. Deep ear cleaning should be done only by a veterinarian.	Do not use alcohol in the ear.
Electric Shock Signs: Burns on lips or gums, burns where wire has contacted animal, difficulty breathing, unconsciousness.	Unplug electric wire from outlet or push animal away from wire with stick. Stand on something dry. Call veterinarian immediately. Administer artificial respiration if necessary.	

252

Eye Injury Signs: Tearing, pawing at eye, swelling, bloodshot eyes, shut eye, visible object in eye	For swelling, apply ice pack or pads soaked in a saline solution. If eye is out, try to calm and immobilize animal. Soak compresses in salt solution (1 tsp. to 1 pt. of water) or thick sugar solution, place over eye or eye socket and secure with tape. Get animal to a veterinarian. Do not attempt to put eye back yourself. DO KEEP eye and eye socket wet. DO NOT USE PLAIN WATER AS THAT MAY INCREASE SWELLING.	Do not use eye drops unless recommended by a veterinarian.
Fishhooks	Muzzle if necessary. Cut off barb end of hook, carefully work out through skin backwards. Apply mild antiseptic.	
Foot Problems	Remove any foreign objects. Soak in mild salt solution. Bandage raw feet. Paint pads with NuSkin.	Do not leave bandage on for more than two days at a time.
Frostbite	Keep in warm room. Call veterinarian.	Do not rub with ice, snow or cold water.
Heat Exhaustion Signs: Semiconsciousness, unconsciousness, panting, muscle twitches and dry, hot skin	Keep animal cool. Pour cool water on animal. Call veterinarian.	Do not put ice on animal.
Paint on Fur	Cut off fur that has paint on it. Soften paint still on animal with mineral oil, then wash with pet or baby shampoo. Wash animal with auto-mechanic grease-cutting hand soap.	Do not put turpentine, kerosene, gasoline, paint thinner or paintbrush cleaner on pet.
Poison Ivy Will not affect animal, but can rub off on people	Using rubber gloves, wash animal with brown laundry soap or tincture of green soap.	
Porcupine Quills	Make sure all quills are removed. Treat for puncture wounds. Check mouth and throat carefully for any remaining quills.	
Puncture Wounds	Pour 3% medical hydrogen peroxide into wound. Wash surrounding area with germicidal soap or mild antiseptic (any mouthwash). Punctures can be serious, so consult veterinarian.	
Skunk Odor	Wash animal in tomato juice.	
Snakebite	Apply tourniquet if you know how. Rush to veterinarian.	Do not let animal walk.
Tar on Fur	Cut off fur that has tar on it. Soften tar still on animal with mineral oil, then wash with pet or baby shampoo. Wash animal with auto-mechanic grease-cutting hand soap.	Do not put turnpentine, kerosene, gasoline, paint thinner or paintbrush cleaner on pet.
Unconsciousness	Keep warm. Check breathing frequently. See veterinarian.	Do not give stimulants.
Worms Signs: Diarrhea, vomiting, loss of weight	See veterinarian and bring a stool sample.	Do not attempt to treat with home remedies.

TRAVELING WITH A PET

Take your pet to the veterinarian before going on a trip to be sure it is healthy. The American Society for the Prevention of Cruelty to Animals offers a pamphlet entitled "Traveling with Your Pet." It includes information on shipping a pet by air (such as "Exercise your dog before placing it in the traveling crate"); traveling with your pet by car (such as "If you must leave the pet in a parked car, lock the car, but leave windows rolled down two inches on all sides for ventilation. The heat in a closed car can reach well over 120 degrees."); requirements for traveling abroad, and requirements for traveling in the different states of this country. You can obtain a copy of this pamphlet by sending a check or money order for $1.25 to the ASPCA at 441 East 92nd Street, New York, NY 10028. Enclose a stamped, self-addressed envelope.

Reentry or importation of pets

It is important that pets in international travel be free of communicable diseases because many animals carry infections that are dangerous to man. The U.S. Public Health Service requires that imported pets—dogs, cats, psittacine birds, and turtles—be examined at the port of entry to make sure they show no evidence of disease that can be passed on to humans. The following requirements must also be met.

Dogs: Except for puppies less than three months of age and for dogs coming from a rabies-free area, dogs must be vaccinated against rabies at least 30 days prior to entry into the United States. A certificate of rabies vaccination, signed by a licensed veterinarian, should accompany the dog. The certificate should identify the breed of dog, date of vaccination, and type of vaccine used.

Cats: Rabies vaccination is not routinely required for domestic cats or for wild members of the cat family.

Psittacine birds (parrots, parakeets, etc.): Import rules for personally owned pet birds from all countries but Canada were tightened on January 15, 1980, to provide greater protection against exotic Newcastle disease, a fatal disease of poultry and other birds.

Among the new Department of Agriculture requirements is a 30-day quarantine in government facilities, an advance reservation and fee for quarantine space, and a national government veterinary health certificate obtained in the country of the bird's origin. Also, entry ports for pet birds will be limited to nine cities, including New York, Miami and Los Angeles, and only two psittacine birds per family per year may be brought in. For details on these and less stringent rules for birds from Canada, write for the Department's free pamphlet, "Importing a Pet Bird," in care of USDA, Animal and Plant Health Inspection Service, 6505 Belcrest Road, Hyattsville, Maryland 20782.

Turtles: A person may import live turtles with a carapace length of less than 4 inches and viable turtle eggs, provided that for each arrival the person imports no more than one lot containing six or fewer live turtles or six or fewer viable turtle eggs, or any combination totaling no more than six. The Public Health Service has no restrictions on the importation of live turtles with a carapace length of more than 4 inches.

Monkeys: Pet monkeys may not be imported. Live monkeys and other primates may be imported into the United States only by a registered importer for scientific, educational or exhibition purposes.

If additional information is needed concerning the importation of these animals, address inquiries to the Center for Disease Control, Attention: Bureau of Epidemiology, Quarantine Division, Atlanta, Georgia 30333.

Persons planning to import horses, ruminants, swine, poultry, birds and dogs used in handling livestock should contact the U.S. Department of Agriculture.

Persons planning to import fish, snakes, spiders, wild birds, rabbits, bears, wild members of the cat family, and other wild animals should contact the U.S. Department of the Interior.

Taking a pet to a foreign country

Travelers planning to take a pet to a foreign country must meet the entry requirements of the country of destination. You can obtain this information by writing directly to that country, to the country's embassy in Washington, D.C., or to the nearest consulate.

Areas reported to be rabies free include:

CARIBBEAN

Anguilla	Martinique
Antigua	Montserrat
Aruba	Nevis
Bahamas	St. Kitts
Barbados	St. Lucia
Bermuda	St. Martin
Curaçao	St. Vincent
Guadeloupe	Virgin Islands
Jamaica	

EUROPE

Faroe Islands	Norway
Finland	Sweden
Iceland	United Kingdom
Ireland	

ASIA

Japan	Taiwan

PACIFIC

American Samoa	Guam
Australia	New Zealand
Fiji	Saipan

The State of Hawaii and the territories of Guam and American Samoa have special requirements. All dogs and cats entering these areas are subject to a 120-day quarantine in accordance with state and territorial regulations.

EMERGENCY INFORMATION FOR YOUR PETS

Registration number _____

License number _____

Veterinarian _____

    Address _____

    Telephone _____

Vaccinations and immunizations

    Type _____   Date _____

    _____   _____

    _____   _____

    _____   _____

Other medical problems _____

_____

_____

Registration number _____

License number _____

Veterinarian _____

    Address _____

    Telephone _____

Vaccinations and immunizations

    Type _____   Date _____

    _____   _____

    _____   _____

    _____   _____

Other medical problems _____

_____

_____

NATURAL DISASTERS

57

NATURAL DISASTERS

No matter where you live, you are subject to a natural disaster of some kind. There are ways, however, of mitigating the consequences of such an attack. With advance planning, there will be fewer lives lost and less property damaged. This chapter covers earthquakes, weather-related disasters—hurricanes, thunderstorms, lightning, tornadoes, flash floods, winter storms, strong winds—and nuclear fallout. Safety rules for each disaster are also included.

THUNDERSTORMS

It has been estimated that at any given moment, nearly 2,000 thunderstorms are in progress over the earth's surface. Their frequency and potential for harm make them one of nature's greatest killers and destroyers.

Thunderstorms, generated by temperature imbalances in the atmosphere, are examples of violent convection. The cooling of cloud tops or warming of cloud bases puts warmer, lighter air layers below the colder, denser layers. The resulting instability causes the cloud layers to overturn. The heavier, denser layers will sink and the lighter, warmer air will rise rapidly. The upward movement produces cumulus cloud formation (rising mounds, domes or towers). Air flows through the cloud's sides, mixing with and feeding the updraft in a process called entrainment. Strong winds above the developing clouds may produce a chimney effect, drawing air upward to augment the updraft. As a cloud forms, water vapor changes to liquid and/or frozen cloud particles. This results in the release of heat, which takes over as the principal source of energy for a developing cloud. Once the cloud is formed by other forces, this release of heat helps keep it growing.

As cloud particles grow, by colliding and combining with one another, they may become rain, snow and/or hail. Precipitation begins when they become heavy enough to fall against an updraft. Having reached the final stage of growth, the cumulonimbus cloud, called a thunderstorm cloud, may be several miles across the base and extend to an altitude of 40,000 feet or more. High-level winds shred the cloud top into the familiar anvil-shaped form. These cloud towers are sometimes visible as lonely giants, or they move several abreast to form a squall line. This stage is often accompanied by strong gusts of cold wind from downdraft or heavy rain or hail. Lightning always accompanies thunder. Lightning is nature's warning that the thunderstorm is in its most active stage. Tornadoes may also be associated with violent thunderstorms.

Thunder

Thunder is the crash and rumble that customarily follows lightning. It is caused by the explosive expansion of the air which has been heated by a lightning stroke. When lightning is close by, thunder sounds like a sharp crack. When lightning is more distant, thunder is a rumbling noise because the sound is refracted and modified by the turbulent environment. Because the speed of light is so many times that of sound, a lightning bolt is seen before the crash of thunder is heard. You can estimate distance (in miles) to a lightning stroke by counting the number of seconds between the lightning and the thunder, and then dividing by five.

Lightning

It is estimated that lightning strikes the earth 100 times each second. It is a gigantic spark between areas having opposite electrical charges during a thunderstorm. As a thunderstorm develops, an intense electrical field is produced within a cloud. A large positive charge is usually concentrated in the frozen upper layers of the cloud. A large negative charge along with a smaller positive area is found in the lower portions. The earth is normally negatively charged with respect to the atmosphere. As the thunderstorm passes over the ground, the negative charge in the base of the cloud induces a positive charge on the ground below and for several miles around the storm. The ground charge follows the storm like an electrical shadow, growing stronger as the negative cloud charge increases. The attraction between positive and negative charges makes the positive ground current flow up buildings, trees and other structures and in effect establishes the conditions for a flow of current. Air, however, which is a poor conductor of electricity, insulates the cloud and the ground charges, preventing a flow of current until huge electrical charges are built up. Lightning occurs when the difference between positive and negative charges—the electrical potential—becomes great enough to overcome the resistance of the insulating air and to force a conductive path for the current to flow between the two charges (see Fig. 57-1).

Lightning presents a double danger. As a carrier of high electrical currents, it can both shock and burn. The typical cloud-to-ground strike takes about one second.

Fig. 57-1

Safety rules

Lightning kills many people each year. About four out of every five deaths or injuries from lightning occur in rural areas. Most who die have sought refuge under a tree, and many of these people are golfers. About two-thirds of the people injured by lightning make a full recovery because most are not struck directly but only receive a shock from being close to the stroke.

If you plan to be outdoors during warm-weather periods and during the passage of cold fronts, check weather forecasts and keep an eye on the sky. When cumulus clouds (clouds with a flat base and rounded, puffy outlines) begin building up and the sky begins to darken, a thunderstorm is about to strike. On the ground, the wind may suddenly reverse direction and rise in speed, and the temperature may sharply drop. Heavy rain, hail and lightning occur only in a thunderstorm's mature stage. The more active the thunderstorm, the greater the potential for tornado formation.

Protect yourself:
1. When a thunderstorm threatens, get inside a home or large building, or inside an all-metal (not convertible) vehicle.
2. Inside a home, avoid using the telephone, except for emergencies.
3. If you are outside, with no time to reach a safe building or an automobile, follow these rules:
• Do not stand underneath a natural lightning rod such as a tall, isolated tree in an open area.
• Avoid projecting above the surrounding landscape, as you would do if you were standing on a hilltop, in an open field, on the beach, or fishing from a small boat.
• Get out of and away from open water.
• Get away from tractors and other metal farm equipment.
• Get off and away from motorcycles, scooters, golf carts and bicycles. Put down golf clubs.
• Stay away from wire fences, clotheslines, metal pipes, rails and other metallic paths which could carry lightning to you from some distance away.
• Avoid standing in small, isolated sheds or other small structures in open areas.
• In a forest, seek shelter in a low area under a thick growth of small trees. In open areas, go to a low place such as a ravine or valley. Be alert for flash floods.
• If you are hopelessly isolated in a level field or prairie and you feel your hair stand on end (indicating lightning is about to strike), drop to your knees and bend forward, putting your hands on your thighs. Do not lie flat on the ground.

First aid: Many people apparently "killed" by lightning can be revived if quick action is taken. When a group is affected, the apparently dead should be treated first; those unconscious but breathing will probably recover spon-

taneously. First aid should be rendered to those not breathing within four to six minutes to prevent irrevocable brain damage. Mouth-to-mouth resuscitation should be administered once every five seconds to adults and once every three seconds to infants and small children (see pages 17–18). If the victim is not breathing and has no pulse, cardiopulmonary resuscitation is necessary. This is a combination of mouth-to-mouth resuscitation and external cardiac compression. It should be administered by persons with proper training (see pages 18–19). Medical attention also should be given to victims who appear only temporarily stunned or otherwise unhurt, since there may be hidden effects.

WINTER STORMS

Every winter is bad for some portion of the country. Winter storms can kill without breaking any climatological records. The National Weather Service, in its forecasts, distinguishes a variety of winter storms. "Snow flurries" are defined as intermittent snowfall that may reduce visibility. The accumulation from snow flurries is usually small. "Snow" is a steady snowfall which continues for several hours. Snow can also be termed "intermittent" or "occasional." "Snow squalls" are brief, intense snowfalls with gusty surface wind. "Blowing and drifting snow" means strong winds and greatly reduced visibility. "Blowing snow" is defined as snow that is lifted from the surface by wind. It restricts horizontal visibility. An "ice storm" creates a substantial coating of ice, whose weight can cause considerable damage. The damage is greater if the freezing rain or drizzle is accompanied by high winds. "Heavy snow" means a fall of at least four to

six inches in a 12-hour period, or six or more inches in a 24-hour period. ("Heavy snow" can also mean an accumulation of two to three inches in a 12-hour period for some parts of the country that have infrequent snow). A "blizzard" means wind speeds of at least 35 mph and considerable falling and/or blowing snow for an extended period of time. Snow accompanying a blizzard is a fine powder often whipped into such quantities that it can reduce visibility to a few yards. A "severe blizzard" means wind speeds of at least 45 mph, dense snow and temperatures of 10° F or below. A combination of wind speed and temperature is called the "Wind-Chill Factor." When very strong winds combine with slightly below freezing temperatures, it can have the same chilling effect as temperatures nearly 50° lower in a calm atmosphere (see Fig. 57-2).

Safety rules

Prior to the siege of winter, all battery-powered equipment should be checked. Make sure that heating fuel and food supplies are adequate for long nonshopping periods. During winter actively work to prevent fires. Coal- or oil-burning stoves, fireplaces, heaters or furnaces should constantly be watched when in use. Remain indoors during storms and cold snaps. If you must go outdoors, wear protective clothing in layers—more effective than a single layer of thick clothing. The layers can be removed to prevent perspiring and subsequent chill. Outer garments should be tightly woven, water repellent and hooded. The hood should protect most of your face. Cover your mouth to insure warm breathing and to protect your lungs from extremely cold air. Entrapped,

WIND-CHILL EQUIVALENT TEMPERATURES (°F)			
Calm air	At 15 mph	At 30 mph	At 40 mph and over
30	9	− 2	− 6
20	− 5	−18	−22
10	−18	−33	−38
0	−31	−49	−54
−10	−45	−64	−70
−20	−58	−78	−87
−30	−72	−93	−101
−40	−85	−109	−116

Fig. 57-2

insulating air, warmed by body heat, is the best protection against the cold. Mittens, snug at the wrists, are much better protection than fingered gloves.

If you must go outside, avoid over-exertion. Shoveling snow is extremely hard work. It can bring on a heart at-tack, a major cause of death during and after winter storms.

Have your car winterized before the storm season begins. Each thing on the following checklist should be in perfect condition: ignition system, battery, lights, tire treads, cooling sys-tem, fuel system, lubrication, exhaust system, heater, defroster, brakes, wip-er blades, snow tires, chains, anti-freeze, winter-grade oil. A good way to keep water out of your fuel tank is to make sure the tank is always full of gasoline.

Carry a winter car kit containing equipment to help you keep alive, warm and visible if you are trapped for a long period: blankets or sleeping bags, extra clothing, high-caloric non-perishable food, facial tissues, paper towels, matches and candles, a com-pass and road maps, knife, first-aid kit, shovel, sack of sand, flashlight with fresh battery, red flares for pro-tection against plows and to help guide rescuers, windshield scraper, booster cables, two chains, fire extin-guisher, catalytic heater, de-icing fluid for windshields, CB radio. Be equipped for the worst conditions, es-pecially if you anticipate driving in heavy snow in open country.

Driving in a winter storm is serious business. If the storm exceeds or even tests your limitations, seek available refuge immediately. Plan your travel carefully; select primary and alternate routes. Check the latest weather infor-mation on your radio. Try not to trav-el alone, but in convoy with another vehicle if possible. Always fill the gas-oline tank before entering open coun-try, even for a short distance. Drive carefully and defensively.

If a blizzard traps you, avoid over-exertion and exposure. Disorientation comes quickly in blowing and drifting snow. Stay in your vehicle, but keep it ventilated. Run the motor and heater sparingly and only with a downwind window open for ventilation. Beware of carbon monoxide. To help circula-tion, exercise by clapping your hands and moving your arms and legs vigor-ously. Turn on the inside dome light at night to make the vehicle visible.

Never eat snow; melt it first. Do not take an alcoholic drink; it opens the blood vessels near the skin and speeds the loss of heat. Do not leave your car. If the storm abates and you decide to risk a trip for help, however, snowshoes are indispensable. If you have none, they can be cut from the fi-berboards of your door. Leggings and snow boots can be cut from the seat covers. If you do have to leave your car (if it is wrecked) and if you cannot find immediate shelter, do not wait too long. Build your own shelter be-fore the cold makes you numb. Hunt for a natural barrier to hide behind such as the hollow under a thick ever-green tree. Weave a windbreak of boughs, with a carpet of boughs for warmth, and cut a hole for your head. Compared to the open air with the cold wind blowing at you, a cave can be snug and warm.

Blizzards take a heavy toll each year on livestock. Always move them into sheltered areas. Haul extra feed to feeding areas before the storm hits.

STRONG WINDS AND THE MOBILE HOME

Compactness, flexibility and economy have made mobile homes popular. Unfortunately, mobile homes are vul-nerable to very strong winds. High winds can cause them to collapse, roll over or even become airborne. Many states and communities have recog-nized the value of safety measures and now require mobile homes to be ade-

Positioning your mobile home with a narrow end facing the direction from which the strongest winds come will provide some degree of protec-tion. Check with the local weather of-fice to find out the direction.

Natural barriers such as trees pro-vide excellent windbreaks. The pro-tection to be gained from trees outweighs the danger from falling limbs in a severe windstorm. Two or more rows of trees are more effective than a single row. Trees at least 30 feet high are the most effective.

Your mobile home unit must also be tied down securely. Ties should be made of wire, rope or rust-resistant steel straps that connect the mobile home and its steel frame to anchors embedded in the ground. The cable or strap should be secured to the anchor with a yoke-type fastener and tension-ing device or with clamps and turn-buckles. Two types of ties are needed: an over-the-top tie and a frame tie. The first keeps the unit from over-turning and the second prevents it from being blown off its support. An over-the-top tiedown is secured to an-chors on each side of the mobile home. Frame ties connect the steel beam supporting the unit to anchors. Several of each type of tie, with con-nections and anchors, are the most ef-

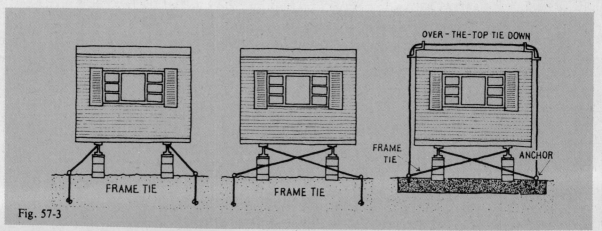

OVER-THE-TOP TIE DOWN

FRAME TIE

FRAME TIE

FRAME TIE

ANCHOR

Fig. 57-3

NATURAL DISASTERS

fective tiedown for the whole unit. In addition, anchors can be embedded in a concrete slab (see Fig. 57-3).

The number of ties required depends on variables such as the length and shape of the mobile home unit, expected wind direction and speed, type of connection between the unit and its steel supporting frame, size and type of tiedown materials, soil condition, and the holding power of the ground anchor (see Fig. 57-4).

You will also have to be sure you have sufficient piers and footings to carry the weight of the mobile home under the supporting steel frame.

Even though your mobile home may be well anchored, you should quickly seek other shelter when warned of an approaching severe thunderstorm, hurricane or tornado. Your mobile home park should have its own safe shelter, and the Red Cross operates many public shelters. If there is time before you must leave an area where hurricanes are threatening, tie down or remove for indoor stowage any cabanas, awnings or other lightweight fixtures that might be blown away. Pack breakables; tape windows; disconnect electrical, sewer and water lines. (When a tornado is approaching, there is no time to do this.) Listen to your radio or television for information and instructions.

FLASH FLOODS

Flash floods are now the number one killer among weather-related disasters in the United States. When heavy rains fall during a short period, the ground cannot absorb all the water, and the resulting runoff flows rapidly into existing channels and may cause flash floods.

Almost every section of the country has suffered from property and life loss due to this least-suspected quick killer. Flooding drives hundreds of thousands of Americans from their homes each year, and from 100 to 200 persons are killed. Property loss can reach more than one billion dollars. Floods also are incredible water wasters, for their by-product is pollution. Floods also cost us other priceless natural resources by eroding land and sweeping away surface vegetation.

Floods begin when soil and vegetation cannot absorb rain or melting snow. Water runs off land in strong rivulets too great to be carried away by normal channels or to be retained in natural ponds or man-made reservoirs. This recurring flooding rips through riverbeds and surges over banks. It sweeps away everything in its path. Flood currents can tear out trees; destroy buildings, crops and bridges; and even wash away cars. People and livestock are often helpless when caught in the powerful pull of rapidly moving water.

Increased flash flooding in recent years has been caused by the spread of urban development and by greater population mobility. In cities, removal of vegetation increases the flow rates of small streams. Bridges, culverts and buildings are often constructed in a manner that impedes the flow of water and results in flooding. In the countryside, the use of mountainous areas and narrow canyons for recreation is exposing growing numbers of unwary visitors to flash floods. This list of danger spots keeps getting larger. Today more than 15,000 U.S. communities and recreational areas are identified by the Flood Insurance Ad-

ministration as being flash-flood prone. Some 3,000 of these areas are high risk in terms of potential deaths and property damage.

Recognition of the need for citizen safety measures has resulted in the establishment of many local flood-warning programs. The National Weather Service recommends a locally operated community warning system as the most effective means of preventing loss of life and reducing property damage from flash flooding. This program of high community involvement can be activated when required by local weather conditions. Surveys following major flash-flood disasters have clearly shown that when federal, state and local agencies work together there is less dollar loss from property damage as well as fewer injuries and deaths. Preparedness plans can be simple or sophisticated. The essential elements are: volunteer rainfall and stream gauge observers; reliable and rapid local communications systems with emergency backup; local flash flood warning coordinator and alternate; forecast procedures developed by National Weather Service hydrologists; warning dissemination plan; adequate preparedness plan including public education. Hydrologists at the National Weather Service's River Forecast Centers constantly monitor the meteorological and hydrological conditions which affect rivers and water supplies at more than 2,500 points on the nation's largest rivers. Reports and forecasts of river conditions are issued many times each day so that flood-prone areas along major rivers can be warned should possible flood conditions occur. The constant monitoring of river and soil conditions en-

Fig. 57-4	TIE-DOWN ANCHORAGE REQUIREMENTS*					
	10- and 12-ft.-wide mobile homes				12- and 14-ft.-wide mobile homes	
Wind velocity in m.p.h.	30 to 50 ft. long		50 to 60 ft. long		60 to 70 ft. long	
	No. of frame ties**	No. of over-the-top ties	No. of frame ties**	No. of over-the-top ties	No. of frame ties**	No. of over-the-top ties
70	3	2	4	2	4	2
80	4	3	5	3	5	3
90	5	4	6	4	7	4
100	6	5	7	5	8	6
110	7	6	9	6	10	7

* Tie-down components used must be able to withstand at least 4,750 lbs. without failure. Anchors capable of withstanding 5,700 lbs. without failure also are required. The holding power of ground anchors can be determined by conducting pullout tests or by consulting with your anchor dealer. He should be able to provide you with data on anchor holding power for various kinds of soils.

** The number of frame ties shown is based on using the Type 2 frame tie system, which can resist a greater horizontal force than Type 1. If Type 1 frame ties are used, the quantity shown in the table should be increased by one additional tie.

ables these hydrologists to provide data on the potential for flash flooding to field offices and local officials over most of the nation.

Safety rules

Before the flood:

1. Keep on hand materials like sand-bags, plywood, plastic sheeting and lumber.
2. Install check valves in building sewer traps to prevent flood water from backing up in sewer drains.
3. Arrange for auxiliary electrical supplies for hospitals and other operations which are critically affected by power failure.
4. Keep first-aid supplies at hand.
5. Keep your automobile fueled; if electric power is cut off, filling stations may not be able to operate pumps for several days.
6. Keep a stock of food which requires little cooking and no refrigeration; electric power may be interrupted.
7. Keep a portable radio, emergency cooking equipment, lights and flash-lights in working order.

When you receive a flood warning:

1. Store drinking water in clean bath-tubs and in various containers. Water service may be interrupted.
2. If forced to leave your home and time permits, move essential items to safe ground; fill tanks to keep them from floating away; grease immovable machinery.
3. Move to a safe area before access is cut off by flood water.

During the flood:

1. Avoid areas subject to sudden flooding.
2. Do not attempt to cross a flowing stream where water is above your knees.
3. Do not attempt to drive over a flooded road—you can be stranded and trapped.

After the flood:

1. Do not use fresh food that has come into contact with flood waters.
2. Test drinking water for potability; wells should be pumped out and the water tested before drinking.
3. Seek necessary medical care at nearest hospital. Food, clothing, shelter, and first aid are available at Red Cross shelters.
4. Do not visit disaster area; your presence might hamper rescue and other emergency operations.

5. Do not handle live electrical equipment in wet areas; electrical equipment should be checked and dried before being used.
6. Use flashlights, not lanterns or torches, to examine buildings; flammables may be inside.
7. Report broken utility lines to appropriate authorities.

The watch: The watch means: Check preparedness requirements, keep informed and be ready for immediate action if a flash flood warning is released. When radar or observer reports indicate that flash flooding is likely or is occurring, a flash flood warning is released.

The warning: The warning requires prompt reaction if you are in an area subject to flooding. Follow flash flood safety rules. Flash flood warnings are one of the most urgent types of weather warnings issued, and they are transmitted to the public by the most rapid means available.

TORNADOES

A tornado is a violent column of air rotating counterclockwise. It descends from an intense thunderstorm cloud system in the form of a funnel (see Fig. 57-5). Not all thunderstorms

Fig. 57-5

spawn tornadoes, but when proper weather conditions are present—unseasonably warm, humid air at the earth's surface, cold air at middle atmospheric levels and strong upper-level jet stream winds—severe thunderstorms and tornadoes are more likely to occur. The funnel of the tornado, which is a violent wind, is initially composed of nothing more than

condensed water vapor. When the circulation of the funnel reaches the ground, it usually picks up dirt and debris, which eventually darken the entire funnel. Damage can occur even though the funnel does not seem to reach the ground. Tornadoes average five to ten minutes on the ground. The path may be only $\frac{1}{8}$ to $\frac{1}{4}$ of a mile wide and seldom more than 15 miles long. The tornado usually moves from the southwest to the northeast at about 30 mph. It may move as quickly as 70 mph. Wind in the rotating funnel is estimated to reach as high as 250 mph in some of the larger, long-lived tornadoes, which are responsible for most tornado-related deaths.

Every tornado is capable of great destruction. It can topple buildings, roll over mobile homes, uproot trees, hurl people and animals through the air for hundreds of yards and turn debris into lethal wind-borne missiles. Tornadoes do their destructive work through the combined action of their violent rotating winds, airborne missiles and the partial vacuum in the center of the vortex. As a tornado passes over a building, the winds twist and rip at the outside while pushing the upwind walls inward. The dynamic pressure reduction pushes downwind walls outward. Mobile homes are particularly vulnerable. Occupants of mobile homes should seek shelter whenever tornadoes threaten.

Tornadoes occur in many parts of the world and in all fifty states of the United States. However, they strike most frequently in the Deep South and the broad, relatively flat basin between the Rockies and the Appalachians. No season is free of them, although they occur most frequently in April, May and June. The southern states are usually hit hardest in winter and spring, the northern states in spring and summer. Maximum frequency in central Gulf states is February. The center moves eastward during March to the southeast Atlantic states, with the peak in April. May tornado migration is to the southern plains states, and June finds them most frequently in the area from the northern plains states to the Great Lakes as far east as western New York State. Most tornadoes occur in late afternoon between 4 and 6 p.m.

The National Severe Storms Forecast Center in Kansas City, Missouri, issues watches when these conditions are imminent. Warnings are issued by area National Weather Service offices.

Safety rules

When a tornado threatens, stay away from windows, doors, and outside walls. Protect your head. If you are inside a home and have time before a tornado strikes, open some windows on the side of the house away from the approaching tornado. In homes and small buildings, go to the basement or to an interior part on the lowest level. Get under something sturdy. In schools, hospitals, and public places, move to predesignated shelter areas. Interior hallways on lowest floors are best. If you are in a mobile home or vehicle, leave it and go to more substantial shelter. If you are outdoors with no shelter available, lie flat in a nearby ditch and shield your head with your arms.

The watch: Tornadoes and severe thunderstorms are possible.

The warning: Tornado detected; take shelter.

HURRICANES

A hurricane is a violent tropical storm of the western North Atlantic which has winds of at least 74 mph. In the northern hemisphere, the winds of tropical storms (low-pressure areas) blow counterclockwise and spiral inward toward the center of the eye. A cyclone is the name given to tropical storms in the Indian Ocean. A typhoon is the same type of storm, but it originates in the western Pacific.

The hurricane season runs from June through November, with the peak usually in September. There have been rare occurrences before June and after November. The most extreme devastation of a hurricane is usually confined to a core area 50 miles or less in diameter around the center, or eye. Squalls extend outward up to 500 miles. Hurricanes develop and intensify over warm waters. On land, they break up rapidly because they have been cut off from their oceanic source of energy. Although hurricanes affecting the United States do most of their damage along the Gulf Coast and eastern coast of Florida, they have moved northward along the Eastern seaboard. It is important for persons living in or visiting these regions during hurricane season to

know what emergency measures to take should a hurricane occur.

The hurricane warning operations of NOAA's (National Oceanic and Atmospheric Administration) National Weather Service begin when the tropical disturbance is first detected. A series of advisory messages is issued every six hours by the National Hurricane Center in Miami, Florida. These warning messages are primarily for marine and aviation interests when the storm is over ocean areas.

If the tropical disturbance later intensifies and becomes a tropical storm (winds of from 39 to 73 mph) or a hurricane, it is given a name. As the hurricane approaches land, the information in the advisory begins to focus on its potential coastal and inland effects. Advisories recommending safety measures are issued to marine interests. The advisories become more frequent so citizens and public officials can take proper precautions.

A *hurricane watch* is issued when there is a threat to a coastal area due to hurricane conditions for the next 24 to 36 hours. A *hurricane warning* headlines the advisory when hurricane conditions are expected within a period of 24 hours. The warning message includes the coastal areas where the effects of a hurricane are expected. Gale warnings (winds up to 39 mph) may also be issued when a hurricane threatens. Hurricane warnings also spell out expected danger from storm surge in coastal areas; possible flooding of inland areas from hurricane rainfall; and the potential of hurricane-spawned tornadoes.

For most hurricanes the National Hurricane Center tries to give residents of threatened coastal areas enough time to carry out recommended evacuation plans. (Many areas are now working on evacuation plans.) A hurricane has a unique atmospheric feature: the storm's center, known as the eye. When a hurricane center passes directly over where you are located, you may experience the following weather: Rain and wind suddenly diminish, skies may clear and there is an interval of relative calm. Suddenly heavy rain and rising wind develop from the opposite direction, for the other side of the storm has arrived. For most people, however, there is no interim calm at all since the width of most eyes ranges from 10 to 40 miles. The time between the first rise in wind and rain squalls and a return to moderate winds after the storm can be 12 to 24 hours. This varies according to the size of the hurricane, its forward speed, and your proximity to its center.

The major threat of a hurricane is storm surge (measured in feet of water above mean sea level). Storm surge (see Fig. 57-6) can cause drowning. It is the storm's worst killer. Other effects are strong winds, the possibility of associated tornadoes, and heavy rains which can cause inland flooding. Storm surge begins over the deep ocean. The very low pressure and strong winds around a hurricane's eye allow the ocean surge under it to rise a foot or two higher than the surrounding ocean surface, forming a dome of water as great as 50 miles across. As the storm moves into shallow coastal water, decreasing water depth transforms the dome into a storm surge that can rise 20 feet or

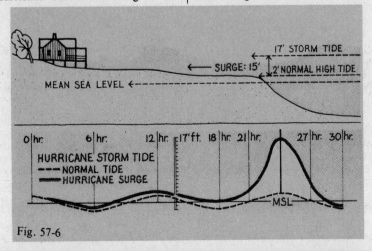

Fig. 57-6

261

more above normal sea level. The result can be massive flooding and shoreline destruction. The high, wind-driven waves of the hurricane are superimposed on the storm surge. The combination of surge and waves produces an extremely effective battering ram capable of smashing structures, eroding long stretches of beach and undermining poorly anchored buildings. The highest and most dangerous portion of the storm surge usually extends some 50 miles along the coast from near the center of the hurricane. Needless to say, this combination of wind and water can be lethal.

Wind speeds vary greatly from hurricane to hurricane, and within each storm. Winds can range from 74 to 200 mph. They may knock down power lines, uproot trees and break windows. They also often carry a deadly barrage of debris. Rainfall varies with the size of the hurricane, its forward speed and other factors. During the time it takes a hurricane to pass through an area, there may be five to ten inches or more of rain. Flash flooding can occur in low-lying areas, ripping up roadbeds and adding to the general destruction.

Safety rules

Stay or leave: When a hurricane threatens your area, you will have to decide whether you should evacuate or whether you can ride out the storm in safety at home. If local authorities recommend evacuation, you should leave. Their advice is based on knowledge of the strength of the storm and its potential for death and destruction.

In general, if you live on the coastline or an offshore island, plan to leave. If you live in a mobile home, plan to leave. If you live near a river or in a flood plain, plan to leave. But if you live on high ground, away from coastal beaches, consider staying.

In any case, the ultimate decision to stay or leave will be yours. Study the following list and carefully consider the factors involved—especially the items pertaining to storm surge.

At the beginning of the hurricane season (June): Make plans for action: Learn the storm surge history and elevation of your area. Learn safe routes inland. Learn the location of official shelters. Determine where to move your boat in an emergency. Trim back deadwood from trees. Check for loose rain gutters and down spouts. If shutters do not protect windows, stock boards to cover glass.

When a hurricane watch is issued for your area: Check often for official bulletins on radio, TV, or NOAA Weather Radio. Fuel your car. Check mobile home tie-downs. Moor small craft or move to safe shelter. Stock up on canned provisions. Check supplies of special medicines and drugs. Check batteries for radio and flashlights. Secure lawn furniture and other loose material outdoors. Tape, board, or shutter windows to prevent shattering. Wedge sliding glass doors to prevent their lifting from their tracks.

When a hurricane warning is issued for your area: Stay tuned to radio, TV, or NOAA Weather Radio for official bulletins. Stay home if your house is sturdy and on high ground. Board up garage and porch doors; move valuables to upper floors; bring in pets, fill containers (bathtub) with several days' supply of drinking water; turn up refrigerator to maximum cold and don't open unless necessary; use telephone only for emergencies; stay indoors on the downwind side of house away from windows; beware of the eye of the hurricane.

Leave mobile homes. Leave areas which might be affected by storm tide or stream flooding, and do so early—in daylight if possible. Also, shut off water and electricity at main stations; take small valuables and papers but travel light; leave food and water for pets (shelters will not take them); lock up house; drive carefully to nearest designated shelter, following recommended evacuation routes.

After the all-clear is given: Drive carefully; watch for dangling electrical wires, undermined roads, flooded low spots. Don't sightsee. Report broken or damaged water, sewer, and electrical lines. Use caution reentering your home, and check for gas leaks and food and water spoilage.

Community action: Beyond individual and family actions during a hurricane emergency, there is much to be done at the community level. Many communities on the Atlantic and Gulf coasts have made plans for action in the event a hurricane threatens, such as delineation of areas to be evacuated, shelter designations, evacuation routes, and emergency operations of fire, police, and other public service units.

But many exposed coastal communities are not prepared for a hurricane, and others have waited for disaster's expensive lesson before taking corrective steps. To encourage community preparedness, NOAA's National Weather Service has invented a town, named Homeport, and made it a model of hurricane preparedness. Copies of the Homeport story are available from the Superintendent of Documents, U.S. Government Printing Office, Washington, D.C. 20402. Stock number 0317-0046. Ask the G.P.O. for the current price.

NOAA WEATHER RADIO

Citizens must rely on the many warning methods available in local communities to advise them of impending weather threats. In 1975, a White House policy statement designated National Oceanic Atmospheric Administration (NOAA) Weather Radio as the sole government-operated method of warning citizens in the event of nuclear attack and severe weather. This increasingly popular VHF radio transmission provides a continuous 24-hour-a-day window on weather. Broadcasts are from area National Weather Service offices. Because the NOAA Weather Radio operates on VHF frequencies, only special all-weather radios or ones equipped with weather bands can receive these broadcasts. These radios are both inexpensive and easily obtainable. Many are built with warning devices which can only be activated from a Weather Service office. This instantaneous method of alerting listeners in time of impending disaster or severe weather usually gives ample time to get ready. It has often saved lives and property. Over 90% of the people in the United States are within listening range of the NOAA Weather Radio broadcasts. At the flick of a button, one can receive a full rundown of the current weather for the area (40–60 miles from the antenna). The program is comprised of several constantly updated brief messages which include current weather and forecasts appropriate to an area's activities. For example, farming communities would receive, as an integral part of programming, information necessary for their work. Lake or sea-

262

coast locations would hear marine information helpful for both recreational and commercial boaters.

The NOAA Weather Radio broadcasts are made on one of three high-band FM radio frequencies—162.40, 162.475, or 162.55 megahertz (MHz). The 162.475 MHz frequency is used only in special cases where required to avoid channel interference.

EARTHQUAKES

Among the most frightening and destructive phenomena of nature are earthquakes and their aftereffects. Most earthquakes occur in the areas bordering the Pacific Ocean called the Ring of Fire, including the Pacific coasts of North and South America, the Aleutians, Japan, Southeast Asia and Australia.

An earthquake is the oscillatory, sometimes violent movements of the earth's surface that follows a release of energy in the earth's crust. This energy can be generated by a sudden dislocation of segments of the crust, by a volcanic eruption or even by manmade explosions. Most of the destructive earthquakes are caused by dislocations of the crust. When subjected to deep-seated forces (whose origins and nature are largely unknown), the crust may first bend and then, when the stress exceeds the strength of the rocks, break and snap to a new position. In the process of breaking, vibrations called seismic waves are generated. These waves travel from the source of the earthquake along the surface and through the earth.

Very shallow earthquakes are probably caused by fracturing of the brittle rock in the crust or by internal stresses that overcome the frictional resistance locking opposite sides of a fault. The immediate cause of intermediate and deep earthquakes is not fully understood yet. The epicenter of an earthquake is the point on the earth's surface directly above the region where an earthquake's energy originates. The focal depth of an earthquake is the depth from the earth's crust to the earthquake's origin. The location of an earthquake is commonly described by the geographic position of its epicenter and by its focal depth (see Fig. 57-7).

Geologists have found that earthquakes tend to recur along faults. A fault is a fracture in the earth's crust

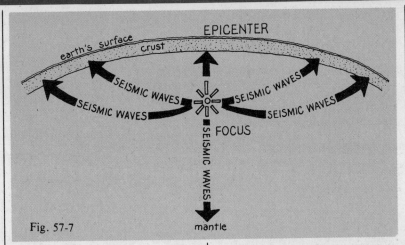

Fig. 57-7

along which two blocks of the crust have slipped with respect to each other. The master fault of an intricate network of faults in the United States that cuts through the coastal region of California is the San Andreas Fault.

The vibrations produced by earthquakes are detected, recorded and measured by instruments called seismographs. From a seismogram, the time, epicenter and focal depth can be determined. There are two types of vibrations: surface waves, which travel along the earth's surface, and body waves, which travel through the earth. Surface waves usually have the strongest vibrations and cause most of the damage. Body waves are of two types: compressional and sheer. Compressional waves travel at great speeds and usually reach the surface first. They are therefore called primary, or P, waves. Sheer waves do not travel so rapidly through the earth's crust and mantle as do compressional waves and are therefore called secondary, or S, waves.

The first indication of an earthquake will often be a sharp thud, signaling the arrival of compressional waves. This is followed by sheer waves and the ground roll caused by the surface waves. The severity of an earthquake can be expressed in several ways. The magnitude of an earthquake, as expressed by the Richter scale, is a measure of the amplitude of the seismic waves and is related to the amount of energy released. The intensity, as expressed by the Modified Mercalli scale, is a subjective measure that describes how severe a shock was felt at a particular location. Damage or loss of life and property is another,

and ultimately the most important, measure of an earthquake's severity.

The Richter scale, named after Dr. Charles F. Richter of the California Institute of Technology, is the best-known scale for measuring the magnitude of earthquakes. The scale is logarithmic, so that a recording of 7, for example, indicates a disturbance with ground motion 10 times as large as a recording of 6. A quake of 2 is the smallest quake normally felt by humans. Earthquakes with a Richter value of 6 or more are commonly considered major. The San Francisco earthquake of 1906 had a magnitude of 8.3.

Earthquakes of large magnitude do not necessarily cause the most intense surface effects. The effect in a given region depends to a large degree on local surface and subsurface geologic conditions. An area underlain by unstable ground such as sand or clay is likely to experience much more noticeable effects than an area equally distant from an earthquake's epicenter but underlain by firm ground such as granite.

An earthquake's destructiveness depends on many other factors, including the density of the population and the construction in the area shaken by the quake. Injuries are commonly caused by collapsing buildings, toppling chimneys, falling brick and roof parapets, and flying glass from broken windows.

The United States Geological Survey attempts to anticipate earthquakes, as do some other scientific groups, but as yet there is no way to predict accurately the time and place an earthquake will strike. The Nation-

263

al Center for Earthquake Research at the Geological Survey's field center in Menlo Park, California, studies earthquake-prone areas in the hope of determining patterns. For the present, the best protection against an earthquake is to avoid construction in high-risk areas and to employ earthquake-resistant construction techniques.

Safety Rules

Before an earthquake occurs: In those areas where damaging earthquakes can be expected, support the enactment of safe building codes and their enforcement. In addition, support school building programs that provide for strengthening old, weak school buildings or replacing them with earthquake-resistant structures on ground reasonably safe from failure during an earthquake; support community efforts to replace other old, weak buildings and to insure that loose objects on the exterior of buildings be removed or fastened; organize and support programs to prepare for future earthquakes, including earthquake drills; support research to learn more about earthquake problems and to supply information needed to plan wisely the siting, design and construction of man-made structures.

If you live in an earthquake-prone area, you should check your home for earthquake hazards. Bolt down or provide other strong support for water heaters and gas appliances because fire damage can result from broken gas lines and appliance connections. Use flexible connections wherever possible. Place large and heavy objects on the lower shelves of a bookcase. Fasten shelves securely to the walls.

As a parent or head of a family, hold occasional home earthquake drills to provide your family with the knowledge to avoid injury and panic during an earthquake. Teach family members how to turn off electricity, gas and water at the main switches and valves. Know basic first-aid techniques because medical facilities may be overloaded after a severe earthquake. Keep a flashlight and battery-powered radio in the home ready for use at all times. Keep immunizations up to date for all family members.

During an earthquake: Remain calm. If you are indoors, watch for falling plaster, brick, light fixtures and other objects. Watch for objects on high bookcases and china cabinets. Watch for shelves that might slide or topple. Stay away from windows, mirrors and chimneys. If in danger, hide under a table, desk or bed, in a corner away from a window, or in a strong doorway. It is usually best not to run outside.

If you are in a high-rise office building when an earthquake strikes, get under a desk. Do not dash for the exit, because stairways may be broken or jammed with people. Power for elevators may fail. If you are in a crowded store, do not rush for a doorway, because hundreds may have the same idea.

If you are caught outside, avoid high buildings, walls, power poles and other objects that could fall on you. Do not run through the streets. Move to an open area away from all hazards. If you are in an automobile, stop at the safest place available, preferably an open area.

When you hear that an earthquake has occurred, stand by for a tsunami, or tidal wave, emergency.

After an earthquake: Check for injuries in your family and neighborhood. Do not attempt to move seriously injured people unless they are in immediate danger of further injury. Check for fires or fire hazards. Wear shoes in all areas where there is debris or broken glass. Check utility lines and appliances for damage. If the gas leaks, shut off the main gas valve. Shut off the electrical power if there is damage to your house wiring. Report the damage to the appropriate utility company and follow their instructions. Do not use matches, lighters or open-flame appliances until you are sure no gas leaks exist. Do not operate electrical switches or appliances if gas leaks are suspected. Do not touch downed power lines or objects in contact with them. Clean up spilled medicines, drugs and other potentially harmful materials. If water is off, emergency water may be obtained from water heaters, toilet tanks, melted ice cubes and canned vegetables. Check to see that sewage tanks are intact before permitting continued flushing of toilets. Do not eat or drink anything from open containers near shattered glass. Liquids may be strained through a clean handkerchief or cloth to eliminate glass splinters. Turn on the radio for up-to-the-minute reports. Check your chimney over its entire length for cracks and damage, particularly in the attic and at the roofline. Unnoticed damage could lead later to a fire. The initial check should be made from a distance. Inspect closets and storage shelf areas. Open closet and cupboard doors carefully because objects may be ready to fall from shelves. Do not go sight-seeing, particularly in beach and waterfront areas where seismic sea waves may strike. Keep the street clear for passage of emergency vehicles. Be prepared for further activity known as earthquake aftershocks. Although smaller than the main shock, they can cause additional damage. Respond to requests for help from fire, police, and Civil Defense officials, but do not go into damaged areas unless your help has been requested. If power is off, check your freezer and plan to use up foods that will spoil quickly. Use outdoor charcoal broilers for emergency cooking. Do not use your telephone except for emergency calls.

RADIATION

People can protect themselves against fallout radiation, and have a good chance of surviving it, by staying inside a fallout shelter. In most cases, the fallout radiation level outside the shelter would decrease rapidly enough to permit people to leave the shelter within a few days.

Even in communities that receive heavy accumulations of fallout particles, people soon might be able to leave shelter for a few minutes or a few hours at a time in order to perform emergency tasks. In most places, it is unlikely that full-time shelter occupancy would be required for more than a week or two. Trained radiology monitors using special instruments to detect and measure the intensity of fallout radiation will advise when it is safe to leave a shelter.

A fallout shelter does not need to be a special type of building or an underground bunker. It can be any space with walls and roofs thick or heavy enough to keep out dangerous amounts of radiation. For example, a shelter can be the basement or inner corridor of any large building, the basement of a private home, a subway or tunnel, or even a backyard trench with some kind of shielding material serving as a roof.

264

In addition to protecting people from fallout radiation, most fallout shelters also would provide limited protection against the blast and heat effects of nuclear explosions that were not close by. To find out more about what types of shelters and what supplies to use, consult the Department of Defense booklet "In Time of Emergency." Write to: Superintendent of Documents, Washington, D.C. 20402.

Radiation sickness

Radiation sickness is caused by the invisible rays given off by particles of radioactive fallout. If a person has received a large dose of radiation in a short period of time—generally less than a week—he will become seriously ill and will probably die. But if he has received only a small or medium dose, his body will repair itself and he will get well. Long-range effects, however, are not well known. No special clothing can protect a person from gamma radiation, and no special medicines can protect a person from or cure radiation sickness.

Symptoms: The effects may not be noticed for several days. Early symptoms include lack of appetite, nausea, vomiting, fatigue, weakness and headache. Later, the patient may suffer a sore mouth, loss of hair, bleeding gums, bleeding under the skin and diarrhea. But these same symptoms can be caused by other diseases, and not everyone who has radiation sickness shows all of these symptoms, or shows them all at once.

If the person has a headache or general discomfort, give one or two aspirin tablets every three or four hours (half a tablet for a child under 12). If he is nauseous, give him motion sickness tablets if available. If his mouth is sore or his gums are bleeding, have him use a mouthwash made up of a half-teaspoon of salt to one quart of water. If there is vomiting or diarrhea, he should drink slowly several glasses each day of a salt-and-soda solution (one teaspoonful of salt and one-half teaspoonful of baking soda to one quart of cool water), plus bouillon or fruit juices. If available, a mixture of kaolin and pectin should be given for diarrhea. Whatever his symptoms, the patient should be kept lying down, comfortably warm and resting. Radiation sickness is not contagious or infectious.

FAMILY FOOD STOCKPILE FOR SURVIVAL

The United States Civil Defense authorities encourage families to have a two-week supply of food and water in order to be self-sufficient in the event of a natural disaster where transportation has been disrupted, or an atomic disaster where radiation would keep rescuers out of the area for up to two weeks.

Storing and replacing foods

To provide a balanced diet, include fruit, vegetables, juices and beverages, milk, soup, cheese, meat, fish, infant foods, bread and crackers. Jellies, jams, sugar, salt and other seasonings make meals more appetizing. Avoid salty foods; they increase water consumption. Dried and canned foods are preferable. They also will last for months without refrigeration. Most of the food you use should be edible unheated. Small cans, preferably for one meal, are recommended because of the difficulty of preserving leftovers safely. Provide medicine and special foods for sick persons.

Food in a full, well-insulated home freezer does not begin to spoil until several days after power goes off. (Food in large freezers will keep longer than food in small freezers.) But once the freezer has been opened, foods should be used promptly.

Food should be stored in a dry, cool, secure place, preferably in a basement. To maintain the eating quality, temperatures should be below 70° F and above freezing. Protect food from rodents and insects by storing the original boxes in tightly closed cans or other metal containers. This also extends the storage life of the food. Most of the foods suggested in the chart on page 268 would be safe to use after longer periods of storage.

It is a good idea to draw regularly on the food stockpile so that foods are used while they are still of good eating quality. As items are used, replace them, putting the fresh supplies at the back of the stockpile.

You may want to label cans and containers with the date of purchase and the approximate date when they should be replaced. Suggested charts for keeping a record of your family food reserves are given on page 269.

Canned foods are generally safe to eat as long as the seal of the can is not broken. Food spoilage may have occurred if a can has bulging ends, is leaking, or if when the can is opened there is spurting liquid, off-odor, or mold on the food.

When food in glass containers becomes spoiled, the cover may bulge or food may leak through the broken seal. Gas bubbles, cloudiness, and films of growth that can be seen through the glass may indicate bacterial growth. If the seal has broken on jars of baby food, the "safety button" in the center of the lid will be pushed upward instead of drawn downward. Food from containers showing any signs of food spoilage should be discarded immediately without tasting.

Equipment for cooking and serving

You should have equipment for emergency cooking, serving and eating. Have on hand a small, compact cooking unit, such as the ones used by campers; one or two cooking pans; disposable knives, forks and spoons; paper plates, towels, cups and napkins; can and bottle openers; nursing bottles and nipples if there is a baby in the family; measuring cup; medicine dropper for measuring water purifier; matches; and a pocket knife. It is better not to use anything that requires water for washing. Each family will need to estimate the number of items required for a two-week period. Store your emergency cooking and serving equipment with or near your reserve food supply.

Water

You and your family can manage for quite a while without food, but only for a short time without liquids. About one-half gallon of water per person per day is optimal for drinking. Large quantities of fruit juice and soft drinks will help satisfy thirst. Minimal handwashing and personal hygiene could be accomplished with another half-gallon of water per person per day.

Some of your water requirements could be met by tapping home hot-water tanks and toilet tanks. Know the location of your main incoming water valve so you can shut it off if directed to do so by local health authorities to prevent the entrance of contaminated water. As a safety measure, the valve on the gas line to your hot-water heater should be turned off also. Water from a hot-water tank can be obtained by opening the drain cock at the bottom of the tank. To get a free flow of water with the water inlet valve turned off, you may need to vent the tank by turning on a faucet somewhere on the water line. Some hot-water tanks are automatically vented.

> It is of the utmost importance that water stored for emergency use be clean and safe. If there is any doubt, treat it to make it safe.

The best method of purifying water is to boil it vigorously for one to three minutes to destroy bacteria that might be present. Boiling, however, does not destroy radioactivity. To improve the taste of boiled water, pour it from one clean container to another several times.

Any household bleach solution that contains hypochlorite, a chlorine compound, as its only active ingredient will purify water easily and inexpensively. Bleach solutions with 5.25 percent of sodium hypochlorite are most common. They are available in grocery stores. Add the bleach solution to the water in any clean container in which it can be thoroughly mixed by stirring or shaking. The following table shows the proper amount of a 5.25-percent solution to add to water.

Add the chlorine solution to the water and stir, then let the mixture stand for 30 minutes. The water should still have a distinct taste or smell of chlorine. If it does not, add another dose of the solution and let the water stand another 15 minutes. The taste or smell of chlorine in water thus treated is a sign of safety. If you cannot detect chlorine in the water you are trying to purify by this method, do not store it. The chlorine solution may have weakened through age or for some other reason.

If you have ordinary household 2-percent tincture of iodine in your home medicine chest, you can use it to purify small quantities of water. Add three drops of tincture of iodine to each quart of clear water and six drops to each quart of cloudy water. For a gallon, add 12 drops for clear water, 24 drops for cloudy water. Stir thoroughly.

Water purification tablets that release chlorine or iodine can be used safely to purify water. They are inexpensive and can be bought at most sporting goods stores and some drugstores. If you use water purification tablets, follow the directions on the package. Usually one tablet is sufficient for one quart of water; double the dosage if the water is cloudy.

Water can be stored in plastic jugs that are thoroughly cleaned, filled and then capped with a tight-fitting lid. Plastic containers are shatter-proof and lighter than glass. Metal containers may give the water an unpleasant taste. Clean water stored in this way should remain palatable for an indefinite period. It is advisable to check the containers every few months for leaks. At the same time examine the water. If undesirable appearances or tastes have developed, the water should be changed.

Warning. Water that has been contaminated by radioactive material should not be used unless no alternate supply is available. The danger is greatest immediately after fallout deposition. Infants and children are more at risk from such water than are adults. Water from springs and covered wells could be used.

Amount of water	Amount of solution to add to	
	Clear water	*Cloudy water*
1 quart (¼ gallon)	2 drops	4 drops
1 gallon	8 drops	16 drops
5 gallons	½ teaspoon	1 teaspoon

RESERVE FOOD SUPPLY

Kind of food	Need per person		Remarks
	Daily	*Two weeks*	
1. Milk	Equivalent of 2 glasses (fluid)	Equivalent of 7 qts. (fluid)	Each of the following is about the equivalent of one quart of fluid milk: Three 6-oz. cans of evaporated milk. One 14½-oz. can of evaporated milk. Three to 3½ ozs. of nonfat dry milk.
2. Canned meat, poultry, fish, dry beans, and peas	2 servings	28 servings (about 8 to 9 lbs.)	Amounts required for one serving of each food are as follows: Canned meat, poultry, fish—2 to 3 ozs. Canned mixtures of meat, poultry, or fish with vegetables, rice, macaroni, spaghetti, noodles, or dry beans—8 ozs. Thick soups containing meat, poultry, fish or dry beans or peas—one-half of a 10½-oz. can (condensed).
3. Fruits and vegetables	3 to 4 servings	42 to 56 servings (about 21 lbs. canned)	Amounts required for one serving of each food are as follows: Canned juices—4 to 6 ozs., single strength. Canned fruit and vegetables—4 ozs. Dried fruit—1½ ozs.
4. Cereals and baked goods	3 to 4 servings	42 to 56 servings (about 5 to 7 lbs.)	Amounts required for one serving of each food are as follows (selection depends on extent of cooking possible): Cereal: Ready-to-eat, puffed—½ oz. Ready-to-eat, flaked—¾ oz. Other ready-to-eat and uncooked—1 oz. Crackers, cooking—1oz. Canned bread, steamed puddings, and cake—1 to 2 ozs. Flour, flour mixes—1 oz. Macaroni, spaghetti, noodles: Dry—¾ oz. Cooked, canned—6 ozs.
5. Spreads for bread and crackers	According to family practices		Examples: Cheese spreads. Peanut and other nut butters. Jam, jelly, marmalade, preserves. Syrup, honey. Apple and other fruit butters. Relish, catsup, mustard.
6. Hydrogenated fats and vegetable oils		Up to 1 lb. or 1 pt.	Amount needed depends upon extent of cooking possible.
7. Sugars, candy, nuts, instant puddings		1 to 2 lbs.	
8. Miscellaneous	According to family practices		Examples (amount needed depends on extent of cooking possible): Instant beverages. Instant, dry cream substitute. Bouillon products. Synthetic beverage products. Salt and spices (e.g., pepper). Flavoring extracts, vinegar. Soda, baking powder.
9. Water (for drinking)	½ gal.	7 gals.	

Note: The amounts listed will supply the calories needed by one adult for two weeks. Teenagers are likely to eat more than the amount in the chart. Younger children need less food.

SAMPLE MEAL PLANS FOR *LIMITED* COOKING FACILITIES

First day	Second day	Third day
Morning		
Citrus fruit juice[1]	Citrus fruit juice[1]	Prunes[1]
Ready-to-eat cereal	Hot cereal (quick-cooking)	Ready-to-eat cereal
Milk	Milk	Milk
Hot coffee,[2] tea,[2] or cocoa[2]	Hot coffee,[2] tea,[2] or cocoa[2]	Crackers
		Cheese
		Hot coffee,[2] tea,[2] or cocoa[2]
Noon		
Vegetable soup[1]	Beef-and-vegetable stew[1]	Chile con carne with beans[1]
Potato salad[1]	Green beans[1]	Tomatoes[1]
Crackers	Crackers	Crackers
Ham spread[1]	Peanut butter	Hot coffee,[2] tea,[2] or cocoa[2]
Milk	Milk	
Candy bar		
Between meals		
Fruit-flavored drink or fruit drink	Tomato juice[1]	Fruit-flavored drink or fruit drink
Night		
Beef and gravy[1]	Tuna fish,[1] cream of celery soup,[1] mixed sweet pickles[1]—combined in one dish	Lunch meat[1]
Noodles[1]		Hominy[1]
Peas and carrots[1]	Fruit[1]	Applesauce[1]
Instant pudding	Cookies	Cookies
Hot coffee,[2] tea,[2] or cocoa[2]	Hot coffee,[2] tea,[2] or cocoa[2]	Hot coffee,[2] tea,[2] or cocoa[2]

[1]Canned   [2]Instant

SAMPLE MEAL PLANS FOR *NO* COOKING FACILITIES

First day	Second day	Third day
Morning		
Citrus fruit juice[1]	Fruit juice[1]	Grapefruit segments[1]
Ready-to-eat cereal	Corned beef hash[1]	Ready-to-eat cereal
Milk, cold coffee,[2] or tea[2]	Crackers	Vienna sausage[1]
Crackers	Spread	Milk, cold coffee,[2] or tea[2]
Peanut butter or other spread	Milk, cold coffee,[2] or tea[2]	
Noon		
Spaghetti with meat sauce[1]	Baked beans[1]	Chile con carne with beans[1]
Green beans[1]	Brown bread[1]	Crackers
Crackers	Tomatoes[1]	Fruit[1]
Spread	Fruit[1]	Cookies
Milk, cold coffee,[2] or tea[2]	Milk, cold coffee,[2] or tea[2]	Milk, cold coffee,[2] or tea[2]
Between meals		
Fruit-flavored drink or fruit drink	Milk	Tomato juice
Night		
Lunch meat[1]	Pork and gravy[1]	Sliced beef[1]
Sweet potatoes[1]	Corn[1]	Macaroni and cheese[1]
Applesauce[1]	Potatoes[1]	Peas and carrots[1]
Milk, cold coffee,[2] or tea[2]	Instant pudding	Crackers
Candy	Fruit juice[1]	Milk, cold coffee,[2] or tea[2]

[1]Canned   [2]Instant

Replacement periods for foods listed in chart

Use within 6 months:
Evaporated milk
Dried fruit, in metal container
Dry crisp crackers, in metal container
Gum

Use within 1 year:
Nonfat dry or whole dry milk, in metal container
Canned meat, poultry, fish
Mixtures of meat, vegetables and cereal products, in sealed cans
Canned condensed meat-and-vegetable soups
Dehydrated soups, in metal container
Canned fruits, fruit juices, and vegetables
Cereal: ready-to-eat cereals, in metal container; uncooked cereal (quick-cooking or instant), in metal container
Hydrogenated fats, vegetable oils
Sweets and nuts: hard candy; nuts, canned; instant puddings
Miscellaneous: coffee, tea, cocoa (instant); dry-cream products (instant); bouillon products; flavored beverage products; flavoring extracts; soda, baking powder

May be stored indefinitely:
Sugar
Salt

268

OUR FAMILY FOOD RESERVE

Kind of Food	Amount Stored	Date Purchased	Suggested Replacement Date

DAILY URINE TEST RECORD

Doctor _____   Phone _____

Date	Medication taken today	Urine Tests							
		Breakfast		Lunch		Dinner		Bedtime	
		sugar	ketones	sugar	ketones	sugar	ketones	sugar	ketones

PAINT SELECTION CHART

	Aluminum Paint	Cement-base Paint	Exterior Clear Finish	House Paint	Metal Roof Paint	Porch-and-Deck Paint	Primer or Undercoater	Rubber-base Paint	Spar Varnish	Transparent Sealer	Trim-and-Trellis Paint	Wood Stain	Metal Primer
WOOD													
Natural finish			X						X			X	
Porch floor						X							
Shingle roof												X	
Shutters and trim				X•			X				X•		
Siding	X			X•			X				X•		
Windows	X			X•			X						
MASONRY													
Asbestos cement				X•			X	X					
Brick	X	X		X•			X	X		X			
Cement and cinder block	X	X		X•			X	X		X			
Cement porch floor						X		X					
Stucco	X	X		X•			X	X		X			
METAL													
Copper									X				
Galvanized	X•			X•			X		X		X•		X
Iron	X•			X•							X•		X
Roofing					X•								X
Siding	X•			X•							X•		X
Windows, aluminum	X			X•							X•		X
Windows, steel	X•			X•							X•		X

Note: Black dot (X•) indicates that a primer or sealer may be necessary before the finishing coat or coats (unless the surface has been previously finished).

INDEX

INDEX

281

285